Student Solutions Manual for

Genetics

Table of Contents
Student Solutions Manual for Genetics, Second Edition, by Hartwell

Chapter 1 Genetics: The Study of Biological Information

Synopsis:

Chapter 1 is an introduction to the study of modern-day genetics. Genetics is the study of genes: how genes are segments of DNA molecules; how genes are inherited; and how genes direct an organism's characteristics. The most important insight from this chapter is that the basic function of most (but not all) genes is to direct the synthesis of (to encode) a particular type of protein.

Key Terms:

mutations heritable changes in *DNA sequence*.

evolution the change in the genetic composition of a population resulting from the *selection* of individuals possessing DNA variants that make them particularly suited to survive and reproduce in a given environment.

genes basic units of biological information; specific segment of DNA in a discrete region of a *chromosome* that serve as a unit of function by encoding a particular *RNA* or *protein*.

chromosomes organelles that package and manage the storage, duplication, expression, and *evolution* of DNA.

genome the entire collection of *chromosomes* in each cell of an organism.

metabolism the chemical and physical reactions that convert sources of energy and matter to fuel growth and repair within a cell.

proteins large polymers composed of hundreds to thousands of *amino acid* subunits strung together in long chains. Proteins are required for the structure, function, and regulation of the body's cells, tissues, and organs.

biological system any complex network of interacting molecules or groups of cells that function in a coordinated manner through dynamic signaling.

central dogma the flow of information from *DNA* to *RNA* to *protein*.

model organisms organisms whose characteristics (e.g., short generation time) facilitate experimental laboratory research.

Problem Solving Tips:

The first chapter of this book provides a broad overview of genetics. Chapter 1 covers a lot of ground, but only superficially. Don't worry if at this point you don't understand all of the information given at a deep level – you will later on. However, you are likely familiar already (from introductory biology classes) with some of the fundamentals of what a gene is and how genes are used to make proteins.

Chapter 1

The problems in this chapter are meant to get you started in the habit of thinking like a geneticist – quantitatively, analytically, carefully, and logically.

Solutions to Problems:

Vocabulary

1-1.

a. 4; **b.** 11; **c.** 7; **d.** 1; **e.** 9; **f.** 8; **g.** 12; **h.** 6; **i.** 2; **j.** 10; **k.** 3; **l.** 5

Section 1.1 DNA: The Molecule That Stores Digitized Biological Information

2. The complementary strand of a DNA molecule is simply the strand with which the original DNA molecule forms base pairs. Remember two things: (1) The two strands of a double-stranded DNA molecule are oriented in the opposite direction with respect to each other (their 5' and 3' ends run in opposite directions), and (2) the base pairs are A-T and G-C. Therefore, the DNA strand complementary to the one shown is: 5' AGCTTAATGCT 3'

3. a. If the 3 billion (3,000,000,000) base pairs of the human genome is divided into 23 chromosomes, the average size of a human chromosome is 3,000,000,000 base pairs/23 chromosomes ≈ 130,435,000 base pairs per chromosome.

b. The human genome contains about 20,000 genes, and assuming that they are spread evenly over the 23 chromosomes, on average there are 20,000 genes/23 chromosomes ≈ 870 genes per chromosome.

c. About half the DNA of the human genome contains genes, meaning that all the genes are found within 1.5 billion (1,500,000,000) base pairs. Therefore, on average there are 1,500,000,000 base pairs / 20,000 genes ≈ 75,000 base pairs per gene.

Section 1.2 Proteins: The Molecules That Govern Life Processes

4. a. Both. Each protein is composed of a "string" of amino acids, and DNA is a "string" of nucleotides.

b. DNA. DNA is double-stranded through complementary base pairing of single strands in opposite orientations. A protein is a single strand of linked amino acids, and the strand folds into a particular shape.

c. DNA. Four different kinds of nucleotides – A, G, C, and T – are present in the DNA polymer. Twenty different common amino acids are present in almost all proteins.

d. Protein. Twenty distinct amino acid subunits are the building blocks of almost all proteins. DNA is made up of only four different types of nucleotides.

e. Protein. Proteins are polymers of amino acids; DNA is a polymer of nucleotides.

f. DNA. DNA is a polymer of nucleotides; proteins are polymers of amino acids.

g. DNA. Genes are segments of DNA; by using the genetic code, most genes encode proteins.

h. Protein. Some proteins (enzymes) perform chemical reactions.

5. a. Each base in a single strand of a DNA molecule can be either an A, G, C or T. Therefore, a specific 100-nucleotide DNA strand could start with any one of the four nucleotides, the second nucleotide could be any one of the four nucleotides, etc. The number of different possible sequences increases by a factor of 4 at each successive step in the addition of a base (see the following figure). Thus, the number of different possible sequences of a 100-nucleotide DNA strand is $4^{100} = {\sim}1.6 \times 10^{60}$. We need not consider the second, complementary strand of DNA, as its base sequence is determined by the sequence of the first strand.

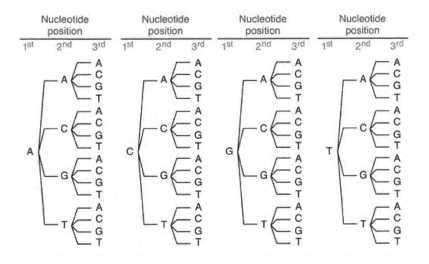

b. Because each amino acid can be 1 of 20 different amino acids, by the same logic as in part (a), the number of different 100-amino acid proteins is $20^{100} = {\sim}1.3 \times 10^{130}$.

Section 1.4   The Molecular Similarity of All Life-Forms

6. Scientists think that all forms of life on earth have a common origin because organisms as distant as humans and bacteria share the same genetic code, and many of their proteins are similar in amino acid sequence and biochemical function.

7. Scientists study model organisms like yeast and fruit flies in order to understand universal biochemical pathways. Because of their common origin and because they have similar genes and

proteins, all organisms share certain universal pathways. For example, many of the genes that help regulate cell division are similar in yeast and humans. Obviously, scientists cannot perform experiments on humans, but researchers can manipulate organisms like yeast, fruit flies, and mice in the laboratory in many useful ways. Universal principles of biology may be learned from these model organisms because of the common origin of all life.

8. To detect proteins in different organisms that have a common origin, scientists use computer analysis of the DNA sequences of genomes to look for genes that encode proteins with large stretches of amino acids that are identical or similar. To assess whether related genes in different organisms have similar functions, scientists can generate mutations in the genes and see if the mutations have similar effects. For example, suppose bacteria with a mutation in a particular gene are unable to grow because the cells cannot divide. If fruit flies with a mutation in a gene with related DNA sequences that encode a similar protein die as very young embryos with very few cells, you could conclude that the genes in each organism have a key function in cell division. In some cases, you could go one step further by placing the normal fruit fly gene into the genome of the mutant bacterial cells (or the normal bacterial gene into the genome of the mutant fruit flies). If the mutant organisms with the gene from the other species were able to grow properly, you could then conclude that the genes from the different organisms do in fact encode proteins that fulfill the same biochemical role in cell division. Because bacteria and fruit flies are so distantly related to each other, this type of "gene rescue" experiment is only rarely successful. But for more closely related species (like fruit flies and yeast cells, both of which are eukaryotic organisms), such experiments have often demonstrated that genes from different species that have related DNA sequences also have similar gene function.

Section 1.5 The Modular Construction of Genomes

9. Scientists think that new genes arise by duplication of an original gene and divergence by mutation because the genomes of all organisms have gene families and superfamilies. These gene families and superfamilies contain genes that encode proteins with with similar amino acid sequences; the proteins in these families fold into similar three-dimensional structures and they perform related functions. The genomes of more complex organisms usually contain more members of the same gene/protein families that exist in the genomes of simpler organisms. It is unlikely that all of these gene/protein families arose anew in each organism.

10. Genes have exons that include protein coding regions, and also regions of DNA between the exons called introns. Exons from different genes could be "shuffled" by chromosome

rearrangements. Modules from different proteins could thus reassort to form new proteins with new functions.

11. A protein is likely to perform the same type of biochemical reaction in different cell types. For example, if a protein is a kinase (a kind of enzyme that adds a phosphate group to other molecules called substrates) it would probably be a kinase in all cells. However, the kinase might add a phosphate group to one substrate in one cell type but a different substrate in other kinds of cells. Therefore, a protein with a particular biochemical activity could function in the same or in different pathways in various cell types.

Section 1.6 Modern Genetic Techniques

12. a. Untrue; the zebrafish that lacks a functional version of the gene is viable.

b. True; the zebrafish that lacks a functional version of the gene lacks stripes.

c. Insufficient information; no information is given as to why the stripes are absent in the mutant zebrafish and many explanations for this observation are possible.

d. Insufficient information; the gene is not required for viability because the fish lacking a functional version of it are alive. However, no information is given about possible abnormalities in the mutant zebrafish other than a failure to form horizontal stripes.

13. a. The DNA sequence of the *WDR62* gene would have enabled scientists to predict the amino acid sequence of the protein it encodes. Conserved regions of amino acid sequence often reveal structural features indicative of the biochemical function of the protein. In fact, *WDR62* is so named because the protein it encodes contains "WD repeats": regions with similar amino acid sequences that are found in several proteins. These WD repeats allow the proteins that contain them to bind to other proteins.

b. Knowing the *WDR62* mutations cause microcephaly indicates that at the level of the organism, the gene and the protein it encodes are required for brain development.

c. If the mutant mice had a syndrome similar to people with microcephaly, then we would know for sure that *WDR62* is the microcephaly disease gene. These mice could also be used in various experiments to study the biochemical pathways in which the WDR62 protein participates, as these pathways are likely to be similar in mice and humans and would be needed for proper brain development in both species.

Section 1.7 Human Genetics and Society

14. Different people may have very different perspectives about their interest in obtaining the DNA sequence of their genome. Genome sequences may be helpful in treating diseases, in making reproductive decisions, and in providing clues about ancestry. At the present time, only a small fraction of the information in genome sequences can be interpreted by scientists because many traits are influenced in very complicated ways by large networks of genes. In some cases, individuals may have excellent reasons for NOT wanting to learn about their genetic predispositions to certain traits. For example, many people whose parents have Huntington disease, a neurodegenerative condition that tends to affect people late in life, can know for certain whether or not they will develop the disease by analysis of the base sequence of a single gene. Some people may wish not to know they will eventually develop this disease because that knowledge may affect their current quality of life. Your own perspectives about this issue may well change as your understanding of genetics increases.

Chapter 2   Mendelian Genetics

Synopsis:

The first part of Chapter 2 covers the basic principles of inheritance that can be summarized as Mendel's Laws of Segregation (for one gene) and Independent Assortment (for more than one gene). You will see in chapter 3 how these laws relate to chromosome segregation during meiosis.

In the second part of Chapter 2, we see that the relationship between genotype and phenotype can be more complicated than envisaged by Mendel. Alleles do not have to be completely dominant or recessive with respect to each other. Not all genotypes are equally viable. Genes can have more than two alleles in a population. One gene can govern more than one phenotype. A single phenotype can be influenced by more than one gene, and these genes can interact in a variety of ways.

Despite these complications, the alleles of individual genes still segregate according to Mendel's Law of Segregation, and different pairs of genes still usually behave as dictated by Mendel's Law of Independent Assortment.

Key Terms:

genes and **alleles** of genes – a gene determines a trait; and there are different alleles or forms of a gene. The <u>colour gene</u> in pea has two alleles: the <u>yellow allele</u> and the <u>green allele</u>.

genotype and **phenotype** – genotype is the genetic makeup of an organism (written as alleles of specific genes), while phenotype is what the organism looks like.

homozygous and **heterozygous** – when both alleles of a gene are the same, the individual is homozygous for that gene (or *pure-breeding*). If the two alleles are different, the organism is heterozygous (also called a *hybrid*).

dominant and **recessive** – the dominant allele is the one that controls the phenotype in the heterozygous genotype; the recessive allele controls the phenotype only in a homozygote since its effect is hidden or masked when the dominant allele is present.

monohybrid or **dihybrid cross** – a cross between individuals who are both heterozygous for one gene (monohybrid) or for two genes (dihybrid).

testcross – performed to determine whether or not an individual with the dominant trait is homozygous or heterozygous; an individual with the dominant phenotype but unknown genotype is crossed with an individual with the recessive phenotype.

wild-type alleles – alleles with a frequency equal to or greater than 1 percent in the population. Colloquially, wild-type alleles are the "normal" alleles found most commonly in the population.

mutant alleles – rare alleles with a frequency of less than 1 percent in the population.

monomorphic gene – a gene with only one common, wild-type allele.

polymorphic gene – a gene with many wild-type alleles. The wild-type alleles of a polymorphic gene are often called **common variants.**

incomplete dominance and **codominance** – cases in which the phenotype of heterozygotes is different than that of either type of homozygote. Incomplete dominance describes alleles where the heterozygote has a phenotype that is in between that of either homozygote, but typically is more similar to one parent than to the other, while heterozygotes for codominant alleles have both of the phenotypes associated with each homozygote. Usually in incomplete dominance one allele is nonfunctional or only partially functional, while in codominance both alleles are fully functional.

recessive lethal allele – an allele (usually a loss-of-function allele) of an **essential gene** necessary to the survival of the individual. A zygote homozygous for a recessive lethal allele cannot survive and thus is not detected among the progeny of a cross.

dominance series of multiple alleles – Although each individual has only two alleles of a gene, many alleles of the gene may exist in the population. These alleles may be completely dominant, incompletely dominant, or codominant with respect to each other as determined by the phenotype of heterozygotes for the particular pair.

pleiotropy – A gene may affect more than one phenotype.

complementary gene action – Function of two different genes is required to produce a phenotype. Nonfunctional recessive alleles of either gene can produce the same abnormal phenotype in homozygotes. Such a phenotype that can be caused by nonfunctional alleles of more than one gene is called a **heterogeneous trait.**

epistasis – An allele of one gene hides the effects of different alleles at a second gene.

redundant genes – Two or more genes provide the same function.

penetrance – the fraction of individuals with a particular genotype who display the genotype's characteristic phenotype.

expressivity – the degree to which an affected individual displays the phenotype associated with that individual's genotype. Expressivity of a genotype can vary due to environment, chance, and alleles of other genes (**modifier genes**).

conditional mutation – a change in the base sequence of a gene that affects gene function only under specific environmental conditions.

continuous (quantitative) trait – a trait whose phenotype varies over a wide range of values that can be measured. Continuous traits are **polygenic** – they are controlled by the combined activities of many genes.

Key Ratios:

3:1 – Ratio of progeny phenotypes in a cross between monohybrids

[$Aa \times Aa \rightarrow$ 3 $A-$ (dominant phenotype) : 1 aa (recessive phenotype)]

1:2:1 – Ratio of progeny genotypes in a cross between monohybrids

($Aa \times Aa \rightarrow$ 1 AA : 2 Aa : 1aa)

1:1 – Ratio of progeny genotypes in a cross between a heterozygote and a recessive homozygote

($Aa \times aa \rightarrow$ 1 Aa : 1aa)

1:0 – All progeny have the same phenotype. Can result from several cases:

[$AA \times -- \rightarrow$ $A-$ (all dominant phenotype)]

[$aa \times aa \rightarrow$ aa (all recessive phenotype)]

9:3:3:1 – Ratio of progeny phenotypes in a dihybrid cross

($Aa\,Bb \times Aa\,Bb \rightarrow$ 9 $A-\,B-$: 3 $A-\,bb$: 3 $aa\,B-$: 1 aa)

1:2:1 – Ratio of progeny genotypes and phenotypes in a cross between hybrids when there is **incomplete dominance** or **codominance**:

($Aa \times Aa \rightarrow$ 1 AA : 2 Aa : 1aa)

Note that in incomplete dominance and codominance, a new (third) phenotype will appear in the hybrids (Aa) of the F_1 generation. In the F_2 generation, this same phenotype must be the largest component of the 1:2:1 monohybrid ratio.

2:1 – Ratio of progeny phenotypes observed in a cross between hybrids when one allele (A^1) is a **recessive lethal allele** that has a dominant effect on a visible phenotype:

($Aa \times Aa \rightarrow$ 1 A^1A^1 : 2 A^1A^2 : 1 A^2A^2)

Note that in this case, homozygotes for the recessive lethal allele A^1 die (*red colour*), but A^1A^2 heterozygotes have a phenotype different from A^2A^2 homozygotes.

Interactions of Two Genes:

You should be able to recognize traits influenced by two genes as variations on the 9:3:3:1 ratio of genotypic classes resulting from a dihybrid cross. For your convenience, an abbreviated version of Table 2.4 summarizing these gene interactions is presented below. It is particularly useful to understand the concepts of complementary gene action, epistasis, and redundancy.

If you are given the details of a biochemical pathway, you should be able to work out the ratios of phenotypes expected among the progeny of a cross. Note that you cannot go in the opposite

Chapter 2

direction: A particular ratio does not tell much about the underlying biochemistry. Thus, you should NOT try to memorize specific examples relating particular ratios to specific biochemical pathways.

F₂ Genotypic Ratios from an F₁ Dihybrid Cross

Gene interaction	A- B-	A- bb	aa B-	aa bb	F₂ Phenotypic Ratio
None: Four distinct F₂ Phenotypes	9	3	3	1	9:3:3:1
Complementary: One dominant allele of each of two genes is necessary to produce the phenotype	9	3	3	1	9:7
Recessive epistasis: Homozygous recessive allele of one gene masks both alleles of another gene	9	3	3	1	9:3:4
Dominant epistasis I: Dominant allele of one gene hides effects of both alleles of another gene	9	3	3	1	12:3:1
Dominant epistasis II: Dominant allele of one gene hides effects of dominant allele of another gene	9	3	3	1	13:3
Redundancy: Only one dominant allele of either of two genes is necessary to produce phenotype	9	3	3	1	15:1

Problem Solving:

The essential component of solving most genetics problems is to DIAGRAM THE CROSS in a consistent manner. In most cases you will be given information about phenotypes, so the diagram would be:

phenotype of one parent x phenotype of the other parent → phenotype(s) of progeny

The goal is to assign genotypes to the parents and then use these predicted genotypes to generate the genotypes, phenotypes, and ratios of progeny. If the predicted progeny match the observed data you were provided, then your genetic explanation is correct.

The points listed below will be particularly helpful in guiding your problem solving:

• Remember that **there are two alleles of each gene when describing the genotypes of individuals.** But if you are describing gametes, remember that **there is only one allele of each gene per gamete.**

• **You will need to determine whether a trait is dominant or recessive.** Two main clues will help you answer this question.

- o First, if the parents of a cross are true-breeding for the alternative forms of the trait, look at the phenotype of the F_1 progeny. Their genotype must be heterozygous, and their phenotype is thus controlled by the dominant allele of the gene.
  - o Second, look at the F_2 progeny (i.e., the progeny of the F_1 hybrids). The 3/4 portion of the 3:1 phenotypic ratio indicates the dominant phenotype.
- You should **recognize the need to set up a testcross** (to establish the genotype of an individual showing the dominant phenotype by crossing this individual to a recessive homozygote).
- You must **keep in mind the basic rules of probability:**
  - o *Product rule*: If two outcomes must occur together as the result of independent events, the probability of one outcome AND the other outcome occurring is the product of the two individual probabilities. So, the probability of getting a 4 on one die AND a 4 on the second die is the product of the two individual probabilities.
  - o *Sum rule*: If there is more than one way in which an outcome can be produced, the probability of either one OR the other occurring is the sum of the two mutually exclusive individual probabilities.
- Remember that **Punnett squares are not the only means of analyzing a cross; branched-line diagrams and calculations of probabilities according to the product and sum rules are more efficient ways of looking at complicated crosses** involving more than one or two genes.
- **You should be able to draw and interpret pedigrees.** When the trait is rare, look in particular for vertical patterns of inheritance characteristic of dominant traits, and horizontal patterns that typify recessive traits. Check your work by assigning genotypes to all individuals in the pedigree and verifying that these make sense.
- The vocabulary problem (the first problem in the set) is a useful gauge of how well you know the terms most critical for your understanding of the chapter.

In the first part of Chapter 2, the major goal was to determine which allele of a gene is dominant and which is recessive, and then to ascribe genotypes to various individuals or classes of individuals based on the ratio of progeny types seen in a cross. The challenges become more difficult in the second part of the chapter, but the first step in problem solving remains the same: You need to DIAGRAM THE CROSS in a consistent manner. The next steps are to answer the following questions:

How many genes are involved in determining the phenotype?

How many alleles of each gene are present?

What phenotypes are associated with which genotypic classes? (The answer to this last question will help you understand the dominance relationships between the alleles of each gene and the interactions between alleles of traits determined by more than one gene.)

The points listed below will be particularly helpful in guiding your problem solving:

- To distinguish between one gene and two gene traits, look for the number of phenotypic classes in the F_2 generation and the ratios in the F_2s among those classes. If a single gene is involved, there will be either two classes (3:1 or 2:1 if an allele is a recessive lethal) or three classes (1:2:1 in the cases of codominance or incomplete dominance). If two genes are involved, you could see two classes (9:7, 13:3, or 15:1) or three classes (9:3:4 or 12:3:1) or four classes (9:3:3:1). [*Note*: These ratios require that the P generation is true-breeding and that the F_1 crosses examined are between hybrids.]

- Understand that when there is codominance or incomplete dominance, a novel phenotype will appear in the F_1 generation. In the F_2 generation, this same phenotype must be the largest component of the 1:2:1 monohybrid ratio.

- If you see a series of crosses involving different phenotypes for a certain trait, for example coat colour, and each individual cross gives a monohybrid ratio (3:1 or 1:2:1), then all the phenotypes are controlled by one gene with many alleles that form an **allelic series**. You should write out the dominance hierarchy for this series (e.g., $a = b > c$) to keep track of the relationships among the alleles. Thus, a is codominant or incompletely dominant to b and both a and b are completely dominant to c.

- Lethal alleles are almost always recessive because a zygote with a dominant lethal allele could not grow into an adult. (The only exceptions to this rule involve **conditional lethal alleles** that survive in some environments but not others.) On the basis of what you have learned in this chapter, you can recognize recessive lethal alleles if they are pleiotropic and show a dominant visible phenotype such that the monohybrid phenotypic ratio is 2 (dominant phenotype) : 1 (recessive phenotype).

- Remember that the 9:3:3:1 dihybrid F_2 phenotypic ratio and its variants represent various combinations of the genotypic classes 9 $A- B-$: 3 $A- bb$: 3 $aa B-$: 1 $aa bb$, where the dashed line (–) indicates either a dominant or recessive allele. Based on the observed ratios, you should be able to tell which genotypic classes correspond to which phenotypes. Although you should not memorize the table on the previous page displaying these variants of 9:3:3:1, you should be able to consider whether particular biochemical explanations fit the ratios seen.

- Don't forget to use the product rule of probability to determine the proportions of genotypes or phenotypes for independently assorting genes

Solutions to Problems:

<u>Vocabulary</u>

2-1a. i. **4**; ii. **3**; iii. **6**; iv. **7**; v. **11**; vi. **13**; vii. **10**; viii. **2**; ix. **14**; x. **9**; xi. **12**; xii. **8**; xiii. **5**; xiv. **1**.

2-1b. i. **2**; ii. **5**; iii. **10;** iv. **7;** v. **6;** vi. **8;** vii. **11;** viii. **3;** ix. **4;** x. **1;** xi. **9**.

<u>Section 2.1 - Background</u>

2-2. Prior to Mendel, **people held two basic misconceptions about inheritance**. First was the common idea of blended inheritance: that the parental traits become mixed and forever changed in the offspring. Second, many thought that one parent contributes the most to an offspring's inherited features (e.g., some people thought they saw a fully formed child in a human sperm).

In addition, **people who studied inheritance did not approach the problem in an organized way**. They did not always control their crosses. They did not look at traits with clear-cut alternative phenotypes. They did not start with pure-breeding lines. They did not count the progeny types in their crosses. For these reasons, they could not develop the same insights as did Mendel.

2-3. There are **several advantages to using peas** for the study of inheritance. **(1) Peas have a fairly rapid generation time** (at least two generations per year if grown in the field, three or four generations per year if grown in greenhouses). **(2) Peas can either self-fertilize or be artificially crossed** by an experimenter. **(3) Peas produce large numbers of offspring** (hundreds per parent). **(4) Peas can be maintained as pure-breeding lines**, simplifying the ability to perform subsequent crosses. **(5) Because peas have been maintained as inbred stocks, two easily distinguished and discrete forms of many traits are known. (6) Peas are easy and inexpensive to grow.**

In contrast, studying **genetics in humans has several disadvantages. (1) The generation time of humans is very long** (roughly 20 years). **(2) There is no self-fertilization in humans, and it is not ethical to manipulate crosses. (3) Humans produce only a small number of offspring per mating** (usually one) **or per parent** (almost always fewer than 20). **(4) Although people who are homozygous for a trait do exist (analogous to pure-breeding stocks), homozygosity cannot be maintained** because mating with another individual is needed to produce the next generation. **(5) Because human populations are not inbred, most human traits show a continuum of phenotypes**; only a few traits have two very distinct forms. **(6) People require a lot of expensive care to "grow".**

There is nonetheless one major advantage to the study of genetics in humans: Because many inherited traits result in disease syndromes, and because the world's population now exceeds 7 billion people, **a very large number of people with diverse, variant phenotypes can be recognized.** These variations are the raw material of genetic analysis.

Section 2.2 – Genetic Analysis According to Mendel

2-4.

a. **Two phenotypes are seen in the second generation of this cross: normal and albino.** Thus, only one gene is required to control the phenotypes observed.

b. Note that the phenotype of the first generation progeny is normal colour, and that in the second generation, there is a ratio of 3 normal : 1 albino. Both of these observations show that **the allele controlling the normal phenotype (*A*) is dominant to the allele controlling the albino phenotype (*a*).**

c. In a testcross, an individual showing the dominant phenotype but that has an unknown genotype is mated with an individual that shows the recessive phenotype and is therefore homozygous for the recessive allele. The male parent is albino, so **the male parent's genotype is *aa*.** The **normal-coloured offspring** must receive an *A* allele from the mother, so **the genotype of the normal offspring is *Aa*.** The albino offspring must receive an *a* allele from the mother, so **the genotype of the albino offspring is *aa*.** Thus, **the female parent must be heterozygous *Aa*.**

2-5. Because two different phenotypes result from the mating of two cats of the same phenotype, the short-haired parent cats must have been heterozygous. The phenotype expressed in the heterozygotes (the parent cats) is the dominant phenotype. Therefore, **short hair is dominant to long hair.**

2-6.

a. Two affected individuals have an affected child and a normal child. This outcome is not possible if the affected individuals were homozygous for a recessive allele conferring piebald spotting, and if the trait is controlled by a single gene. Therefore, **the piebald spotting trait must be the dominant phenotype.**

b. If the trait is dominant, the piebald parents could be either homozygous (*PP*) or heterozygous (*Pp*). However, because the two affected individuals have an unaffected child *(pp)*, **they both must be heterozygous (*Pp*).** A diagram of the cross follows:

piebald x piebald → 1 piebald : 1 normal

Pp   x   *Pp* →   1 *Pp*   : 1 *pp*

Note that although the apparent ratio is 1:1, this is not a testcross but is instead a cross between two monohybrids. The reason for this discrepancy is that only two progeny were obtained, so this number is insufficient to establish what the true ratio would be (it should be 3:1) if many progeny resulted from the mating.

2-7. You would conduct a testcross between your normal-winged fly (*W*-) and a short-winged fly that must be homozygous recessive (*ww*). The possible results are diagrammed here; the first genotype in each cross is that of the normal-winged fly whose genotype was originally unknown.

WW x $ww \rightarrow$ **all Ww (normal wings)**

Ww x $ww \rightarrow$ **1/2 Ww (normal wings) : 1/2 ww (short wings).** (1:1 ratio)

2-8. First diagram the crosses:

closed x open $\rightarrow$ F$_1$ open $\rightarrow$ F$_2$ 145 open : 59 closed

F$_1$ open x closed $\rightarrow$ 81 open : 77 closed

The results of the crosses fit the pattern of inheritance of a single gene, with the open trait being dominant and the closed trait recessive. The first cross is similar to those Mendel did with pure-breeding plants, although you were not provided with the information that the starting plants were true-breeding. **The phenotype of the F$_1$ plants is open, indicating that open is dominant. The closed parent must be homozygous for the recessive allele. Because only one phenotype is seen among the F$_1$ plants, the open parent must be homozygous for the dominant allele.** Thus, the parental cucumber plants were indeed true-breeding homozygotes.

The result of the self-fertilization of the F$_1$ plants shows a 3:1 ratio of the open : closed phenotypes among the F$_2$ progeny. **The 3:1 ratio in the F$_2$ shows that a single gene controls the phenotypes and that the F$_1$ plants are all hybrids (i.e., they are heterozygotes).**

The final cross confirms that the F$_1$ plants from the first cross are heterozygous because **this testcross yields a 1:1 ratio of open: closed progeny.** In summary, all the data are consistent with the trait being determined by one gene with two alleles, and open being the dominant trait.

2-9. The dominant trait (short tail) is easier to eliminate from the population by selective breeding. The reason is you can recognize every animal that has inherited the short tail allele, because only one such dominant allele is needed to see the phenotype. If you prevent all the short-tailed animals from mating, then the allele would become extinct.

On the other hand, the recessive dilute coat colour allele can be passed unrecognized from generation to generation in heterozygous mice (who are *carriers*). The heterozygous mice do not express the phenotype, so they cannot be distinguished from homozygous dominant mice with normal coat colour. You could prevent the homozygous recessive mice with the dilute phenotype from mating, but the allele for the dilute phenotype would remain among the carriers, which you could not recognize.

2-10.

a. The problem already states that only one gene is involved in this trait, and that the dominant allele is dimpled (*D*) while the recessive allele is nondimpled (*d*). Diagram the cross described in this part of the problem:

nondimpled ♂ x dimpled ♀→ proportion of F_1 with dimple?

Note that the dimpled woman in this cross had a *dd* (nondimpled) mother, so the dimpled woman MUST be a heterozygote. We can thus rediagram this cross with genotypes:

dd (nondimpled) ♂ x *Dd* (dimpled) ♀ → **1/2 *Dd* dimpled** : 1/2 *dd* nondimpled

One half of the children produced by this couple would be dimpled.

b. Diagram the cross:

dimpled (*D?*) ♂ x nondimpled (*dd*) ♀ → nondimpled (*dd*) F_1

Because they have a nondimpled child (*dd*), the husband must have a *d* allele to contribute to the offspring. **The husband is thus of genotype *Dd*.**

c. Diagram the cross:

dimpled (*D?*) ♂ x nondimpled (*dd*) ♀ → eight F_1, all dimpled (*D–*)

The *D* allele in the children must come from their father. The father could be either *DD* or *Dd*, but **it is most probable that the father's genotype is *DD*.** We cannot rule out completely that the father is a *Dd* heterozygote. However, if this was the case, the probability that all 8 children would inherit the *D* allele from a *Dd* parent is only $(1/2)^8 = 1/256$.

2-11.

a. The only unambiguous cross is:

homozygous recessive x homozygous recessive → all homozygous recessive

The only cross that fits this criteria is: dry x dry → all dry. Therefore, **dry is the recessive phenotype (*ss*) and sticky is the dominant phenotype (*S–*).**

b. A 1:1 ratio comes from a testcross of heterozygous sticky (*Ss*) x dry (*ss*). However, **the sticky x dry matings here include both the *Ss* x *ss* AND the homozygous sticky (*SS*) x dry (*ss*).**

A 3:1 ratio comes from crosses between two heterozygotes, *Ss* x *Ss*. However, the sticky individuals are not only *Ss* heterozygotes but also *SS* homozygotes. Thus the sticky x sticky matings in this human population are a mix of matings between two heterozygotes (*Ss* x *Ss*), between two homozygotes (*SS* x *SS*), and between a homozygote and heterozygote (*SS* x *Ss*). **The 3:1 ratio of the heterozygote cross is therefore obscured by being combined with results of the two other crosses.**

2-12. Diagram the cross:

black x red → 1 black : 1 red

No, you cannot tell how coat colour is inherited from the results of this one mating. In effect, this was a testcross – a cross between animals of different phenotypes resulting in offspring of two phenotypes. This does not indicate whether red or black is the dominant phenotype. To determine which phenotype is dominant, remember that an animal with a recessive phenotype must be homozygous. Thus, **if you mate several red horses to each other and also mate several black horses to each other, the crosses that always yield only offspring with the parental phenotype must have been between homozygous recessives.** For example, if all the black x black matings result in only black offspring, black is recessive. Some of the red x red crosses (that is, crosses between heterozygotes) would then result in both red and black offspring in a ratio of 3:1. To establish this point, you might have to do several red x red crosses, because some of these crosses could be between red horses homozygous for the dominant allele. You could of course ensure that you were sampling heterozygotes by using the progeny of black x red crosses (such as that described in the problem) for subsequent black x black or red x red crosses.

2-13.

a. **1/6** because a die has 6 different sides.

b. There are three possible even numbers (2, 4, and 6). The probability of obtaining any one of these is 1/6. Because the 3 events are mutually exclusive, use the sum rule: $1/6 + 1/6 + 1/6 = 3/6 = $ **1/2.**

c. You must roll either a 3 or a 6, so $1/6 + 1/6 = 2/6 = $ **1/3.**

d. Each die is independent of the other, thus the product rule is used: $1/6 \times 1/6 = $ **1/36.**

e. The probability of getting an even number on one die is $3/6 = 1/2$ (see part *b*). This is also the probability of getting an odd number on the second die. This result could happen either of 2 ways – you could get the odd number first and the even number second, or *vice versa*. Thus the probability of both occurring is $1/2 \times 1/2 \times 2 = $ **1/2.**

f. The probability of any specific number on a die = 1/6. The probability of the same number on the other die =1/6. The probability of both occurring at the same time is 1/6 x 1/6 = 1/36. The same probability is true for the other 5 possible numbers on the dice. Thus the probability of any of these mutually exclusive situations occurring is 1/36 + 1/36 + 1/36 + 1/36 + 1/36 + 1/36 = 6/36 = **1/6**.

g. The probability of getting two numbers both over four is the probability of getting a 5 or 6 on one die (1/6 + 1/6 = 1/3) and 5 or 6 on the other die (1/3). The results for the two dice are independent events, so 1/3 x 1/3 = **1/9**.

2-14. The **probability of drawing a face card** = 12 face cards / 52 cards = **0.231**. The **probability of drawing a red card** = 26 / 52 = **0.5**. The **probability of drawing a red face card** = probability of a red card x probability of a face card = 0.231 x 0.5 [or 6 red face cards / 52 cards] = **0.116**

2-15.

a. The *Aa bb CC DD* woman can produce 2 genetically different eggs that vary in their allele of the first gene (*A* or *a*). She is homozygous for the other 3 genes and can only make eggs with the *b C D* alleles for these genes. Thus, using the product rule (because the inheritance of each gene is independent), she can make 2 x 1 x 1 x 1 = **2 different types of gametes**: (*A b C D* and *a b C D*).

b. Using the same logic, an *AA Bb Cc dd* woman can produce 1 x 2 x 2 x 1 = **4 different types of gametes**: *A* (*B* or *b*) (*C* or *c*) *d*.

c. A woman of genotype *Aa Bb cc Dd* can make 2 x 2 x 1 x 2 = **8 different types of gametes**: (*A* or *a*) (*B* or *b*) *c* (*D* or *d*).

d. A woman who is a quadruple heterozygote can make 2 x 2 x 2 x 2 = **16 different types of gametes**: (*A* or *a*) (*B* or *b*) (*C* or *c*) (*D* or *d*). This problem (like those in parts *a-c* above) can also be visualized with a branched-line diagram.

2-16.

a. The probability of any phenotype in this cross depends only on the gamete from the heterozygous parent. The probability that a child will resemble the quadruply heterozygous parent is thus $1/2$ A x $1/2$ B x $1/2$ C x $1/2$ D = $1/16$. The probability that a child will resemble the quadruply homozygous recessive parent is $1/2$ a x $1/2$ b x $1/2$ c x $1/2$ d = $1/16$. **The probability that a child will resemble either parent is then $1/16 + 1/16 = 1/8$**. This cross will produce 2 different phenotypes for each gene or 2 x 2 x 2 x 2 = **16 potential phenotypes.**

b. The probability of a child resembling the recessive parent is 0; the probability of a child resembling the dominant parent is 1 x 1 x 1 x 1 = 1. **The probability that a child will resemble one of the two parents is 0 + 1 = 1. Only 1 phenotype is possible in the progeny (dominant for all 4 genes),** as $(1)^4 = 1$.

c. The probability that a child would show the dominant phenotype for any one gene is 3/4 in this sort of cross (remember the 3/4 : 1/4 monohybrid ratio of phenotypes), so the **probability of resembling the parent for all four genes is $(3/4)^4 = 81/256$**. There are 2 phenotypes possible for each gene, so $(2)^4 =$ **16 different kinds of progeny.**

d. **All progeny will resemble their parents** because all of the alleles from both parents are identical, so the **probability = 1**. There is only 1 phenotype possible for each gene in this cross; because $(1)^4 = 1$, the child can have only **one possible phenotype** when considering all four genes.

2-17.

a. The combination of alleles in the egg and sperm allows only one genotype for the zygote: *aa Bb Cc DD Ee*.

b. Because the inheritance of each gene is independent, you can use the product rule to determine the number of different types of gametes that are possible: 1 x 2 x 2 x 1 x 2 = **8 types of gametes** (as in problem 2-15). To figure out the types of gametes, consider the possibilities for each gene separately and then the possible combinations of genes in a consistent order. For each gene the possibilities are: *a*, (*B* : *b*), (*C* : *c*), *D*, and (*E* : *e*). The possibilities can be determined using the product rule. Thus for the first 2 genes [*a*] x [*B* : *b*] gives [*a B* : *a b*] x [*C* : *c*] gives [*a B C* : *a B c* : *a b C* : *a b c*] x [*D*] gives [*a B C D* : *a B c D* : *a b C D* : *a b c D*] x [*E* : *e*] gives [*a B C D E* : *a B C D e* : *a B c D E* : *a B c D e* : *a b C D E* : *a b C D e* : *a b c D E* : *a b c D e*]. This problem can also be visualized with a branched-line diagram:

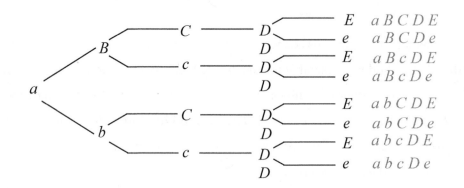

2-18. The first two parts of this problem involve the probability of occurrence of two independent traits: the sex of a child and galactosaemia. The parents are heterozygous for galactosaemia, so there is a 1/4 chance that a child will be affected (that is, homozygous recessive). The probability that a child is a girl is 1/2. The probability of an affected girl is therefore 1/4 x 1/2 = 1/8.

a. Fraternal (non-identical) twins result from two independent fertilization events and therefore the probability that both will be girls with galactosaemia is the product of their individual probabilities (see above); 1/8 x 1/8 = **1/64**.

b. For identical twins, one fertilization event gave rise to two individuals. The probability that both are girls with galactosaemia is **1/8**.

For parts *c-g*, remember that each child is an independent genetic event. The sex of the children is not at issue in these parts of the problem.

c. Both parents are carriers (heterozygous), so the probability of having an unaffected child is 3/4. The probability of 4 unaffected children is 3/4 x 3/4 x 3/4 x 3/4 = **81/256**.

d. The probability that at least one child is affected is all outcomes except the one mentioned in part *c*. Thus, the probability is 1 - 81/256 = **175/256**. Note that this general strategy for solving problems, where you first calculate the probability of all events except the one of interest, and then subtract that number from 1, is often useful for problems where direct calculations of the probability of interest appear to be very difficult.

e. The probability of an affected child is 1/4 while the probability of an unaffected child is 3/4. Therefore 1/4 x 1/4 x 3/4 x 3/4 = **9/256**.

f. The probability of 2 affected and 1 unaffected in any one particular birth order is 1/4 x 1/4 x 3/4 = 3/64. There are 3 mutually exclusive birth orders that could produce 2 affected and 1 unaffected – unaffected child first born, unaffected child second born, and unaffected child third born. Thus, there is a 3/64 + 3/64 + 3/64 = **9/64** chance that 2 out of 3 children will be affected.

g. The phenotype of any particular child is independent of all others, so the probability of an affected child is **1/4**.

2-19. Diagram the cross, where *P* is the normal pigmentation allele and *p* is the albino allele:

normal (*P?*) x normal (*P?*) → albino (*pp*)

An albino must be homozygous recessive *pp*. The parents are normal in pigmentation and therefore could be *PP* or *Pp*. Because they have an albino child, **both parents must be carriers (*Pp*). The probability that their next child will have the *pp* genotype is 1/4.**

2-20. Diagram the cross:

yellow round x yellow round → 156 yellow round : 54 yellow wrinkled

The monohybrid ratio for seed shape is 156 round : 54 wrinkled = 3 round : 1 wrinkled. The parents must therefore have been heterozygous (*Rr*) for the pea shape gene. All the offspring are yellow and therefore have the *Yy* or *YY* genotype. **The parent plants were *Y– Rr* x *YY Rr*** (that is, you know at least one of the parents must have been *YY*).

2-21. Diagram the cross:

smooth black ♂ x rough white ♀ → F₁ rough black

→ F₂ 8 smooth white : 25 smooth black : 23 rough white : 69 rough black

a. Since only one phenotype was seen in the first generation of the cross, we can assume that the parents were true-breeding, and that the F₁ generation consists of heterozygous animals. **The phenotype of the F₁ progeny indicates that rough and black are the dominant phenotypes. Four phenotypes are seen in the F₂ generation so there are two genes controlling the phenotypes in this cross. Therefore, *R* = rough, *r* = smooth; *B* = black, *b* = white.** In the F₂ generation, consider each gene separately. For the coat texture, there were 8 + 25 = 33 smooth : 23 + 69 = 92 rough, or a ratio of ~1 smooth : ~3 rough. For the coat colour, there were 8 + 23 = 31 white : 25 + 69 = 94 black, or about ~1 white : ~3 black, so the F₂ progeny support the conclusion that the F₁ animals were heterozygous for both genes.

b. An F₁ male is heterozygous for both genes, or *Rr Bb*. The smooth white female must be homozygous recessive; that is, *rr bb*. Thus, *Rr Bb* x *rr bb* → 1/2 *Rr* (rough) : 1/2 *rr* (smooth) and 1/2 *Bb* (black) : 1/2 *bb* (white). The inheritance of these genes is independent, so apply the product rule to find the expected phenotypic ratios among the progeny, or **1/4 rough black : 1/4 rough white : 1/4 smooth black : 1/4 smooth white**.

2-22. Diagram the cross:

$YY\,rr\ \times\ yy\,RR\ \rightarrow$ all $Yy\,Rr\ \rightarrow$ 9/16 $Y{-}\,R{-}$ (yellow round) : 3/16 $Y{-}\,rr$ (yellow wrinkled) : 3/16 $yy\,R{-}$ (green round) : 1/16 $yy\,rr$ (green wrinkled).

Each F_2 pea results from a separate fertilization event. The probability of 7 yellow round F_2 peas is $(9/16)^7 = 4{,}782{,}969/268{,}435{,}456 = \mathbf{0.018}$.

2-23.

a. First diagram the cross, and then figure out the monohybrid ratios for each gene:

$Aa\,Tt\ \times\ Aa\,Tt\ \rightarrow$ 3/4 $A{-}$ (achoo) : 1/4 aa (non-achoo) and 3/4 $T{-}$ (trembling) : 1/4 tt (non-trembling).

The probability that a child will be $A{-}$ (and have achoo syndrome) is independent of the probability that it will lack a trembling chin, so the probability of a child with achoo syndrome but without trembling chin is 3/4 $A{-}$ x 1/4 tt = **3/16**.

b. The probability that a child would have neither dominant trait is 1/4 aa x 1/4 tt = **1/16**.

2-24. The F_1 must be heterozygous for all the genes because the parents were pure-breeding (homozygous). The appearance of the F_1 establishes that the dominant phenotypes for the four traits are tall, purple flowers, axial flowers and green pods.

a. From a heterozygous F_1 x F_1, both dominant and recessive phenotypes can be seen for each gene. Thus, you expect 2 x 2 x 2 x 2 = 16 different phenotypes when considering the four traits together. The possibilities can be determined using the product rule with the pairs of phenotypes for each gene, because the traits are inherited independently. Thus: [tall : dwarf] x [green : yellow] gives [tall green : tall yellow : dwarf green : dwarf yellow] x [purple : white] gives [tall green purple : tall yellow purple : dwarf green purple : dwarf yellow purple : tall green white : tall yellow white : dwarf green white : dwarf yellow white] x [terminal : axial] which gives **tall green purple terminal : tall yellow purple terminal : dwarf green purple terminal : dwarf yellow purple terminal : tall green white terminal : tall yellow white terminal : dwarf green white terminal : dwarf yellow white terminal : tall green purple axial : tall yellow purple axial : dwarf green purple axial : dwarf yellow purple axial : tall green white axial : tall yellow white axial : dwarf green white axial : dwarf yellow white axial**. The possibilities can also be determined using the branched-line method shown below, which might in this complicated problem be easier to track.

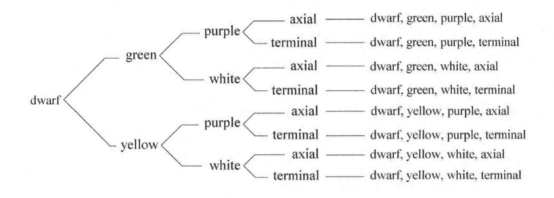

b. Designate the alleles: *T* = tall, *t* = dwarf; *G* = green; *g* = yellow; *P* = purple, *p* = white; *A* = axial, *a* = terminal. The cross *Tt Gg Pp Aa* (an F$_1$ plant) x *tt gg pp AA* (the dwarf parent) will produce 2 phenotypes for the tall, green and purple genes, but only 1 phenotype (axial) for the fourth gene or 2 x 2 x 2 x 1 = **8 different phenotypes**. The first 3 genes will give a 1/2 dominant : 1/2 recessive ratio of the phenotypes (for example 1/2 *T* : 1/2 *t*) as this is in effect a testcross for each gene. Thus, **the proportion of each phenotype in the progeny will be 1/2 x 1/2 x 1/2 x 1 = 1/8.**

   Using either of the methods described in part *a*, the progeny will be **1/8 tall green purple axial : 1/8 tall yellow purple axial : 1/8 dwarf green purple axial : 1/8 dwarf yellow purple axial : 1/8 tall green white axial : 1/8 tall yellow white axial : 1/8 dwarf green white axial : 1/8 dwarf yellow white axial**.

2-25. For each separate cross, determine the number of genes involved. Remember that 4 phenotypic classes in the progeny means that 2 genes control the phenotypes. Next, determine the phenotypic ratio for each gene separately. A 3:1 monohybrid ratio tells you which phenotype is dominant and that both parents were heterozygous for the trait; in contrast, a 1:1 ratio results from a testcross where the dominant parent was heterozygous.

Chapter 2

a. There are 2 genes in this cross (4 phenotypes). One gene controls purple : white with a monohybrid ratio of 94 + 28 = 122 purple : 32 + 11 = 43 white or ~3 purple : ~1 white. The second gene controls spiny : smooth with a monohybrid ratio of 94 + 32 =126 spiny : 28 + 11 = 39 smooth or ~3 spiny : ~1 smooth. Thus, designate the alleles for the flower colour trait as *P* = **purple**, *p* = **white**, **with the *P* allele dominant to the *p* allele; and for the pod shape trait as *S* = spiny, *s* = smooth, with the *S* allele dominant to the *s* allele**. This is a straightforward dihybrid cross: ***Pp Ss* x *Pp Ss*** → **9 *P– S–* : 3 *P– ss* : 3 *pp S–* : 1 *pp ss*.**

b. The 1 spiny : 1 smooth ratio indicates a testcross for the pod shape gene. Because all progeny were purple, at least one parent plant must have been homozygous for the *P* allele of the flower colour gene. The cross was **either *PP Ss* x *P– ss* or *P– Ss* x *PP ss*.**

c. This is similar to part *b*, except that here all the progeny were spiny so at least one parent must have been homozygous for the *S* allele. The 1 purple : 1 white testcross ratio indicates that **the parents were either *Pp S–* x *pp SS* or *Pp SS* x *pp S–*.**

d. Looking at each trait individually, there are 89 + 31 = 120 purple : 92 + 27 = 119 white. A 1 purple : 1 white monohybrid ratio denotes a testcross. For the other gene, there are 89 + 92 = 181 spiny : 31 + 27 = 58 smooth, or a 3 spiny : 1 smooth ratio indicating that the parents were both heterozygous for the *S* gene. **The genotypes of the parents were *pp Ss* x *Pp Ss*.**

e. There is a 3 purple : 1 white ratio among the progeny, so the parents were both heterozygous for the *P* gene. All progeny have smooth pods so the parents were both homozygous recessive *ss*. **The genotypes of the parents were *Pp ss* x *Pp ss*.**

f. There is a 3 spiny : 1 smooth ratio, indicative of a cross between heterozygotes (*Ss* x *Ss*). All progeny were white so the parents must have been homozygous recessive *pp*. **The genotypes of the parents were *pp Ss* x *pp Ss*.**

2-26. Three characters (genes) are being analyzed in this cross. While we can usually tell which alleles are dominant from the phenotype of the heterozygote, we are not told the phenotype of the heterozygote (that is, the original pea plant that was selfed). Instead, use the monohybrid phenotypic ratios to determine which allele is dominant and which is recessive for each gene. Consider height first. There are 272 + 92 + 88 + 35 = 487 tall plants and 93 + 31 + 29 + 11 = 164 dwarf plants. This is a ratio of ~3 tall : ~1 dwarf, indicating that **tall is dominant**. Next consider pod shape, where there are 272 + 92 + 93 + 31 = 488 inflated pods and 88 + 35 + 29 + 11 = 163 flat pods, or approximately 3 inflated : 1 flat, so **inflated is dominant**. Finally, consider flower colour. There were 272 + 88 + 93 + 29 = 482 purple flowers and 92 + 35 + 31 + 11 = 169 white flowers, or ~3 purple : ~1 white. Thus, **purple is dominant**.

2-27. Diagram each of these crosses, remember that you were told that tiny wings = *t*, normal wings = *T*, narrow eye = *n* and oval (normal) eye = *N*. You thus know that one gene determines the wing trait and one gene determines the eye trait, and you further know the dominance relationship between the alleles of each gene.

In **cross 1**, all of the parents and offspring show the tiny wing phenotype so there is no variability in the gene controlling this trait, and all flies in this cross are *tt*. Note that the eye phenotypes in the offspring are seen in a ratio of 3 oval : 1 narrow. This phenotypic monohybrid ratio means that both parents are heterozygous for the gene (*Nn*). Thus **the genotypes for the parents in cross 1 are**: *tt Nn* ♂ x *tt Nn* ♀.

In **cross 2** consider the wing trait first. The female parent is tiny (*tt*) so this is a testcross for the wings. The offspring show both tiny and normal in a ratio of 82 : 85 or a ratio of 1 tiny : 1 normal. Therefore the normal male parent must be heterozygous for this gene (*Tt*). For eyes the narrow parent is homozygous recessive (*nn*) so again this is a testcross for this gene. Again both eye phenotypes are seen in the offspring in a ratio of 1 oval : 1 narrow, so the oval female parent is a *Nn* heterozygote. Thus **the genotypes for the parents in cross 2 are**: *Tt nn* ♂ x *tt Nn* ♀.

Consider the wing phenotype in the offspring of **cross 3**. Both wing phenotypes are seen in a ratio of 64 normal flies : 21 tiny or a 3 normal : 1 tiny. Thus both parents are *Tt* heterozygotes. The male parent is narrow (*nn*), so cross 3 is a testcross for eyes. Both phenotypes are seen in the offspring in a 1 normal : 1 narrow ratio, so the female parent is heterozygous for this gene. **The genotypes of the parents in cross 3 are**: *Tt nn* ♂ x *Tt Nn* ♀.

When examining **cross 4** you notice a monohybrid phenotypic ratio of 3 normal : 1 tiny for the wings in the offspring. Thus both parents are heterozygous for this gene (*Tt*). Because the male parent has narrow eyes (*nn*), this cross is a testcross for eyes. All of the progeny have oval eyes, so the female parent must be homozygous dominant for this trait. Thus **the genotypes of the parents in cross 4 are**: *Tt nn* ♂ x *Tt NN* ♀.

2-28.

a. Analyze each gene separately: *Tt* x *Tt* will give 3/4 *T–* (normal wing) offspring. The cross *nn* x *Nn* will give 1/2 *N–* (normal eye) offspring. To calculate the probability of the normal offspring apply the product rule to the normal portions of the monohybrid ratios by multiplying these two fractions: 3/4 *T–* x 1/2 *N–* = 3/8 *T– N–*. Thus **3/8 of the offspring of this cross will have normal wings and oval eyes**.

b. Diagram the cross:

$Tt\ nn\ ♀\ \times\ Tt\ Nn\ ♂ \rightarrow\ ?$

Find the phenotypic monohybrid ratio separately for each gene in the offspring. Then multiply these monohybrid ratios to find the phenotypic dihybrid ratio. A cross of $Tt \times Tt \rightarrow 3/4$ $T–$ (normal wings) : $1/4$ tt (tiny wings). For the eyes the cross is $nn \times Nn \rightarrow 1/2$ $N–$ (oval) : $1/2$ nn (narrow). Applying the product rule gives $3/8$ $T– N–$ (normal oval) : $3/8$ $T– nn$ (normal narrow) : $1/8$ $tt\ N–$ (tiny oval) : $1/8$ $tt\ nn$ (tiny narrow). When you multiply each fraction by 200 progeny you will see **75 normal oval : 75 normal narrow : 25 tiny oval : 25 tiny narrow**.

2-29.

a. **The protein specified by the pea colour gene is an enzyme called Sgr**, which is required for the breakdown of the green pigment chlorophyll. (See Figure A in the Fast Forward box "Genes Encode Proteins").

b. **The y allele could be a null allele** because it does not specify the production of any of the Sgr enzyme.

c. The Y allele is dominant because in the heterozygote, **the single Y allele will lead to the production of some Sgr enzyme**, even if the y allele cannot specify any Sgr. **The amount of the Sgr enzyme made in heterozygotes is sufficient for yellow colour.**

d. **In yy peas, the green chlorophyll cannot be broken down**, so this pigment stays in the peas, which remain green in colour.

e. If the amount of Sgr protein is proportional to the number of functional copies of the gene, then YY homozygotes should have twice the amount of Sgr protein as do Yy heterozygotes. Yet both YY and Yy peas are yellow. These observations suggest that **half the normal amount of Sgr enzyme is sufficient for the pea to break down enough chlorophyll so that the pea will still be yellow.**

f. Just as was seen in part e, for many genes (including that for pea colour), half the amount of the protein specified by the gene is sufficient for a normal phenotype. Thus, in most cases, even if the gene is essential, heterozygotes for null alleles will survive. **The advantage of having two copies of essential genes is then that even if one normal allele becomes mutated (changed) so that it becomes a null allele, the organism can survive because half the normal amount of gene product is usually sufficient for survival.**

g. **Yes, a single pea pod could contain peas with different phenotypes because a pod is an ovary that contains several ovules (eggs), and each pea represents a single fertilization event involving one egg and one sperm (from one pollen grain).** If the female plant was Yy, or yy, then it is possible that some peas in the same pod would be yellow and others green. For example, fertilization of a y egg with Y pollen would yield a yellow pea, but if the pollen grain was y, the pea would be green. However, a pea pod could not contain peas with different phenotypes if the female plant was *YY*, because all the peas produced by this plant would be yellow.

h. **Yes, it is possible that a pea pod could be different in colour from a pea growing within it.** One reason is that, as just seen in part *g*, **a single pod can contain green and yellow peas**. But a more fundamental reason is that **one gene controls the phenotype of pea colour, while a different gene controls the separate phenotype of pod colour.**

2-30. If the alleles of the pea colour and pea shape genes inherited from a parent in the P generation always stayed together and never separated, then the gametes produced by the doubly heterozygous F₁ individuals in Figure 2.14 would be either *Y R* or *y r*. (Note that only two possibilities would exist, and these would be in equal frequencies.) On a Punnett square (male gametes shaded in *blue*, female gametes in *pink*):

	Y R ½	*y r* ½
Y R ½	*YY RR* ¼	*Yy Rr* ¼
y r ½	*Yy Rr* ¼	*yy rr* ¼

Thus **the genotypic ratios of the F₂ progeny would be 1/4 *YY RR*, 1/2 *Yy Rr* , and 1/4 *yy rr*. The phenotypic ratios among the F₂ progeny would be 3/4 yellow round and 1/4 green wrinkled.** These results make sense because if the alleles of the two genes were always inherited as a unit, you would expect the same ratios as in a monohybrid cross.

2-31. Similar to what you saw in Figure A in the Fast Forward box "Genes Encode Proteins", **the most likely biochemical explanation is that the dominant allele *L* specifies functional G3βH enzyme, while the recessive allele *l* is incapable of specifying any functional enzyme** (in nomenclature you will see in later chapters, *l* is a *null allele*). The functional enzyme can synthesize the growth hormone gibberellin, so plants with the *L* allele are tall. **Even half the normal amount of this enzyme is sufficient for the tall phenotype, explaining why *Ll* heterozygotes are tall.**

2-32.

a. As in Problem 31 above, **the dominant allele *P* most likely specifies a functional product (in this case, the protein bHLH), while the recessive *p* allele cannot specify any functional protein.** The fact that the hybrid is purple (as shown on Figure 2.7) indicates that half the normal amount of active bHLH protein is sufficient for purple colour.

Chapter 2

b. **Yes, flower colour could potentially be controlled by genes specifying the enzymes DFR, ANS, or 3GT in addition to the gene specifying the bHLH protein.** Alleles specifying functional enzymes would yield purple colour, while those that could not produce functional enzymes would cause white colour. It is likely that the alleles for purple colour would be dominant.

Section 2.3 – Mendelian Inheritance in Humans

2-33.

a. **Recessive** - two unaffected individuals have an affected child— **II-1, V-2 (*aa*)**. Therefore, the parents in generation I and those involved in the consanguineous marriage must all be carriers – **I-1, I-2, IV-1, IV-2 (*Aa*)**.

b. **Dominant** - the trait is seen in each generation and every affected person (*A–*) has an affected parent. Note that III-3 is unaffected (*aa*) even though both his parents are affected; this would not be possible for a recessive trait. The term "carrier" is not applicable, because everyone with a single *A* allele shows the trait.

c. **Recessive** - two unaffected, carrier parents – **II-4, II-5 (*Aa*)** have an affected child— **III-4 (*aa*)**, as in part *a*. Individual **I-2** is also affected (*aa*) and thus has transmitted a recessive disease allele to all of his children, making individuals **II-1, II-2, and II-3** carriers (*Aa*) also.

2-34.

a. Cutis laxa must be a recessive trait because affected child II-4 has normal parents. Because II-4 is affected she must have received a disease allele (*CL*) from both parents. The mother (I-3) and the father (I-4) are both heterozygous ($CL^+ CL$). **The trait is thus recessive.**

b. You are told that this trait is rare, so unrelated people in the pedigree, like I-2, are almost certainly homozygous normal ($CL^+ CL^+$). Diagram the cross that gives rise to II-2: $CL CL$ (I-1) x $CL^+ CL^+$ (I-2) → $CL^+ CL$. Thus the **probability that II-2 is a carrier is very close to 100 percent**. (In Chapter 12 you will find the definition of a term called the *allele frequency*; if the value of the allele frequency in the population under study is known, you can calculate the very low likelihood that II-2 is a carrier.)

c. As described in part *a* both parents in this cross are carriers: $CL^+ CL$ x $CL^+ CL$. II-3 is <u>not</u> affected so he cannot have the *CL CL* genotype. Therefore there is a 1/3 probability that he has the $CL^+ CL^+$ genotype and a **2/3 probability that he is a carrier ($CL^+ CL$)**.

d. As shown in part *b*, II-2 must be a carrier ($CL^+ CL$). In order to have an affected child II-3 must also be a carrier. The probability of this is 2/3 as shown in part *c*. The probability of two heterozygous parents having an affected child is 1/4. Apply the product rule to these probabilities: (1 probability that II-2 is $CL^+ CL$) x (2/3 probability that II-3 is $CL^+ CL$) x (1/4 probability of an affected child from a mating of two carriers) = 2/12 = **1/6**.

2-35. Diagram the cross! In humans, this is usually done as a pedigree. Remember that the affected siblings must be *CF CF*.

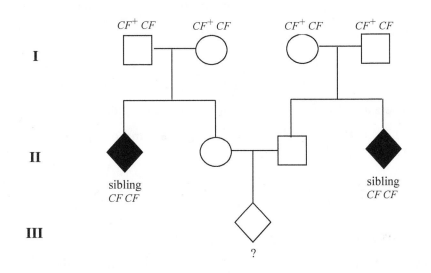

a. **The probability that II-2 is a carrier is 2/3.** Both families have an affected sibling, so both sets of parents (that is, all the people in generation I) must have been carriers. Thus, the expected genotypic ratio in the children is 1/4 affected : 1/2 carrier : 1/4 homozygous normal. II-2 is NOT affected, so she cannot be *CF CF*. Of the remaining possible genotypes, 2 are heterozygous. There is therefore a 2/3 chance that she is a carrier.

b. **The probability that II-2 x II-3 will have an affected child** is 2/3 (the probability that the mother is a carrier as seen in part *a*) x 2/3 (the probability the father is a carrier using the same reasoning) x 1/4 (the probability that two carriers can produce an affected child) = 4/36 = **1/9**.

c. The probability that both parents are carriers and that their child will be a carrier is 2/3 x 2/3 x 1/2 = 2/9 (using the same reasoning as in part *b*, except asking that the child be a carrier instead of affected). However, it is also possible for $CF^+ CF^+$ x $CF^+ CF$ parents to have children that are carriers. Remember that there are 2 possible ways for this particular mating to occur – homozygous father x heterozygous mother or *vice versa*. Thus the probability of this sort of mating is 2 x 1/3 (the probability that a particular parent is $CF^+ CF^+$) x 2/3 (the probability that the other parent is $CF^+ CF$) x 1/2 (the probability that such a mating could produce a carrier child) = 2/9. **The probability that a child could be a carrier** from either of these two scenarios (where both parents are carriers or where only one parent is a carrier) is the sum of these mutually exclusive events, or $2/9 + 2/9 = \textbf{4/9}$.

2-36.

a. Because the disease is rare the affected father is most likely to be heterozygous ($HD^+ HD$). **There is a 1/2 chance that the son** inherited the HD allele from his father and **will develop the disease.**

b. **The probability of an affected child is:** 1/2 (the probability that Joe is $HD^+ HD$) x 1/2 (the probability that the child inherits the HD allele if Joe is $HD^+ HD$) = **1/4.**

2-37. The trait is recessive because pairs of unaffected individuals (I-1 x I-2 as well as II-3 x II-4) had affected children (II-1, III-1, and III-2). There are also two cases in which an unrelated individual must have been a carrier (II-4 and either I-1 or I-2), so **the disease allele appears to be common in the population.**

2-38.

a. **The inheritance pattern seen in Figure 2.20 could be caused by a rare dominant mutation.** In this case, the affected individuals would be heterozygous ($HD^+ HD$) and the normal individuals would be $HD^+ HD^+$. Any mating between an affected individual and an unaffected individual would give 1/2 normal ($HD^+ HD^+$) : 1/2 affected ($HD^+ HD$) children. **However, the same pattern of inheritance could be seen if the disease were caused by a common recessive mutation.** In the case of a common recessive mutation, all the affected individuals would be $HD\ HD$. Because the mutant allele is common in the population, most or even all of the unrelated individuals could be assumed to be carriers ($HD^+ HD$). Matings between affected and unaffected individuals would then also yield phenotypic ratios of progeny of 1/2 normal ($HD^+ HD$) : 1/2 affected ($HD\ HD$).

b. **Determine the phenotype of the 14 children of III-6 and IV-6. If the disease is due to a recessive allele,** then III-6 and IV-6 must be homozygous for this recessive allele, and **all their children must have the disease. If the disease is due to a dominant mutation,** then III-6 and IV-6 must be heterozygotes (because they are affected but they each had one unaffected parent), and **1/4 of their 14 children would be expected to be unaffected.**

Alternatively, you could **look at the progeny of matings between unaffected individuals** in the pedigree such as III-1 and an unaffected spouse. **If the disease were due to a dominant mutation, these matings** would all be homozygous recessive x homozygous recessive and **would never give affected children. If the disease is due to a recessive mutation,** then many of these individuals would be carriers, and if the trait is common then at least some of the spouses would also be carriers, so **such matings could give affected children**.

2-39. Diagram the cross by drawing a pedigree:

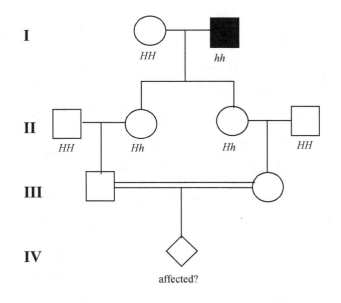

affected?

a. Assuming the disease is very rare, the first generation is *HH* unaffected (I-1) x *hh* affected (I-2). Thus, both of the children (II-2 and II-3) must be carriers (*Hh*). Again assuming this trait is rare in the population, those people marrying into the family (II-1 and II-4) are homozygous normal (*HH*). Therefore, the probability that III-1 is a carrier is 1/2; III-2 has the same chance of being a carrier. **Thus the probability that a child produced by these two first cousins would be affected** is 1/2 (the probability that III-1 is a carrier) x 1/2 (the probability that III-2 is a carrier) x 1/4 (the probability the child of two carriers would have an *hh* genotype) = **1/16 = 0.0625**.

b. If 1/10 people in the population are carriers, then the probability that II-1 and II-4 are *Hh* is 0.1 for each. In this case an affected child in generation IV can only occur if III-1 and III-2 are both carriers. III-1 can be a carrier as the result of 2 different matings: (i) II-1 homozygous normal x II-2 carrier or (ii) II-1 carrier x II-2 carrier. (Note that whether I-1 is *HH* or *Hh*, II-2 must be a carrier because of the normal phenotype (II-2 cannot be *hh*) and the fact that one parent was affected.) The probability of III-1 being a carrier is thus the probability of mating (i) x the probability of generating an *Hh* child from mating (i) + the probability of mating (ii) x the probability of generating an *Hh* child from mating (ii) = 0.9 (the probability II-1 is *HH*, which is the probability for mating [i]) x 1/2 (the probability that III-1 will inherit *h* in mating [i]) + 0.1 (the probability II-1 is *Hh*, which is the probability for mating [ii]) x 2/3 (the probability that III-1 will inherit *h* in mating [ii]; remember that III-1 is known not to be *hh*) = 0.45 + 0.067 = 0.517. The chance that III-2 will inherit *h* is exactly the same. **Thus, the probability that IV-1 is *hh*** = 0.517 (the probability

III-1 is *Hh*) x 0.517 (the probability that III-2 is *Hh*) x 1/4 (the probability the child of two carriers will be *hh*) = 0.067. **This number is slightly higher than the answer to part *a*, which was 0.0625, so the increased likelihood that II-1 or II-4 is a carrier makes it only slightly more likely that IV-1 will be affected.**

2-40.

a. Both diseases are known to be rare, so normal people marrying into the pedigree are assumed to be homozygous normal. **Nail-patella (*N*) syndrome is dominant** because all affected children have an affected parent. **Alkaptonuria (*a*) is recessive** because the affected children are the result of a consanguineous mating between 2 unaffected individuals (III-3 x III-4). Because alkaptonuria is a rare disease, it makes sense to assume that III-3 and III-4 inherited the same *a* allele from a common ancestor. Genotypes: **I-1 *nn Aa*; I-2 *Nn AA* (or I-1 *nn AA* and I-2 *Nn Aa*); II-1 *nn AA*; II-2 *nn Aa*; II-3 *Nn A–*; II-4 *nn A–*; II-5 *Nn Aa*; II-6 *nn AA*; III-1 *nn AA*; III-2 *nn A–*; III-3 *nn Aa*; III-4 *Nn Aa*; III-5 *nn A–*; III-6 *nn A–*; IV-1 *nn A–*; IV-2 *nn A–*; IV-3 *Nn A–*; IV-4 *nn A–*; IV-5 *Nn aa*; IV-6 *nn aa*; IV-7 *nn A–*.**

b. The cross is *nn A–* (IV-2) x *Nn aa* (IV-5). The ambiguity in the genotype of IV-2 is due to the uncertainty of his father's genotype (III-2). His parents' genotypes are *nn AA* (II-1) x *nn Aa* (II-2) so there is a 1/2 chance III-2 is *nn AA* and a 1/2 chance he is *nn Aa*. Thus, for each of the phenotypes below you must consider both possible genotypes for IV-2. For each part below, calculate the probability of the child inheriting the correct gametes from IV-2 x the probability of obtaining the correct gametes from IV-5 to give the desired phenotype. If both the possible IV-2 genotypes can produce the needed gametes, you will need to sum the two probabilities.

- For the child to have **both syndromes** (*N– aa*), IV-2 would have to contribute an *n a* gamete. This could only occur if IV-2 were *nn Aa*. The probability IV-2 is *nn Aa* is 1/4: For IV-2 to be *nn Aa*, III-2 would have had to be *nn Aa* and would also have had to give an *n a* gamete to IV-2. The probability of each of those events is 1/2, so the chance of both of them occurring is 1/2 x 1/2 = 1/4. (Note that we can assume that II-2 is *nn Aa* because III-3 must have given two of her children an *a* allele. Therefore, both II-2 and III-3 must be *nn Aa*). If IV-2 is *nn Aa*, the chance that he would give a child an *n a* gamete is 1/2. The probability that IV-5 would supply an *N a* gamete is also 1/2. Thus, **the probability that the child would have both syndromes is 1/4 x 1/2 x 1/2 = 1/16**. There is no need to sum probabilities in this case because IV-2 cannot produce an *n a* gamete if his genotype is *nn AA*.

- For the child to have only **nail-patella syndrome** (*N– A–*), IV-2 would have to provide an *n A* gamete and IV-5 an *N a* gamete. This could occur if IV-2 were *nn Aa*; the probability is 1/4 (the probability IV-2 is *Aa*) x 1/2 (the probability of an *A* gamete if IV-2 is *Aa*) x 1/2 (the probability of an *N a* gamete from IV-5] = 1/16. This could also occur if IV-2 were *nn AA*. Here, the probability is 3/4 (the probability IV-2 is *nn AA*) x 1 (the probability of an *n A* gamete if IV-2 is *nn AA*) x 1/2 (the probability of an *N a* gamete from IV-5) = 3/8. Summing the probabilities for the two mutually exclusive IV-2 genotypes, **the probability that the child of IV-2 and IV-5 would have only nail-patella syndrome is 1/16 + 3/8 = 7/16.**

- For the child to have just alkaptonuria (*nn aa*), IV-2 would have to contribute an *n a* gamete. This could only occur if IV-2 were *nn Aa*. The probability IV-2 is *nn Aa* is 1/4, and the probability of receiving an *n a* gamete from IV-2 if he is *nn Aa* is 1/2. The probability that IV-5 would supply an *n a* gamete is also 1/2. Thus, **the probability that the child of IV-2 and IV-5 would have only alkaptonuria** is 1/4 x 1/2 x 1/2 = **1/16**. There is no need to sum probabilities in this case because IV-2 cannot produce an *n a* gamete if his genotype is *nn AA*.

- **The probability of neither defect** is 1 – (sum of the first 3) = 1 - (1/16 + 7/16 + 1/16) = 1 - 9/16 = **7/16**. You can make this calculation because there are only the four possible outcomes and you have already calculated the probabilities of three of them.

2-41. Diagram the cross(es):

midphalangeal x midphalangeal → 1853 midphalangeal : 209 normal

M? x M? → M? : *mm*

The following crosses are possible:

MM	x	*MM*	→	all *MM*
Mm	x	*MM*	→	all *M–*
MM	x	*Mm*	→	all *M–*
Mm	x	*Mm*	→	3/4 *M–* : 1/4 *mm*

The 209 normal children must have arisen from the last cross, so approximately 3 x 209 = ~630 children should be their *M–* siblings. Thus, about 840 of the children or **~40% came from the last mating** and the other 60% of the children were the result of one or more of the other matings. This problem illustrates that much care in interpretation is required when the results of many matings in mixed populations are reported (as opposed to the results of matings where individuals have defined genotypes).

2-42. Draw a Punnett square (male gametes shaded in *blue*, female gametes in *pink*):

	HD $\frac{1}{2}$	HD$^+$ $\frac{1}{2}$
HD$^+$ $\frac{1}{2}$	HD HD$^+$ $\frac{1}{4}$ **affected**	HD$^+$ HD$^+$ $\frac{1}{4}$ **Unaffected**
HD$^+$ $\frac{1}{2}$	HD HD$^+$ $\frac{1}{4}$ **affected**	HD$^+$ HD$^+$ $\frac{1}{4}$ **Unaffected**

a. An equally likely possibility exists that any child produced by this couple will be affected (A) or unaffected (U) . For two children, the possibilities are: AA, AU, UA, UU. The case in which only the second child is affected is UA; this is one of the four possibilities so **the probability that only the second child is affected is 1/4.**

b. From the list just presented in part *a*, you can see that there are two possibilities in which only one child is affected: AU and UA. The probability that either of these two mutually exclusive possibilities will occur is the sum of their independent probabilities: 1/4 + 1/4 = **1/2.**

c. From the list just presented in part *a*, you can see that there is only one possibility in which no child is affected: UU. The probability of this event is **1/4.**

d. If this family consisted of 10 children, **the case in which only the second child out of 10 is affected** (that is, UAUUUUUUUU) **has a probability of** $1/2^{10}$ **= 1/1024 = ~0.00098.** This probability is based on the facts that each birth is an independent event, and that the chance of U and A are each 1/2. We thus use the product rule to determine the chance that each of those 10 independent events will occur in a particular way – a particular birth order.

In a family of ten children, 10 different outcomes (birth orders) exist that satisfy the criterion that only 1 child has the disease. Only the first child could have the disease, only the second   child, only the third child, etc. :

1. **A**UUUUUUUUU
2. U**A**UUUUUUUU
3. UU**A**UUUUUUU
4. UUU**A**UUUUUU
5. UUUU**A**UUUUU
6. UUUUU**A**UUUU
7. UUUUUU**A**UUU
8. UUUUUUU**A**UU
9. UUUUUUUU**A**U
10. UUUUUUUUU**A**

We have already calculated that the chance of one of these outcomes in particular (#2) is 1/1024. As each of the 10 possibilities has the same probability, **the probability that only one child is affected would be 10 x (1/1024) = 10/1024 = ~0.0098.**

Only one possibility exists in which no child would be affected (UUUUUUUUUU), and just like any other specific outcome, this one has a probability of 1/1024 = ~0.00098.

e. One way to determine the probability that four children in a family of ten will have the disease is to write down all possible outcomes for the criterion, as we did above for the second answer in part *d*. Then, also as we did above, sum their individual probabilities, each of which is $(1/2)^{10}$ just as before. If you start to do this……

1. **AAAAUUUUUU**
2. **AAAUAUUUUU**
3. **AAAUUAUUUU**
4. **AAAUUUAUUU**
5. **AAAUUUUAUU**
6. **AAAUUUUUAU**
7. **AAAUUUUUUA**
8. **AAUAAUUUUU**
9. **AAUAUAUUUU**
10. **AAUAUUAUUU**

etc.

…..you will realize fairly quickly that writing down every possible birth order in this case is quite a difficult task and you are likely to miss some outcomes. In short – this is not a good way to find the answer! For questions like this, it is far preferable to use a mathematical tool called the *binomial theorem* in order to determine the number of possible outcomes that satisfy the criterion. The binomial theorem looks like this:

P (**X** will occur **s** times, and **Y** will occur **t** times, in **n** trials) =

$$\frac{n!}{s! \times t!} (p^s \times q^t)$$

P = the probability of what is in parentheses
p = P(**X**)
q = P(**Y**)

X and **Y** are the only two possibilities, so **p** + **q** = 1.
Also, **s** + **t** = **n**.

Remember that **!** means *factorial*: for example, 5! = 5 × 4 × 3 × 2 × 1.

To apply the binomial theorem to the question at hand (assuming you can still remember what the question was!), we'll let X = a child has the disease (A), and Y = a child does not have the disease (U). Then, $s = 4$, $t = 6$, $n = 10$, $p = 1/2$, and $q = 1/2$. The answer to the question is then:

$$P \text{ (4 A and 6 U children out of 10)} = (10! \, / \, 4! \times 6!) \, (1/2^4 \times 1/2^6).$$

Notice that $(p^s \times q^t) = (1/2^4 \times 1/2^6) = 1/2^{10}$. This factor of the binomial theorem equation is the probability of each single birth order, as we saw previously in part *d* above. To get the answer to our question, we need to multiply this factor (the probability of each single birth order) by the number of different birth orders that satisfy our criterion. From the equation in the box above, this second factor is $[n!/(s! \times t!)] = (10! \, / \, 4! \times 6!) = 210$. Thus, **the probability (P) of only 4 children having the disease in a family of 10 children is $1/2^{10} \times 210 \approx 21\%$.**

2-43. In the case of cystic fibrosis, the alleles causing the disease do not specify active protein [in this case, the cystic fibrosis transmembrane receptor (CFTR)]. Some *CF* disease alleles specify defective CFTR proteins that do not allow the passage of chloride ions, while other *CF* disease alleles do not specify any CFTR protein at all. As you will learn in a later chapter, such alleles are called *loss-of-function* alleles. In a heterozygote, the normal CF^+ allele still specifies active CFTR protein, which allows for the passage of chloride ions. Because the phenotype of the heterozygote is unaffected, the amount of active CFTR protein allows passage of enough chloride ions for the cells to function normally. Again as you will see, most loss-of-function alleles are recessive to normal alleles for similar reasons. (But it is important to realize that important exceptions are known in which loss-of-function mutations are actually dominant to normal alleles.)

In the case of Huntington disease, the disease-causing allele is dominant. The reason is that **the huntingtin protein specified by this *HD* allele has, in addition to its normal function** (which is not entirely understood), **a second function that is toxic to nerve cells.** This makes the *HD* disease allele a *gain-of-function* allele. The reason *HD* is dominant to HD^+ is that the protein specified by the disease allele will be toxic to cells even if the cells have normal huntingtin protein specified by the normal allele. Most (but again not all) gain-of-function mutations are dominant for similar reasons.

Section 2.4 – Extensions to Mendel for Single-Gene Inheritance

2-44. The problem states that the intermediate pink phenotype is caused by incomplete dominance between the alleles of a single gene. We suggest that you employ genotype symbols that can show the lack of complete dominance; the obvious *R* for red and *r* for white does not reflect the complexity of this situation. In such cases we recommend using a base letter as the gene symbol and then employing superscripts to show the different alleles. To avoid any possible misinterpretations, it is always advantageous to include a separate statement making the complexities of the dominant/recessive complications clear. Designate the two alleles f^r = red and f^w = white, so the possible genotypes are $f^r f^r$ = red; $f^r f^w$ = pink; and $f^w f^w$ = white. Note that the phenotypic ratio is the same as the genotypic ratio in incomplete dominance.

a. Diagram the cross: $f^r f^w$ x $f^r f^w$ → **1/4 $f^r f^r$ (red) : 1/2 $f^r f^w$ (pink) : 1/4 $f^w f^w$ (white)**.

b. $f^w f^w$ x $f^r f^w$ → **1/2 $f^r f^w$ (pink) : 1/2 $f^w f^w$ (white)**.

c. $f^r f^r$ x $f^r f^r$ → **1 $f^r f^r$ (red)**.

d. $f^r f^r$ x $f^r f^w$ → **1/2 $f^r f^r$ (red) : 1/2 $f^r f^w$ (pink)**.

e. $f^w f^w$ x $f^w f^w$ → **1 $f^w f^w$ (white)**.

f. $f^r f^r$ x $f^w f^w$ → **1 $f^r f^w$ (pink)**.

The cross shown in **part f** is the most efficient way to produce pink flowers, because all the progeny will be pink.

2-45. Diagram the cross: yellow x yellow → 38 yellow : 22 red : 20 white

Three phenotypes in the progeny show that the yellow parents are not true breeding. The ratio of the progeny is close to 1/2 : 1/4 : 1/4. This is the result expected for crosses between individuals heterozygous for incompletely dominant genes. Thus:

$c^r c^w$ **x** $c^r c^w$ → **1/2 $c^r c^w$ (yellow) : 1/4 $c^r c^r$ (red) : 1/4 $c^w c^w$ (white)**.

2-46.

a. Diagram the cross: $e^+ e^+$ x $e^+ e$ → 1/2 $e^+ e^+$: 1/2 $e^+ e$. The trident marking is only found in the heterozygotes, so the probability is **1/2**.

b. The offspring with the trident marking are $e^+ e$, so the cross is $e^+ e$ x $e^+ e$ → 1/4 ee : 1/2 $e^+ e$: 1/4 $e^+ e^+$. Therefore, of 300 offspring, **75 should have ebony bodies, 150 should have the trident marking, and 75 should have honey-coloured bodies**.

2-47. The cross is: white long x purple short → 301 long purple : 99 short purple : 612 long pink : 195 short pink : 295 long white : 98 short white

Deconstruct this dihybrid phenotypic ratio for two genes into separate constituent monohybrid ratios for each of the 2 traits, flower colour and pod length. For flower colour note that there are 3 phenotypes: 301 + 99 purple : 612 +195 pink : 295 + 98 white = 400 purple : 807 pink : 393 white = 1/4 purple : 1/2 pink : 1/4 white. This is a typical monohybrid ratio for incompletely dominant alleles, so **flower colour is caused by incompletely dominant alleles of a gene, with c^p giving purple when homozygous, c^w giving white when homozygous, and the $c^p c^w$ heterozygotes giving pink.** For pod length, the phenotypic ratio is (301 + 612 + 295) long : (99 + 195 + 98) short = 1208 long : 392

short = 3/4 long : 1/4 short. This 3:1 ratio is that expected for a cross between individuals heterozygous for a gene in which one allele is completely dominant to the other, so **pod shape is controlled by a single gene with the long allele (L) completely dominant to the short allele (l)**.

2-48. A cross between individuals heterozygous for incompletely dominant alleles of a gene give a ratio of 1/4 (one homozygote) : 1/2 (heterozygote with the same phenotype as the parents) : 1/4 (other homozygote). Because the problem already states which genotypes correspond to which phenotypes, you know that the colour gene will give a monohybrid phenotypic ratio of 1/4 red : 1/2 purple : 1/4 white, while the shape gene will give a monohybrid phenotypic ratio of 1/4 long : 1/2 oval : 1/4 round.

Because the inheritance of these two genes is independent, use the product rule to generate all the possible phenotype combinations (note that there will be 3 x 3 = 9 classes) and their probabilities, thus generating the dihybrid phenotypic ratio for two incompletely dominant genes: **1/16 red long : 1/8 red oval : 1/16 red round : 1/8 purple long : 1/4 purple oval : 1/8 purple round : 1/16 white long : 1/8 white oval : 1/16 white round**. As an example, to determine the probability of red long progeny, multiply 1/4 (probability of red) x 1/4 (probability of long) = 1/16. If you have trouble keeping track of the 9 possible classes, it may be helpful to list the classes in the form of a branched-line diagram or table as follows:

Phenotype	Probability of phenotype
red, long	$1/4 \times 1/4 = 1/16$
red, oval	$1/4 \times 1/2 = 1/8$
red, round	$1/4 \times 1/4 = 1/16$
purple, long	$1/2 \times 1/4 = 1/8$
purple, oval	$1/2 \times 1/2 = 1/4$
purple, round	$1/2 \times 1/4 = 1/8$
white, long	$1/4 \times 1/4 = 1/16$
white, oval	$1/4 \times 1/2 = 1/8$
white, round	$1/4 \times 1/4 = 1/16$

2-49. In Mendel's *Pp* heterozygotes, the amount of enzyme leading to purple pigment is sufficient to produce purple colour as intense as the purple colour in *PP* homozygotes. Presumably the heterozygote has enough enzyme P so that the maximal level of purple pigment is produced; more enzyme cannot make more purple pigment.

In the snapdragons in Figure 2.24, the amount of red pigment in the *Aa* heterozygote is less than that in the *AA* homozygote. Presumably here, the amount of enzyme A catalyzing the production of the red pigment in the heterozygotes is insufficient to produce the maximum level of the red pigment seen in the *AA* homozygote. That is, in this case **the intensity of the phenotype is proportional to the dosage of functional alleles (1 in the *Aa* heterozygote, 2 in the *AA* homozygote).**

2-50.

a. A person with sickle-cell anaemia is a homozygote for the sickle-cell allele: *Hbβ^S Hbβ^S*.

b. The child must be homozygous *Hbβ^S Hbβ^S* and therefore must have inherited a mutant allele from each parent. Because the parent is phenotypically normal, he/she must be a **carrier with genotype *Hbβ^S Hbβ^A*.**

c. Each individual has two alleles of every gene, including the β-globin gene. If an individual is heterozygous, he/she has two different alleles. Thus, if each parent is heterozygous for different alleles, there are **four possible alleles** that could be found in the five children. This is the maximum number of different alleles possible (barring the very rare occurrence of a new, novel mutation in a gamete that gave rise to one of the children). If one or both of the parents were homozygous for any one allele, the number of alleles distributed to the children would of course be less than four.

2-51. Remember that the gene determining ABO blood groups has 3 alleles and that $I^A = I^B > i$.

a. The O phenotype means the girl's genotype is *ii*. Each parent contributed an *i* allele, so her parents could be ***ii* (O) or *I^{A}i* (A) or *I^{B}i* (B).**

b. A person with the B phenotype could have either genotype *I^{B}I^B* or genotype *I^{B}i*. The mother is A and thus could not have contributed an *I^B* allele to this daughter. Instead, because the daughter clearly does not have an *I^A* allele, the mother must have contributed the *i* allele to this daughter. The mother must have been an *I^{A}i* heterozygote. The father must have contributed the *I^B* allele to his daughter, so he could be **either *I^{B}I^B*, *I^{B}i*, or *I^{A}I^B*.**

c. The genotypes of the girl and her mother must both be *I^{A}I^B*. The father must contribute either the *I^A* or the *I^B* allele, so there is only one phenotype and genotype which would exclude a man as her father - **the O phenotype (genotype *ii*).**

2-52. To approach this problem, look at the mother/child combinations to determine what alleles the father must have contributed to each child's genotype.

a. The father had to contribute *I^B, N,* and *Rh$^-$* alleles to the child. The only male fitting these requirements is **male d** whose phenotype is B, MN, and Rh$^+$ (note that the father must be *Rh$^+$Rh$^-$* because the daughter is Rh$^-$).

b. The father had to contribute *i, N,* and *Rh$^-$* alleles. The father could be either male c (O MN Rh$^+$) or male d (B MN Rh$^+$). As we saw previously, male c is the only male fitting the requirements for the father in part *a*. Assuming one child per male as instructed by the problem, the father in part *b* must be **male c.**

c.   The father had to contribute I^A, M, and Rh^- alleles. Only **male b** (A M Rh^+) fits these criteria.

d.   The father had to contribute either I^B or i, M, and Rh^-. Three males have the alleles required: these are male a, male c, and male d. However, of these three possibilities, only **male a** remains unassigned to a mother/child pair.

2-53. Designate the alleles: p^m (marbled) $> p^s$ (spotted) $= p^d$ (dotted) $> p^c$ (clear).

a.   The expected phenotypes of the F_1 plants from the two original parental crosses are **marbled ($p^m p^s$)** from the first cross **and dotted ($p^d p^c$)** from the second cross.

b.   Diagram the crosses:

      1. $p^m p^m$ (homozygous marbled) x $p^s p^s$ (spotted) $\rightarrow$ $p^m p^s$ (marbled F_1)

      2. $p^d p^d$ x $p^c p^c$ $\rightarrow$ $p^d p^c$ (dotted F_1)

      3. $p^m p^s$ x $p^d p^c$ $\rightarrow$ 1/4 $p^m p^d$ (marbled) : 1/4 $p^m p^c$ (marbled) : 1/4 $p^s p^d$ (spotted dotted) : 1/4 $p^s p^c$ (spotted) = **1/4 spotted dotted : 1/2 marbled : 1/4 spotted**.

2-54. Suppose, as maintained by your fellow student, that spotting is due to the action of one gene with alleles S (spotting) and s (no spots), and that dotting is due to the action of a second gene with alleles D (dotting) and d (no spots). The cross series shown in Figure 2.25a, starting with true-breeding spotted and true-breeding dotted strains, could be diagrammed as:

    $SS\ dd$ x $ss\ DD$ $\rightarrow$ $Ss\ Dd$ (spotted and dotted F_1) $\rightarrow$ F_2 consisting of 9 $S- D-$ (spotted and dotted) : 3 $S- dd$ (spotted, not dotted) : 3 $ss\ D-$ (not spotted, dotted) : 1 $ss\ dd$ (not spotted, not dotted)

Thus, the alternative hypothesis suggested by your fellow student would predict that some lentils would be found in the F_2 generation that would be neither spotted nor dotted. The results shown in Figure 2.25 do not include any such lentils. **If you counted a large number of F_2 individuals and you failed to see lentils that were neither spotted nor dotted, you would be able to exclude the hypothesis that two genes were involved.**

2.55.

a.   All of the crosses have results that can be explained by one gene - either a 3:1 phenotypic monohybrid ratio showing that one allele is completely dominant to the other, or a 1:1 ratio showing that a testcross was done for a single gene, or all progeny with the same phenotype as the parents. You can thus conclude that all of the coat colours are controlled by the alleles of **one gene, with chinchilla (C) > himalaya (c^h) > albino (c^a).**

b.   1. $c^h c^a$ x $c^h c^a$

    2. $c^h c^a$ x $c^a c^a$

3. Cc^h x $C(c^h$ or $c^a)$

4. CC x c^h (c^h or c^a)

5. Cc^a x Cc^a

6. c^hc^h x c^ac^a

7. Cc^a x c^ac^a

8. c^ac^a x c^ac^a

9. Cc^h x $c^h(c^h$ or $c^a)$ or Cc^a x c^hc^h

10. Cc^a x c^hc^a.

c. **Cc^h (from cross 9)** x **Cc^a (from cross 10)** → 1/4 CC (chinchilla) : 1/4 Cc^a (chinchilla) : 1/4 Cc^h (chinchilla) : 1/4 c^hc^a (himalaya) = **3/4 chinchilla : 1/4 himalaya**, or Cc^a **(cross 9)** x Cc^a **(cross 10)** → **3/4 C– chinchilla : 1/4 c^ac^a albino.**

2-56. There are two keys to this problem: (1) Pollen grains and ovules are gametes that have only one copy of the *S* incompatibility gene, while the stigma (the part of the female plant on which the pollen grains land) has two copies of this gene. (2) Pollen with a particular *S* gene allele cannot fertilize any ovules in a plant whose stigma has the same *S* allele, because the pollen will not grow a tube allowing it to fertilize an ovule.

a. In the cross *S1 S2* x *S1 S2* all of the pollen grains (whether they are *S1* or *S2*) will land on the stigmas of plants that have the same alleles, and therefore **no progeny would be produced at all**.

b. The way this cross was written is ambiguous because the male and female parents were not specified. The cross could be ♂ *S1 S2* x ♀ *S2 S3*, or ♀ *S1 S2* x ♂ *S2 S3*, or both (because the flowers of these plants have both male and female parts). For the cross ♂ *S1 S2* x ♀ *S2 S3*, the pollen grains would be *S1* or *S2*. The *S2* pollen could not fertilize the female plant, but the *S1* pollen could. **The progeny of the ♂ *S1 S2* x ♀ *S2 S3* cross would thus be *S1 S2* and *S1 S3* (in a 1:1 ratio).** For the cross written the opposite way (♀ *S1 S2* x ♂ *S2 S3*), the pollen would be *S2* or *S3*. The *S2* pollen would not produce any progeny, but the *S3* pollen could produce both *S1 S3* progeny and *S2 S3* progeny. **The progeny of the ♀ *S1 S2* x ♂ *S2 S3* cross would thus be a 1:1 ratio of *S1 S3* and *S2 S3*.**

c. Because of the ambiguity in the way the cross was written, there are again two possibilities: The cross could be ♂ *S1 S2* x ♀ *S3 S4*, or ♀ *S1 S2* x ♂ *S3 S4*, or both. Regardless of these possibilities, all pollen grains would be able to fertilize all ovules, because the pollen grains do not share any alleles with the female parent. **As a result, any of these crosses could produce four types of progeny in equal numbers: *S1 S3, S1 S4, S2 S3,* and *S2 S4*.**

d. **This mechanism would prevent plant self-fertilization because any pollen grain produced by any plant would land on a stigma sharing the same allele.** For example, if an *S1* pollen grain produced by an *S1 S2* plant lands on a stigma from the same plant, the stigma would have the same allele   and no pollen tube would be able to grow to allow fertilization. The same would be   true for an *S2* pollen grain from the same plant. (Of interest, tomato plants in the wild cannot self-fertilize because of this incompatibility mechanism; they proliferate only through cross-   fertilization. However, many domesticated cultivars of tomatoes can self-fertilize because they   were selected for varieties that have mutations causing the failure of the incompatibility   mechanism.)

e. **Plants with functioning incompatibility systems must be heterozygotes because a pollen grain cannot fertilize a female plant sharing the same allele of the *S* incompatibility gene.** For example, an *S1* pollen grain cannot fertilize successfully any female plant that also has an *S1* allele. No way thus exists to create *S1 S1* homozygous progeny.

f. **Peas cannot be governed by this mechanism because you already saw in this chapter that Gregor Mendel routinely self-fertilized his peas in the F_1 generation to produce the F_2 generation.**

g. **The larger the number of different alleles of the *S* gene that are present in the population, the more likely it is that any given pollen grain of any genotype would land on the stigma of a flower that did not share the same allele, and the less likely that the pollen will interact unproductively with flowers that share the same allele.** Within the population, the proportion of matings that could produce progeny would increase with a greater variety in *S* gene alleles; this would clearly increase the fertility (and thus the average evolutionary fitness) of the population as a whole.

2-57.

a. This ratio is approximately **2/3 curly : 1/3 normal**.

b. The expected result for this cross is: $Cy^+Cy \times Cy^+Cy \rightarrow$ 1/4 $Cy\ Cy$ (?): 1/2 Cy^+Cy (curly) : 1/4 Cy^+Cy^+ (normal). If the ***Cy/ Cy*** genotype **is lethal** then the expected ratio will match the observed data.

c. The cross is $Cy^+Cy \times Cy^+Cy^+ \rightarrow$ 1/2 Cy^+Cy : 1/2 Cy^+Cy^+, so there would be approximately **90 curly-winged and 90 normal-winged flies**.

2-58. Designate the gene *p* (for pattern). There are 7 alleles, p^1-p^7, with p^7 being the allele that codes for absence of pattern and $p^1 > p^2 > p^3 > p^4 > p^5 > p^6 > p^7$.

a. There are **7 different patterns** possible. These are associated with the following genotypes: p^1-, p^2p^a (where $p^a = p^2, p^3, p^4 \ldots p^7$), p^3p^b (where $p^b = p^3, p^4, p^5 \ldots p^7$), p^4p^c (where $p^c = p^4, p^5, p^6,$ and p^7), p^5p^d (where $p^d = p^5, p^6,$ and p^7), p^6p^e (where $p^e = p^6$ and p^7), and p^7p^7.

b. The phenotype dictated by the allele p^1 has the greatest number of genotypes associated with it = 7 (p^1p^1, p^1p^2, p^1p^3, etc.). **The absence of pattern** is caused by just one genotype, p^7p^7.

c. This finding suggests that **the allele determining absence of pattern (p^7) is very common** in these clover plants with the p^7p^7 genotype being the most frequent in the population. The other alleles are present, but are much less common in this population.

2-59.

a. The 2/3 montezuma : 1/3 wild-type phenotypic ratio, and the statement that montezumas are never true-breeding, together suggest that there is a **recessive lethal allele** of this gene. When there is a recessive lethal, crossing two heterozygotes results in a 1:2:1 genotypic ratio, but one of the 1/4 classes of homozygotes do not survive. **The result is the 2:1 phenotypic ratio as seen in this cross. Both the montezuma parents were therefore heterozygous, *Mm*.** The *M* allele must confer the montezuma colouring in a dominant fashion, but homozygosity for *M* is lethal.

b. Designate the alleles: *M* = montezuma, *m* = green; *F* = normal fin, *f* = ruffled fin. Diagram the cross: ***Mm FF* x *mm ff*** → expected monohybrid ratio for the *M* gene alone: 1/2 *Mm* (montezuma) : 1/2 *mm* (wild-type); expected monohybrid ratio for the *F* gene alone: all *Ff*. The expected dihybrid ratio = **1/2 *Mm Ff* (montezuma, normal fin) : 1/2 *mm Ff* (green, normal fin).**

c. *Mm Ff* x *Mm Ff* → expected monohybrid ratio for the *M* gene alone: 2/3 montezuma (*Mm*) : 1/3 green (*mm*); expected monohybrid ratio for the *F* gene alone: 3/4 normal fin (*F–*) : 1/4 ruffled fin (*ff*). The expectations when considering both genes together is: **6/12 montezuma normal fin : 2/12 montezuma ruffled fin : 3/12 green normal fin : 1/12 green ruffled fin.**

Section 2.5 – Extensions to Mendel for Gene Interactions

2-60.

a. The mutant plant lacks the function of all three genes, so **its genotype must be *aa bb cc*.**

b. Considering each gene separately, 3/4 of the F_2 progeny will have at least one dominant allele, whereas 1/4 will be homozygous for the recessive allele. As just seen in part *a*, mutant plants must be triply homozygous recessive. The chance that a plant will have the *aa bb cc* genotype is 1/4 x 1/4 x 1/4 = 1/64. All other F_2 plants will be normal for this phenotype, so **the fraction of normal plants = 1 – 1/64 = 63/64.**

c. **The most likely explanation for redundant gene function is that in the relatively recent past, a single gene became duplicated (or in this case, triplicated).** The three copies of the *SEP* gene are nearly identical to each other and thus fulfill the same function. Only if the functions of all three genes are lost does a mutant phenotype result. In fact, these kinds of gene duplication events occur often enough in nature that redundant gene function is a common phenomenon.

2-61. The cross is: black x chestnut → F_1 bay → F_2 black : bay : chestnut : liver

Four phenotypes in the F_2 generation means there are two genes determining coat colour. The F_1 bay animals produce four phenotypic classes, so they must be doubly heterozygous, *Aa Bb*. Crossing a liver-coloured horse to either of the original parents resulted in the parent's phenotype. The liver horse's alleles do not affect the phenotype, suggesting the recessive genotype *aa bb*. Though it is probable that the original black mare was *AA bb* and the chestnut stallion was *aa BB,* each of these animals only produced 3 progeny, so it cannot be definitively concluded that these animals were homozygous for the dominant allele they carry. Thus, **the black mare was *A– bb*, the chestnut stallion was *aa B–*, and the F_1 bay animals are *Aa Bb*. The F_2 horses were: bay (*A– B–*), liver (*aa bb*), chestnut (*aa B–*), and black (*A– bb*).**

2-62. The cross is: walnut x single $\rightarrow$ F_1 walnut x F_1 walnut $\rightarrow$ 93 walnut : 29 rose : 32 pea : 11 single

a. How many genes are involved? The four F_2 phenotypes means there are 2 genes, *A* and *B*. Both genes affect the same structure, the comb. The F_2 phenotypic dihybrid ratio among the progeny is close to 9:3:3:1, so there is no epistasis. Because walnut is the most abundant F_2 phenotype, it must be the phenotype due to the *A– B–* genotype. Single combs are the least frequent class, and are thus *aa bb*. Now assign genotypes to the cross. If the walnut F_2 are *A– B–*, then the original walnut parent must have been *AA BB*:

  AA BB x *aa bb* $\rightarrow$ *Aa Bb* (walnut) $\rightarrow$ 9/16 *A– B–* (walnut) : 3/16 *A– bb* (rose) : 3/16 *aa B–* (pea) : 1/6 *aa bb* (single).

b. Diagram the cross, recalling that the problem states the parents are homozygous:

  AA bb (rose) x *aa BB* (pea) $\rightarrow$ *Aa Bb* (walnut) $\rightarrow$ 9/16 *A– B–* (walnut) : 3/16 *A– bb* (rose) : 3/16 *aa B–* (pea) : 1/6 *aa bb* (single). Notice that this F_2 is in identical proportions as the F_2 generation in part *a.*

c. Diagram the cross: *A– B–* (walnut) x *aa B–* (pea) $\rightarrow$ 12 *A– B–* (walnut) : 11 *aa B–* (pea) : 3 *A– bb* (rose) : 4 *aa bb* (single). Because there are pea and single progeny, you know that the walnut parent must be *Aa*. The 1 *A–* : 1 *aa* monohybrid ratio in the progeny also tells you the walnut parent must have been *Aa.* Because some of the progeny are single, you know that both parents must be *Bb*. In this case, the monohybrid ratio for the *B* gene is 3 *B–* : 1 *bb*, so both parents were *Bb*. The original cross must have been *Aa Bb* x *aa Bb*. You can verify that this cross would yield the observed ratio of progeny by multiplying the probabilities expected for each gene alone. For example, you anticipate that 1/2 the progeny would be *Aa* and 3/4 of the progeny would be *Bb*, so 1/2 x 3/4 = 3/8 of the progeny should be walnut; this is close to the 12 walnut chickens seen among 30 total progeny.

d. Diagram the cross: *A– B–* (walnut) x *A– bb* (rose) → all *A– B–* (walnut). The progeny are all walnut, so **the walnut parent must be *BB***. No pea progeny are seen, so **both parents cannot be *Aa,* so one of the two parents must be *AA***. This could be either the walnut or the rose parent or both.

2-63. green x yellow → F_1 green → F_2 9 green : 7 yellow

a. The 9:7 ratio is a variant of the 9:3:3:1 phenotypic dihybrid ratio arising from complementary gene action, suggesting that **two genes are controlling colour**. The genotypes are:
    AA BB (green) x *aa bb* (yellow) → F_1 *Aa Bb* (green) → F_2 9/16 *A– B–* (green) : 3/16 *A– bb* (yellow) : 3/16 *aa B–* (yellow) : 1/16 *aa bb* (yellow).

b. F_1 *Aa Bb* x *aa bb* → 1/4 *Aa Bb* (green) : 1/4 *aa Bb* (yellow) : 1/4 *Aa bb* (yellow) : 1/4 *aa bb* (yellow) = 1/4 green : 3/4 yellow.

2-64.

a. Because unaffected individuals had affected children, the **trait is recessive**. From affected individual II-1, you know the mutant allele is present in this generation. The trait was passed on through II-2 who was a carrier. All children of affected individuals III-2 x III-3 are affected, as predicted for a recessive trait. However, generation V seems inconsistent with recessive inheritance of a single gene. This result is consistent with two different genes involved in hearing with a defect in either gene leading to deafness: The trait is polymorphic. **The two family lines shown contain mutations in two separate genes, and the mutant alleles of both genes determining deafness are recessive.**

b. Individuals in generation V are doubly heterozygous (*Aa Bb*), having inherited a dominant and recessive allele of each gene from their parents (*aa BB* x *AA bb*). The people in generation V are not affected because **the product of the dominant allele of each gene is sufficient for normal function.** This is an example of *complementation*: For each gene, the gamete from one parent provided the dominant allele that the gamete from the other parent lacked.

2-65. Dominance relationships are between alleles of the same gene. **Only one gene is involved when considering dominance relationships. Epistasis involves two genes.** The alleles of one gene affect the phenotypic expression of the second gene.

2-66.

a. white x white → F_1 white → F_2 126 white : 33 purple

    At first glance this cross seems to involve only one gene, as true-breeding white parents give white F_1s. However, if this were true, then the F_2 MUST be totally white as well. The purple F_2 plants show that this cross is NOT controlled by 1 gene. These results may be **due to 2 genes**. To determine if this is the case, it makes sense to ask: Does a ratio of 126 : 33 represent a variant of the 9:3:3:1 dihybrid ratio? Usually when you are given raw numbers of individuals for the classes, you divide through by the smallest number, yielding in this case 3.8 white : 1 purple. This is neither a recognizable monohybrid nor dihybrid ratio. Dividing through by the smallest class is NOT the correct way to convert raw numbers to a ratio. Assuming that the F_1 in this case are dihybrids, there must have been 16 different equally likely fertilization events that produced the F_2 progeny (16 boxes in the 4 x 4 Punnett square), even though the phenotypes may not be distributed in the usual 9/16 : 3/16 : 3/16 : 1/16 ratio. If the 159 F_2 progeny are divided equally into 16 fertilization types, then there are 159/16 = ~10 F_2 plants/fertilization type. The 126 white F_2s therefore represent 126/10 = ~13 of these fertilizations. Likewise the 33 purple plants represent 33/10 = ~3 fertilization types. **The F_2 phenotypic ratio is thus 13 white : 3 purple. The data fit the hypothesis that two genes control colour, and that the F_1 are dihybrids.**

You can now assign genotypes to the parents in the cross. Because the parents are homozygous (true-breeding) and there are 2 genes controlling the phenotypes, there are two

possible ways to set up the genotypes of the parents so that the F_1 dihybrids are heterozygous for dominant and recessive alleles of each gene. One option is: *AA BB* **(white)** x *aa bb* **(white)** → *Aa Bb* **(white, same as *AA BB* parent)** → 9 *A– B–* **(white)** : 3 *A– bb* **(unknown phenotype)** : 3 *aa B–* **(unknown phenotype)** : 1 *aa bb* **(white, same as *aa bb* parent)**. If you assume that *A– bb* is white and *aa B–* is purple (or *vice versa*), then this is a match for the observed data presented in the cross above [(9 + 3 + 1) = 13 white : 3 purple].

Alternatively, you could try to diagram the cross as *AA bb* (white) x *aa BB* (white) → *Aa Bb* (whose phenotype is unknown as this is NOT a genotype seen in the parents) → 9 *A– B–* (same unknown phenotype as in the F_1) : 3 *A– bb* (white like the *AA bb* parent) : 3 *aa B–* (white like the *aa BB* parent) : 1 *aa bb* (unknown phenotype). Such a cross cannot give an F_2 phenotypic ratio of 13 white : 3 purple. The only F_2 classes that could be purple are *A– B–* , but this is impossible because this class is larger than the number of purple plants observed and because the F_1 plants must then have been purple; or the *aa bb* class which is smaller than the number of purple plants observed. Therefore, the first set of possible genotypes (written in bold above) is the best fit for the observed data.

Assume that *A– bb* plants are white, and *aa B–* plants are purple. Our model above states that in order to be purple, a plant must have a *B* allele and no *A* allele. Thus, we can say that *A* is epistatic to *B*.

b. white F_2 x white F_2 (self-cross) → 3/4 white : 1/4 purple. Assume again that the *aa B–* class is purple in part *a* above. A 3:1 monohybrid ratio means the parents are both heterozygous for one gene with purple due to the recessive allele. The second gene is not affecting the ratio, so both parents must be homozygous for the same allele of that gene. Thus the cross must be: *Aa BB* **(white)** x *Aa BB* (white self-cross) → 3/4 *A– BB* (white) : 1/4 *aa BB* (purple).

c. purple F_2 x self → 3 purple : 1 white. Again, the selfed parent must be heterozygous for one gene and homozygous for the other gene. Because purple is *aa B–*, the genotype of the purple F_2 plant must be *aa Bb*.

d. white F_2 x white F_2 (not a self-cross) → 1/2 purple : 1/2 white. The 1:1 monohybrid ratio means a testcross was done for one of the genes. The second gene is not altering the ratio in the progeny, so the parents must be homozygous for that gene. If purple is *aa B–*, then the genotypes of the parents must be *aa bb* **(white)** x *Aa BB* **(white)** → 1/2 *Aa Bb* (white) : 1/2 *aa Bb* (purple).

2-67. $I^A I^B\ Ss$ x $I^A I^A\ Ss$ → expected monohybrid ratio for the *I* gene of 1/2 $I^A I^A$: 1/2 $I^A I^B$; expected ratio for the *S* gene considered alone of 3/4 *S–* : 1/4 *ss*. Use the product rule to generate the phenotypic ratio for both genes considered together and then assign phenotypes, remembering that all individuals with the *ss* genotype **look like type O**. The apparent phenotypic ratio for both genes is: 3/8 $I^A I^A\ S–$: 3/8 $I^A I^B\ S–$: 1/8 $I^A I^A\ ss$: 1/8 $I^A I^B\ ss$ = 3/8 A : 3/8 AB : 1/8 O : 1/8 O = **3/8 Type A : 3/8 Type AB : 2/8 Type O.**

2-68.

a. The cross is between two normal flies that carry *H* and *S*. These individuals cannot be homozygous for *H* or for *S*, because we are told that both are lethal in homozygotes. Thus, the mating described is a dihybrid cross: *Hh Ss* x *Hh Ss*. The genotypic classes among the progeny zygotes should be 9 *H– S–*, 3 *H– ss*, 3 *hh S–*, and 1 *hh ss*. However, all zygotes that are *HH* or *SS* or both will die before they hatch into adult flies. You could do this problem as a branched-line diagram as shown in the following figure, in which the progeny should be 2/3 *Hh* and 1/3 *hh* (considering the *H* gene alone) and 2/3 *Ss* and 1/3 *ss* (considering the *S* gene alone). As can be seen from the diagram, **7/9 of the adult progeny will be normal, and 2/9 will be hairless.**

b. As just seen in the diagram, the hairless progeny of the cross in part *a* are *Hh ss*, and these are mated with parental flies that are *Hh Ss*. You could again portray the results of this cross as a branched-line diagram. For the *H* gene, again 2/3 of the viable adult progeny will be *Hh* and 1/3 will be *hh*. The cross involving the *S* gene is a testcross, and all the progeny will be viable, so 1/2 the progeny will be *Ss* and 1/2 will be *ss*. As seen in the diagram that follows, **2/6 = 1/3 of the progeny will be hairless and the remaining 2/3 will be normal.**

2-69.

a. blood types: **I-1 AB; I-2 A; I-3 B; I-4 AB; II-1 O; II-2 O; II-3 AB; III-1 A; III-2 O.**

b. genotypes: **I-1 *Hh* $I^A I^B$; I-2 *Hh* $I^A i$ (or $I^A I^A$); I-3 *H– $I^B i$ (or $I^B I^B$); I-4 *H– $I^A I^B$; II-1 *H– ii*; II-2 *hh* $I^A I^A$ (or $I^A i$ or $I^A I^B$); II-3 *Hh* $I^A I^B$; III-1 *Hh* $I^A i$; III-2 *hh* $I^A I^A$ (or $I^A I^B$ or $I^A i$ or $I^b i$ or $I^B I^B$)**

At first glance, you find inconsistencies between expectations and what could be inherited from a parent. For example, I-1 (AB) × I-2 (A) could not have an O child (II-2). The epistatic *h* allele (which causes the Bombay phenotype) could explain these inconsistencies. If II-2 has an O phenotype because she is *hh*, her parents must both have been *Hh*. The Bombay phenotype would also explain the second seeming inconsistency of two O individuals (II-1 and II-2) having an A child. II-2 could have received an I^A allele from one of her parents and passed this on to III-1 together with one *h* allele. Parent II-1 would have to contribute the *H* allele so that the I^A allele would be expressed; the presence of *H* means that II-1 must also be *ii* in order to be type O. A third inconsistency is that individuals II-2 and II-3 could not have an *ii* child since II-3 has the $I^A I^B$ genotype, but III-2 has the O phenotype. This could also be explained if II-3 is *Hh* and III-2 is *hh*.

2-70. The difference between traits determined by a single pleiotropic gene and traits determined by several genes would be seen if crosses were done using pure-breeding plants (wild-type x mutant), then selfing the F₁ progeny. If **several genes** were involved there **would be several different**

combinations of the petal colour, markings, and stem position phenotypes in the F$_2$ generation. If all 3 traits were due to an allele present at **one gene**, the **three phenotypes would always be inherited together** and the F$_2$ plants would be either yellow, dark brown, and erect OR white, no markings, and prostrate.

2-71. Diagram the cross. Figure out an expected monohybrid ratio for each gene separately, then apply the product rule to generate the expected dihybrid ratio.

A^yA Cc x A^yA cc → monohybrid ratio for the A gene alone: 1/4 A^yA^y (dead) : 1/2 A^yA (yellow) : 1/4 AA (agouti) = 2/3 A^yA (yellow) : 1/3 AA (agouti); monohybrid ratio for the C gene: 1/2 Cc (non-albino) : 1/2 cc (albino).

Overall there will be 2/6 A^yA Cc (yellow) : 2/6 A^yA cc (albino) : 1/6 AA Cc (agouti) : 1/6 AA cc (albino) = **2/6 A^yA Cc (yellow) : 3/6 $--$ cc (albino) : 1/6 AA Cc (agouti)**. Note that the A^yA cc animals must be albino because the albino parent had exactly the same genotype; this indicates that cc is epistatic to all alleles of gene A. Although you were not explicitly told that the AA cc animals are also albino, this makes sense because in Figure 2.44, cc is epistatic to all alleles of another gene B in animals that must have been AA. (Another way to think of this is that the cc albino colour must be epistatic to alleles of all genes that confer colour because no pigments are produced.)

2-72.

a. Diagram one of the crosses:

white-1 x white-2 → red F$_1$ → F$_2$ 9 red : 7 white

Even though there are only 2 phenotypes in the F$_2$, colour is not controlled by one gene - the 9:7 ratio is a variation of 9:3:3:1, so there are 2 genes controlling these phenotypes. Individuals must have at least one dominant allele of each gene in order to get the red colour; this is an example of *complementary gene action*. Thus the genotypes of the two pure-breeding white parents in this cross are *aa BB* x *AA bb*. The same conclusions hold for the other 2 crosses.

If white-1 is *aa BB* and white-2 is *AA bb*, then white-3 must be *AA BB cc*. The reason is that if white-3 had the same genotype as white-1 or white-2, then one of the three crosses would have produced an all white F$_1$ (no complementation). Because none of the crosses had an all white F$_1$, we can conclude that **three genes are involved.**

b. **white-1 is *aa BB CC*; white-2 is *AA bb CC*; and white-3 is *AA BB cc*.**

c. ***aa BB CC* (white-1) x *AA bb CC* (white-2) → *Aa Bb CC* (red) → 9/16 *A– B– CC* (red) : 3/16 *A– bb CC* (white) : 3/16 *aa B– CC* (white) : 1/6 *aa bb CC* (white). Red colour requires a dominant, functional allele of each of the three genes (*A– B– C–*).**

2-73. You know about the alleles of the *A* gene (*A* for agouti, a^t for black/yellow, *a* for black, and A^y for recessive lethal yellow) from Figure 2.28 and Figure 2.29. You know about the interaction of the *B* and *C* genes governing the variation in black, brown, and albino colours from Figure 2.44.

a. The yellow parent must have an A^y allele, but we don't know the second allele of the *A* gene (A^y–). We don't know at the outset what alleles this yellow mouse has at the *B* gene, so we'll leave these alleles for the time being as *??*. Since this mouse does show colour we know it is not *cc* (albino), so it must have at least one *C* allele (*C–*). The brown agouti parent has at least one *A* allele (*A–*); it must be *bb* at the *B* gene; and since there is colour it must also be *C–*. The mating between these two can thus be represented as A^y– *?? C–* x *A– bb C–*.

Now consider the progeny. Because one pup was albino (*cc*), the parents must both be *Cc*. A brown pup (*bb*) indicates that both parents had to be able to contribute a *b* allele, so we now know the first mouse (the yellow parent) must have had at least one *b* allele. The fact that this brown pup was non-agouti means both parents carried an *a* allele. The black agouti progeny tells us that the first mouse must have also had a *B* allele. This latter fact also clarifies that A^y is epistatic to *B* because this parent was yellow rather than black. The complete genotypes of the mice are therefore: A^y*a Bb Cc* x *Aa bb Cc*.

b. Think about each gene individually, then the effect of the other genes in combination with that phenotype. *C–* leads to a phenotype with colour; *cc* gives albino (which is epistatic to all colours determined by the other genes because no pigments are produced). The possible genotypes of the progeny of this cross for the *A* gene are A^y*A*, A^y*a*, *Aa*, and *aa*, giving yellow, yellow, agouti, and non-agouti phenotypes, respectively. Since yellow (A^y) is epistatic to *B*, non-albino mice with A^y will be yellow regardless of the genotype of the *B* gene. *Aa* is agouti; with the *aa* genotype there is no yellow on the hair (non-agouti). The type of colouration depends on the *B* gene. For *B* the offspring could be *Bb* (black) or *bb* (brown). In total, **six different coat colour phenotypes are possible: albino (– – – – *cc*), yellow (A^y(*A* or *a*) – – *C–*), brown agouti (*A– bb C–*), black agouti (*A– B– C–*), brown (*aa bb C–*), and black (*aa B– C–*).** [Note: Although A^y (yellow colour) is in fact epistatic to *B* (black) or *bb* (brown) colours governed by the *B* gene, you were not explicitly told this. Thus, based on the information provided, you might have included an additional colour phenotype if you considered that A^y (*A* or *a*) *bb C–* had a lighter colour than the yellow of A^y (*A* or *a*) *Bb C–* animals.]

2-74.

a. **No**, a single gene cannot account for this result. While the 1:1 ratio seems like a testcross, the fact that **the phenotype of one class of offspring (linear) is not the same as either of the parents** argues against this being a testcross.

b. The appearance of four phenotypes means **two genes** are controlling the phenotypes.

c. The 3:1 ratio suggests that **two alleles of one gene** determine the difference between the wild-type and scattered patterns.

d. The true-breeding wild-type fish are homozygous by definition, and the scattered fish have to be homozygous recessive according to the ratio seen in part *c*, so the cross is: *bb* **(scattered) x** *BB* **(wild-type)** → **F$_1$** *Bb* **(wild-type)** → **3/4** *B–* **(wild-type) : 1/4** *bb* **(scattered)**.

e. The inability to obtain a true-breeding nude stock suggests that the nude fish are heterozygous (*Aa*) and that the *AA* genotype dies. Thus *Aa* **(nude) x** *Aa* **(nude)** → **2/3** *Aa* **(nude) : 1/3** *aa* **(scattered)**.

f. Going back to the linear cross from part *b*, the fact that there are four phenotypes led us to propose two genes were involved. The 6:3:2:1 ratio looks like an altered 9:3:3:1 ratio in which some genotypes may be missing, as predicted from the result in part *e* that *AA* animals do not survive. The 9:3:3:1 ratio results from crossing double heterozygotes, so **the linear parents are doubly heterozygous** *Aa Bb*. **The lethal phenotype associated with the** *AA* **genotype produces the 6:3:2:1 ratio. The phenotypes and corresponding genotypes of the progeny of the linear x linear cross are: 6 linear,** *Aa B–* **: 3 wild-type,** *aa B–* **: 2 nude,** *Aa bb* **: 1 scattered,** *aa bb*. Note that the *AA BB, AA Bb, AA Bb,* and *AA bb* genotypes are missing due to lethality.

2-75.

a. *Aa Bb Cc* x *Aa Bb Cc* → 9/16 *A– B–* x 3/4 *C–* : 9/16 *A– B–* x 1/4 *cc* : 3/16 *A– bb* x 3/4 *C–* : 3/16 *A– bb* x 1/4 *cc*: 3/16 *aa B–* x 3/4 *C–* : 3/16 *aa B–* x 1/4 *cc* : 1/16 *aa bb* x 3/4 *C–* : 1/16 *aa bb* x 1/4 *cc* = 27/64 *A– B– C–* (wild-type) : 9/64 *A– B– cc* : 9/64 *A– bb C–* : 3/64 *A– bb cc* : 9/64 *aa B– C–* : 3/64 *aa B– cc* : 3/64 *aa bb C–* : 1/64 *aa bb cc* = **27/64 wild-type : 37/64 mutant**.

b. Diagram the crosses:

      1. unknown male x *AA bb cc* → 1/4 wild-type (*A– B– C–*) : 3/4 mutant

      2. unknown male x *aa BB cc* → 1/2 wild-type (*A– B– C–*) : 1/2 mutant

      3. unknown male x *aa bb CC* → 1/2 wild-type (*A– B– C–*) : 1/2 mutant

The 1:1 ratio in testcrosses 2 and 3 is expected if the unknown male is heterozygous for one of the genes that are recessive in the testcross parent. The 1 wild-type : 3 mutant ratio arises when the male is heterozygous for two of the genes that are homozygous recessive in the testcross parent. (If you apply the product rule to 1/2 *B–* : 1/2 *bb* and 1/2 *C–* : 1/2 *cc* in the first cross, then you find 1/4 *B– C–*, 1/4 *B– cc*, 1/4 *bb C–*, and 1/4 *bb cc*. Only *B– C–* will be wild-type, the other 3 classes will be mutant.) Thus the unknown male must be *Bb Cc*. In testcross 1 the male could be either *AA* or *aa*. Crosses 2 and 3 show that the male is only heterozygous for one of the genes in each case: gene *C* in testcross 2 and gene *B* in testcross 3. In order to get wild-type progeny in both crosses, the male must be *AA*. Therefore the genotype of the unknown male is ***AA Bb Cc***.

2-76. In **Figure 2.48b** the A^1 and B^1 alleles each have the same effect on the phenotype (plant height in this example), while the A^0 and B^0 alleles are non-functional. Thus, the shortest plants are $A^0A^0B^0B^0$, and the tallest plants are $A^1A^1B^1B^1$. **The phenotypes are determined by the total number of A^1 and B^1 alleles in the genotype.** Thus, $A^1A^0B^0B^0$ plants are the same phenotype as $A^0A^0B^0B^1$. In total there will be 5 different phenotypes: 4 '0' alleles (total = 0); 1 '1' allele + 3 '0' alleles (total = 1); 2 '1' alleles + 2 '0' alleles (total = 2); 3 '1' alleles + 1 '0' allele (total = 3); and 4 '1' alleles (total = 4).

In **Figure 2.43** the *a* allele = *b* allele = no function (in this case no colour = white). If the *A* allele has the same level of function as a *B* allele then you would see 5 phenotypes as was the case for **Figure 2.48b**. But since there are a total of 9 phenotypes, this cannot be true so *A≠B*. Notice that *aa Bb* is lighter than *Aa bb* even though both genotypes have the same number of dominant alleles. Thus, **in Figure 2.43 an *A* allele has more effect on colouration than a *B* allele**. If you assume, for example, that *B* = 1 unit of colour and *A* = 1.5 units of colour, then 16 genotypes lead to 9 phenotypes.

2-77.

a. Analyze each cross by determining how many genes are involved in the phenotypes and the relationships between the alleles of these genes. In cross 1, there are 2 genes because there are 3 classes in the F$_2$ showing a modified 9:3:3:1 ratio (12:1:3), and LR is the doubly homozygous recessive class. In cross 2, only 1 gene is involved because there are 2 phenotypes in a 3:1 ratio; WR>DR. In cross 3, there is again only 1 gene involved (2 phenotypes in a 1:3 ratio); DR>LR. In cross 4, there is 1 gene (2 phenotypes, with a 3:1 ratio); WR>LR. In cross 5, there are again 2 genes (and as in cross 1, there is a 12:1:3 ratio of three classes); LR is the double homozygous recessive. In total, **there are 2 genes controlling these phenotypes in foxgloves**.

b. Remember that all four starting strains are true-breeding. In cross 1 the parents can be assigned the following genotypes: *AA BB* **(WR-1)** x *aa bb* **(LR)** → *Aa Bb* (WR) → 9 *A– B–* (WR) : 3 *A– bb* (WR; this class displays the epistatic interaction) : 3 *aa B–* (DR) : 1 *aa bb* (LR). The results of cross 2 suggested that DR differs from WR-1 by one gene, so **DR is *aa BB***; cross 3 confirms these genotypes for DR and LR. Cross 4 introduces WR-2, which differs from LR by one gene and differs from DR by 2 genes, so **WR-2 is *AA bb***. Cross 5 would then be *AA bb* (WR-2) x *aa BB* (DR) → *Aa Bb* (WR) → 9 *A– B–* (WR) : 3 *A– bb* (WR) : 3 *aa B–* (DR) : 1 *aa bb* (LR) = 12 WR : 3 DR : 1 LR.

c. WR from the F$_2$ of cross 1 x LR → 253 WR : 124 DR : 123 LR. Remember from part *b* that LR is *aa bb* and DR is *aa B–* while WR can be either *A– B–* or *A– bb* = *A– ??*. The experiment is essentially a testcross for the WR parent. The observed monohybrid ratio for the *A* gene is 1/2 *Aa* : 1/2 *aa* (253 *Aa* : 124 + 123 *aa*), so the WR parent must be *Aa*. The DR and LR classes of progeny show that the WR parent is also heterozygous for the *B* gene (DR is *Bb* and LR is *bb* in these progeny). Thus, the cross is *Aa Bb* **(WR)** x *aa bb* **(LR)**.

2-78.

a. For all 5 crosses, determine the number of genes involved in the trait and the dominance relationships between the alleles. Cross 1: 1 gene, red > blue. Cross 2: 1 gene, lavender > blue. Cross 3: 1 gene, codominance/incomplete dominance (1:2:1), bronze is the phenotype of the heterozygote. Cross 4: 2 genes with epistasis (9 red : 4 yellow : 3 blue). Cross 5: 2 genes with epistasis (9 lavender : 4 yellow : 3 blue). **In total there are 2 genes. One gene controls blue (c^b), red (c^r), and lavender (c^l), where $c^r = c^l > c^b$. The second gene controls the yellow phenotype: *Y* seems to be colourless (or has no effect on colour), so the phenotype is** determined by the alleles of the *c* gene. The *y* allele makes the flower yellow, and is epistatic to all alleles of the *c* gene.

b. cross 1: $c^r c^r$ YY (red) x $c^b c^b$ YY (blue) → $c^r c^b$ YY (red) → 3/4 c^r– YY (red) : 1/4 $c^b c^b$ YY (blue)

cross 2: $c^l c^l$ YY (lavender) x $c^b c^b$ YY (blue) → $c^l c^b$ YY (lavender) → 3/4 c^l– YY (lavender) : 1/4 $c^b c^b$ YY (blue)

cross 3: $c^l c^l$ YY (lavender) x $c^r c^r$ YY (red) → $c^l c^r$ YY (bronze) → 1/4 $c^l c^l$ YY (lavender) : 1/2 $c^l c^r$ YY (bronze) : 1/4 $c^r c^r$ YY (red)

cross 4: $c^r c^r$ YY (red) x $c^b c^b$ yy (yellow) → $c^r c^b$ Yy (red) → 9/16 c^r– Y– (red) : 3/16 c^r– yy (yellow) : 3/16 $c^b c^b$ Y– (blue): 1/16 $c^b c^b$ yy (yellow)

cross 5: $c^l c^l$ yy (yellow) x $c^b c^b$ YY (blue) → $c^l c^b$ Yy (lavender) → 9/16 c^l– Y– (lavender) : 3/16 c^l– yy (yellow) : 3/16 $c^b c^b$ Y– (blue) : 1/16 $c^b c^b$ yy (yellow)

c. $c^r c^r$ yy (yellow) x $c^l c^l$ YY (lavender) → $c^r c^l$ Yy (bronze) → monohybrid ratio for the *c* gene is 1/4 $c^r c^r$: 1/2 $c^r c^l$: 1/4 $c^l c^l$ and monohybrid ratio for the *Y* gene is 3/4 Y– : 1/4 yy. Using the product rule, these generate a dihybrid ratio of **3/16 $c^r c^r$ Y– (red) : 3/8 $c^r c^l$ Y– (bronze) : 3/16 $c^l c^l$ Y– (lavender) : 1/16 $c^r c^r$ yy (yellow) : 1/8 $c^r c^l$ yy (novel genotype) : 1/16 $c^l c^l$ yy (yellow)**. You expect the $c^r c^l$ yy genotype to be yellow as *y* is normally epistatic to the *c* gene. However, you have no direct evidence from the data in any of these crosses that this will be the case, so it is possible that this genotype could cause a different and perhaps completely new phenotype.

2-79. This problem shows that gene interactions producing variations of the 9:3:3:1 ratio in addition to those shown in Table 2.5 are possible though rare.

a. Using the information provided, it is clear that one of the pure-breeding white strains must be homozygous for recessive alleles of gene *A* and the other pure-breeding white strain must be homozygous for recessive alleles of gene *B*. That is, the cross was *AA bb* (white) x *aa BB* (white) → F_1 *Aa Bb* (all blue).

b. In the F_2 generation produced by self-mating of the F_1 plants, you would find a genotypic ratio of 9 *A– B–* : 3 *A– bb* : 3 *aa B–* : 1 *aa bb*. The *A– B–* plants would have blue flowers because colourless precursor 1 would be converted into blue pigment. (Colourless precursor 2 would not produce blue pigment in these flowers because the pathway is suppressed by the proteins specified by the dominant alleles of the two genes.) The *A– bb* plants would be white because the first pathway could not produce blue pigment in the absence of the protein specified by *B*, while the second pathway would be shut off by the protein specified by *A*. The *aa B–* plants would be white because the first pathway could not produce blue pigment in the absence of the protein specified by *A*, while the second pathway would be shut off by the protein specified by *B*. Interestingly, the *aa bb* plants would be blue because even though the first pathway would not function, the second would as it is not suppressed. **You would thus expect in the F₂ generation a ratio of 10 blue (9 *A– B–* + 1 *aa bb*) : 6 white (3 *A– bb* + 3 *aa B–*).**

2-80. The answers are presented in the table below. Different colours in the table represent different phenotypes; these colours are chosen arbitrarily and do not signify anything. The numbers in parentheses indicate the compounds that are present to produce the colours.

Part	9 *A– B–*	3 *A– bb*	3 *aa B–*	1 *aa bb*	Ratio
A	(2 + 4)	(2 + 3)	(1 + 4)	(1 + 3)	9:3:3:1
B	(2)	(2)	(2)	(1)	15:1
C	(3)	(2)	(1)	(1)	9:3:4
D	(2)	(1)	(1)	(1)	9:7
E	(2 + 3)	(2)	(3)	(1)	9:3:3:1
F	(2 + 4) = (2)	(2 + 3) = (2)	(1 + 4)	(1 + 3)	12:3:1
G	(3)	(2) = (1)	(1) = (2)	(1) = (2)	9:7
H	(2)	(1)	(2)	(2)	13:3

[Note: In part *e*, you could have interpreted a limitless supply of compound 1 to mean that compound 1 would be present in all the phenotypes (for example, the *A– B–* genotype would have compounds 1 + 2 + 3, etc.). The ratio would still be the same under this assumption as the ratio listed in the table.]

2-81. A particular phenotypic ratio does not allow you to infer the operation of a specific biochemical mechanism because as can be seen from the answers to Problem 80, **different biochemical mechanisms can produce the same ratio of phenotypes** (for example, the pathways in parts *d* and *g* are different yet both yield 9:7 ratios). The particular ratio seen in a cross may nonetheless provide information about types of biochemical pathways you could exclude from consideration because those pathways could not produce the observed ratio.

In contrast, **if you know the biochemical mechanism behind a gene interaction** and you also know the dominance relationships of the alleles, you can then trace out the consequences of each genotypic class and thus **you can predict the ratios of phenotypes you would see among the F_2 progeny.**

2-82.

a.   There are actually **two different phenotypes** mentioned in this problem. One phenotype is the shape of the erythrocytes. All people with the genotype $SPH\ SPH^+$ have **spherical erythrocytes**. Therefore this phenotype **is fully penetrant and shows no variation in expression.** The second **phenotype is anaemia. Here the expressivity among anaemic patients varies from severe to mild.** There are even **some people with the $SPH\ SPH^+$ genotype (150/2400) with no symptoms of anaemia at all. Thus the penetrance of the anaemic phenotype is 2250/2400 or 0.94.**

b.   The disease-causing phenotype is the anaemia and the severity of the anaemia is greatly reduced when the spleen functions poorly and does not "read" the spherical erythrocytes. Therefore **treatment might involve removing the spleen (an organ which is not essential to survival). The more efficiently the spleen functions, the earlier in a patient's life it should be removed.** $SPH\ SPH^+$ individuals with no symptoms of anaemia should not be subjected to this drastic treatment.

2-83.

a.   The most likely mode of inheritance is a **single gene with incomplete dominance** such that $f^n f^n$ = normal (<250 mg/dl), $f^n f^a$ = intermediate levels of serum cholesterol (250-500 mg/dl), and $f^a f^a$ homozygotes = elevated levels (>500 mg/dl). Some of the individuals in the pedigrees do not fit this hypothesis. In 2 of the families (Families 2 and 4), two normal parents have a child with intermediate levels of serum cholesterol. **One possibility is that in each family, at least one of these normal parents (I-3 and/or I-4 in Family 2; I-1 and/or I-2 in Family 4) was actually a $f^n f^a$ heterozygote who did not have elevated cholesterol in excess of 250 mg/dl. In this scenario, familial hypercholesterolaemia is a trait with incomplete penetrance**, so that some unaffected people have a genotype that causes the disease in other people. It is also possible that the affected children of these parents do not have an f^a allele associated with elevated serum cholesterol, but they show the trait for other reasons such as diet, level of exercise, or other genes. This explanation is reasonable, but perhaps less likely because multiple children would have to have the trait but not the f^a allele.

b. **Familial hypercholesterolaemia also shows variable expressivity**, meaning that people with the same genotype have the condition, but to different extents. This suggests that factors other than just the genotype are involved in the expression of the phenotype. Such factors could again include diet, level of exercise, and other genes.

2-84. If polycystic kidney disease is dominant, then the child is Pp and inherited the P disease allele from one parent or the other, yet phenotypically the parents appear to be pp. Perhaps one of the parents is indeed Pp, but this parent does not show the disease phenotype for some reason. Such situations are not uncommon: the unexpressed dominant allele is said to have **incomplete penetrance** in these cases. Alternatively, it could be that both parents are indeed pp and the P allele inherited by the child was due to a **spontaneous mutation** during the formation of the gamete in one of the parents; we will discuss this topic in Chapter 8. It is also possible that the **father of the child is not the male parent of the couple**. In this case the biological father must have the disease.

2-85.

a. The pattern in both families **looks like a recessive trait** since unaffected individuals have affected progeny and the trait skips generations. For example, in the Smiths II-3 must be a carrier, but in order for III-5 to be affected II-4 must also be a carrier. **If the trait is rare (as is this one) you wouldn't expect two heterozygotes to marry by chance as many times as required by these pedigrees. The alternative explanation is that the trait is dominant but not 100% penetrant.**

b. Assuming this is a dominant but not completely penetrant trait, **individuals II-3 and III-6 in the Smiths' pedigree and individual II-6 in the Jeffersons' pedigree** must carry the dominant allele but not express it in their phenotypes.

c. If the trait were common, **recessive inheritance** is the more likely mode of inheritance.

Chapter 2

d. **None**; in cases where two unaffected parents have an affected child, both parents would be carriers of the recessive trait.

2-86. The hairy x hairy → 2/3 hairy : 1/3 normal cross described in the first paragraph of the problem tells us that the hairy flies are heterozygous, that the hairy phenotype is dominant to normal, and that the homozygous hairy progeny are lethal (that is, hairy is a recessive lethal). Thus, hairy wings is *Hh*, normal wings is *hh,* and the lethal genotype is *HH*. Normal flies therefore should be **hh (normal-1)** and a cross with hairy (*Hh*) would be expected to always give 1/2 *Hh* (hairy) : 1/2 *hh* (normal) as seen in cross 1.

In cross 2, the progeny MUST for the same reasons be 1/2 *Hh* : 1/2 *hh*, yet they ALL appear normal. This suggests the normal-2 stock has another mutation that suppresses the hairy wing phenotype in the *Hh* progeny. The hairy parent must have the recessive alleles of this suppressor gene (*ss*), while the normal-2 stock must be homozygous for the dominant allele (*SS*) that suppresses the hairy phenotype. Thus cross 2 is **hh SS (normal-2)** x *Hh ss* (hairy) → 1/2 *Hh Ss* (normal because hairy is suppressed) : 1/2 *hh Ss* (normal).

In cross 3, the normal-3 parent is heterozygous for the suppressor gene: **hh Ss (normal-3)** x *Hh ss* (hairy) → the expected ratios for each gene alone are 1/2 *Hh* : 1/2 *hh*, and 1/2 *Ss* : 1/2 *ss*, so the expected ratio for the two genes together is 1/4 *Hh Ss* (normal) : 1/4 *Hh ss* (hairy) : 1/4 *hh Ss* (normal) : 1/4 *hh ss* (normal) = 3/4 normal : 1/4 hairy.

In cross 4 you see a 2/3 : 1/3 ratio again, as if you were crossing hairy x hairy. After a bit of trial-and-error examining the remaining possibilities for these two genes, you will be able to demonstrate that this cross was **Hh Ss (normal-4)** x *Hh ss* (hairy) → expected ratio for the individual genes are 2/3 *Hh* : 1/3 *hh*, and 1/2 *Ss* : 1/2 *ss*, so the expected ratio for the two genes together from the product rule is 2/6 *Hh Ss* (normal) : 2/6 *Hh ss* (hairy) : 1/6 *hh Ss* (normal) : 1/6 *hh ss* (normal) = 2/3 normal : 1/3 hairy.

2-87. The Black Lab: A solid black dog must: deposit eumelanin (*E–*); not be brown (*B–*); have no pheomelanin striping in the hairs [(*K^B–* and any *A* gene alleles) or (*aa* and any *K* gene alleles)]; must not be diluted to gray (*D–*); no spotting (*S–*); and no merle (*M^2M^2*). Because Labs always breed true for solid colours (black, brown, or some light yellow colour), the black Lab cannot be heterozygous at any gene for recessive alleles that specify non-solid colours. So **the Black Lab is most likely: *EE* or *Ee*, *BB* or *Bb*, (*K^B K^B* and any gene *A* alleles) or (*K^B k^y aa*), *DD*, *SS*, *M²M²*.**

The Chocolate Lab: A solid chocolate brown dog would be the same genotype as solid black, except *bb*.

The Yellow Lab: A solid yellow dog must not deposit eumelanin (*ee*). Any alleles of gene *B* are possible, and as above, the dog must be *DD*, *SS*, and *M²M²*. The same considerations for genes *A* and *K* apply as for the other Labs above. The yellow dog pictured cannot be *aa*, however, or it would be white. Therefore, **yellow labs are *ee*, *B–* or *bb*, *K^B K^B*, any gene *A* alleles except *aa*, *DD*, *SS*, *M²M²*.**

Chapter 3   The Chromosome Theory of Inheritance

Synopsis:

Chapter 3 is critical for understanding genetics because it connects Mendel's laws for the transmission of genes with the behaviour of chromosome during meiosis. Genes are located on chromosomes and travel with them during cell division, gamete formation, and fertilization. Mendel's first law of segregation is the consequence of the fact that homologous chromosomes segregate from each other (move to opposite spindle poles) during the first meiotic division in germ cells. Mendel's second law of independent assortment results from the independent alignment of each pair of homologous chromosomes during the first meiotic divison.

Many of the experiments that verified the Chromosome Theory of Inheritance relied on the facts that, in many organisms, the two sex chromosomes are morphologically distinct and do not carry the same genes. As a result, the inheritance patterns of X-linked genes in fruit flies and humans differ from those of autosomal genes, and scientists were able to correlate these unusual inheritance patterns with the presence of particular sex chromosomes.

Key Terms:

haploid (n) – cells such as gametes that contain only one copy of each chromosome pair.

diploid ($2n$) – cells that contain both copies of a homologous chromosome pair.

sister chromatids – the two copies of a single chromosome that result after chromosome replication during S phase. The sister chromatids are connected to each other at the **centromere**.

metacentric/acrocentric – terms that describe the position of the centromere on a chromosome. In *metacentric chromosomes*, the centromere is near the centre so the chromosome contains two long *arms*. In *acrocentric chromosomes*, the centromere is near (but not quite at) one of the ends.

homologous chromosomes (homologues) – chromosomes that match in shape, size, and banding pattern because they have the same set of genes. Normally, in a pair of homologous chromosomes, one chromosome is of maternal origin, while the other is of paternal origin. As a result, homologous chromosomes may carry different alleles of genes.

nonhomologous chromosomes – chromosomes that do not match because they have different sets of genes.

karyotype – a representation of an organism's genome made by arranging micrographs of each chromosome as homologous pairs of decreasing size.

sex chromosomes – the chromosomes that determine an individual's sex; in humans and *Drosophila*, these are the **X chromosome** and the **Y chromosome**.

SRY – the gene found on the Y chromosome in humans and other mammals whose presence is the primary determinant of maleness. In rare cases of **sex reversal**, the *SRY* gene has shifted from the Y chromosome to the X chromosome.

autosomes – chromosomes that do not determine sex and that are found as homologous pairs.

pseudoautosomal regions (PARs) – regions containing about 30 genes that are found on both the X and Y chromosomes in humans. The presence of PARs allows the X and Y chromosomes to pair with each other during the first meiotic division.

cell cycle – repeating pattern of cell growth and division. **Interphase** (the period between cell divisions) consists of G_1, **S** (the time of chromosome replication), and G_2. The cells divide during **M phase**, and the daughter cells separate from each other through **cytokinesis** at the end of M phase. (See Figure 3.8 for details.)

spindle – cellular structure made of **microtubules** emanating from two **spindle poles** that forms during M phase and guides chromosome movements.

kinetochores – structures found at centromeres that connect the chromosomes to the microtubule fibres of the spindle.

mitosis – cell division that preserves the number and kinds of chromosomes. Successive rounds of mitosis starting from a fertilized zygote create a multicellular organism whose **somatic cells** are genetically identical.

prophase/prometaphase/metaphase/anaphase/telophase – successive stages of M phase (see Figure 3.9 for details).

germ cells – cells destined for a specialized role in the production of gametes. In animals, the germ cells are set aside as the **germ line** early in embryogenesis.

meiosis – cell divisions of germ cells that result in the formation of gametes. Meiosis consists of two rounds of division (Meiosis I and Meiosis II) that follow a single round of chromosome replication; as a result, the gametes are haploid.

synapsis – the pairing of homologous chromosome during Meiosis I. Synapsis is mediated by a protein structure called the **synaptonemal complex**. The paired chromosomes during prophase and metaphase of meiosis I are called **bivalents** or **tetrads**.

crossing-over – exchange of genetic material between homologous chromosomes that takes place during prophase of meiosis I at sites called **chiasmata**. Crossing-over results in the **recombination** of genetic material between nonsister chromatids.

Chapter 3

nondisjunction – rare mistakes that occur during cell division in which chromosomes or chromatids that should separate from each other fail to separate from each other.

gametogenesis/oogenesis/spermatogenesis – processes that produce gametes.

oogonia/spermatogonia – germline cells in the ovaries or testes that undergo mitotic divisions.

oocytes/spermatocytes – germline cells in the ovaries or testes that undergo meiosis. Primary oocytes/spermatocytes are the cells that undergo meiosis I; secondary oocytes/spermatocytes undergo meiosis II.

polar bodies – small cells produced in females at the end of meiosis I or meiosis II that disintegrate and cannot become eggs.

ovum – the haploid egg cell produced at the end of meiosis II in females.

spermatid – haploid cells produced at the conclusion of meiosis II in males that will undergo additional development to become sperm.

X linkage – inheritance pattern seen for genes located on the X chromosome but not the Y chromosome. X-linked genes may exhibit crisscross inheritance in which the sons look like their mothers and the daughters resemble their fathers. Males are hemizygous for X-linked genes because they have only one copy of these genes.

dosage compensation – processes that ensure that cells in males and females produce the same amount of protein encoded by X-linked genes. In humans, dosage compensation occurs due to X chromosome inactivation: when an individual has two or more X chromosomes, all of the X chromosomes but one are "turned off" because they become inactive Barr bodies.

sex-limited traits – traits that affect a structure or process found in one sex but not the other. Sex-influenced traits can be seen in both sexes, but the expression differs between the sexes. The terms sex-limited and sex-influenced do not say anything about a gene's location, because both sex-linked and autosomal genes may affect the two sexes differently.

The Keys to Mitosis and Meiosis:

The figures starting at the bottom of the next page depict metaphase of mitosis and meiosis I and summarize how chromosomes are transmitted during these types of cell division. You should note the following points:

• Just as in Figure 3.3, sister chromatids are shown in the same shade of the same colour, homologous chromosomes are shown in different shades of the same colour, and nonhomologous chromosomes are shown in different colours. This scheme reflects the facts that sister chromatids have identical DNA sequences, homologous chromosomes are nearly the same (they have the same genes but may have different alleles of those genes), and nonhomologous chromosomes have different genes.

- In metaphase of mitosis, the sister chromatids are connected through their kinetochores to microtubules emanating from the opposite spindle poles. The chromosomes congress to the metaphase plate because the microtubules exert forces on the sister chromatids in opposite directions, but these counterbalance each other because the sister chromatids are connected at the centromere. During anaphase, the centromeric connection is dissolved, so the sister chromatids can move to the opposite poles.

- In metaphase of meiosis I, the two sister chromatids of each chromosome attach to microtubules from the same spindle pole. It is the homologous chromosomes that attach to microtubules from opposite spindle poles; at anaphase of meiosis I, it is the homologous chromosomes that go to opposite spindle poles. During anaphase of meiosis I, the centromeres remain intact, so the sister chromatids remain together as the homologous chromosome go to opposite spindle poles. The separation of homologous chromosomes during meiosis I explains Mendel's first law of allele segregation.

- The reason homologous chromosomes connect to opposite spindle poles and can congress to the metaphase plate during meiosis I is that the homologues are attached to each other by crossing-over at chiasmata (*not shown*). Crossing-over is thus critical for ensuring that the homologous chromosomes pair so that they can separate from each other at anaphase of meiosis I when the chiasmata are dissolved. In the absence of crossing-over, homologous chromosomes are likely to behave incorrectly and go to the same spindle pole at anaphase of meiosis I; this is one cause of *nondisjunction*. In Chapter 4, you will learn more about how crossing-over ensures proper chromosome behaviour during meiosis I.

- During metaphase of meiosis I, two different pairs of homologous chromosomes can connect to the spindle in two equally likely ways, explaining Mendel's second law of independent assortment.

- (*Not shown*). Metaphase of meiosis II is similar to metaphase of mitosis, but the cells have only half the number of chromosomes. For example, cells in metaphase of meiosis II would have only one *blue* chromosome and one *red* chromosome.

Chapter 3

Metaphase of Mitosis

Metaphase of Meiosis I

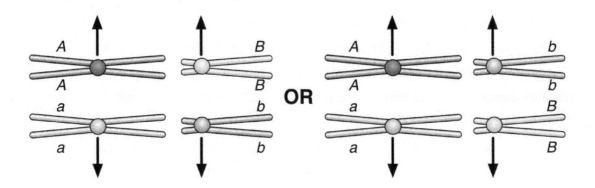

Problem Solving:

For problems involving mitosis and meiosis, you should make sure you can draw from memory the two figures on this page and understand the forces that pull sister chromatids (mitosis and meiosis II) or homologous chromosomes (meiosis I) to opposite spindle poles and the structures (centromeres in mitosis and meiosis II; the chiasmata resulting from crossing-over during meiosis I) that keep the sister chromatids or homologous chromosomes together at the metaphase plate until the centromeres or chiasmata are dissolved. Remember that in this book, a chromosome consists of all chromatids connected through a common centromere. Thus, a single chromosome during mitotic metaphase has two sister chromatids, but then these chromatids become two chromosomes during anaphase of mitosis.

Remember that you should start each problem involving the outcomes of crosses by diagramming the crosses, determining the number of genes involved and the phenotypes associated with each of the alleles. Based on what you learned in this chapter, you can see that you need to consider the possibility that a gene controlling a phenotype is X-linked. You can determine whether a gene involved in the cross is X-linked by looking for a clear phenotypic difference between the sexes in one generation's progeny of a cross. This is NOT a difference in the absolute numbers of males and females of a certain phenotype, but instead a trait that is present in one sex and totally absent in the other sex. This difference between the sexes will be seen in <u>either</u> the F_1 generation <u>or</u> the F_2 generation, but **not** in both generations in the same cross series. It is not possible to make a definitive conclusion about X-linkage based on just one generation of a cross - you **must** see the data from **both** the F_1 and F_2 progeny. For X-linked recessive traits, if the sex difference is seen in the F_1 generation, then the female parent had the X-linked phenotype. If the sex difference is seen in the F_2 generation, then the male parent had the X-linked trait. The opposite is true for X-linked dominant traits. X-linked genes usually show a 1:1 monohybrid ratio.

Once you have generated a model to explain the data, use your model to re-diagram the cross by assigning genotypes to the parental (P) generation. Then follow the cross through, figuring out the expected genotypes and phenotypes in the F_1 and F_2 generations. Remember that your genotype-phenotype assignments must always agree with those initially assigned to the parents. Next, compare your predicted results to the observed data you were given. If the two sets of information match, then your initial genotypes were correct! In many cases, there may seem to be two possible sets of genotypes for the parents. If your predicted results do not match the data given, try the other possible set of genotypes for the parents.

Solutions to Problems:

Vocabulary

3-1. i. **13**; ii. **7**; iii. **11**; iv. **10**; v. **12**; vi. **8**; vii. **9**; viii. **1**; ix. **6**; x. **15**; xi. **3**; xii. **2**; xiii. **16**; xiv. **4**; xv. **14**; xvi. **5**.

Section 3.1 – Chromosomes: The Carriers of Genes

3-2. A diploid number of 46 means there are 23 homologous pairs of chromosomes.

a. A child receives **23 chromosomes from the father**.

b. Each somatic cell has **44 autosomes** (22 pairs) and **2 sex chromosomes** (1 pair).

c. **A human ovum (female gamete) contains 23 chromosomes** - one of each homologous pair (22 autosomes and one X chromosome).

d. **One sex chromosome (an X chromosome) is present in a human ovum.**

Section 3.2 – Sex Chromosomes and Sex Determination

3-3.

a.   **7 centromeres** are shown.

b.   There are **7 chromosomes** in the diagram. Note that by definition the number of chromosomes is equal to the number of centromeres.

c.   There are **14 chromatids**.

d.   There are **3 pairs** of homologous chromosomes and one chromosome without a partner.

e.   There are **4 metacentric** chromosomes and **3 acrocentric** chromosomes.

f.   **This is an organism in which males are XO**, so it is most likely that **females would be XX. The karyotype of females would be the same as the one shown, except that there would be 2 copies of the left-most chromosome instead of one copy.**

3-4. Sex-reversed XX individuals are males because they have a functional *SRY* gene whose presence activates testes development in embryos. The embryonic testes secrete hormones that trigger the development of other male sex organs. However, **sex-reversed XX males lack the male fertility genes found in the MSY region of the Y chromosome, so they are infertile** (compare Figures 3.6 and 3.7).

3-5.

a.   If the purpose of the SRY protein is to activate the *Sox9* gene, then male development takes place when *Sox9* is active, but female development occurs when *Sox9* is inactive. Thus, **an XY individual who is homozygous for a nonfunctional mutant allele of *Sox9* would develop as a female.** Even though the SRY protein is made, it will not be able to activate copies of *Sox9* that are inherently nonfunctional.

b.   In the experiment described in the Fast Forward Box "Transgenic Mice Show that *SRY* is the Maleness Factor", researchers added an *SRY* gene to the genomes of XX mice, and these mice developed as males. Suppose now that instead of *SRY,* you added a *Sox9* transgene to an XX mouse. **This XX mouse with a *Sox9* transgene would develop as a female, not a male.** The reason is that the *Sox9* transgene could not be activated in the absence of the SRY protein. (In fact, XX mice already have two copies of *Sox9* even without the transgene because *Sox9* is autosomal.)

Section 3.3 – Mitosis: Cell Division That Preserves Chromosome Number

3-6. Mitosis maintains the chromosome number. Thus, **mitosis produces 2 daughter cells each with 14 chromosomes (2*n*, diploid).**

3-7.

a. iii. In anaphase, the sister chromatids separate and move to opposite spindle poles. Note in the figure that each chromatid assumes a V-shaped configuration because the chromatid is being pulled towards the pole along the microtubules that connect the pole to the kinetochore in the centromeric region. As a result, the centromeric region "leads" the chromatid towards the pole, and the telomeres at the ends of the arms lag behind as the chromatid moves towards the poles.

b. i. In prophase, the chromosomes have already replicated so that they consist of two sister chromatids. These chromosomes have not yet attached to the spindle because the nuclear envelope is still intact.

c. iv. In metaphase, the chromosomes (consisting at this stage of two sister chromatids connected to each other at the centromere) are found at the metaphase plate at the centre of the cell. There is no nuclear envelope because it broke down previously, allowing the kinetochores of the two sister chromatids to connect to spindle fibres emanating from opposite spindle poles. (These spindle fibre attachments are what allow the chromosomes to congress to the metaphase plate.)

d. ii. During G_2 of the cell cycle, the chromosomes, which have not yet condensed, are still contained in an intact nucleus.

e. v. During telophase, the sister chromatids, which already moved to opposite spindle poles during anaphase, are incorporated into the nuclei of the two daughter cells. Cytokinesis is the process that separates the cytoplasms of these two daughter cells.

3-8.

a. G_1, S, G_2 and M (see Figure 3.8).

b. G_1, S and G_2 are all part of interphase.

c. **G_1 is the time of major cell growth that precedes DNA synthesis and chromosome replication. Chromosome replication occurs during S phase. G_2 is another phase of cell growth after chromosome replication during which the cell synthesizes many proteins needed for mitosis.**

3-9.

	G_1	S	G_2	Prophase	Metaphase	Anaphase	Telophase
a. # of chromatids/chromosome	1	1 → 2	2	2	2	1	1
b. nucleolus?	yes	yes	yes	yes → no	no	no	no → yes
c. spindle?	no	no	no	no → yes	yes	yes	yes → no

d. nuclear membrane?	yes	yes	yes	yes → no	no	no	no → yes

3-10. No, mitosis can (and does) occur in haploid cells. This is because each chromosome aligns independently at the metaphase plate; there is no requirement for homologous chromosome pairing.

Section 3.4 – Meiosis: Cell Divisions That Halve Chromosome Number

3-11. Meiosis produces 4 cells (n, haploid), each with 7 chromosomes (one half the number of chromosomes of the starting cell).

3-12. In order to answer this question count the number of independent centromeres. If two sister chromatids are connected by one centromere this counts as one chromosome. **Meiosis I is the only division that reduces the chromosome number by half, so it is a reductional division**. A cell undergoing meiosis II or mitosis has the same number of centromeres (and thus chromosomes) as each daughter cell. Therefore, the **meiosis II and mitotic divisions are both equational**.

3-13.

a. **mitosis, meiosis I, meiosis II**

b. **mitosis, meiosis I**

c. **mitosis**

d. Mitosis is obviously excluded, but the rest of the answer depends on whether your definition of ploidy counts chromosomes or chromatids. Meiosis I in a diploid organism produces daughter cells with n chromosomes but $2n$ chromatids; meiosis II produces haploid daughter cells with n chromosomes or n chromatids. Thus, there are **2 possible answers: meiosis II (if you count chromatids or chromosomes) and meiosis I (if you count chromosomes but not if you count chromatids)**. To avoid potential confusion, geneticists usually use the terms "n", "$2n$", and "ploidy" only to describe cells with unreplicated chromosomes, so they don't often use these terms when talking about the cells produced at the end of meiosis I.

e. **meiosis I**

f. **none**

g. **meiosis I**

h. **meiosis II, mitosis**

i. **mitosis, meiosis I**

3-14. Remember that the problem states that all cells are from the same organism. This fact is needed to allow the designation of mitosis, meiosis I and II. The stage of the cell cycle can be inferred from the morphology of the spindle, the presence or absence of the nuclear membrane, and whether homologous chromosomes (or sister chromatids) are paired (or connected through a centromere) or separated. **The** *n* **number is 3 chromosomes** (this is the number of chromosomes in the haploid gametes).

a. **anaphase of meiosis I**

b. **metaphase of mitosis** (<u>not</u> meiosis II because there are 6 chromosomes or 2*n* in this cell)

c. **telophase of meiosis II**

d. **anaphase of mitosis**

e. **metaphase of meiosis II**

3-15.

a. The cell is in **metaphase/early anaphase of meiosis I in a male**, assuming the heterogametic sex (that is, the sex with two different sex chromosomes) in *Tenebrio* is male. Note the *heteromorphic* chromosome pair (with non-identical chromosomes) in the centre of the cell.

b. It is **not possible to distinguish any structure other than the number of chromosomes**.

c. ***n* = 5**.

3-16. In the following figures, chromosomes are drawn in the same style as in Figure 3.3: Nonhomologous chromosomes are in different colours (here, blue and red); homologous chromosomes are represented in different shades (dark or light) of the same colour, while sister chromatids are in the same shades of the same colour. In this scheme, the relative degree of similarity in colour and shade illustrates the degree of nucleotide sequence similarity. Nonhomologous chromosomes are unrelated and do not have the same genes. Homologous chromosomes have DNA sequences that are about 99.9 percent identical (they have the same genes, but different alleles of those genes). Sister chromatids have identical DNA sequences, excepting very rare new mutations.

To further your understanding of chromosome behaviours during the various types of cell division, the figures also have arrows showing the direction in which the chromatids or chromosomes will move during the subsequent anaphase. (This was not requested in the instructions to the problem.)

a. Metaphase of mitosis:

b. Metaphase of meiosis I: (Note the pairing of homologous chromosomes and the two possible alignments of the 2 non-homologous chromosome pairs.)

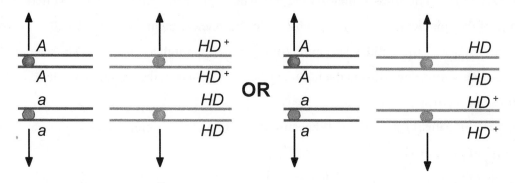

c. Metaphase of meiosis II: Shown below is only one of the two products of meiosis I from the cell diagrammed at the left in part *b*; the other product of this meiosis I would have chromosomes bearing *a* and *HD*. The other alignment in meiosis I (shown at the right in part *b*) will give two *A HD* and two *a HD*$^+$ daughter cells.

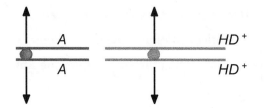

3-17. Using the assumptions given, each person can produce 2^{23} genetically different gametes. Thus, the couple could potentially produce 2^{23} x $2^{23} = 2^{46}$ or **70,368,744,177,664 different zygotic combinations**. That is 70 trillion, 368 billion, 744 million, 177 thousand, 664 genetically different children.

It is **very realistic to assume that homologous chromosomes carry different alleles of some genes**. As we will see later in the book there are about 3 million differences between the DNA sequences in the two haploid human genomes in any one human being, or on average about 130,000 differences between any two homologous chromosomes. In contrast, **crossing-over almost always occurs between homologous chromosomes in any meiosis**; you will remember that crossing-over is needed to allow the homologous chromosomes to segregate properly during meiosis I. Thus, **the second assumption is much less realistic**.

The fact that crossing-over occurs between homologous chromosomes means that even though the 2^{46} number just calculated is enormous, it is nonetheless a gross under-estimate of the number of different zygotes two people could produce. As you will see in the next chapter, crossing-over leads to *genetic recombination*, meaning that a chromosome in a gamete is a composite of pieces from the chromosomes the parent obtained from his or her parents. Different gametes from any one parent have different mixtures of genomic segments from that person's mother and father. So, when someone says they have never known anyone genetically like you, they are exactly right (unless you are an identical twin or triplet)!

3-18. The diploid sporophyte contains 7 homologous pairs of chromosomes. One chromosome in each pair came from the male gamete and the other from the female gamete. When the diploid cell undergoes meiosis one homologue of each pair ends up in the gamete (spore). For each homologous pair, the probability that the gamete contains the homologue inherited from the father = 1/2. **The probability that a gamete contains only the homologues inherited from the father is $(1/2)^7 =$ 0.78%.**

3-19. Absolutely. **Meiosis requires the pairing of homologous chromosomes during meiosis I, so meiosis cannot occur in a haploid organism.**

3-20.

a. **The diagram at left (i) is correct. In this diagram the connection between sister chromatids is maintained in the region between the chiasma and the telomeres**; in the diagram on the right this connection is incorrectly shown as it occurs between the chromatids of homologous chromosomes. If you trace out the chromatids you will notice that the sister chromatid cohesion in the region between the chiasma and the telomeres provides a physical connection that joins homologous chromosomes, allowing them to stay together at the metaphase plate during meiosis I. This shows why recombination is so important for proper meiotic chromosome behaviour.

b. **The cohesin complexes at the centromere must be different than those along the chromosome arms, at least during meiosis I. At anaphase I the cohesin complexes along the arms must be destroyed in order to allow the homologous chromosomes to separate. However, the cohesin at the centromeres must remain because sister chromatids stay together until anaphase of meiosis II.** Research suggests that this difference between the cohesin complexes occurs because centromeric cohesin is specifically protected from destruction at anaphase I by a protein called *shugoshin* (Japanese for *guardian spirit*).

3-21. Most likely, **some kind of crossing-over event occurred between a normal X chromosome and a normal Y chromosome,** as shown by the *red* "X" at the left of the figure below. This crossing-over event would then move the *SRY* gene from the Y onto the X chromosome, making an *SRY*⁺ X chromosome and an *SRY*⁻ Y chromosome. A person with a normal X chromosome and an *SRY*⁺ X chromosome would be a sex-reversed male. A person with a normal X chromosome and an *SRY*⁻ Y chromosome would be a sex-reversed female.

This crossing-over event must have occurred in a male, and it must have occurred between the centromere of the Y chromosome and the *SRY* gene in order to move the gene from the Y to the X. [You should note that this crossing-over event must be "illegitimate" (meaning that it is a rare mistake in meiosis) because the X and Y chromosome are not homologous (do not share the same DNA sequences) in the region where the crossing-over event occurred]. In contrast, crossing-over does occur at least once in each meiosis between either the PAR1 regions on the X and Y and/or the PAR2 regions on the X and Y; it is crossing-over in the PAR regions that ensures the X and Y chromosomes pair and then disjoin properly during meiosis I in normal males.

Section 3.5 - Gametogenesis

3-22. Remember that this textbook uses the convention that the number of chromosomes is equal to the number of separate centromeres. Therefore, after DNA synthesis each chromosome has replicated and thus has 2 chromatids held together at the attached centromeres. This structure is one chromosome with two chromatids. The centromeres separate at anaphase in mitosis or at anaphase II in meiosis; at this point, the two chromatids now become two chromosomes. For an overview of egg formation in humans **see Figure 3.19**; for an overview of sperm formation in humans **see Figure 3.20**.

a.   **96 chromosomes** with 1 chromatid each = **96 chromatids**;

b.   **48 chromosomes** with 2 chromatids each = **96 chromatids**;

c.   **48 chromosomes** with 1 chromatid each = **48 chromatids**;

d.   **48 chromosomes** with 1 chromatid each (unreplicated in G_1) = **48 chromatids**;

e.   **48 chromosomes** with 2 chromatids each (replicated in G2) = **96 chromatids**;

f.   **48 chromosomes** (unreplicated in G_1 preceding meiosis) = **48 chromatids;**

g.   **48 chromosomes** with 2 chromatids each = **96 chromatids**;

h.   **48 chromosomes** with 1 chromatid each (unreplicated before S) = **48 chromatids**;

i.   **24 chromosomes** with 1 chromatid each = **24 chromatids**;

j.   **48 chromosomes** with 2 chromatids each = **96 chromatids**;

k.   **24 chromosomes** with 2 chromatids each = **48 chromatids**;

l.   **24 chromosomes** with 1 chromatid each = **24 chromatids**;

m.   **24 chromosomes** with 1 chromatid each = **24 chromatids**.

3-23.

a.   **400 sperm** are produced from 100 primary spermatocytes;

b.   **200 sperm** are produced from 100 secondary spermatocytes;

c.   **100 sperm** are produced from 100 spermatids;

d.   **100 ova** are formed from 100 primary oocytes. Remember that although each primary oocyte will produce three or four meiotic products (depending on whether the first polar body undergoes meiosis II), only one will become an egg (ovum);

e.   **100 ova** develop from 100 secondary oocytes - the other 100 haploid products are polar bodies;

f.   **No ova** are produced from polar bodies.

3-24. The primary oocyte is arrested in prophase I, so it contains a duplicated set of the diploid number of chromosomes (46 chromosomes and 92 chromatids). During meiosis I, the homologous chromosomes segregate into two separate cells, so the chromosome carrying the *A* alleles will segregate into one cell while the chromosome carrying the *a* alleles will segregate into the other cell. (This outcome assumes that no crossing-over has occurred between the *A* gene and the centromere of the chromosome that carries this gene.) One of these cells becomes the secondary oocyte (containing 23 chromosomes each with 2 chromatids and more of the cytoplasm) and the other becomes the polar body. **The genotype of the dermoid cyst that develops from a secondary oocyte could be either *AA* or *aa*.** Note that the attached sister chromatids in the secondary oocyte must separate from each other before the first mitosis leading to cyst formation.

3-25. Remember that in turkeys, ZW is ♀, ZZ is ♂, and WW is lethal.

a.   The ZW eggs would give rise to **only ZW females**.

b.   Cells resulting from meiosis will be 1/2 Z : 1/2 W. Upon chromosomal duplication they would become ZZ or WW. ZZ cells develop into males and WW is lethal, so **only males** are produced by this mechanism.

c. After eggs have gone through meiosis I, they will contain either a replicated Z or a replicated W chromosome. If the sister chromatids separate to become the chromosomes you will have 1/2 ZZ : 1/2 WW. Again, **only ZZ males** are produced since WW cells are inviable.

d. Meiosis of a ZW cell produces 4 haploid products, 2 Z : 2 W, one of which is the egg and the other 3 are the polar bodies. If the egg is Z then it has a 1/3 chance of fusing with a Z polar body and a 2/3 chance of fusing with a W polar body = 1/3 ZZ ($\male$) : 2/3 ZW ($\female$). If the egg is W then the fusion products will be 1/3 WW (lethal) : 2/3 ZW ($\female$). Because these 2 types of eggs are mutually exclusive, you add these 2 probabilities: 1/2 (probability of Z egg) x (1/3 ZZ : 2/3 ZW) + 1/2 (probability of W egg) x (1/3 WW : 2/3 WZ) = 1/6 ZZ : 2/6 ZW + 1/6 WW : 2/6 WZ = 1/6 ZZ ($\male$) : 4/6 ZW ($\female$) : 1/6 WW (lethal) = **1/5 ZZ ($\male$) : 4/5 ZW ($\female$)**.

Section 3.6 – Validation of the Chromosome Theory

3-26. In birds males are ZZ, females are ZW. Diagram the crosses between true-breeding birds: yellow $\female$ x brown $\male$ $\rightarrow$ brown $\female$ and brown $\male$; brown $\female$ x yellow $\male$ $\rightarrow$ yellow $\female$ and brown $\male$

These two crosses are reciprocal crosses, and the progeny show a sex-associated difference in phenotypes - both sexes are the same phenotype (brown) in the first cross but different phenotypes in the second cross (brown $\female$ and yellow $\male$). This finding indicates the **trait is sex-linked**; a single sex-linked gene is sufficient to explain the results. Also, the second cross shows crisscross inheritance - brown females x yellow males $\rightarrow$ brown sons and yellow daughters. Crisscross inheritance is also characteristic of a sex-linked trait. Because the parents are true-breeding, the first cross shows that brown > yellow. **Therefore, the alleles of the gene are Z^B (brown allele on Z chromosome) and Z^b (yellow allele on Z chromosome); the W chromosome does not carry the feather colour gene.** The first cross was Z^b W x $Z^B Z^B$ $\rightarrow$ Z^B W (brown females) and $Z^B Z^b$ (brown males). The second cross was Z^B W x $Z^b Z^b$ $\rightarrow$ $Z^B Z^b$ (brown males) and Z^b W (yellow females).

3-27.

a. Ivory eyes is the recessive phenotype and brown is the dominant phenotype; females have 2 alleles of every gene and males have only one. Diagram the cross: ivory $\female$ (*bb*) x brown $\male$ (*B*) $\rightarrow$ fertilized eggs are *Bb* $\female$ (**brown**); unfertilized eggs are *b* $\male$ (**ivory**).

b. The cross is *Bb* F_1 $\female$ x *B* $\male$ $\rightarrow$ fertilized eggs are **1/2 *Bb* $\female$ (brown) : 1/2 *BB* $\female$ (brown) = all brown $\female$ progeny**; unfertilized eggs are **1/2 *B* $\male$ (brown) : 1/2 *b* $\male$ (ivory)**.

3-28. The answer to this question depends upon when the nondisjunction occurs. Nondisjunction in meiosis I in the male results in one secondary spermatocyte that contains both sex chromosomes (the X and the Y) and the other secondary spermatocyte that lacks sex chromosomes. If the red-eyed males are X^{w+} Y, then the sperm that are formed after nondisjunction in meiosis I are X^{w+} Y and nullo (O) sex chromosome. The $X^w X^w$ female makes X^w eggs, so fertilization will produce **X^w O (white-eyed, sterile male) and $X^{w+} X^w$ Y (red-eyed female)** progeny. If nondisjunction occurred in meiosis II in the male, the sperm would be $X^{w+} X^{w+}$ or YY and nullo (O) sex chromosome. After fertilization of the X^w eggs, the zygotes would be **$X^{w+} X^{w+} X^w$ (lethal)** or **X^w Y Y (fertile white-eyed males)** and **X^w O (sterile white-eyed males)**. Notice that the normal progeny of this cross will be $X^{w+} X^w$ (red-eyed females) and X^w Y (white-eyed males), which are indistinguishable from the nondisjunction progeny in terms of their eye colours.

3-29. In birds, females are the heterogametic sex (ZW); Z^B represents the Z chromosome with the barred allele, Z^b is non-barred.

a. Z^B W (barred hen) x $Z^b Z^b$ (non-barred rooster) → **Z^b W (non-barred females) and $Z^B Z^b$ (barred males)**.

b. $Z^B Z^b$ F$_1$ x Z^b W → **Z^B W (barred) and Z^b W (non-barred) females and $Z^B Z^b$ and $Z^b Z^b$ (barred and non-barred) males**.

3-30. Brown eye colour (*bw*) and scarlet (*st*) are autosomal recessive mutations while vermilion (*v*) is an X-linked recessive trait. The genes interact such that both brown, vermilion (*bw v*) double mutants and brown, scarlet (*bw st*) double mutants are white-eyed. When diagramming a cross involving more than one gene you <u>must</u> start with a genotype for each parent that includes information on <u>both genes</u>. Then figure out the genotype of the F$_1$ progeny. In order to predict the F$_2$ results, find the expected ratio for each gene separately, and then cross-multiply the ratios to generate the F$_2$. Diagram the following crosses. [*Note*: In this answer as well as those to several problems that follow, X-linked genes will not be written as a superscript of the X symbol. Instead only the gene symbol will be used, as is done for the autosomal genes. You can determine that the gene in question is X-linked because it will be paired with the Y chromosome in the male genotypes.]

a. vermilion ♀ (*v v bw$^+$bw$^+$*) x brown ♂ (*v$^+$Y bw bw*) → **F$_1$ *v v$^+$ bw$^+$ bw* (wild-type females)** x

_v_ Y _bw$^+$ bw_ (vermilion males) → F$_2$ ratio for brown alone = 3/4 *bw$^+$*– : 1/4 *bw bw*; the ratio for vermilion alone in both F$_2$ females and males = 1/2 v^+ : 1/2 v (the other sex chromosome will be either v or Y); **the ratio for both genes in both F$_2$ females and males = 3/8 v^+ bw^+– (wild-type) : 3/8 v bw^+– (vermilion) : 1/8 v^+ bw bw (brown) : 1/8 v bw bw (white).**

b. brown ♀ (v^+v^+ bw bw) x vermilion ♂ (vY bw^+bw^+) → **F$_1$ v v^+ bw^+ bw (wild-type females) x v^+ Y bw^+ bw (wild-type males)** → F$_2$ ratio for brown alone = 3/4 bw^+– : 1/4 bw bw; ratio for vermilion alone in the F$_2$ females = 1 v^+– and in the males = 1/2 v^+: 1/2 v. The ratio for both genes in the **F$_2$ females is 3/4 v^+– bw^+– (wild-type) : 1/4 v^+– bw bw (brown)** and the dihybrid ratio in the **F$_2$ males is 3/8 v^+Y bw^+– (wild-type) : 3/8 vY bw^+– (vermilion) : 1/8 v^+Y bw bw (brown) : 1/8 vY bw bw (white).**

c. scarlet ♀ (bw^+bw^+ st st) x brown ♂ (bw bw st^+st^+) → **F$_1$ bw^+ bw st^+ st (wild-type,** males and females are the same because both genes are autosomal) → F$_2$ monohybrid ratio for scarlet = 3/4 st^+– : 1/4 st st and for brown = 3/4 bw^+– : 1/4 bw bw. **The F$_2$ dihybrid ratio (which holds for both sexes) = 9/16 st^+– bw^+– (wild-type) : 3/16 st^+– bw bw (brown) : 3/16 st st bw^+– (scarlet) : 1/6 st st bw bw (white).**

d. brown ♀ (bw bw st^+st^+) x scarlet ♂ (bw^+bw^+ st st) → **F$_1$ bw^+ bw st^+ st (wild-type)** → **F$_2$ ratio as in part c above.**

3-31. It is most likely that **the bag-winged females have one mutation on the X chromosome that has a dominant effect on wing structure and that also causes lethality in homozygous females or hemizygous males.** This is analogous to the A^y allele in mice discussed in Chapter 2, except here the bag gene is on the X chromosome. Thus, all of the bag-winged flies are heterozygous for this mutation.

Diagram the cross: Bg Bg^+ (bag-winged female) x Bg^+ Y (normal-winged male) → 1/4 Bg Bg^+ (bag-winged females) : 1/4 Bg^+ Bg^+ (normal-winged females) : 1/4 Bg Y (dead) : 1/4 Bg^+ Y (normal-winged males). Thus, the ratio of the surviving progeny is 1/3 bag-winged females : 1/3 normal-winged females : 1/3 normal-winged males.

3-32.

a. Eosin is an X-linked recessive mutation. The cream-coloured variants were found occasionally in the eosin true-breeding stock. This suggests that the cream flies have the eosin genotype and <u>also</u> have a second mutation that further lightens the eosin phenotype. Diagram the cross:

wild-type ♀ x cream ♂ → F$_1$ wild-type → F$_2$ 104 wild-type ♀ : 52 wild-type ♂ : 44 eosin ♂ :

14 cream ♂ (8:4:3:1 ratio)

How many genes are controlling the phenotype? There are 3 phenotypes seen in the F$_2$ males. This number of phenotypes could be due to one gene with codominance/incomplete dominance, but the phenotypes are not present in a 1:2:1 ratio. Instead the F$_2$ phenotypic ratio seems to be an epistatic modification of 9:3:3:1. Therefore, the eye colours must be controlled by 2 genes whose mutant alleles are recessive. The fact that the cream eye colour initially arose in the eosin mutant stock suggests that cream is a modifier of eosin. This sort of modifier only alters the mutant allele of the gene it is modifying and has no effect on the wild-type allele. The F$_1$ shows you that the wild-type phenotype is dominant. As expected, the difference in the phenotypes between the F$_2$ males and females shows that eosin (*e*) is X-linked, but the cream modifier (*cr*) is probably not on the X chromosome (that is, it is autosomal) because some F$_2$ animals are eosin but not cream. These considerations suggest that the crosses observed were as follows:

e^+e^+ cr^+cr^+ ♀ x e Y cr cr ♂ → F$_1$ e^+e cr^+c ♀ x e^+ Y cr^+cr ♂ → F$_2$ ratios for each gene alone = 1/2 e^+– ♀ : 1/4 e^+ Y : 1/4 e Y and 3/4 cr^+– : 1/4 cr cr. When these are cross multiplied, the **F$_2$ ratio for both genes = 3/8 e^+– cr^+– (wild-type)** ♀ : **1/8 e^+– cr cr (wild-type)** ♀ : **3/16 e^+ Y cr^+– (wild-type)** ♂ : **1/16 e^+ Y cr cr (wild-type)** ♂ : **3/16 e Y cr^+– (eosin)** ♂ : **1/16 e Y cr cr (cream)** ♂ = **8 wild-type** ♀ : **4 wild-type** ♂ : **3 eosin** ♂ : **1 cream** ♂.

b. e Y cr^+cr^+ (eosin ♂) x e e cr cr (cream ♀) → **F$_1$** e e cr^+cr ♀ x e Y cr^+cr ♂ → F$_2$ ratios for each gene alone = 1/2 e e ♀ : 1/2 e Y ♂ and 3/4 cr^+– : 1/4 cr cr. The **F$_2$ ratios for both genes = 3/8 e e cr^+– (eosin ♀) : 3/8 e Y cr^+– (eosin ♂) : 1/8 e e cr cr (cream ♀) : 1/8 e Y cr cr (cream ♂).**

c. e e cr^+cr^+ (eosin ♀) x e Y cr cr (cream ♂) → **F$_1$** e e cr^+cr ♀ x e Y cr^+cr ♂ → F$_2$ ratios for each gene alone = 1/2 e e ♀ : 1/2 e Y ♂ and 3/4 cr^+– : 1/4 cr cr. **F$_2$ ratios for both genes = 3/8 e e cr^+– (eosin ♀) : 3/8 e Y cr^+– (eosin ♂) : 1/8 e e cr cr (cream ♀) : 1/8 e Y cr cr (cream ♂).** This is the same result as in part *b*.

3-33. wild-type ♀ x yellow vestigial ♂ → F$_1$ wild-type ♀ and ♂ → F$_2$ 16 yellow vestigial ♂ : 48

yellow ♂ : 15 vestigial ♂ : 49 wild-type ♂ : 31 vestigial ♀: 97 wild-type ♀

There are 4 different phenotypes in the F$_2$, so 2 genes are involved. One gene determines body colour, and the F$_1$ shows that wild-type is dominant to yellow. The other gene determines wing length, and the F$_1$ shows that wild-type is dominant to vestigial. This conclusion is reinforced by the F$_2$ progeny where there are 48 + 49 + 97 normal-winged individuals : 16 + 15 + 31 vestigial-winged flies = 194 normal : 61 vestigial = 3:1. In the F$_2$ there are wild-type and vestigial males and females in a 3:1 ratio, so wing shape is an autosomal trait; in the F$_2$ there are yellow males but no yellow females, so body colour is an X-linked trait. Thus, **vestigial is the recessive allele of an autosomal gene and yellow is the recessive allele of an X-linked gene**. The original cross was thus:

$X^{y+} X^{y+}$ vg^+vg^+ ♀ x X^y Y vg vg ♂.

3-34.

a. The white eye allele is an X-linked, recessive mutation. Diagram the cross:

white ♂ x purple ♀ → F$_1$ wild-type eye colour → F$_2$ 3/8 wild-type ♀ : 1/8 purple ♀ : 3/16

wild-type ♂ : 1/4 white ♂ : 1/16 purple ♂.

How many genes are involved? The white and purple eye colours cannot be caused by two different alleles of the same gene because then the F$_1$ males would be purple due to crisscross inheritance. Because white and purple are mutant eye colours, the parental cross can also be considered to be a *complementation test*; the wild-type phenotype of the F$_1$ heterozygotes means that there are 2 different genes controlling eye colour (review **Figure 2.42**). The mutant allele of one of the genes causes white eye colour, the mutant allele of the other gene causes purple eye colour. The wild-type alleles of both genes contribute to wild-type eye colour. **In both cases the mutant allele is recessive ($w < w^+$ and $p < p^+$)** as demonstrated by the wild-type phenotype of the F$_1$ animals. **You also expect that white (the absence of pigment) should be epistatic to eyes with red or purple pigmentation.** Although you are already told that **white is X-linked; purple is an autosomal trait** because it shows no difference between the sexes in either the F$_1$ or the F$_2$ generation - there is a 3 p^+- : 1 $p\,p$ ratio in both males and females in the F$_2$. The original cross was thus: w Y p^+p^+ (white ♂) x w^+w^+ $p\,p$ (purple ♀).

b. $w\,w\,p^+p^+$ (white ♀) x w^+ Y $p\,p$ (purple ♂) → **F$_1$ w^+w p^+p (wild-type eye colour ♀) x w Y p^+p (white ♂)** → F$_2$ ratio for white alone = 1/2 w^+w : 1/2 $w\,w$ females and 1/2 w^+ Y : 1/2 w Y males; for the purple gene alone the ratio is 3/4 p^+- : 1/4 $p\,p$. **The F$_2$ ratio for both genes in females = 3/8 w^+- p^+- (wild-type) : 1/8 w^+- $p\,p$ (purple) : 3/8 $w\,w\,p^+-$ (white) : 1/8 $w\,w\,p\,p$ (white) = 3/8 wild-type : 1/2 white : 1/8 purple. The ratio for the males is the same.** Note that in this reciprocal cross there is a phenotypic difference between the sexes in the F$_1$ generation and no difference in the F$_2$ generation.

Section 3.7 – Sex-Linked and Sexually Dimorphic Traits in Humans

3-35. Colour blindness in this family is an X-linked recessive condition, because two unaffected parents have affected children, and because two unrelated individuals would have to carry rare alleles if the trait were autosomal. Since the males are hemizygous with only one allele for this trait, their phenotype directly represents their genotype. **II-2 and III-3 are affected, so they must be X^{cb} Y.** Now consider the parents of II-2. **I-2 is normal and therefore X^{CB} Y. I-1 must be a carrier so her genotype is $X^{CB} X^{cb}$. II-1 can be either $X^{CB} X^{CB}$ or $X^{CB} X^{cb}$** (but she is more likely to be a normal homozygote if the trait is rare). **II-3 must be a carrier ($X^{CB} X^{cb}$) since she had an affected son. II-4 is X^{CB} Y; III-1 must be $X^{CB} X^{cb}$** (because she has normal colour vision yet she must have received X^{cb} from her father); **III-2 is either $X^{CB} X^{CB}$ or $X^{CB} X^{cb}$; III-4 is an unaffected male and therefore must be X^{CB} Y.**

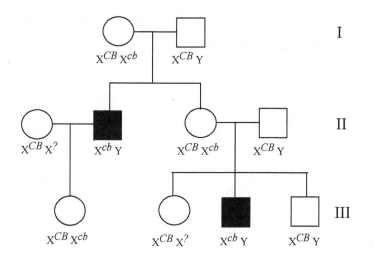

3-36. Pedigrees 1-4 show examples of each of the four modes of inheritance.

a. **Pedigree 1** represents a recessive trait because two unaffected individuals have affected children. If the trait were X-linked, then I-1 would have to be affected in order to have an affected daughter. The trait is **autosomal recessive. Pedigree 2** represents recessive inheritance (see part *a*). This is **X-linked recessive** inheritance as autosomal recessive inheritance was already accounted for in part *a*. This conclusion is supported by the data showing that the father (I-1) is unaffected and only sons show the trait in generation II, implying that the mother must be a carrier. **Pedigree 3** shows the inheritance of a dominant trait because affected children always have an affected parent (remember that all four diseases are rare). The trait must be **autosomal dominant** because the affected father transmits it to a son. **Pedigree 4** represents an **X-linked dominant** trait as characterized by the transmission from affected father to all of his daughters but none of his sons.

b. **Pedigree 1** - both parents are carriers for this autosomal recessive trait so there is a **1/4 chance** that the child will be affected (*aa*). **Pedigree 2** – individual I-2 is a carrier for this X-linked trait. The probability is 1/2 that she will pass on X^a to her daughter II-5. The unaffected father (I-1) contributes a normal X^A chromosome, so the probability that II-5 is a carrier = 1/2. The **probability of an affected son** = 1/2 (probability II-5 is a carrier) x 1/2 (probability II-5 contributes X^a) x 1/2 (probability of Y from father II-6) = **1/8**. The **probability of an affected daughter = 0** because II-6 must contribute a normal X^A. **Pedigree 3** - for an autosomal dominant trait there is a **1/2 chance** that the heterozygous mother (II-5) will pass on the mutant allele to a child of either sex. **Pedigree 4** - the father (I-1) passes on the mutant X chromosome to all his daughters and none of his sons. Therefore II-6 does not carry the mutation, as shown by his normal phenotype. The **probability of an affected child = 0**.

3-37.

a. Unaffected individuals have affected children, so albinism is **recessive**.

b. If albinism were X-linked, then I-9 would have to be an affected hemizygote in order to have an affected daughter. As this is not the case, albinism is **autosomal**.

c. *aa*

d. *Aa*

e. *Aa*

f. *Aa*

g. *Aa*

h. **Aa**

3-38.

a. Draw the pedigree:

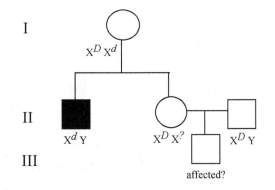

The grandmother (I-1) of the child in question must have been heterozygous for the *d* allele causing the disease because her son (II-1) was affected. The probability that II-2 will have an affected son = 1/2 (the probability that II-1 inherited the X^d chromosome from I-1) x 1/2 (the probability that II-1's son receives the X^d chromosome from her if she is $X^D X^d$) = **1/4**.

b.

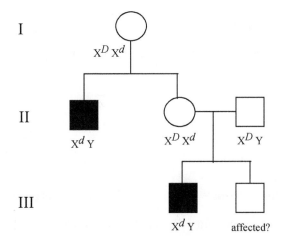

We now know that II-2 is in fact a carrier since she had an affected son. Therefore the probability is **1/2** that she will pass on the X^d chromosome to III-2.

c.

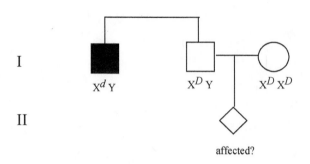

I

$X^d Y$ $X^D Y$ $X^D X^D$

II

affected?

The mother of these two men was a carrier. She passed on the X^d chromosome to the affected son and she passed on the X^D chromosome to the unaffected son. For individual I-3, since the disease allele is relatively rare in the population and there is no indicated family history of DMD, I-3 is not a carrier and is homozygous for the D allele. Thus, there is **no chance** that the unaffected man will pass the disease allele to his children.

d.

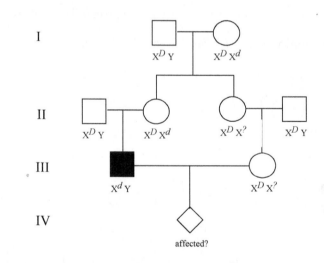

I

$X^D Y$ $X^D X^d$

II

$X^D Y$ $X^D X^d$ $X^D X^?$ $X^D Y$

III

$X^d Y$ $X^D X^?$

IV

affected?

The probability of IV-1 being an affected son = 1/2 (probability that II-3 is a carrier) x 1/2 (probability that III-2 inherits X^d) x 1/2 (probability that IV-1 inherits X^d) x 1/2 (probability IV-1 inherits the Y from III-1) = **1/16. The probability that IV-1 is an affected girl** = 1/2 (probability that II-3 is a carrier) x 1/2 (probability that III-2 inherits X^d) x 1/2 (probability that IV-1 inherits X^d) x 1/2 (probability IV-1 inherits X^d from III-1) = **1/16. The chance that IV-1 is not affected** = 1 - (1/16 probability of an affected male + 1/16 probability of an affected female) = 1 - 2/16 = **7/8.**

e.

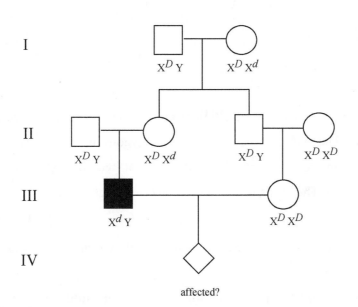

I

X^D Y $\quad$ $X^D X^d$

II

X^D Y $\quad$ $X^D X^d$ $\qquad$ X^D Y $\quad$ $X^D X^D$

III

X^d Y $\qquad\qquad$ $X^D X^D$

IV

affected?

II-2 must be a carrier in order for her son to inherit the disease. II-3 is the brother and he is normal, so his genotype must be X^D Y. Therefore III-2, his daughter, must be homozygous normal. The probability that the fetus (diamond) will be an **affected boy = 0**; the probability of an **affected daughter = 0 (but she will be a carrier)**; the probability of an **unaffected child = 100%.**

3-39.

a. Hypertrichosis is almost certainly an **X-linked dominant trait**.

b. **The trait is dominant because every affected child has an affected parent**. If the trait were recessive then several of the people marrying into the family would have to be carriers, yet this trait is rare. Hypertrichosis is highly likely to be **X-linked because two affected males (II-4 and IV-3) pass the trait on to all of their daughters but none of their sons**.

We can actually calculate the probability that the trait is autosomal dominant rather than X-linked dominant. If the trait is autosomal dominant, then the fathers would have to be heterozygous *Hh* because they have unaffected children; the mothers of these children are unaffected so the mothers would have to be *hh*. The probability of an unaffected male child from such matings = 1/2 (probability of inheriting *h*) × 1/2 (probability the child will be male) = 1/4. The probability of an affected daughter = 1/4. The probability of having 9 unaffected sons and 5 affected daughters = $(1/4)^9 \times (1/4)^5 = (1/4)^{14} = 3.7 \times 10^{-9}$. In other words, the probability that the trait is autosomal dominant is only about 4 in a billion. (The 9 unaffected sons and 4 of the 5 affected daughters are the children of II-4, while the last affected daughter is the progeny of IV-3.)

c.   **III-2 had 4 mates and III-9 had 6 mates!**

3-40.

a.   If the trait is autosomal dominant, then the fathers must be heterozygous *Rr* because they have unaffected daughters. The mothers would then be homozygous normal, *rr*. The probability of an affected male child from such matings = 1/2 (probability of inheriting *R*) x 1/2 (probability the child will be male) = 1/4. The probability of an unaffected daughter = 1/4. The probability of having 6 affected sons and 5 unaffected daughters = $(1/4)^6$ x $(1/4)^5$ = $(1/4)^{11}$ = **2 x 10^{-7}** or extremely unlikely! (The reasoning here is the same as that used previously in Problem 39b above.)

b.   **This trait could be an example of Y-linked inheritance or it could represent sex-limited expression of the mutant allele** (that is, the allele is dominant in males and recessive or otherwise unexpressed in females, like male pattern baldness). There is no direct evidence to support one hypothesis over the other. However, there are no known examples of Y-linked inheritance other than maleness, while there are several examples of sex-influenced traits that are male dominant and female recessive.

3-41.

a.   The father contributed the *i* or I^A, Rh^+, *M* or *N*, and $Xg^{(a-)}$ alleles. Only **alleged father #3** fits these criteria.

b.   Alleged father #1 was ruled out based on his X chromosome genotype. He is $Xg^{(a+)}$ and cannot have an XX daughter who is $Xg^{(a-)}$. If the daughter was XO (Turner), she could have inherited the one X from either mother or father. If the X came from her mother (who must have been heterozygous for *Xg*), then her father did not contribute an X chromosome. Therefore **alleged fathers #1 and #3** both fit the criteria for paternity.

3-42. When nondisjunction occurs in meiosis I (MI), there are two types of affected gametes. Half of the gametes receive no sex chromosomes (nullo) while the rest of the gametes receive one copy of each of the sex chromosomes in the parent. Thus MI nondisjunction in a male will give XY sperm and nullo sperm. If the nondisjunction occurs in MII, then half of the affected gametes are nullo while the rest receive 2 copies of one of the original sex chromosomes. MII nondisjunction in a male will therefore give either XX sperm or YY sperm and nullo sperm with no sex chromosomes.

a. The boy received both an X^B and a Y from his father. Because both the X and Y segregated into the same gamete, the nondisjunction occurred in **meiosis I in the father**.

b. The son could have received both the X^A and X^B from the mother and the Y from the father, or alternatively the X^B from the mother and the X^A and Y from the father. You can determine that the nondisjunction occurred in **meiosis I, but you cannot determine in which parent**.

c. The son has two X^A chromosomes and a Y. Therefore the nondisjunction occurred in the **mother, but because she is homozygous $X^A X^A$ you cannot determine during which meiotic division**.

3-43.

a. **Individual III-5** was not related to anyone in the previous generation. Therefore the cancer with which he was afflicted is not likely to be caused by the rare mutation in *BRCA2*. Instead his cancer may have been due to a mutation in another gene that can predispose one to cancer or exposure to environmental influences like carcinogens.

b. There is a vertical pattern of inheritance of the cancers, so **the *BRCA2* mutation has a dominant effect on causing cancer**. Most of the affected children in this pedigree have an affected parent, although there are a few cases where this is not seen (for example, V-1 and V-8). It is very unlikely that the mutant *BRCA2* allele is recessive because then many unrelated people would have to be carriers of the rare mutant allele.

c. The *BRCA2* mutation is not Y-linked as affected males (for example III-9 and IV-6) pass the trait to their daughters. **The data do not clearly distinguish between X-linked and autosomal inheritance**. The X-linked hypothesis is supported by the fact that all of the daughters of men who could transmit the mutant allele are affected (for example, the five daughters of IV-6). *BRCA2* is actually on autosome 13.

d. **The penetrance of the cancer phenotype is incomplete**. For example, if the mutant allele is dominant then women II-4 and III-8 should have had cancer if the mutant disease-causing allele is dominant. It is critical to note that the presence of the *BRCA2* mutation does not always cause cancer. Instead the mutation increases the predisposition to cancer. The reasons for this will be explained in Chapter 16.

e. **The expressivity is variable**. Some of the women who have inherited the mutant cancer-causing allele do not have breast cancer but instead have ovarian or other cancers. This suggests that the *BRCA2* mutation can predispose one to cancers other than breast cancer, even though breast tumours are the most likely outcome.

f. **Ovarian cancer is sex-limited** since males don't have ovaries . Although the data are fragmentary, **the penetrance of breast cancer may be sex-influenced**. Of the five males who should be carrying the *BRCA2* mutant allele (II-5, III-9, IV-2, IV-9, IV-4), only one has breast cancer (III-9), giving a rate of 20% affected men. Of the 21 women who must be carrying the mutant *BRCA2* allele, 16 have breast cancer - a rate of 80% affected women. Perhaps the hormonal environment or the amount of breast tissue helps determine whether a person with the *BRCA2* mutation will develop breast cancer. Thus, the cancers most often associated with the *BRCA2* mutation (ovarian and breast cancers) usually appear in females.

g. The absence of cancer in the first two generations **could be explained by the low penetrance of the cancer phenotype, particularly among men**. Three individuals in generations I and II must have carried the mutant allele of *BRCA2*, but only one of these was a woman. Other explanations are also possible. One interesting hypothesis has to do with the fact that cancer is a disease whose frequency increases with age and life expectancies have improved only in recent times. Thus, the individuals in the first two generations of this pedigree may have died early of other causes before they had the chance to develop cancer.

3-44. Remember that white tigers are shown by <u>unshaded</u> symbols. Test each possibility by assigning genotypes based on the mode of inheritance.

a. **No**. Y-linked genes are only expressed in males. Since there are white females, the trait could not be Y-linked.

b. **No**. White males would have to have white daughters but not white sons. Mohan's daughter is not white and Tony has a normally-coloured daughter, Kamala, and a white son, Bim.

c. **Yes**. The information in the pedigree is consistent with dominant autosomal inheritance.

d. **Yes**. The information in the pedigree is consistent with a recessive X-linked trait.

e. **Yes**. There is no data in the cross scheme to allow you to rule out recessive autosomal inheritance in this highly inbred family.

3-45.

a. **The *SHOX* allele that causes LWD is dominant**. You can easily see this because of the vertical inheritance pattern in which the rare disease is transmitted from parent to child in every generation.

b. **An X-linked dominant trait would travel from mother to daughter and son, and from father to daughter. In this pedigree, you can see transmission from father (II-3) to both daughter (III-7) and son (III-5). In addition, all of the daughters of affected fathers should be affected, and III-6 is unaffected.** Even though the *SHOX* gene is located on the sex chromosomes, the disease shows an inheritance pattern similar to that of a condition caused by an autosomal dominant allele. This is the reason PAR1 is called a *pseudoautosomal region*.

c. The *SHOX* disease allele is located on the indicated sex chromosomes in the following affected individuals: **I-2 X, II-2 X, II-3 X, III-3 X, III-5 Y, III-7 X, IV-1 X, IV-2 X.**

d. One unusual observation is the transmission of the disease allele from father (II-3) to both his son (III-5) and his daughter (III-7). **The father (II-3) got the *SHOX* disease allele on an X chromosome from his mother. He gives his X chromosome (with the *SHOX* disease allele) to his daughter, and he also gives his son a Y chromosome with the *SHOX* disease allele.** The second unusual observation is that **III-6 is unaffected, although she must have inherited her father's X chromosome, and the X chromosome that her father (II-3) inherited had the mutant *SHOX* allele because it came from his mother (I-2).** Both of these observations can be explained by crossing-over between the PAR1 regions of the X and Y chromosomes during meiosis I. **Mutant and normal *SHOX* alleles can be transferred between the X and Y chromosomes by crossing-over.**

e. The crossing-over event that switches the *SHOX* alleles between the X and Y chromosomes is shown on the following diagram. This figure focuses only on the short arms of the two sex chromosomes that include the *SHOX* gene in PAR1 and (on the Y) the *SRY* gene specifying male development. (The diagram does not show the centromeres or the long arms of these chromosomes; for a more complete picture, see the answer to Problem 21 above.)

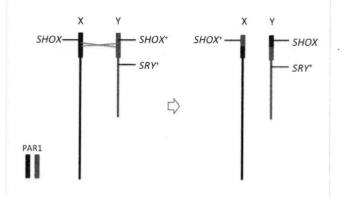

You should note an important difference between the crossing-over event depicted here and the crossover shown in the answer to Problem 21 earlier in this chapter that leads to the phenomenon of sex reversal. In this case, the crossing-over that shifts the *SHOX* gene alleles between the X and Y chromosomes occurs in PAR1. This region is homologous in the X and Y chromosomes, and thus crossing-over occurs regularly during almost every meiosis in PAR1.

(Such crossing-over is necessary for the X and Y chromosomes to pair and then separate from each other during meiosis I in males.) In contrast, the crossing-over between the X and Y that causes sex reversal is a mistake (an illegitimate recombination) because sex reversal requires a crossover in the interval between the Y chromosome centromere and the *SRY* gene (see the answer to Problem 21). The X and Y chromosomes do not share DNA sequences in this region, so crossing-over does not usually occur there.

Chapter 4   Linkage, Recombination, and the Mapping of Genes on Chromosomes

Synopsis:

In this chapter, we learn the consequences of the fact that hundreds or even thousands of genes can be found on one chromosome. Gene pairs that assort independently exhibit a recombination frequency of 50% because the number of parental types = the number of recombinants. Genes may assort independently either because they are on different chromosomes or because they are far apart on the same chromosome. If two genes lie close together on a chromosome, their alleles do not assort independently; instead, the genes are linked and parental classes of gametes will be formed more frequently than recombinant classes. The Recombination Frequency (RF) increases to a maximum of 50% as the distance between the two genes increases. The formation of recombinant classes depends on the occurrence of physical crossovers between nonsister chromatids that take place during prophase of the first meiotic division, after the chromosomes have replicated and homologous chromosomes have paired with each other. The greater the distance between the genes, the more likely the chance a crossover event occurs and the greater the RF; the 50% limit to RF occurs when genes are sufficiently far apart that at least one crossover occurs between them in every meiosis, and thus for linked genes, RF is less than 50%. By measuring RF, geneticists can map the location of genes along the chromosomes. RF can be tracked by looking at individual progeny of a cross involving at least one parent who is a heterozygote for the two genes in question.

This chapter also discusses what happens when recombination takes place during mitosis, rather than meiosis. In contrast with meiotic recombination, which is a programmed event that must occur at least once on every chromosome during every meiosis, mitotic recombination reflects rare mistakes that occur (usually in response to DNA damage). Mitotic recombination provides a valuable tool to researchers because it allows them to create mosaic organisms in which different cells have different genotypes.

Key Terms:

syntenic genes – genes located on the same chromosome.

parental types/classes – gametes whose alleles are in the same combinations as in the gametes that gave rise to the previous generation; or progeny generated by parental gametes.

recombinant types/classes – gametes whose alleles are in different combinations than in the gametes that gave rise to the previous generation; or progeny generated by recombinant gametes. Although recombinant types can also form from independent assortment if the two genes are on nonhomologous chromosomes (see Chapter 3), in this chapter the term refers exclusively to gametes or progeny resulting from a meiosis in which a crossover took place between the two genes in question.

linkage – when two genes are located close enough to each other on the same chromosome so that a doubly heterozygous parent makes more parental-type than recombinant-type gametes.

recombination frequency (RF) – the proportion of the total number of gametes or progeny that are recombinant types (recombinants/total).

map unit (m.u.)/centimorgan (cM) – a measure of genetic distance between linked genes; 1 mu = 1 cM = 1% RF.

locus (singular)/**loci** (plural) – a specific location on a particular chromosome.

interference – a phenomenon in which a crossover event on a chromosome prevents or limits the occurrence of a second crossover event nearby on the same chromosome. Interference is thought to take place as a way to help ensure that at least one crossover occurs on each bivalent, so that homologous chromosomes segregate accurately during the first meiotic division.

coefficient of coincidence (c.o.c.) – the ratio of the number of double crossovers observed in a cross to the number of double crossovers expected if the two crossovers were independent of each other. The *interference* = 1 – c.o.c. This makes sense because the amount of interference reflects a decrease in the frequencies of double crossovers (DCOs).

chi-square test – a statistical device used to measure the likelihood that a particular set of observed experimental results could have been obtained as chance deviations from the expectations from a particular hypothesis to be tested (the **null hypothesis**).

significant result – experimental results that are highly unlikely to be explained by the null hypothesis. A significant result allows you to reject the null hypothesis. An **insignificant result** does not allow you to reject the null hypothesis. Note that these definitions mean that the chi-square test can never prove a null hypothesis, but can only reject the null hypothesis.

degrees of freedom (d.o.f) – In the chi-square test for the goodness of fit, the d.o.f. = number of classes – 1. The d.o.f. is required for interpreting the chi-square test.

***p* value** – the probability that the observed results could be obtained by chance deviations from the expectations of the null hypothesis. If the *p* value is low (usually below 0.05 for genetic analysis), you can reject the null hypothesis.

twin spots – adjacent patches of tissues that are phenotypically and genotypically different from each other, and phenotypically and genotypically different from the surrounding cells. Twin spots can result from **mitotic crossing-over** depending on the arrangement of alleles and the sites of the mitotic crossovers.

mosaic – an organism harbouring cells of different genotypes. For example, a fruit fly with twin spots is a mosaic.

sector – in yeast, a region of a colony of cells in which the cells have a different phenotype and genotype from the other cells in the same colony.

Key Equations:

- Recombination Frequency (RF) = # of recombinant progeny / total # of progeny. (Multiply × 100 to express the RF as %).

- 1% RF = 1 m.u. or 1 cM.

- Coefficient of coincidence (c.o.c) = # DCOs (double crossovers) observed / # DCOs expected. To calculate the # DCOs expected, multiply the crossover frequency in interval 1 × crossover frequency in interval 2, and then multiply this value by the total number of progeny.

- Interference = 1 – c.o.c.

- $\chi^2 = \Sigma$ [(# observed – # expected)^2 / # expected].
  (In other words, χ^2 is the sum over all classes of [$(O - E)^2$ / E] calculated for each class.)

- Degrees of freedom (d.o.f.) = # classes – 1.

- In χ^2 analysis, the ultimate goal is to determine the probability p that the observed results could have been obtained by chance if the null hypothesis is correct. To determine p, you need to calculate χ^2 and d.o.f., and then you must consult a table of critical values such as Table 4.3.

Problem Solving:

For many of the problems in this chapter, you will still need to start by answering the same questions you dealt with in the first three chapters:

How many genes are involved in the cross?

For each of these genes, what is the dominance relationship between the alleles?

For each of these genes, is it X-linked or autosomal?

In the problems in this chapter, you now have to consider the additional possibility that genes may be syntenic (on the same chromosome) and that they are genetically linked.

When thinking about genes that are linked, you must write the genotypes in a way that represents the linkage. Remember that there is one allele per homologue, so *aa* becomes *a / a* . It is usually advantageous to indicate the homologous chromosomes with horizontal, parallel lines so that you can track which alleles of which genes were present on which chromosomes. Thus, $a^+ b^+ c / a b c^+$ would be diagrammed as:

$$\frac{a^+ \qquad b^+ \qquad c}{a \qquad b \qquad c^+}$$

Although the two lines in the diagram above represent the two homologous chromosomes, you should always keep in mind that recombination actually occurs at the four-strand stage, after each chromosome has replicated into two sister chromatids. This fact plays an important role in understanding why there is a 50% limit of the RF measured between two genes.

Tips for two-point crosses:

♦ The minimum requirement for detecting recombination is that one parent must be heterozygous for 2 genes. The recombination events that can be detected are the ones that occur between the 2 genes, giving recombinant gametes instead of parental gametes.

♦ It is easiest to detect the parental versus recombinant gametes if you do a testcross.

♦ If the genes are assorting independently, in a testcross of $a^+a\ b^+b$ x $aa\ bb$, the expected phenotypic frequencies and classes of progeny are 1 $a^+a\ b^+b$: 1 $aa\ bb$: 1 $a^+a\ bb$: 1 $aa\ b^+b$. However, the genes are genetically linked if you see more parental than recombinant progeny.

♦ Recombination Frequency (RF) = # of recombinant progeny / total # of progeny. (Multiply × 100 to express the RF as %). 1% RF = 1 m.u. or 1 cM.

♦ Genes on the X chromosome can be mapped without a testcross. Just use the hemizygous male progeny as in Problem 4-6.

Tips for three-point crosses:

♦ In a three-point cross, a parent heterozygous for the three genes generates the progeny. Therefore, all classes (parental, etc.) will occur as reciprocal pairs of progeny. These reciprocal pairs will be both genetic reciprocals and numerically equivalent.

♦ Designate the different gametes or offspring as noncrossover (NCO; parental), single crossover (SCO) or double crossover (DCO). The NCO classes are those classes of progeny who have one of the intact, non-recombinant homologues from the parent. The NCO classes will be represented by the reciprocal pair with the greatest numbers of offspring. There will be SCOs occurring between the gene on the left and the gene in the middle (two reciprocal classes), and SCOs occurring between the gene in the middle and the gene on the right (another two reciprocal classes). The DCO classes will be represented by the reciprocal classes with the smallest numbers of offspring (**Figure 4.15**). However, sometimes one or both double crossover classes are missing because they are rare.

- ◆ By examining the pattern of data seen in a problem, you can often start solving the problem with a basic understanding of the linkage relationships of the genes. Some of the more common patterns of data are:

  - 3 unlinked genes gives 8 classes of data that occur as 4 genetically reciprocal pairs, but all classes are seen in a 1:1:1:1:1:1:1:1 ratio;

  - 3 linked genes give 8 classes of data that occur as 4 reciprocal pairs genetically and numerically unless one or both of the DCO classes are missing, in which case you will see 6 classes as 3 reciprocal pairs or 7 classes as 3 reciprocal pairs plus an additional unpaired class;

  - 2 linked genes plus one unlinked gene will yield 8 classes of data. 4 of these classes will be numerically equal to each other, while the other 4 classes will also be numerically equal to each other. The group of 4 classes with larger numbers will consist of the reciprocal parental classes for the linked genes together with either allele of the unlinked gene. The group of 4 classes with the smaller numbers will be the reciprocal recombinant classes of the linked genes together with either allele of the unlinked gene.

- ◆ Begin the process of mapping the genes by ordering the genes. To figure out which gene is in the middle of a group of three genes, choose one of the double crossover classes. Compare it to the most similar parental class of progeny where two of the three genes will have the same combination of alleles. The gene that differs is the gene in the middle. See problem 4-22c for further explanation.

- ◆ The last step is to determine the distance between the genes on each end and the gene in the middle. Use the formula RF = # of recombinants between the 2 genes / total # of progeny. Remember for each interval that the # of recombinants is the number of progeny in the reciprocal SCO classes representing crossovers in that interval, plus the number of recombinants in the reciprocal DCO classes.

Tips for crosses involving four genes:

- ◆ A few problems in this chapter deal with crosses involving 4 genes. You should realize that to provide you with easily solvable problems, the arrangements of the 4 genes were carefully chosen such that the data patterns immediately suggest rather simple solutions. If you had 4 linked genes in a group, you would get 16 classes of progeny in 8 reciprocal pairs, but this would be extremely difficult to analyze because you would have to consider many types of double crossovers as well as triple crossovers, in addition to the SCOs in each interval. You should thus be on the lookout for the following patterns with simpler solutions:

- 4 unlinked genes give 16 classes of progeny in a 1:1:1:1:1:1:1:1:1:1:1:1:1:1:1:1 ratio;

- 3 linked genes and 1 gene assorting independently gives 16 classes of data occurring as 8 reciprocal pairs genetically and 4 groups of 4 numerically;

- 4 linked genes that show only 8 classes of data indicate that two of these genes are so tightly linked to each other that they never separate by crossing over. You can thus deal with this as a three-point cross.

Tips for mitotic recombination problems:

♦   For mitotic recombination in a heterozygous parental cell to produce daughter cells homozygous for either allele, mitotic recombination must take place between the gene and the centromere.

♦   Any mitotic recombination between a gene and the centromere will automatically make homozygous any other gene that is even further from the centromere.

Solutions to Problems:

Vocabulary

4-1. i. **7**; ii. **3**; iii. **1**; iv. **8**; v. **4**; vi. **5**; vii. **2**; viii. **6**

Section 4.1 – Gene Linkage and Recombination

4-2.

a.   Diagram the cross. WT = wild type.

scabrous $\male$ ($sc\ sc\ j^+j^+$) x javelin $\female$ ($sc^+sc^+\ jj$) → F$_1$ WT $\female$ ($sc\ sc^+\ j^+j$) x scabrous javelin $\male$ ($sc\ sc\ jj$) → 1/4 scabrous (P) : 1/4 javelin (P) : 1/4 WT (R) : 1/4 scabrous javelin (R).

This F$_1$ female will make four different types of gametes in equal frequency – 1/4 $sc^+\ j$: 1/4 $sc\ j^+$: 1/4 $sc^+\ j^+$: 1/4 $sc\ j$. Because this is a testcross, the male parent will always provide the recessive alleles of the genes. Thus, the phenotypes of the progeny will be determined by the gamete they receive from the heterozygous F$_1$ female. (Recall that in *Drosophila*, meiotic recombination does not occur in the male germline, and so testcrosses are almost always set up like the one here.)

Of course these genes may be linked. In this case the cross would be diagrammed as follows:

Gametes	A b 0.40	a B 0.40	A B 0.10	a b 0.10
A b 0.40	AA bb 0.16	Aa Bb 0.16	AABb 0.04	Aabb 0.04
a B 0.40	Aa Bb 0.16	aa BB 0.16	AaBB 0.04	aaBb 0.04
A B 0.10	AA Bb 0.04	Aa BB 0.04	AABB 0.01	AaBb 0.01
a b 0.10	Aa bb 0.04	aa Bb 0.04	AaBb 0.01	aabb 0.01

Section 4.2 – Recombination: A Result of Crossing-Over During Meiosis

Careful observation of the drawing will also illustrate some additional points of interest. (i) Note that these are acrocentric mouse chromosomes, so the centromeres are found at one chromosome end. The centromeres (*dark green* and *light green ovals*) are made of many cohesin complexes that are not shown. The spindle fibres exerting poleward forces (*black arrows*) are connected to the kinetochores (*not shown*), which are found at the centromeres but which involve proteins other than the cohesin complexes. (ii) At anaphase of meiosis I, the cohesin complexes along the arms (both proximal and distal to the chiasmata) dissolve, allowing the homologous chromosomes to be pulled to opposite spindle poles. (iii) Note that the cohesin complexes are rings inside of which are the two sister chromatids. In other words, the rings include two *light green* chromatids or two *dark green* chromatids, but never a *light green* and a *dark green* chromatid. The reason for this is straightforward: The cohesin rings are made immediately after chromosomes replicate into sister chromatids, before the homologous chromosomes pair with each other.

4-6. The parents are from true-breeding stocks. Diagram the cross:

raspberry eye colour ♂ x sable body colour ♀ → F$_1$ wild-type eye and body colour ♀ x sable body colour ♂ (if no mention is made of the eye colour, then it is assumed to be wild type) → F$_2$ 216 wild-type ♀ : 223 sable ♀ : 191 sable ♂ : 188 raspberry ♂ : 23 wild-type ♂ : 27 raspberry sable ♂

The phenotypes seem to be controlled by 2 genes, one for eye colour and the other for body colour. The F$_1$ female progeny show that the wild-type allele is dominant for body colour ($s^+ > s$) and the wild-type allele is also dominant for eye colour ($r^+ > r$). Sable body colour is seen in the F$_1$ males but not the F$_1$ females, so the s gene is X-linked. In the F$_2$ generation, the raspberry eye colour is seen in the males but not in the females, so r is also an X-linked gene. We can now assign genotypes to the true-breeding parents in this cross:

$r\ s^+$ / Y (raspberry ♂) x $r^+\ s$ / $r^+\ s$ ♀ → F$_1$ $r\ s^+$ / $r^+\ s$ ♀ (wild-type) x $r^+\ s$ / Y (sable ♂) →

[the heterozygous F$_1$ female can make the following gametes: (parentals) $r\ s^+$, $r^+\ s$ and (recombinants) $r\ s$, $r^+\ s^+$; the F$_1$ male can make Y and $r^+\ s$ gametes] → F$_2$ will be $r\ s^+$ / $r^+\ s$ (wild-type females), $r^+\ s$ / $r^+\ s$ (sable females), $r\ s$ / $r^+\ s$ (sable females), $r^+\ s^+$ / $r^+\ s$ (wild-type females), $r^+\ s$ / Y (sable males), $r\ s^+$ / Y (raspberry males), $r\ s$ / Y (raspberry sable males), $r^+\ s^+$ / Y (wild-type males)

The F$_1$ female is heterozygous for both genes and will therefore make parental and recombinant gametes. The F$_1$ male is not a true testcross parent, because he does not carry the recessive alleles for both of the X-linked genes. However, this sort of cross <u>can</u> be used for mapping, because F$_2$ sons receive only the Y chromosome from the F$_1$ male and are hemizygous for the X chromosome from the F$_1$ female. Thus the phenotypes in the F$_2$ males represent the array of parental and recombinant gametes generated by the F$_1$ female as well as the frequencies of these gametes. Using the F$_2$ males, the **recombination frequency (RF) and map distance between sable and raspberry = 23 (wild-type males) + 27 (raspberry sable males) / 429 (total males) = 0.117 x 100 = 11.7 cM.**

4-7.

a. The parental females are heterozygous for the X-linked dominant *Greasy* (*Gs*) and *Broadhead* (*Bhd*) genes. They are crossed to homozygous recessive males. The male progeny of this cross will show four phenotypes, which will fall into two genetic reciprocal pairs. One pair will be shiny fur skeletal abnormalities and wild type (*Gs Bhd* and *Gs$^+$ Bhd$^+$*) while the other pair will be shiny fur and skeletal abnormalities (*Gs Bhd⁺* and *Gs⁺ Bhd*). If the genes are far apart on the X chromosome, then they will assort independently and all four classes will show equal frequency. If the genes are linked, then there will be a more frequent reciprocal pair (the parental pair) and a less frequent pair (the recombinant pair). There are 49 *Gs Bhd⁺* and 48 *Gs⁺ Bhd* male progeny. Thus, this is the parental pair and the genotype of the female is *Gs Bhd⁺ / Gs⁺ Bhd*. **The cross can be diagrammed:**

> ***Gs Bhd⁺ / Gs⁺ Bhd ♀ x Gs⁺ Bhd⁺ / Y ♂ → 49 Gs Bhd⁺ ♂ : 48 Gs⁺ Bhd ♂ : 2 Gs Bhd ♂ : 1 Gs⁺ Bhd⁺ ♂.***

The distance between these two genes: RF = 2 + 1 / 100 = 0.03 = 3 m.u.

b. The daughters in this cross must inherit the *Gs⁺ Bhd⁺* X chromosome from their fathers. This chromosome carries the recessive alleles of both genes, so this is a true testcross. Thus the **genotypes, phenotypes, and frequencies of the female progeny would be the same as their brothers**.

4-8.

a. Diagram the cross:

CC DD x *cc dd* → F₁ *C D / c d* x *cc dd* → 997 *Cc Dd*, 999 *cc dd*, 1 *Cc dd*, 3 *cc Dd*.

Because the gamete from the homozygous recessive parent is always *c d*, we can ignore one *c* and one *d* allele (the *c d* homologue) in each class of the F₂ progeny. The remaining homologue in each class of F₂ is the one contributed by the doubly heterozygous F₁, the parent of interest when considering recombination. In the F₂ the two classes of individuals with the greatest numbers represent parental gametes (*C D* or *c d* from the heterozygous F₁ parent combining with the *c d* gamete from the homozygous recessive parent). The other two types of progeny result from recombinant gametes (*C d* or *c D* combining with the *c d* gamete from the homozygous recessive parent). The number of recombinants divided by the total number of offspring x 100 gives the map distance: (1 + 3)/(997 + 999 + 1 + 3) = 4/2000 = 0.002 x 100 = 0.2% RF or **0.2 map units (m.u.) or 0.2 cM**.

b. *CC dd* x *cc DD* → F₁ *C d / c D* x *c d / c d* → ?

As determined in part *a*, *C* and *D* are 0.2 cM apart. Thus the gametes produced by the heterozygous F₁ will be 49.9% *C d*, 49.9% *c D*, 0.1% *C D*, 0.1% *c d*. After fertilization with *c d* gametes, there would be **49.9% Cc dd, 49.9% cc Dd, 0.1% Cc Dd, 0.1% cc dd**. Because this is a testcross, the gametes from the doubly heterozygous F_1 parent determine the phenotypes of the progeny.

c. Because the RF is so low (0.2%), very few crossovers occur between genes C and D. A single crossover in a single meiosis would produce 2 Recombinant progeny. With an RF = 0.002, you would have 2 Recombinant progeny out of 1000 total progeny. 1000 progeny could be obtained in 1000/4 = 250 meioses. Thus, only 1 out of every 250 meioses would have a crossover between genes C and D; in any one meiosis, the chance of a crossover occurring between the genes would be 1/250 = 0.004 = 0.04%. Thus, **in a typical meiosis, no crossovers would occur between genes C and D.**

d. In this case, you see equal frequencies of all progeny classes, so the number of Recombinants equals the number of Parentals. In other words, the genes are syntenic but so far apart that they are genetically unlinked; the RF is ~50%. You should realize that when genes are unlinked, every meiosis must have at least one recombination event occurring between the two genes in question (in other words, when RF = 50%, no meiosis can be an NCO). However, we cannot determine the average number of crossovers between the two genes other to say that this number must be greater than 1. The reason is that as the physical distance between syntenic but unlinked genes increases, the number of double crossovers (DCOs) and triple or higher level crossovers increases yet the RF still remains ~50%. **Thus, in a typical meiosis, at least one crossover occurs between genes C and D.**

4-9. To determine the probability that a child will have a particular genotype, look at the gametes that can be produced by the parents. In this example, A and B are 20 m.u. apart, so in a doubly heterozygous individual 20% of the gametes will be recombinant and the remaining 80% will be parental. The $a\ b/a\ b$ homozygous man can only produce $a\ b$ gametes. The doubly heterozygous woman, with a genotype of $A\ B/a\ b$, can produce 40% $A\ B$, 40% $a\ b$, 10% $A\ b$ and 10% $a\ B$ gametes. (Total of recombinant classes = 20%.) **The probability that a child receives the $A\ b$ gamete from the female (and is therefore $A\ b/a\ b$) = 10%.**

4-10.

a. Designate the alleles: HD = Huntington disease allele, hd = normal allele; B = brachydactyly, b = normal fingers. Because both traits are rare in the population, we assume that the parents are heterozygous for the mutant allele of the gene dictating their traits. **John's father is $bb\ HDhd$; his mother is $Bb\ hdhd$.**

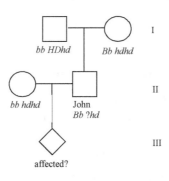

b. We know the John is *Bb* because he has brachydactyly. **His complete genotype could be *Bb HDhd* or *Bb hdhd*.**

In order to answer part *c* below, it would be helpful here to calculate the probability that John is *HDhd* rather than *hdhd*. This calculation is a bit tricky – it requires you to use *conditional probability*. If we had no information about John, the probability that John is *HDhd* because he inherited *HD* from his *HDhd* father would be 1/2. However, we do have some information about John – he is 50 and has no symptoms of Huntington disease; this fact – or *condition* – as well as the information that 2/3 of people who inherit *HD* have symptoms of the disease by age 50 – has to be used to calculate the chance that John inherited the *HD* allele from his father. The easiest way to think about this conditional probability is the following:

John's father or anyone else who is *HDhd* could have two classes of children: those who inherit the *HD* allele (*HDhd*), and those who inherit the *hd* allele (*hdhd*). As we said previously, with no other knowledge, the ratio of John's progeny would be 1 *HDhd* : 1 *hdhd*. However, we know that John is 50 and has no symptoms. All of the *hdhd* progeny will have no symptoms at 50, and also 1/3 of the *HDhd* progeny will have no symptoms. These facts change the genotypic ratio, because we are considering the symptom-free people only; for symptom-free people, the ratio is 1/3 *HDhd* : 1 *hdhd*. Another way to express the same ratio is 1/3 *HDhd* : 3/3 *hdhd*, or 1 *HDhd* : 3 *hdhd*. Thus, **the chance that John is *Bb HDhd* is 1/4.**

c. In order for the child to express both diseases, the child must be *Bb HDhd*, and so John must be *Bb HDhd*. We just calculated in part *b* that the probability John is *Bb HDhd* is 1/4. The chance that the child is *Bb HDhd* is 1/4 (the chance that John has the *HD* allele) × 1/2 (the chance that the child inherits *HD* from John) × 1/2 (the chance that the child inherits *B* from John) = 1/16. The chance that a *Bb HDhd* child will express brachydactyly is 90%, and the chance such a child will have Huntington disease by age 50 is 2/3. Therefore, **if the two genes are not linked, the probability that the child will express both brachydactyly and Huntington disease by age 50 is 1/16 × 0.90 × 2/3 = 0.0375 = 3.75%.**

d. If the two loci are linked, the alleles on each of John's homologues will be either *B hd / b HD* or *B hd / b hd*. The *B HD* gamete could only be produced if John is *B hd / b HD* and recombination occurs. The probability of that specific recombinant gamete = 10% (the other 10% of the recombinant gametes are *b hd*). As shown in part *b*, the probability that John's genotype is *B hd / b HD* = 1/4. **The probability that John's child will have both Huntington disease and brachydactyly = 1/4 (probability that John is *B hd / b HD*) x 1/10 (probability of child inheriting *B HD* recombinant gamete from John) x 9/10 (probability of expressing brachydactyly) x 2/3 (probability of expressing Huntington disease by age 50) = 0.015 = 1.5%.**

4-11. Designate the alleles of the genes: A = normal pigmentation and a = albino allele; $Hb\beta^A$ = normal globin and $Hb\beta^S$ = sickle-cell allele.

a. Because both traits are rare in the population, we assume that the parents are homozygous for the wild-type allele of the gene dictating their normal traits (that is, they are not carriers). Diagram the cross: $a\ Hb\beta^A / a\ Hb\beta^A$ (father) x $A\ Hb\beta^S / A\ Hb\beta^S$ (mother) $\rightarrow$ $a\ Hb\beta^A / A\ Hb\beta^S$ (son). Given that the genes are separated by 1 map unit, parental gametes = 99% and recombinant gametes = 1% of the gametes. **The son's gametes will consist of: 49.5% *a* $Hb\beta^A$, 49.5% *A* $Hb\beta^S$, 0.5% *a* $Hb\beta^S$ and 0.5% *A* $Hb\beta^A$.**

b. In this family, the cross is $A\ Hb\beta^A / A\ Hb\beta^A$ (father) x $a\ Hb\beta^S / a\ Hb\beta^S$ (mother) $\rightarrow$ $a\ Hb\beta^S / A\ Hb\beta^A$ (daughter). **The daughter's gametes will be: 49.5% *a* $Hb\beta^S$, 49.5% *A* $Hb\beta^A$, 0.5% *a* $Hb\beta^A$ and 0.5% *A* $Hb\beta^S$.**

c. The cross is: $a\ Hb\beta^A / A\ Hb\beta^S$ (son) x $a\ Hb\beta^S / A\ Hb\beta^A$ (daughter). **The probability of an *a* $Hb\beta^S / a\ Hb\beta^S$ child (sickle-cell anaemic and albino) = 0.005 (probability of *a* $Hb\beta^S$ from son) x 0.495 (probability of *a* $Hb\beta^S$ from daughter) = 0.0025.**

4-12. Diagram the cross:

blue smooth x yellow wrinkled $\rightarrow$ 1447 blue smooth, 169 blue wrinkled, 186 yellow smooth, 1510 yellow wrinkled.

a. To determine if the genes are linked, first predict the results of the cross if the genes are unlinked. In this case, a plant with blue, smooth kernels (*A– W–*) is crossed to a plant with yellow, wrinkled kernels (*aa ww*). Since there are four classes of progeny, the parent with blue, smooth kernels must be heterozygous for both genes (*Aa Ww*). From this cross, **we would predict equal** numbers of all four phenotypes in the progeny if the genes were unlinked. Since the numbers are very skewed, with the smaller classes representing recombinant offspring, the *A* and *W* genes are linked. RF = (169 + 186) / (1447 + 169 + 186 + 1510) = 355/3312 = 10.7% = **10.7 cM**.

b. The genotype of the blue smooth parent was *Aa Ww*. The arrangement of alleles in the parent is determined by looking at the phenotypes of the largest classes of progeny (the parental reciprocal pair). Since blue smooth and yellow wrinkled are found in the highest proportion, *A W* must be on one homologue and *a w* on the other = *A W / a w*.

c. The genotype of the blue wrinkled progeny is *A w /a w*. This genotype can produce *A w* or *a w* gametes in equal proportions. Recombination *cannot* be detected here, as this genotype is only heterozygous for one gene. Recombination between these homologues yields the same two combinations of alleles (*A w* and *a w*) as the parental, so each type of gamete is expected 50% of the time. The yellow smooth progeny plant has a genotype of *a W / a w*. Again, since recombination cannot be detected, the frequency of each type is 50%. Thus the cross is *A w / a w* (blue wrinkled) x *a W / a w* (yellow smooth). **Four types of kernels are expected in equal proportions: 1/4 *A w / a W* (blue smooth) : 1/4 *A w / a w* (blue wrinkled) : 1/4 *a w / a W* (yellow smooth) : 1/4 *a w / a w* (yellow wrinkled).**

4-13. Diagram the cross: *CC bb* (brown rabbits) x *cc BB* (albinos) → F_1 *Cc Bb* x *cc bb* → 34 black : 66 brown : 100 albino.

a. If the genes are unlinked, the F_1 will produce *C B, c b, C b,* and *c B* gametes in equal proportions. A mating to animals that produce only *c b* gametes will produce four genotypic classes of offspring: 1/4 *Cc Bb* (black) : 1/4 *cc Bb* (albino) : 1/4 *Cc bb* (brown) : 1/4 *cc bb* (albino). The ratio would be **1/4 black : 1/2 albino : 1/4 brown**.

b. If gene *C* and gene *B* are linked, then the genotype of the F_1 class is *C b / c B* and you would expect the parental type *C b* and *c B* gametes to predominate; *c b* and *C B* are the recombinant gametes present at lower levels. The parental gametes are represented in the F_2 by the *Cc bb* (brown) and *cc Bb* (albino) classes. Since we cannot distinguish between the albinos resulting from fertilization of recombinant gametes (*c b*), and those resulting from parental gametes (*c B*), we have to use the proportion of the *C B* recombinant class and assume that the other class of recombinants (*c b*) is present in equal frequency. Since the crossing-over is a reciprocal exchange, this assumption is reasonable. There were 34 black progeny; assuming that 34 of the 100 albino progeny were the result of recombinant gametes, **the genes are (34 + 34) recombinant / 200 total progeny = 34% RF = 34 cM apart.**

4-14. Notice that you are asked for the <u>number of different *kinds* of phenotypes</u>, not the number of individuals with each of the different phenotypes.

a. **2** (*A–* and *aa*).

b. **3** (*AA*, *Aa*, and *aa*).

c. **3** (*AA*, *Aa*, and *aa*).

d. **4** (*A– B–*, *A– bb*, *aa B–*, and *aa bb*).

e. **4** (*A– B–*, *A– bb*, *aa B–*, and *aa bb*; because the genes are linked, the frequency of the four classes will be different than that seen in part *d*).

f. **Nine** phenotypes in total. There are three phenotypes possible for each gene. The total number of combinations of phenotypes is $(3)^2 = 9$ [(*AA*, *Aa*, and *aa*) x (*BB*, *Bb*, and *bb*)].

g. Normally there are four phenotypic classes, as in parts *d* and *e*: (*A– B–*, *A– bb*, *aa B–*, and *aa bb*); however, because the genes are linked, the frequency of the four classes will be different than that seen in part *d*. Also, in this case, there is recessive epistasis, so two of the classes (for example, *A– bb* and *aa bb*) have the same phenotype, **giving 3 phenotypic classes**.

h. Two genes means four phenotypic classes (*A– B–*, *aa B–*, *A– bb*, and *aa bb*). Because gene function is duplicated (redundant), the first three classes are all phenotypically equivalent in that they have function, and only the *aa bb* class will have a different phenotype, being without function. Thus there are only **2 phenotypic classes**.

i. There is 100% linkage between the two genes. The number of phenotypic classes will depend on the arrangement of alleles in the parents. **If the parents are *A B / a b* x *A B / a b*, the progeny will be 3/4 *A– B–* : 1/4 *aa bb* and there will be two phenotypic classes. If the parents are *A b / a B* x *A b / a B*, the progeny will be 1/4 *AA bb* : 1/2 *Aa Bb* : 1/4 *aa BB* and there will be three phenotypic classes in the offspring.**

4-15.

a. *AA BB* x *aa bb* → F$_1$ *A B / a b* (*A B* on one homologue and *a b* on the other homologue). The F$_1$ progeny will produce parental-type gametes *A B* and *a b*, and the recombinant types *A b* and *a B*. The genes are 40 cM apart, so **the recombinants will make up 40% of the gametes (20% *A b* and 20% *a B*). The remaining 60% of the gametes are parental: 30% *A B* and 30% *a b*.** Set up a Punnett square to calculate the frequency of the 4 phenotypes in the F$_2$ progeny. In the Punnett square the phenotypes are shown in parentheses (*Aa bb*). **The F$_2$ phenotypic ratio is: 0.59 *A– B–* : 0.16 *A– bb* : 0.16 *aa B–* : 0.09 *aa bb*.**

Gametes	0.3 *A B*	0.3 *a b*	0.2 *A b*	0.2 *a B*
0.3 *A B*	*A B / A B* (0.09 *AA BB*)	*A B / a b* (0.09 *Aa Bb*)	*A B / A b* (0.06 *AA Bb*)	*A B / a B* (0.06 *Aa BB*)
0.3 *a b*	*a b / A B* (0.09 *Aa Bb*)	*a b / a b* (0.09 *aa bb*)	*a b / A b* (0.06 *Aa bb*)	*a b / a B* (0.06 *aa Bb*)
0.2 *A b*	*A b / A B* (0.06 *AA Bb*)	*A b / a b* (0.06 *Aa bb*)	*A b / A b* (0.04 *AA bb*)	*A b / a B* (0.04 *Aa Bb*)
0.2 *a B*	*a B / A B* (0.06 *Aa BB*)	*a B / a b* (0.06 *aa Bb*)	*a B / A b* (0.04 *Aa Bb*)	*a B / a B* (0.04 *aa BB*)

b. If the original cross was *AA bb* x *aa BB*, the allele combinations in the F$_1$ would be *A b / a B*. Parental gametes in this case are 30% *A b* and 30% *a B* and the recombinant gametes are 20% *A B* and 20% *a b*. Set up a Punnett square, as in part *a*. **The F$_2$ phenotypic ratio is: 0.54 *A– B–* : 0.21 *A– bb* : 0.21 *aa B–* : 0.04 *aa bb*.**

Gametes	0.3 *A b*	0.3 *a B*	0.2 *A B*	0.2 *a b*
0.3 *A b*	*A b / A b* (0.09 *AA bb*)	*A b / a B* (0.09 *Aa Bb*)	*A b / A B* (0.06 *AA Bb*)	*A b / a b* (0.06 *Aa bb*)
0.3 *a B*	*a B / A b* (0.09 *Aa Bb*)	*a B / a B* (0.09 *aa BB*)	*a B / A B* (0.06 *Aa BB*)	*a B / a b* (0.06 *aa Bb*)
0.2 *A B*	*A B / A b* (0.06 *AA Bb*)	*A B / a B* (0.06 *Aa BB*)	*A B / A B* (0.04 *AA BB*)	*A B / a b* (0.04 *Aa Bb*)
0.2 *a b*	*a b / A b* (0.06 *Aa bb*)	*a b / a B* (0.06 *aa Bb*)	*a b / A B* (0.04 *Aa Bb*)	*a b / a b* (0.04 *aa bb*)

4-16. V^1, V^2, and V^3 are codominant alleles of the DNA variant marker locus, while *D* and *d* are alleles of the disease gene. The marker and the disease locus are linked. Diagram the cross:

$V^1 D / V^2 d$ (father) x $V^3 d / V^3 d$ (mother) → $V^2 ? / V^3 d$.

The fetus <u>must</u> get a $V^3 d$ homologue from the mother. The fetus also received the V^2 allele of the marker. The father could have given a $V^2 d$ (non-recombinant) or a $V^2 D$ (recombinant) gamete.

a. If the *D* locus and the V^1 allele of the marker are 0 m.u. apart (there is no recombination between them; they appear to be the same gene), **the probability that the child, who received the V^2 allele of the marker, has the *D* allele = 0.**

Parts *b-d* require thinking in terms of *conditional probability* – similar to Problem 10 above. In this case, the *condition* is the fact that you already know that the child received the V^2 marker allele. This fact alters the otherwise simple expectations based on recombination frequency and equal segregation of alleles into gametes.

b. If the distance between the disease locus and marker is 1 m.u., 1% of the father's gametes are recombinant between D and the marker locus, and 99% of his gametes are parental types. Half of the recombinant gametes will be $V^2 D$, and the other half will be $V^1 d$; half of the parental gametes will be $V^1 D$, and the other half will be $V^2 d$. If we consider 200 of his gametes, there will be 1 $V^2 D$: 1 $V^1 d$: 99 $V^1 D$: 99 $V^2 d$. As we already know that the child inherited V^2, and the ratio of gametes with the V^2 allele is 1 $V^2 D$: 99 $V^2 d$, you can see that **the chance that the fetus has the D allele is 1/100 = 1%.** Parts $b - d$ are solved using the same logic.

c. **5%.**

d. **10%.**

e. **50%.**

Section 4.3 – Mapping: Locating Genes Along a Chromosome

4-17.

a. There are four equally frequent phenotypic classes in the progeny; these must include a reciprocal pair of parentals and a reciprocal pair of recombinants. The parental reciprocal pair could either be [(wild-type wings, wild-type eyes) and (dumpy wings, brown eyes)] or [(wild-type wings, brown eyes) and (dumpy wings, wild-type eyes)]. The first possibility means the genotype of the heterozygous female was $dp^+ bw^+ / dp\ bw$ while the second pair means the genotype of the female was $dp\ bw^+ / dp^+ bw$. In either case the recombination frequency is 50% (178 + 181 / 716 or 185 + 172 / 716) so **the two genes are assorting independently**.

b. In this cross the heterozygous parent is the male and there is no recombination in *Drosophila* males. If dumpy and brown were on separate chromosomes then they must assort independently and there would be four classes of progeny as in part *a*. We can tell that **the two genes are on the same chromosome** because the lack of recombination in the male parent then explains why only two (parental) classes of progeny are seen. **The genotype of the heterozygous male must have been $dp^+ bw^+ / dp\ bw$.**

c. If the genes are far enough apart on the same chromosome they will assort independently in the first cross. This is because (1) **recombination occurs at the four-strand stage of meiosis**; and (2) **in every meiosis, at least one crossover will occur between the two genes.** Independent assortment does not occur in the second cross because there is no recombination in *Drosophila* males. In *Drosophila*, therefore, **it is a simple matter to decide if genes are syntenic** (located on the same chromosome), **even if the alleles of these genes assort independently**. A cross between a male heterozygous for the two genes of interest and a recessive female will clearly distinguish between genes on separate chromosomes and syntenic genes. In the case of genes on separate chromosomes, there will be four equally frequent classes of progeny. In the case of genes on the same chromosome (even genes that are very far apart on the same chromosome), there will only be two classes of progeny – the parental classes.

d. The $dp \leftrightarrow bw$ distance cannot be measured in any two-point cross. The measured recombination frequency can be no higher than 50% when looking at data involving a single pair of genes. **Large genetic distances can be measured accurately only by summing up the values obtained for smaller distances separating other genes in between those at the ends**.

4-18. Diagram the cross:

wild-type ♀ x reduced cinnabar ♂ → F_1 ♀ x F_1 ♂ → F_2 292 wild-type, 9 cinnabar, 7 reduced, 92 reduced cinnabar.

Two genes are involved in this cross, but the frequencies of the phenotypes in the second generation offspring do not look like frequencies expected for a cross between double heterozygotes for two independently assorting genes (9:3:3:1). The genes must be linked. Designate the alleles: cn^+ = wild type, cn = cinnabar; rd^+ = wild type, rd = reduced. The cross is:

$cn^+ rd^+ / cn^+ rd^+$ ♀ x $cn\,rd / cn\,rd$ ♂ → F_1 $cn^+ rd^+ / cn\,rd$.

Recombination occurs in *Drosophila* females but <u>not</u> in males. Thus males can only produce the parental $cn^+ rd^+$ or $cn\,rd$ gametes. The females produce both the parental gametes and the recombinant gametes $cn^+ rd$ and $cn\,rd^+$. These gametes can combine as shown in the Punnett square that follows.

female gametes	male gamete $cn^+ rd^+$	male gamete $cn\,rd$
$cn^+ rd^+$ (parental)	$cn^+ rd^+ / cn^+ rd^+$ (wild type)	$cn^+ rd^+ / cn\,rd$ (wild type)
$cn\,rd$ (parental)	$cn\,rd / cn^+ rd^+$ (wild type)	$cn\,rd / cn\,rd$ (cinnabar reduced)
$cn^+ rd$ (recombinant)	$cn^+ rd / cn^+ rd^+$ (wild type)	$cn^+ rd / cn\,rd$ (reduced)

cn rd⁺	*cn rd⁺ / cn⁺ rd⁺*	*cn rd⁺ / cn rd*
(recombinant)	(wild type)	(cinnabar)

The reduced flies and the cinnabar flies are recombinant classes. However, there should be an equal number of recombinant types that have a wild-type phenotype because they received a $cn^+ rd^+$ gamete from the male parent. If we assume that these recombinants are present in the same proportions, then RF = 2 x (7+9)/400 = 8%. **The genes are separated by 8 cM.**

4-19.

The shortest distances are the most accurate. Therefore begin assembling a map using the genes that are closest together. *MAT-LEU2* are 16 cM apart and *MAT-THR4* are 20 cM apart. This gives two possible maps: *MAT* - (16 cM) - *LEU2* - (4 cM) - *THR4* or *LEU2* - (16 cM) - *MAT* - (20 cM) - *THR4*. Because *THR4* is 35 cM from *LEU2* the second map must be the correct one. Note that the two smaller distances do not sum up to the longer distance because these recombination frequencies are based on two-point crosses. The *HIS4* gene is 23 cM from *LEU2*. This initially leads to two possible maps: *HIS4* - (23 cM) - *LEU2* - *MAT* - *THR4* or *LEU2* - (16 cM) - *MAT*- (7 cM) - *HIS4* - *THR4*. The first map is the most likely because *HIS4* is 37 cM from *MAT* instead of being very close to *MAT*. So **the order of the genes is *HIS4* - *LEU2* - *MAT* - *THR4*** (or the inverse).

4-20.

a. A testcross is the best way to find the map distance between two genes. One parent must the heterozygous for both genes and the other parent must be homozygous recessive. Thus the cross would be ***Bb Cc*** **x** ***bb cc***. Because these genes are syntenic the heterozygous parent may be either *B C / b c* or *B c / b C*.

b. There are two possible orders for these genes, shown in the following figure:

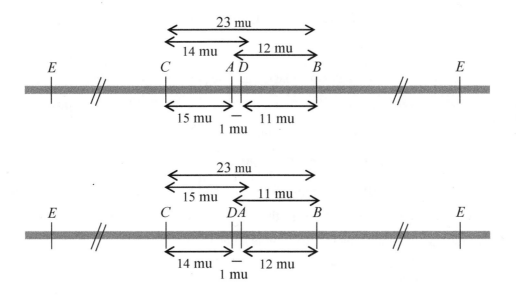

c. Because the map positions of *A* and *D* are so close, **the relative order of *A* and *D* is not clear.**
Another uncertainty is the location of gene *E*. This gene must be on this chromosome because
we are told all of these genes are syntenic. However the *E* gene is genetically unlinked to any of
the other genes (*A*, *B*, *C*, and *D*).

d. To figure out the actual order of the genes you must **do a three-point cross with either *B A D* or**
A D C and order the genes by finding the double crossover class, comparing this to the parental
class and ascertaining the order of the genes. This is described in the 'Tips for Three-Point
Crosses' section at the beginning of this chapter. Also see Problem 4-22c for a further explanation
of this method of determining the gene order.

   The location of the *E* gene can be determined by finding new genes that are genetically
linked to the left of *C* and to the right of *B* in the maps seen in part *b*. This **extension of the**
linkage group will eventually allow the placement of gene *E* when it shows genetic linkage to
one of these new genes.

4-21.

   Although this problem considers three different genes, each cross only considers two at a time.
You are thus asked to construct a map of the three genes based on 3 two-point crosses. Note the space
separating the genes in the genotypes written for the parents of each cross. This is meant to show that
we don't know if any of the genes are on the same chromosome. If the two genes in each cross are
assorting independently then the four phenotypic classes in the testcross progeny must occur in equal
frequencies. This is clearly not the case in any of the three crosses. Therefore the *mb*, *e*, and *k* genes

Chapter 4

are all linked. The genotypes of the parents in the first cross may be correctly written as $mb^+ e^+ /$ $mb^+ e^+$ x $mb\ e / mb\ e$.

In the first cross, the $mb^+ e^+$ and $mb\ e$ classes are the parentals. This is based both on the known genotypes of the true-breeding parental generation and on the fact that this reciprocal pair is the most frequent. The recombinants are the $mb^+ e$ and the $mb\ e^+$ flies, so the RF = 11 + 15 / 250 = 0.104 = 10.4 m.u. In the second cross the recombinant reciprocal pair is $k^+ e^+$ and $k\ e$, so the recombination frequency is 11 + 7 / 312 = 0.058 = 5.8 m.u. The $k\ mb^+$ and $k^+ mb$ classes are the recombinant reciprocal pair for the third cross. In this case the RF = 11 + 15 / 422 = 0.062 = 6.2 m.u. The mb and e genes in the first cross are the furthest apart, so the k gene must be in between them. Thus the map for this data is:

Note that the distance calculated between e and mb in cross one (10.4 m.u.) does NOT equal the sum of the two shorter distances (12.0 m.u.). The distance calculated from cross one is less accurate because it is based on single crossovers between e and mb and does not include any of the double crossovers that occurred in the $e \leftrightarrow k$ and $k \leftrightarrow mb$ regions simultaneously. Thus, the best map of these genes is:

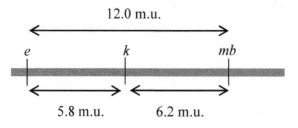

4-22. In foxgloves, wild-type flower colour is red and the mutant colour is white; the mutation *peloria* causes the flowers at the apex of the stem to be very large; normal foxgloves are very tall, and *dwarf* affects the plant height. When you describe the phenotype of an individual you usually only refer to the non-wild type traits. The cross is:

white-flowered x dwarf peloria $\rightarrow$ F$_1$ white-flowered x dwarf peloria $\rightarrow$ 172 dwarf peloria, 162 white, 56 dwarf peloria white, 48 wild type, 51 dwarf white, 43 peloria, 6 dwarf, 5 peloria white.

a. Because there is only 1 phenotype of F$_1$ plant, the parents must have been homozygous for all three genes. The phenotype of the F$_1$ heterozygote indicates the **dominant alleles: white flowers, tall stems, and normal-sized flowers**.

b. Designate the alleles for the 3 genes: W = white, w = red; P = normal-sized flowers, p = peloria; T = tall, t = dwarf. The cross is: **WW PP TT (white-flowered) x ww dd pp (dwarf peloria)**.

c. Note that all 3 of these genes are genetically linked. There are only 2 classes of parental progeny as defined both phenotypically and numerically. In order to draw a map of these genes, organize the testcross data (see the Table that follows), figure out which of the 3 genes is in the middle and calculate the recombination frequencies in regions 1 and 2. By definition, the parentals are the class with the same phenotype as the original parents of the cross, and the double crossover (DCO) class is the least frequent reciprocal pair of progeny. At this point, arbitrarily one of the remaining 2 reciprocal pairs of progeny is single crossover (SCO) 1 and the last remaining pair is SCO 2.

Classes of gametes	Genotype	Numbers
Parental (P)	*W P T*	162
	w p t	172
SCO 1	*W p t*	56
	w P T	48
SCO 2	*W P t*	51
	w p T	43
DCO	*w P t*	6
	W p T	5

Compare the DCO class with the parental class. Remember that a DCO comes from a meiosis with a simultaneous crossover in regions 1 and 2. As a result, the allele of the gene in the middle switches with respect to the alleles of the genes on the ends. In this data set, take one of the DCO classes (for example *W p T*) and compare it to the most similar parental gamete (*W P T*). Two alleles out of three are in common; the one that differs (*p* in this case) is the gene in the middle. Thus, the order is *W P T* (or *T P W*).

Once you know the order of the 3 genes, you must calculate the 2 shortest distances - from the end to the centre ($W \leftrightarrow P$) and from the centre to the other end ($P \leftrightarrow T$). The total number of progeny in this testcross = 543. RF $W \leftrightarrow P$ = (56 + 48 + 6 + 5)/543 = 115/543 = 21.2 cM; RF $P \leftrightarrow T$ = (51 + 43 + 6 + 5)/543 = 19.3 cM.

The map is:

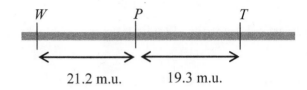

d. Interference (I) = 1 - coefficient of coincidence (c.o.c.)

c.o.c. = frequency of observed DCO / frequency of expected DCO

The expected percentage of double crossovers is the product of the RF in each interval: (0.193) x (0.212) = 0.0409. The observed DCO frequency = 11/543 = 0.0203; **c.o.c. = 0.0203/0.0409 = 0.496; I = 1 - 0.496 = 0.504**; **yes, there is interference.**

4-23.

a. See problem 4-29 for a detailed explanation of the methodology. Diagram the cross:

$$a^+ b^+ c^+ / a b c ♀ \; x \; a b c / a b c ♂ → \; ?.$$

Recombination occurs in *Drosophila* females, so the female parent will make the following classes of gametes. Because this is a testcross, these gametes will determine the phenotypes in the progeny. The Table that follows indicates the kinds of gametes that the female parent will produce and their frequencies.

Classes of gametes	Genotype	Frequency of reciprocal pair	Numbers	Frequency of each class	# of progeny = Freq x 1000
Parental (P)	$a^+ b^+ c^+$ $a\ b\ c$	1 - all else	1 - (0.18 + 0.08 + 0.02) = 0.72	0.36 0.36	**360** **360**
SCO 1	$a^+ b\ c$ $a\ b^+ c^+$	RF in region 1 = SCO 1 + DCO	SCO 1 = 0.2 - 0.02 = 0.18	0.09 0.09	**90** **90**
SCO 2	$a^+ b^+ c$ $a\ b\ c^+$	RF in region 2 = SCO 2 + DCO	SCO 2 = 0.1 - 0.02 = 0.08	0.04 0.04	**40** **40**
DCO	$a^+ b\ c^+$ $a\ b^+ c$	(RF in region 1) x (RF in region 2)	(0.2) x (0.1) = 0.02	0.01 0.01	**10** **10**

b. Diagram the cross: $a^+ b^+ c^+ / a b c ♂ \; x \; a b c / a b c ♀ → \; ?$. Here, the heterozygous parent is the male. Recombination does <u>not</u> occur in male *Drosophila*. Thus, the heterozygous parent will generate only 2 types of gametes, the parental types. If you score 1000 progeny of this cross, you will find **500 $a^+ b^+ c^+$ and 500 $a b c$ progeny.**

4-24. Diagram the cross:

pink petals, black anthers, long stems x pink petals, black anthers, long stems → the progeny listed in the table.

a. Looking at flower colour alone, the cross is pink x pink → (78 + 26 + 44 + 15) red : (39 + 13 + 204 + 68) pink : (5 + 2 + 117 + 39) white = 163 red : 324 pink : 163 white. The appearance of two new phenotypes (red and white) suggest that flower colour shows incomplete dominance. This is confirmed by the 1:2:1 monohybrid ratio seen in the self-cross progeny. **The pink-flowered plants are *Pp*, red are *PP*, and white are *pp*.**

b. The expected ratio of red: pink: white would be 1:2:1. Calculating for the 650 plants, this equals **162.5 red, 325 pink, and 162.5 white.**

c. The monohybrid ratio of the black and tan anthers = (78+26+39+13+5+2) tan : (44 + 15 + 204 + 68 + 117 + 39) black = 163 tan : 487 black = ~ **1 tan : 3 black. Therefore black (*B*) is dominant to tan (*b*).** The monohybrid ratio for the stem length = 487 long stems : 163 short stems = ~ **3 long : 1 short, so long (*L*) is dominant to short (*l*).**

d. Designate the alleles: *P* = red, *Pp* = pink, *p* = white; *B* = black, *b* = tan, *L* = long, *l* = short. Because all 3 monohybrid phenotypic ratios are characteristic of heterozygous crosses, **the genotype of the original plant is *Pp Bb Ll*.**

e. If the stem length and anther colour genes assort independently, the 9:3:3:1 phenotypic ratio should be seen in the progeny. Totaling all the progeny in each of the classes: 365 long black : 122 short black : 122 long tan : 41 short tan. The observed dihybrid ratio is close to a 9:3:3:1 ratio, so **the genes for anther colour (*B*) and stem length (*L*) are unlinked.**

The expected monohybrid ratio for flower colour is 1 red : 2 pink : 1 white, while that for stem length is 3 long : 1 short. If the two genes are unlinked, the expected dihybrid ratio can be calculated using the product rule to give 6/16 long pink : 3/16 long red : 3/16 long white : 2/16 short pink : 1/16 short red : 1/16 short white, or a 6 *L– Pp* : 3 *L– PP* : 3 *L– pp* : 2 *ll Pp* : 1 *ll PP* : 1 *ll pp* ratio. The observed numbers are: 243 long pink : 122 long red : 122 long white : 81 short pink : 41 short red : 41 short white. This observed ratio is close to the predicted ratio, so **the genes for flower colour (*P*) and stem length (*L*) are unlinked.**

The same analysis is done for flower colour and anther colour. The expected dihybrid ratio here is also 6:3:3:2:1:1. The observed numbers are: 272 black pink : 59 black red : 156 black white : 52 tan pink : 104 tan red : 7 tan white. Because these numbers do not fit a 6:3:3:2:1:1 ratio, we can conclude that **flower colour (*P*) and anther colour (*B*) are linked genes.**

f. It is clear that the original snapdragon was heterozygous for *Pp* and *Bb*. However the genotype of this heterozygous plant could have been either *P B / p b* or *P b / p B*. If it is the former and the genes are closely linked, then the *pp bb* phenotype will be very frequent (almost 1/4 of the progeny because it is non-recombinant). Instead the *pp bb* class is very infrequent, accounting for only about 1% (7/650) of the progeny. **Thus, the parental genotype must have been *P b / p B*. In this case, the infrequent *pp bb* class received a *p b* recombinant gamete from each parent. The frequency of the *pp bb* genotype = (frequency of the *p b* recombinant gamete)^2. The recombination frequency (RF) between the *P* gene and the *B* gene = frequency of *P B* + *p b* gametes = 2(($\sqrt{}$ #*pp bb*)/# total progeny) = 2(($\sqrt{7}$)/650) = 0.008 = 0.8 map units.**

4-25.

a. wild-type ♀ x scute (*sc*) echinus (*ec*) crossveinless (*cv*) black (*b*) ♂ → 16 classes of data
Among the 16 classes there are wild type for all traits and scute, echinus, crossveinless, and black. This tells you that the parental female was heterozygous for all 4 traits. The fact that the parental female is wild type also tells you that the wild-type alleles of all 4 genes are dominant. Remember that if you do a testcross with a female that is heterozygous for 3 linked genes, the data shows a very specific pattern. Because each type of meiosis (no recombination, DCO, etc.) gives a pair of gametes, you will see 8 classes of data that will occur in 4 pairs, both genetically and numerically. Thus, if you begin a cross with a female that is heterozygous for 4 linked genes, you should see 16 classes of progeny in a pattern of 8 genetic and numeric pairs. Although we have 16 classes of data, they do not occur in numeric pairs – instead we see numeric groups of 4. If one (or more) of the genes instead assorts independently of the others, then in a testcross you must see numeric groups of 4. For example, the most frequent classes will be parental, and there will be a 1:1:1:1 ratio of the 4 parental types.

  Which gene is assorting independently relative to the other 3 genes? To answer this question, list the genotypes of the gametes that came from the heterozygous parent in the largest group of 4. This group should include the parental classes for the 3 linked genes; there are 4 genotypes here to account for the independent assortment of the unlinked gene. Then choose one of the 4 genes, and remove the allele of that gene from all 4 groups. When you do this with the gene that is assorting independently of the rest, you will find there are only 2 reciprocal classes of data left, which are the parental classes for the linked genes. If you choose one of the linked genes to remove, you will still have 4 different phenotypic classes left. Try removing the *b* gene first. You see that when the *b* allele is removed, only 2 classes are left: *sc ec cv* and + + +. But when this analysis is repeated removing the allele of the *sc* gene there are still 4 different phenotypes left (see the *right column* of the Table).

Genotype	Numbers	remove *b*	remove *s*
b sc ec cv	653	*sc ec cv*	*b ec cv*
+ sc ec cv	670	*sc ec cv*	*+ ec cv*
+ + + +	675	*+ + +*	*+ + +*
b + + +	655	*+ + +*	*b + +*

The *b* gene is therefore assorting independently of the other 3 genes. When the *b* gene is removed from all 16 classes of data, you can see that the data reduces to 8 classes that form 4 genetic and numeric reciprocal pairs, just as in any three-point cross (see answer to part *b* below). Thus, the genotype of the parental female is:

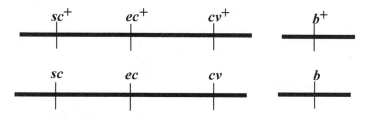

b. Write the classes out as reciprocal pairs.

Classes of gametes	Genotype	Numbers
Parental (P)	*+ + +*	1330
	sc ec cv	1323
SCO 1	*sc + +*	144
	+ ec cv	147
SCO 2	*sc ec +*	171
	+ + cv	169
DCO	*sc + cv*	2
	+ ec +	2

Compare the DCO *sc + cv* to the parental *sc ec cv*; this shows that *ec* is in the middle. Calculate RF *sc ↔ ec* = (144 + 147 + 2 + 2)/3288 = 9.0 cM; RF *ec ↔ cv* = (171 + 169 + 2 + 2)/3288 = 10.5 cM. Remember that the *b* gene assorts independently of the other 3 genes, and thus cannot be included on the map below since it is located on a nonhomologous chromosome.

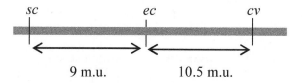

c. Interference (I) = 1 – coefficient of coincidence

c.o.c. = observed DCO frequency / expected DCO frequency = (4/3288) / (0.09 x 0.105) = 0.001 / 0.009 = 0.11

I = 1 – 0.11 = 0.89; yes, there is interference.

4-26.

First re-write the data as genotypes grouping the genetic reciprocal pairs.

Classes of gametes	Genotype	Numbers
Parental (P)	th h st	432
	+ + +	429
Recombinant	th h +	37
	+ + st	33
Recombinant	th + st	35
	+ h +	34

The *th h st* and wild-type (+ + +) classes are defined as parental because they are the most frequent reciprocal pair.

a. Each class of the parental reciprocal pair corresponds to one homologue of the heterozygous *Drosophila* female that was testcrossed to the homozygous recessive male. Thus the genotype of this female is **$th\ h\ st\ /\ th^{+}\ h^{+}\ st^{+}$**.

b. This is a testcross with three linked genes, but there are only 6 classes of data (3 reciprocal pairs) instead of 8 classes. The missing reciprocal pair is *th + +* and *+ h st*. This pair must be the least frequent DCO class. Comparing the *th + +* DCO class to the *+ + +* parental class (the most similar) shows that *th* is the gene that differs, so *th* must be the gene in the middle. The $h \leftrightarrow th$ distance is 35 + 34 / 1000 = 0.069 = 6.9 m.u. The $th \leftrightarrow st$ distance is 37 + 33 / 1000 = 0.07 = 7 m.u. **The best map is:**

6.9 m.u.   7.0 m.u.

c. I = 1 – coefficient of coincidence; coefficient of coincidence = observed DCO / expected DCO. Thus coefficient of coincidence = 0 / (0.069)(0.07) = 0 and **I = 1 – 0 = 1. The interference is complete.**

4-27. Diagram the cross:

$M\ C\ S\ /\ M\ C\ S$ (Virginia strain) x $m\ c\ s\ /\ m\ c\ s$ (Carolina strain) $\rightarrow$ $F_1\ M\ C\ S\ /\ m\ c\ s$ x $m\ c\ s\ /\ m\ c\ s \rightarrow$?

Assume no interference, and remember the map of these 3 genes:

You are being asked to calculate the proportion of the testcross progeny that will have the Virginia parental phenotype. In Chapter 2 we could answer this question by calculating the monohybrid ratios for each pair of alleles ($M : m$, $C : c$, and $S : s$) in the heterozygous parent. The testcross parent can only provide the recessive alleles for each gene, so the probabilities of the various phenotypes can be determined by applying the product rule. Unfortunately, this method of arriving at the probability of the progeny phenotypes only works when the genes under discussion are assorting independently. When the 3 genes are linked, as in this problem, to calculate the frequency of a parental class we must first calculate the frequencies of *all* of the phenotypes expected in the testcross progeny.

A parent that is heterozygous for 3 genes will give 8 classes of gametes. In a testcross, the gamete from the heterozygous parent determines the phenotype of the progeny. When the 3 genes are genetically linked, these 8 classes will be found as 4 reciprocal pairs. In other words, each meiosis in the heterozygous parent must give 2 reciprocal products that occur at equal frequency. For instance, a meiosis with no recombination will produce the parental gametes, $M\,C\,S$ and $m\,c\,s$ at equal frequency. This particular reciprocal pair will also be the most likely event and so the most frequent pair of products. The least probable meiotic event is a double crossover which is a recombination event in the region between M and C (region 1) and simultaneously in the region between C and S (region 2). The remaining gametes are produced by a single crossover in region 1 (the reciprocal pair known as <u>s</u>ingle <u>cross</u>overs in region <u>1</u> or <u>SCO 1</u>) and a single crossover in region 2 (the reciprocal pair known as <u>s</u>ingle <u>cross</u>overs in region <u>2</u> or <u>SCO 2</u>).

The numbers shown on the map of this region of the chromosome represent the recombination frequencies in the gene-gene intervals. There are 6 m.u. between the M and C genes, so 6% (RF = 0.06) of the progeny of this cross will have had a recombination event in region 1. This recombination frequency includes all detectable recombination events between these 2 genes – both SCO in region 1 *and* DCO. Likewise, 17% of all the progeny will be the result of a recombination event in region 2. The DCO class is the result of a simultaneous crossover in region 1 and region 2. Recombination in two separate regions of the chromosome should be independent of each other, so we can apply the product rule to calculate the expected frequency of DCOs. Thus, the frequency of DCO = (0.06) × (0.17) = 0.01. Remember that the recombination frequency between M and C (region 1) includes both SCO 1 and DCO. Thus, 0.06

= SCO 1 + 0.01; solve for SCO 1 = 0.06 − 0.01 = 0.05. The same calculation for region 2 shows that SCO 2 = 0.16. The parental class = 1 − (SCO 1 + SCO 2 + DCO). Also remember that each class of gametes (parental, etc.) is made up of a reciprocal pair. If the frequency of the DCO class is 0.01, then the frequency of the *M c S* gamete is half of that = 0.005. This logic is summarized in the table below.

Classes of gametes	Genotype	Frequency of reciprocal pair	Numbers	Frequency of each class
Parental (P)	*M C S* *m c s*	1 − all else	1 − (0.05 + 0.16 + 0.01) = 0.78	0.39 0.39
SCO 1	*M c s* *m C S*	RF in region 1 = SCO 1 + DCO	SCO 1 = 0.06 − 0.01 = 0.05	0.025 0.025
SCO 2	*M C s* *m c S*	RF in region 2 = SCO 2 + DCO	SCO 2 = 0.17 − 0.01 = 0.16	0.08 0.08
DCO	*M c S* *m C s*	(RF in region 1) x (RF in region 2)	(0.06) x (0.17) = 0.01	0.005 0.005

a. **The proportion of backcross progeny resembling Virginia (parental, *M C S*) = 0.39.**

b. **Progeny resembling *m c s* (P) = 0.39.**

c. **Progeny with *M c S* (DCO) = 0.005.**

d. **Progeny with *M C s* (SCO 2) = 0.08.**

4-28.

a. Recombination does <u>not</u> occur in male *Drosophila*. Therefore, in the cross *A b / a B* ♀ x *A b / a B* ♂ → F_1, the females will make 4 types of gametes (parental *A b* and *a B*; recombinant *A B* and *a b*). The frequencies of the 2 parental gametes will be equal to each other, and the frequency of the *A B* recombinant will be equal to the frequency of its reciprocal recombinant, *a b*.

female gametes	male gamete *A b*	male gamete *a B*
A b [parental]	*A b / A b* (*A− bb*)	*A b / a B* (*A− B−*)
a B [parental]	*a B / A b* (*A− B−*)	*a B / a B* (*aa B−*)
A B [recombinant]	*A B / A b* (*A− B−*)	*A B / a B* (*A− B−*)
a b [recombinant]	*a b / A b* (*A− bb*)	*a b / a B* (*aa B−*)

There is a ratio of 1/4 *A– bb* : 1/2 *A– B–* : 1/4 *aa B–* for the progeny receiving the parental gametes AND the same ratio among the progeny receiving the recombinant gametes. Thus, **the overall phenotypic dihybrid ratio will <u>always</u> be 1/4 *A– bb* : 1/2 *A– B–* : 1/4 *aa B–*, independent of the recombination frequency between the *A* and *B* genes.**

This will **not** be true of the cross *A B / a b* ♀ x *A B / a b* ♂ (see Table below). The male will make the parental gametes, *A B* and *a b*, while the female will make 4 types of gametes: parental *A B* and *a b*; recombinant *A b* and *a B*. In this case, half of the progeny will look *A– B–* because they received the *A B* gamete from the male parent irrespective of the gamete from the female parent. When the male parent donates the *a b* gamete, then it is the gamete from the female parent that determines the phenotype of the offspring. The progeny that are *A– bb* and *aa B–* have received a recombinant gamete from the female parent (and the *a b* gamete from the male). These classes of progeny can then be used **to estimate the recombination frequency between the *A* and *B* genes: RF = 2(# of *A– bb* + # of *aa B–*)/total progeny.** (The factor of 2 is included because you cannot see half of the recombinants.)

female gametes	male gamete *A B*	male gamete *a b*
A B [parental]	*A B / A B* (*A– B–*)	*A B / a b* (*A– B–*)
a b [parental]	*a b / A B* (*A– B–*)	*a b / a b* (*aa bb*)
A b [recombinant]	*A b / A B* (*A– B–*)	*A b / a b* (*A– bb*)
a B [recombinant]	*a B / A B* (*A– B–*)	*a B / a b* (*aa B–*)

b. In mice, recombination occurs in both females and males. Therefore, in the cross *A b / a B* ♀ x *A b / a B* ♂ both sexes will make the same array of gametes (parental *A b* and *a B*; recombinant *A B* and *a b*). In this case, the only phenotype of progeny with a singular genotype will be *aa bb*. In the cross under consideration here, the *aa bb* phenotype can only arise if both parents donate the *a b* recombinant gamete. Of course, the other recombinant gamete, *A B*, occurs with equal frequency. The probability of the *aa bb* genotype = (probability of an *a b* recombinant gamete)^2. If you know the frequency of the *aa bb* phenotypic class in the progeny, **recombination**

Chapter 4

frequency (frequency of recombinant products) between the *A* and *B* genes = 2(($\sqrt{\#aa\ bb}$)/# total progeny)).

In the case of the *A B* / *a b* ♀ x *A B* / *a b* ♂ cross in mice, both sexes are making the same parental gametes (*A B* and *a b*) and recombinant gametes (*A b* and *a B*). Again, the only phenotype of progeny with a singular genotype will be *aa bb*. In this example, this phenotype is the result of the fusion of the *a b* parental gamete from each parent. The frequency of the *aa bb* phenotype = (the frequency of the *a b* gamete) x (the frequency of the *a b* gamete). If you know the frequency of the *aa bb* phenotypic class in the progeny, **the frequency of non-recombinant products between the *A* and *B* genes = 2(($\sqrt{\#aa\ bb}$)/# total progeny)). Recombination frequency = 1 - frequency of non-recombinant products between the *A* and *B* genes.**

4-29. In cross #1 the criss-cross inheritance of the recessive alleles for *dwarp* and *rumpled* from mother to son tells you that all these genes are X-linked. In cross #2, you see the same pattern of inheritance for *pallid* and *raven*, so these genes are X-linked as well. The fact that the F_1 females in both crosses were wild type tells you that the wild-type allele of all 4 genes is dominant to the mutant allele. Designate alleles: dwp^+ and *dwp* for the *dwarp* gene, rmp^+ and *rmp* for the *rumpled* gene, pld^+ and *pld* for the *pallid* gene, and rv^+ and *rv* for the *raven* gene. Assign the genes an arbitrary order to write the genotypes. If you keep the order the same throughout the problem, it is sufficient to represent the wild-type allele of a gene with +.

Cross 1: *dwp rmp + +* / *dwp rmp + +* x *+ + pld rv* / Y → *dwp rmp + +* / *+ + pld rv* (wild-type females) and *dwp rmp + +* / Y (dwarp rumpled males).

Cross 2: *+ + pld rv* / *+ + pld rv* x *dwp rmp + +* / Y → *+ + pld rv* / *dwp rmp + +* (wild-type females) and *+ + pld rv* / Y (pallid raven males).

Final cross: *dwp rmp + +* / *+ + pld rv* (cross 1 F_1 females) x *dwp rmp pld rv* / Y → 428 *+ + pld rv*, 427 *dwp rmp + +*, 48 *+ rmp pld rv*, 47 *dwp + + +*, 23 *+ rmp pld +*, 22 *dwp + + rv*, 3 *+ + pld +*, 2 *dwp rmp + rv*.

All 4 genes might be genetically linked, as they are all on the X chromosome. If so, you expect 16 classes of progeny (2 x 2 x 2 x 2) in 8 genetic and numeric pairs. Notice that there are only 8 classes of progeny. The data that is seen shows exactly the pattern you expect for a female that is heterozygous for 3 linked genes. If 2 of the 4 genes never recombine then you would expect the pattern of data that is seen. If 2 genes never recombine, they will always show the parental configuration of alleles. Thus, examine the various pairs of genes for the presence or absence of recombinants. Note that you never see recombinants between *pallid* and *dwarp*: all the progeny are either pallid or dwarp, but never pallid and dwarp nor wild type for both traits. This suggests that the two genes are so close together that there is essentially no recombination between the loci. If a much larger number of progeny were examined, you might observe recombinants. Treat *dwp* and *pld* as 2 genes at the same location, so one of them (*dwp*, for instance) can be ignored, and this problem becomes a three-point cross between *pld, rv,* and *rmp*.

Classes of gametes	Genotype	Numbers
Parental (P)	*dwp rmp + +*	427
	+ + pld rv	428
SCO 1	*+ rmp pld rv*	48
	dwp + + +	47
SCO 2	*dwp + + rv*	22
	+ rmp pld +	23
DCO	*+ + pld +*	3
	dwp rmp + rv	2

When the *rmp + rv* DCO class is compared to the *rmp + +* parental class, you can see that **rv is in the middle. The *rv ↔ rmp* RF = (48 + 47 + 3 + 2)/1000 = 10 cM; the *pld/dwp ↔ rv* RF = (22 + 23 + 3 + 2)/1000 = 5 cM.** I = 1 − c.o.c.; c.o.c. = observed frequency of DCO/expected frequency of DCO. Thus, c.o.c. = (5/1000)/(0.05)(0.1) = 0.005/0.005 = 1; I = 1 - 1 = 0, so **there is no interference.**

4-30. On the basis of a recombination frequency (RF) of 5%, the physical distance between the *HD* gene and the *G8* marker was estimated to be 5 million bp, but when the human genome was sequenced, the actual physical distance between the gene and the marker was found to be only 500 000 bp. Why is the actual distance much lower than the estimated distance? The reason is that the estimate of the distance on the basis of the RF assumes that recombination is uniform over the entire genome. This assumption is not true. Although over the whole genome the *average* relationship is that 1% RF corresponds to 1 million bp everywhere in the genome, this value hides a great deal of variation in the relationship in different regions of the genome.

In this particular case, it appears that about 10× more crossovers occur in the interval between the *HD* gene and the *G8* marker than in the average 500 000 bp interval in the genome. Clearly then, **the genomic DNA between *HD* and *G8* contains a recombination hotspot.**

4-31. To answer this question, you first need to count the number of recombination nodules visible in the whole genome depicted in Figure 4.10a. There is at least one nodule per bivalent, and there are 20 bivalents in mice. By our own count, we see 29 nodules, but you may see (or imagine you see) a few more or less. We will take 29 as the proper count here. In this meiotic figure, the 29 nodules are distributed among 1386 cM in the male genetic map. If the same mouse genome corresponds to 1817 cM in the female genetic map, this must be because more recombination events take place in the average primary oocyte than in the average primary spermatocyte. So you would multiply 29 times the ratio of the cM in the female : male genetic maps (1817 / 1386) = **~38 recombination nodules in the average prophase I primary oocytes.** [Your final answer may vary depending on how many nodules you counted in Figure 4.10a, but your answer must be more than 20 × (1817 / 1386) = 26.]

Section 4.4 – The Chi-Square Test and Linkage Analysis

4-32. The null hypothesis is that there is independent assortment of 2 genes yielding a dihybrid phenotypic ratio of 9/16 R– Y– : 3/16 R– yy : 3/16 rr Y– : 1/16 rr yy. Use the chi-square (χ^2) test to compare Mendel's observed data with the 9:3:3:1 ratio expected for 2 genes that assort independently.

Genotypes	Observed #	Expected #	χ^2 equation	Sum of χ^2
R– Y–	315	9/16 (556) = 313	$(315 - 313)^2 / 313$	0.01
R– yy	108	3/16 (556) = 104	$(108 - 104)^2 / 104$	0.15
rr Y–	101	3/16 (556) = 104	$(101 - 104)^2 / 104$	0.09
rr yy	32	1/16 (556) = 35	$(32 - 35)^2 / 35$	0.26
				0.51

The number of classes is 4, so the degrees of freedom is 4–1 or 3. Using **Table 4-3** in the text, the probability of having obtained this level of deviation by chance alone is between 0.9 and 0.99 (90 % – 99%). Thus we *cannot* reject the null hypothesis. In other words, **the data are consistent with independent assortment and we therefore conclude that Mendel's data could indeed result from the independent assortment of the 2 genes.**

You should note, however, that although Mendel's data are consistent with independent assortment, this chi-square analysis does not prove that these genes assort independently. This analysis did not exclude any hypothesis. We could not formulate the null hypothesis as stating that the genes do not assort independently; we cannot predict the expected number of progeny under this hypothesis given that linked genes can have RF anywhere from 0% to just under 50%.

4-33.

a.   Diagram the cross.

orange (*O– bb*) x black (*oo B–*) → F$_1$ brown (*O– B–*) → 100 brown (*O– B–*) : 25 orange (*O–bb*) : 22 black (*oo B–*) : 13 albino (*oo bb*)

Because the F$_1$ snakes were all brown, we know that the orange snake could not have contributed an *o* allele, or there would have been some black snakes. The orange snake must be *OO bb*. The black snake could not have contributed a *b* allele or there would have been some orange snakes, so the black parent must be *oo BB*. Therefore **the F$_1$ snakes must be *Oo Bb*.**

b. The F$_1$ snakes are heterozygous for both genes (*Oo Bb*). If the two loci assort independently, we expect the F$_2$ snakes to show a 9 brown : 3 orange : 3 black : 1 albino ratio. The total number of F$_2$ progeny is 160. **We expect 90 (160 x 9/16) of these progeny to be brown, 30 (160 x 3/16) to be orange, 30 to be black, and 10 (160 x 1/16) to be albino.**

c.

Genotypes	Observed #	Expected #	χ^2 equation	Sum of χ^2
O– B–	100	90	$(100–90)^2 / 90$	1.11
O– bb	25	30	$(25–30)^2 / 30$	0.83
oo B–	22	30	$(22–30)^2 / 30$	2.13
oo bb	13	10	$(13–10)^2 / 10$	0.9
				4.97

There are three degrees of freedom (4 classes − 1) and the *p* value is between 0.5 and 0.1. **The observed values do not differ significantly from the expected.**

d. There is a 10% − 50% probability that these results would have been obtained by chance if the null hypothesis were true; this is simply another way of writing the meaning of the *p* value.

4-34.

a. The cross is:

normal (*DD*) x dancer (*dd*) → F$_1$ normal (*Dd*) → F$_2$ 3/4 *D–* (normal) : 1/4 *dd* (dancer)

1/4 of the F$_2$ mice will be dancers if the trait is determined by a single gene with complete dominance.

b. Diagram the cross:

normal (*AA BB*) x dancer (*aa bb*) → F$_1$ normal (*Aa Bb*) → F$_2$ 15/16 normal (*A– B– + A– bb + aa B–*) : 1/16 dancer (*aa bb*)

1/16 of the mice would be expected to be dancers given the second hypothesis that dancing mice must be homozygous for the recessive alleles of two genes.

c. Calculate the chi-square values for each situation. Null hypothesis #1: Dancing is caused by the homozygous recessive allele of one gene, so 1/4 of the F2 mice should be dancers. Calculating the expected numbers, $1/4 \times 50$ mice or 13 should have been dancers, 37 should have been normal.

Genotypes	Observed #	Expected #	χ^2 equation	Sum of χ^2
normal	42	$(3/4) \times 50 = 37$	$(42-37)^2 / 37$	0.68
dancers	8	$(1/4) \times 50 = 13$	$(8-13)^2 / 13$	1.92
				2.60

With one degree of freedom, the p value is between 0.5 and 0.1 and we cannot reject the null hypothesis. The hypothesis that dancing is caused by the homozygous recessive allele of one gene is therefore a good fit with the data.

Null hypothesis #2: Dancing is caused by being homozygous for the recessive alleles of two genes (*aa bb*), so 1/16 of the F2 mice should be dancers.

Genotypes	Observed #	Expected #	χ^2 equation	Sum of χ^2
normal	42	47	$(42-47)^2 / 47$	0.53
dancers	8	3	$(8-3)^2 / 3$	8.33
				8.86

With one degree of freedom, the p value is between 0.01 and 0.001 (and thus < 0.005), so the null hypothesis that two genes control the dancer phenotype is not a good fit; in fact, the hypothesis can be rejected by the criteria employed by most geneticists. **The one gene hypothesis is a better fit with the data**.

4-35. This question asks you to weigh the advantages and disadvantages of using chi-square analysis to test for linkage between two genes using two different assumptions.

a. In assumption #1, as seen in Figure 4.22, the expectation of independent assortment is that the frequency of parental genotypes is the same as the frequency of recombinants. In assumption #2, the expectation of independent assortment is that the parental and recombinant progeny should be present in a ratio of 1:1:1:1. **Notice that the null hypothesis is the same in both cases: that the genes are assorting independently.**

b. Assumption #1, 50 progeny:

Genotypes	Observed #	Expected #	χ^2 equation	Sum of χ^2
Parental	31	25	$(31 - 25)^2 / 25$	1.44
recombinant	19	25	$(19 - 25)^2 / 25$	1.44
				2.88

1 df (degree of freedom), $0.05 < p < 0.1$ and the null hypothesis cannot be rejected – the data is compatible with the hypothesis that the genes are assorting independently.

Assumption #2, 50 progeny:

Genotypes	Observed #	Expected #	χ^2 equation	Sum of χ^2
AB	17	12.5	$(17 - 12.5)^2 / 12.5$	1.62
ab	14	12.5	$(14 - 12.5)^2 / 12.5$	0.18
Ab	8	12.5	$(8 - 12.5)^2 / 12.5$	1.62
aB	11	12.5	$(11 - 12.5)^2 / 12.5$	0.18
				3.6

3 df, $0.10 < p < 0.5$ and the null hypothesis cannot be rejected – the data is compatible with the hypothesis that the genes are assorting independently.

Assumption #1, 100 progeny:

Genotypes	Observed #	Expected #	χ^2 square equation	Sum of χ^2
parental	62	50	$(62 - 50)^2 / 50$	2.88
recombinant	38	50	$(38 - 50)^2 / 50$	2.88
				5.76

1 df, $0.01 < p < 0.05$ and the null hypothesis is rejected – the genes are not assorting independently, so they must be linked.

Assumption #2, 100 progeny:

Genotypes	Observed #	Expected #	χ^2 equation	Sum of χ^2
AB	34	25	$(34 - 25)^2 / 25$	3.24
ab	28	25	$(28 - 25)^2 / 25$	0.36
Ab	16	25	$(16 - 25)^2 / 25$	3.24
aB	22	25	$(22 - 25)^2 / 25$	0.36
				7.2

3 df, $0.05 < p < 0.1$ and the null hypothesis cannot be rejected – the data is compatible with the hypothesis that the genes are assorting independently.

In the first experiment with only 50 progeny, $p < 0.05$ using both the 2 class and 4 class assumptions, so neither assumption supports the idea that the genes are linked (although the test with 2 classes is closer to significance). When more progeny are scored, the null hypothesis (that the genes are assorting independently) is rejected when you look at the data as 2 classes but not as 4 classes. This suggests that **using 2 classes is a more sensitive test for linkage than using 4 classes**.

c.   There is actually a subtle difference in the null hypotheses: in the 2 class situation the null hypothesis is no linkage; in the 4 class situation it is 1:1:1:1, which not only means no linkage but also equal viability of the 4 classes. You could imagine a situation in which certain classes are sub-viable, for example any class with the *a* allele. In such a case, you might see linkage with the 2 class test, but you would miss the even more important point that one allele causes reduced viability. **This ability to see the relative viability of the alleles is an advantage to the 4 class method**.

Section 4.5 – Mitotic Recombination and Genetics Mosaics

4-36. In a normal mitosis (with no recombination), all of the daughter cells produced are genotypically $a\ b\ c\ leth\ d\ e\ /\ a^+\ b^+\ c^+\ leth^+\ d^+\ e^+$ and are phenotypically wild type, like the original cell. Rarely, however, after the chromosomes have replicated into sister chromatids, recombination can occur between nonsister chromatids. The figure below shows the possible locations for such recombination events; these are indicated by Roman numerals I to V. Assume that no crossovers can occur between gene *a* and the centromere because they are so closely linked. The centromeres on sister chromatids split and segregate from each other during mitosis. The centromeres are numbered in the figure below so you can follow them more easily. For example, cen1 and cen2 segregate from each other, so chromatids 1 or 2 and 3 or 4 will end up in a daughter cell.

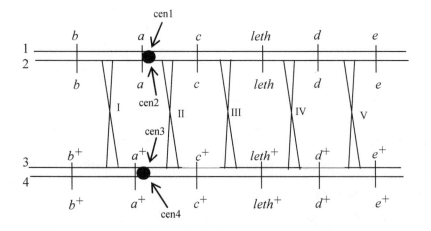

If you review Figure 4.24, you will see that after mitotic recombination, only one orientation of the chromatids on the homologous chromosomes will segregate to yield progeny genotypically different from the parents, and we will only discuss this orientation here. The important rule to keep in mind is that daughter cells of an originally heterozygous parental cell will become homozygous for an allele only if the mitotic crossover occurs between the centromere and the gene. If the mitotic crossover occurs further away from the centromere than the gene, all daughter cells will remain heterozygotes for that gene (see again Figure 4.24).

Consider now the results of a crossover in region I of the figure. In the segregation pattern of interest, one daughter cell will be homozygous for the b^+ allele and heterozygous for the rest of the genes on the chromosome. Thus, this cell will be phenotypically wild type and indistinguishable from the non-recombinant cells surrounding it. However, the reciprocal product of this mitosis will be a daughter cell whose genotype will be homozygous mutant for gene b and heterozygous wild type for everything else. This cell will continue to divide mitotically and yield a patch of b mutant tissue in a sea of wild-type tissue.

Next consider a crossover in region II. In this case, the segregation pattern of interest will yield one wild-type cell and a reciprocal daughter cell which will be $b^+\ a^+\ c\ leth\ d\ e\ /\ b\ a\ c\ leth\ d\ e$. Because this cell is homozygous for the recessive lethal mutation, it will die and you will never see it. A crossover in region III will also give a lethal recombinant product (genotypically $b^+\ a^+\ c^+\ leth\ d\ e\ /\ b\ a\ c\ leth\ d\ e$) that again you will never see.

A crossover in region IV will give a $d\ e$ patch of mutant tissue product (genotypically $b^+\ a^+\ c^+\ leth^+\ d\ e\ /\ b\ a\ c\ leth\ d\ e$), while a crossover in region V will give a patch of e mutant tissue (genotypically $b^+\ a^+\ c^+\ leth^+\ d^+\ e\ /\ b\ a\ c\ leth\ d\ e$).

Thus, **the only phenotypes that will be found in sectors as a result of mitotic recombination will be those associated with (2) b, (9) $d\ e$, and (5) e** (representing crossovers in regions I, IV, and V, respectively).

4-37.

a. The colony is mostly white because the cells are heterozygotes ($ade2^+/ade2^-$) and the $ade2^+$ allele is dominant. Red sectors arise when one cell in the growing colony becomes $ade2^-/ade2^-$. As all the cells continue to grow, the colony continues to expand and the $ade2^-/ade2^-$ cells form a red sector within the white colony (**Figure 4.25**). **Red cells of the $ade2^-/ade2^-$ genotype could arise by mitotic recombination (Figure 4.24), by loss of the entire chromosome containing the $ade2^+$ allele, by a deletion of the portion of the chromosome containing the $ade2^+$ allele, or by spontaneous mutation of the $ade2^+$ allele to an $ade2^-$ allele.** (Note: Using the usual genetic nomenclature in yeast, the $ade2^+$ allele could be written as $ADE2$ and the $ade2^-$ allele as $ade2$. These are alternative ways of representing the same things.)

b. The size of the red sectors depends on when in the formation of the colony the event occurred to form the initial $ade2^-$ / $ade2^-$ cell. If the event occurred early in the formation of the colony there will be a larger red sector than if the event occurred near the end of colony formation. All of the events mentioned in part *a* are rare, so in general they will occur later in colony formation when there are more cells in which they could occur. As a result, **most of the red sectors will be small**. (The colonies in Figure 4.25 actually contain several very small sectors that are too tiny to show up in the photograph.)

4-38. List the phenotypes seen in the normal tissue and the 20 tumours and their frequency of occurrence:

- normal tissue = $A^F A^S$ $B^F B^S$ $C^F C^S$ $D^F D^S$

- tumour type 1 = A^F $B^F B^S$ $C^F C^S$ D^F = 12 tumours

- tumour type 2 = A^F $B^F B^S$ $C^F C^S$ $D^F D^S$ = 6 tumours

- tumour type 3 = A^F B^S $C^F C^S$ D^F = 2 tumours

Remember that all of the tumour tissues were also homozygous for $NF1^-$ while the normal tissue is heterozygous $NF1^+ NF1^-$.

a. **Mitotic recombination** could have caused all 3 types of tumours.

b. Remember that mitotic recombination causes genes further from the centromere to become homozygous, while genes between the recombination event and the centromere, or those on the other side of the centromere, remain heterozygous (review problem 4-36). Notice that all 3 types of tumour cells are homozygous for $NF1^-$, so by definition all 20 mitotic recombination events that gave rise to the 20 tumours occurred between the centromere and the $NF1$ gene. Notice also that all 20 tumours are homozygous for gene *A*, specifically the A^F allele. Because gene *A* is affected by all of the mitotic recombination events, it must be further from the centromere than the $NF1$ gene. Because these tumours become homozygous for the A^F allele, that allele must be on the same homologue with the $NF1^-$ allele. There are 6 tumours that are homozygous for these 2 genes (*A* and *NF1*) (tumour type 2).

As you work your way along the chromosome from *NF1* toward the centromere, the next gene to also become homozygous is the *D* gene (tumour type 1), specifically the D^F allele, then the *B* gene (tumour type 3), specifically the B^S allele. Gene *C* never becomes homozygous, yet we are told it is on this chromosome as well. Thus it could either be on the other side of the centromere from *NF1*, *A*, *D*, and *B* or it could be on the same side of the centromere as the rest of the genes but very closely linked to the centromere (like the *a* gene in problem 4-36). **The order of the genes and coupling of the alleles in normal tissue (prior to mitotic recombination) is shown in the following figure**:

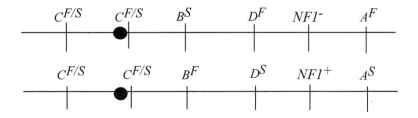

It is possible to use the **mitotic** recombination frequencies with which the various genotypes of tumours arose as a rough, relative approximation of the distances between the genes. These numbers are not to be confused with the meiotic recombination frequency we have been calculating in the other problems in this and other chapters. In tumour type 2 the mitotic recombination event happened between gene *NF1* and gene *D* (*NF1⁻* is homozygous, and so further from the centromere than the recombination event while gene *D* is still heterozygous), and this occurred in 6/20 tumours = 0.3, so **the relative recombination frequency between *NF1* and gene *D* is 0.3**. In tumour type 1 the mitotic recombination event happened between gene *B* and gene *D* (*B* is still heterozygous in these tumours while *D* is homozygous D^F), and this happened in 12/20 tumours = 0.6, so **the relative recombination frequency between genes *B* and *D* is 0.6**. In tumour type 3 the mitotic recombination event happened between the centromere and gene *B* (or between gene *C* and gene *B* if you place gene *C* on the same side of the centromere as the *NF1* gene). This event happened in 2/10 tumours = 0.2 so **the relative recombination frequency between the centromere and gene *B* is 0.2**.

c. In this mechanism an entire homologue of one chromosome is lost. If the lost homologue were the one with the $NF1^+$ allele, then **the resulting cell would be hemizygous for the $NF1^-$ allele, and would develop into a tumour. This did not occur here, because all 3 genotypes of tumours are still heterozygous for at least the *C* gene**.

d. **Yes, deletions of portions of the $NF1^+$ homologue which cause loss of the $NF1^+$ allele** could cause tumours to develop in the resulting *NF1⁻* cells. If these deletions extended to the neighbouring genes *A, D,* or *B,* the tumour cells could show the same protein variants as in the problem. Although point mutations which inactivate the $NF1^+$ allele could cause tumours to develop in the resulting *NF1⁻* cells, this mechanism does not seem to be responsible for any of the particular tumours seen, because all of the tumours express only one allele of gene A (the A^F allele), and this should not be the case if a point mutation occurred in the *NF* gene.

4-39. The genotype of the female fly is $y^+\ sn^+\ /\ y\ sn$. A diagram of potential mitotic crossovers in the cells of this animal is shown in the following figure:

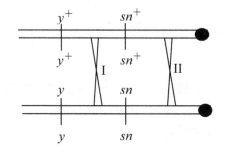

a. **The larger patch of yellow tissue arises from a mitotic crossover in region I. This mitotic recombination will generate a cell of the genotype $y\ sn^+/y\ sn$ (problem 4-36). The smaller patch of yellow and singed tissue must have arisen from a second mitotic recombination between the centromere and *sn*, in region II.** This would produce cells that are $y\ sn/y\ sn$. Because the yellow patch is larger, the recombination in region I occurred earlier in development. The yellow, singed cells are a small patch within a larger patch of yellow cells, so the mitotic crossover in region II happened after (later in development than) the crossover in region I, and this second crossover happened in a recombinant daughter cell of the first recombination event. No wonder these patches within patches are rare!

b. If the genotype of the female was $y^+\ sn/y\ sn^+$, then **a recombination event in region I would give you a detectably recombinant cell (yellow phenotype) with the genotype $y\ sn/y\ sn^+$. A subsequent second mitotic crossover in region II in one of these originally recombinant $y\ sn$ /y\ sn^+$ cells will give you a patch of $y\ sn$ tissue inside a patch of yellow tissue, as in part a.**

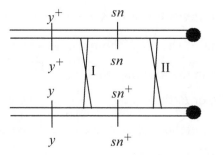

Although the problem did not explicitly ask, you should note that one kind of mitotic crossover can occur which will give a different result in a $y^+\ sn^+\ /\ y\ sn$ female (part a) than a $y^+\ sn\ /\ y\ sn^+$

female (part *b*). After a recombination event in region II the female from part *a* will show a *y sn* patch of tissue. The other recombinant product will be homozygous $y^+ sn^+$, and this cell and its descendants will be indistinguishable from non-recombinant cells. The same sort of recombination event in region II in the female from part *b* will yield one daughter cell of genotype $y^+ sn / y^+ sn$ which will give a patch of *sn* tissue. The reciprocal product of this mitotic recombination will be y $sn^+ / y sn^+$ and will give an adjacent patch of yellow tissue. This phenomenon is called *twin spots* and was depicted in Figures 4.23 and 4.24 of the text.

4-40. This problem illustrates how scientists studying the development of multicellular organisms can use GFP (green fluorescent protein) and mitotic crossing-over to create *mosaic* animals in which different cells have different genotypes. This technique has the additional virtue that the scientists can recognize these different cells within the body of the animal to see how gene function in various cells influence the organism's development.

a. **See the following diagram.**

b. To study the importance of the smc^+ gene, scientists want to study what happens when the gene function is removed; that is, to "knock out" the function of the gene. Because animals homozygous for the loss-of-function *smc* mutation die as early embryos, you cannot obtain any adult mice that completely lack *smc* function. **By using mitotic recombination, researchers can create animals in which most cells are heterozygotes (smc^+/ smc), but some cells are *smc* / *smc* homozygotes without *smc* function.** As long as the lack of the *smc*-encoded protein in those particular cells does not prevent mice from being born, scientists can then study what happens to the animal if the protein is removed from specific cells.

c. **The light green cells (most of the cells in the heterozygous animal) are cells with one copy of the *GFP* gene. The dark green cells are those with two copies of *GFP*** that are formed from mitotic recombination (these are homozygous for GFP^+). Because these cells have two copies of this gene, they make more GFP protein and fluoresce green more brightly. **The cells with no**

***GFP+* gene fail to fluoresce and are shown in white in the figure.** These are the other, reciprocal daughter cells produced from the same mitotic recombination events giving rise to the bright green cells.

d. As just mentioned in the answer to part *c*, **the bright green cells (clone 2) and the white cells (clone 1) are next to each other because they are the reciprocal products of the same mitotic recombination events**. Right after mitosis, these cells are adjacent to each other because they were produced from the same parent cell. If the progeny of these reciprocal daughter cells do not move in the epithelium, they will stay in the same general area and make the *twin spots* that are shown.

e. **See the mitotic recombination event "e" depicted in the diagram shown in the solution to part *a*.** The mitotic crossover must occur in the interval between the centromere and the *GFP* gene so as to create daughter cells homozygous for *GFP+* (the bright green cells) or homozygous for no *GFP* gene (the white cells). Because the *smc* gene is further away from the centromere than the *GFP* gene, the mitotic crossover shown in the diagram will make a daughter cell that is homozygous for both *GFP+* for bright green and *smc+* for normal sized, and a daughter cell that is homozygous for no *GFP* gene and for the *smc* mutation (no fluorescence, small sized).

f. There are more cells in clone 1 than in clone 2 because **the cells in clone 2 are homozygous for the recessive *smc* mutation that causes these cells to divide prematurely** before they reach normal size, making the cells smaller than the normal cells (like those in clone 2) with one or more copies of the *smc+* allele. There will be more of such small white cells because **in any given period of time, they will undergo more rounds of cell division than the normal-sized cells.**

g. **See the mitotic recombination event "g" depicted in the diagram shown in the solution to part *a*.** This event occurs in the interval between *GFP* and *smc*. These daughter cells will be light green (one copy of *GFP+*) and small (because they are homozygous for *smc*). No twin spots will result from this type of mitotic crossover because the reciprocal daughter cell will be light green (*GFP+*/ no GFP) and normal sized (*smc+*/ *smc+*), just like all the surrounding cells.

Chapter 5   The Multifaceted Nature of the DNA Molecule

Synopsis:

The statement "DNA's genetic functions flow directly from its molecular structure" is a good focus for reviewing DNA structure. By focusing on function, the beauty of the structure will become more evident. Make sure you really understand the structure and get a good mental image of the DNA molecule and its construction. Understanding where hydrogen and covalent bonds are found, the polarity of the strands of DNA, and why complementarity is important will provide a good basis for understanding many of the cellular processes (for example transcription, translation and recombination) and the manipulations of recombinant DNA technology, from cloning to genetic screening.

DNA is the nearly universal genetic material. Experiments showing that DNA causes bacterial transformation and that DNA is the agent of virus production in phage-infected bacteria demonstrated this fact.

According to the Watson-Crick model the DNA molecule is a double helix composed of two antiparallel strands of nucleotides; each nucleotide consists of one of four nitrogenous bases (A, T, G or C), a deoxyribose sugar and a phosphate. An A on one strand pairs with a T on the other, and a G pairs with a C. DNA carries information in the sequence of its bases, which may follow one another in any order.

The DNA molecule reproduces by semiconservative replication. In this type of replication the two DNA strands separate and the cellular machinery then synthesizes a complementary strain for each. By producing exact copies of the base sequence information in DNA, semiconservative replication allows life to reproduce itself.

Key Terms:

deoxyribonucleic acid (DNA)   the molecule of heredity that encodes genetic information.

nucleotide a subunit of DNA or RNA consisting of a nitrogenous base (adenine, guanine, thymine, or cytosine in DNA; adenine, guanine, uracil, or cytosine in RNA), a phosphate group, and a sugar (deoxyribose in DNA; ribose in RNA).

phosphodiester bonds covalent bonds joining one *nucleotide* to another. Phosphodiester bonds between nucleotides form the backbone of DNA.

transformation one of the mechanisms by which bacteria transfer genes from one strain to another; occurs when DNA from a *donor* is added to the bacterial growth medium and is then taken up from the medium by the recipient. The recipient cell is known as a *transformant*. Contrast with *conjugation*.

hydrogen bonds weak electrostatic bonds that result in a partial sharing of hydrogen atoms between reacting groups.

major groove in a space-filling representation of the DNA *double helix* model, the wider of the two grooves resulting from the vertical displacement of the two backbone threads. See *minor groove*.

minor groove in a space-filling representation of the DNA *double helix* model, the narrower of the two grooves resulting from the vertical displacement of the two backbone threads. See *major groove*.

ribonucleic acid (RNA) a *polymer* of ribonucleotides found in the nucleus and cytoplasm of cells; it plays an important role in protein synthesis. There are several classes of RNA molecules, including *messenger RNA (mRNA)*, *transfer RNA (tRNA)*, ribosomal RNA (rRNA), and other small RNAs, each serving a different purpose.

template a strand of *DNA or RNA* that is used as a model by DNA or RNA *polymerase* or by *reverse transcriptase* for the creation of a new complementary strand of DNA or RNA.

complementary base-pairing during *DNA replication*, base-pairing in which a complementary strand aligns opposite the exposed bases on the parent strand to create the nucleotide sequence of the new strand of DNA. Refer to *base pair, complementary sequences*.

semiconservative replication a pattern of double helix duplication in which *complementary base-pairing* followed by the linkage of successive nucleotides yields two daughter double helixes that each contain one of the original DNA strands intact (conserved) and one completely new strand.

polymerization the linkage of subunits to form a multi-unit chain. In DNA *replication*, the polymerization of nucleotides occurs through the formation of *phosphodiester bonds* by DNA polymerase III.

leading strand during *replication*, a DNA strand synthesized continuously $5'$ to $3'$ toward the unwinding Y-shaped *replication fork*. Compare with *lagging strand*.

lagging strand during *replication*, the DNA strand whose polarity is opposite to that of the *leading strand*. The lagging strand must be synthesized discontinuously as small *Okazaki fragments* that are ultimately joined into a continuous strand.

Okazaki fragments during *DNA replication*, small fragments of about 1000 bases that are joined after synthesis to form the *lagging strand*.

Significant Elements:

After reading the chapter and thinking about the concepts, you should:

♦ Become familiar with semiconservative replication and understand the general processes of initiation and elongation.

♦ Think about why special enzymes (such as topoisomerases and telomerases) are needed for replication of the genome.

♦ Assign the 5' and 3' designations to backbone strands of DNA and RNA.

♦ Indicate complementary bases to an RNA or DNA template.

♦ Explain the importance of structural features of DNA with respect to copying information.

♦ Think about experimental design.

Problem Solving Tips:

♦ The nature of the problems changes with this material. The problems still require that you have a basic understanding of the concepts and use that knowledge, but the problems are more based on experimental design. These problems can be viewed as more creative synthesis problems.

♦ The experimental type of question may cause you to go back and refresh your understanding of some techniques.

♦ A good way to approach these problems is to identify concepts relevant to the problem and review your knowledge of the topic and any relevant experimentation.

♦ One technique that comes up frequently is tagging a molecule with a label so the molecule can be followed. This is often done using radioactivity. Radioactive label can be incorporated into protein or DNA if a cell or organisms is grown in or fed a radioactive precursor that goes specifically into the type of molecule you want to follow. In designing experiments using radioactive labeling, be sure to consider how you can get a unique label into the molecule of interest.

Solutions to Problems:

Vocabulary

5-1.

i. 6; **ii.** 10; **iii.** 8; **iv.** 2; **v.** 4; **vi.** 7; **vii.** 9; **viii.** 11; **ix.** 3; **x.** 5; **xi.** 1

Section 5.1 - Evidence that DNA is the Genetic Material

5-2.

The proof that DNA was the transforming principle was the treatment of the transforming extract with an enzyme (DNase) that degrades DNA. After this treatment, the extract was no longer able to transform rough, nonvirulent strains of *Streptococcus pneumoniae* bacteria into smooth, virulent cells that could kill host mice. Avery, MacCleod and McCarty also showed that treatments with RNase and proteinase did not abolish the transforming activity of their extracts, indicating that the transforming principle was not RNA or protein. These experiments using enzymatic treatments were important because it could be argued that the purified "transforming principle" these investigators isolated as DNA might have contained proteins or other molecules. Even with this extensive evidence, many scientists still remained unconvinced the DNA carries genes for almost 20 more years.

5-3.

Chapter 5

In DNA transformation, the DNA that enters the cell is in the form of randomly sized fragments, usually generated by mechanical forces that shear the DNA while it is prepared from the bacterial cell. Therefore, 2 genes that are closer together on the chromosome will end up on the same fragment more often than genes that are far apart. A high cotransformation frequency between 2 genes indicates that they are close together. Gene *a* is closer to *c* than it is to gene *b* because there are many instances when *a* and *c* were cotransformed but only a few instances when *a* and *b* were cotransformed.

5-4.

Sulfur is found only in proteins, never in DNA, while phosphorus is a major constituent of the backbone of the DNA molecule and is found only very rarely in proteins (none of the amino acids in proteins contain phosphorous). Nitrogen and carbon, on the other hand, are found in both proteins and DNA. Hershey and Chase needed to differentiate between protein and DNA, so they needed to be able to specifically label the proteins and not the DNA and vice-versa. If they had used labeled nitrogen or carbon, there would be no way to differentiate protein and nucleic acid.

5-5.

In Tube #1 all the sugar phosphate bonds are broken. You would see individual pairs of complementary nucleotides held together by hydrogen-bonds and attached to a sugar with no phosphate group and free phosphates. In reality, the hydrogen bonds that hold together individual complementary nucleotides (2 for A-T pairs and 3 for G-C pairs) are not very stable. These hydrogen bonds would be disrupted by the thermal forces working at room temperature. You usually need at least 4 nucleotide pairs in order to have DNA that is stably double stranded at room temperature. In Tube #2 the bonds that attach the bases to the sugars are broken. You would see base pairs and sugar phosphate chains without the bases. Tube #3 would contain single strands of DNA since the hydrogen bonds between bases were broken.

5-6.

X-ray diffraction studies yielded a crosswise pattern of spots, indicating that DNA is a helix containing repeating units spaced every 3.4 Å. One complete turn of the helix occurs every 34 Å. The diameter of the molecule is 20 Å, indicating that DNA must be composed of more than one polynucleotide chain. The key X-ray diffraction pictures were taken by Rosalind Franklin and

5-7.

a. Human DNA is double stranded. If 30% of the bases are A, and A pairs with an equal amount of T (30%), that leaves 40% to be C + G. Thus, there will be 20% C.

b. 30% T.

c. 20% G (must equal the amount of C).

5-8.

Remember that in double stranded DNA the amount of A (purine) = T (pyrimidine) and the amount of G (purine) = C (pyrimidine). Therefore one of the purines + one of the pyrimidines must equal the other purine + the other pyrimidine. The true statements are: a, b, e, and f.

5-9.

In double stranded DNA adenine pairs with thymine so the percentage of A must equal the percentage of T (same for G and C). Here the amount of A is not equal to the amount of T (nor does C equal G), so the chromosome of this virus must be single stranded.

5-10.

a. The A-T base pairs have only two hydrogen bonds, so it takes less heat energy to denature these base pairs. G-C base pairs have three hydrogen bonds holding them together. It thus takes more energy to break the bonds between Cs and Gs.

b. The denatured single stranded DNA must contain stretches of nucleotides that are complementary to a nearby sequence on its own strand, but in an inverted orientation. These 'stem-and-loop' structures are regions where the single strand of DNA formed a double-stranded region. The loops and the strings holding the stems together are still single-stranded DNA.

5-11.

5'…CAG AAT GGT GCT CTG CTA T…3' This could also be written backwards as 3'….TAT CGT CTC GTG GTA AGA C…5' It is best to indicate polarity by showing the 5' and 3' directions on a strand of DNA or RNA. If no polarity is indicated then the 5' direction is at the right end of the sequence. The dots show that this is a short region of a much longer nucleotide chain.

Chapter 5

Section 5.3 – Genetic Information

5-12.

a.   The information is contained in the order of those building blocks; there are 3 billion nucleotides in the complete haploid set of 23 human chromosomes. This amount of sequence can potentially provide a huge amount of information. Although there are only 4 different building blocks they can be combined in a huge number of combinations. For instance, when considering a short 10 nucleotide long piece of DNA there are 4^{10} or 1,048,576 different possible sequence permutations. The information may be recognized by proteins that bind directly to DNA, or it can be copied into RNA to direct synthesis of proteins.

b.   Each of the four building blocks is a nucleotide. Each nucleotide is made of the sugar deoxyribose and one of the four nitrogenous bases (A, C, G or T) and a phosphate group. Deoxyribose plus a base makes a nucleoside. When phosphate groups are added these become nucleotides. In the DNA strand the adjacent nucleotides are connected by phosphodiester bonds that link a phosphate group to both the 3'-carbon atom of the deoxyribose of one nucleotide and the 5' carbon atom of the deoxyribose of the next nucleotide in the chain.

c.   There are four major differences between DNA and RNA. (i) In RNA the sugar is ribose instead of deoxyribose. (ii) RNA contains the base U instead of T. (iii) Most DNA molecules found in nature are double stranded and most RNA molecules are single stranded, but there are exceptions to both of these cases. (iv) DNA strands can be very long – more than 100,000,000 nucleotides in a human chromosome, for example. The longest naturally occurring RNA molecules are much shorter – about 20,000 nucleotides at most.

5-13.

The complementary DNA would have the complementary sequence with the opposite polarity. Note also the presence of T in DNA in contrast with U in RNA.

    3' GGG AAC CTT GAT GTT TCG GCT CTA ATT 5'

5-14.

Mix RNA from virus type 1 with protein from virus type 2 to reconstitute a "hybrid" virus. In a parallel experiment, mix RNA from virus type 2 with protein from virus type 1. Infect cells with each of these reconstituted hybrid viruses separately, and analyze the protein in the progeny viruses that result from each infection. You will find that the progeny viruses in each case have the protein that corresponds to the type of RNA in the parent hybrid virus. The protein in the progeny did not correspond to the protein in the parent hybrid virus.

Section 5.4 – DNA Replication

5-15.

a. 1/4 of the DNA is in an H/H band near the bottom of the gradient; 3/4 of the DNA is in an L/L band near the top.

b. 1/4 of the DNA is in an L/H band in the middle of the gradient; 3/4 of the DNA is in an L/L band near the top.

c. After one round, a single L/H band near the middle of the gradient would be expected. In subsequent rounds this band would be expected to spread gradually toward the top of the gradient as the heavy DNA is diluted across all of the new molecules in a random fashion. As a result you would not expect discrete bands. Instead you would see a broad "smear."

d. 1/8 of the DNA is in an H/H band near the bottom of the gradient; 7/8 of the DNA is in an L/L band near the top.

5-16.

It is best to consider the individual strands of DNA when calculating the amount of DNA of different densities. Meselson and Stahl started with H:H double stranded DNA (with nucleotides only containing ^{15}N). After one generation in ^{14}N media (with L or light ^{14}N nitrogen), this original molecule becomes two molecules - H:L and H:L, both of which have an intermediate density. After a second generation these 2 molecules will become 4 - H:L, L:L and H:L, L:L. Thus there will be equal amounts of the intermediate band and the light band, as stated in the problem. After another round of DNA replication in the light media (round 3) these 4 molecules will become 8 - H:L, L:L, L:L, L:L and H:L, L:L, L:L, L:L. Thus after 3 rounds 1/4 of the total DNA will be intermediate density and 3/4 will be light density. After the next round of replication (round 4) the 8 molecules will become 16 - H:L, L:L, L:L, L:L, L:L, L:L, L:L, L:L and H:L, L:L, L:L, L:L, L:L, L:L, L:L, L:L. At this point (after round 4), 1/8 of the double-stranded DNA molecules would be of the intermediate density and the remaining 7/8 would be light density.

5-17.

After one S phase, the label would be in one strand of each DNA double helix (call this the round 1 helix), so each chromatid (a double-stranded molecule) contains label on one of its two strands. The labeled ^{3}H-thymidine was removed before the next S phase, so the next set of new strands are not labeled. When the unlabeled strand of each round 1 chromatid is used as a template in round 2, the resulting double stranded chromatid will be unlabeled. When the labeled strand in the round 1 helix is replicated, the resultant chromatid contains this labeled strand and an unlabelled, newly synthesized complementary strand. Thus, after this second round of replication is complete every chromosome would have one labeled chromatid (but the label is only on one strand) and one unlabeled chromatid. Therefore, for each homologous chromosome pair, one chromatid of each of the two chromosomes would contain label. This is option c.

5-18.

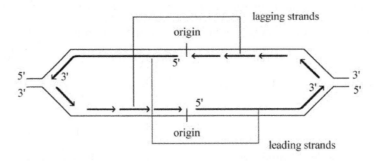

5-19.

a.   DNA polymerase needs to interact with the high energy phosphate groups at the 5'-end of the incoming nucleotide triphosphate and the 3'-end of the previously incorporated nucleotide. This action of the DNA polymerase automatically dictates the 5'-to-3' growth of the DNA chain during replication.

b.   DNA ligase also catalyzes the formation of a phosphodiester bond between the nucleotides located at the 3' end of one Okazaki fragment and the 5' end of the next Okazaki fragment. Because only a single phosphate group is attached to the 5'-carbon atom of the nucleotide at the 5'-end of an Okazaki fragment after the primer is removed, DNA ligase needs an external source of energy to catalyze the formation of a phosphodiester bond. Ligase obtains this energy by hydrolyzing ATP. This lack of a triphosphate group at the 5' end of an Okazaki fragment also explains why DNA polymerase cannot be used to join Okazaki fragments – this enzyme would have no energy source to catalyze the formation of a phosphodiester bond to a nucleotide without a high energy bond.

5-20.

Primers for DNA synthesis are RNA molecules that are made by the "Primase" enzyme. The primer is complementary to the DNA sequence shown and has the opposite polarity:

5' UAU ACG AAU U 3'

5-21.

A bubble is formed by 2 replication forks proceeding in opposite directions form a single origin of replication.

a. There are 3 bubbles in this figure, so there must be 3 origins of replication in this DNA molecule.

b. There are 6 replication forks, one at each of the two ends of each of the 3 replication bubbles.

c. If all replication forks move at the same rate, then the largest bubble was the first one activated. The smallest bubble (the one in the middle) was the last origin of replication to be activated.

5-22.

a. Helicase unwinds the DNA by breaking hydrogen bonds between base pairs to expose the single strand templates for replication.

b. Primase synthesizes a short RNA oligonucleotide, which DNA polymerase requires as a primer in order to copy the template.

c. DNA ligase joins the sugar phosphate backbones of adjacent Okazaki fragments through formation of phosphodiester bonds in order to construct a continuous strand of newly synthesized DNA.

5-23.

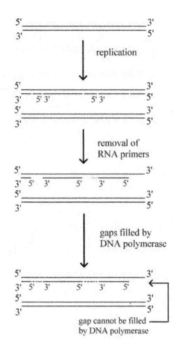

Normally, after an RNA primer is removed from the 5' end of an Okazaki fragment, the "lost" information in the strand being synthesized can be replaced. This occurs when DNA polymerase extends the 3' end of the preceding Okazki fragment by copying the template strand exposed by primer removal. However, this cannot occur at the 5' ends of the new DNA strands, because there is no preceding Okazaki fragment that could be extended. In other words, when the primer is removed from the very 5' end of a newly synthesized strand in a linear chromosome, bases are exposed at the 3' end of the (old) template strand. There is no way to synthesize complementary DNA for those exposed nucleotides. As a result, you would expect that information equal to the length of the removed primer will be lost from the 5' end of the new strand at each end of the chromosome if there is not some sort of alternate replication methodology at the chromosome ends. This leads to a successive shortening of the chromosomes in each generation of cells. It turns out that linear chromosomes in eukaryotic organisms have special structures called "telomeres" at their ends that allow them to overcome this obstacle. Chapter 6 discusses the nature of these telomeres in detail. The figure above shows the situation at the right end of a linear chromosome. The same loss of DNA sequence happens at the left end of the chromosome as well. You can picture this by rotating this diagram 180° while remembering that the RNA primer on the left end of the chromosome will be found on the pair of strands that is continuous at the right end of the chromosome.

5-24.

The figure shows both strands of DNA being replicated in the same direction relative to the replication fork. We now know that each replication fork has a lagging strand and a leading strand because DNA polymerase only catalyzes the addition of nucleotides to the 3' end of the growing chain. Watson and Crick's figure also makes it seem as if DNA replication happens spontaneously without the participation of any of the many proteins that are now known to be involved in the process. In spite of these simplifications this drawing was one of the most influential in the history of modern biology. Watson and Crick's simplification made it intuitively obvious how double helical DNA could be passed from one generation to the next. This was very important in convincing scientists of the time that their model was valid.

5-25.

Remember that DNA polymerase requires a primer supplying a free 3' end so that nucleotides can be added to the growing new strand, a single stranded template DNA to copy and a source of dNTPs. The dNTPs have been already added to the reaction tubes.

a. The reaction tube with DNA #1 + DNA #3 has two DNA strands. They can base pair with each other as follows

```
                          5'-CTACTACGGATCGGG-3'
          3'-GGTCACCCCAAAAAGGGGTGACCGATGA-5'
```

However, in this configuration the free 3'-ends can not be used to to attach new nucleotides as they are outside the region of complementarity (compare the above arrangement to the one that forms in part c of this question).

The DNA polymerase cannot function to produce a new strand, so no new DNAs will be formed.

b. The reaction tube with DNA #2 + DNA #3 has two DNA strands, however insufficient complementarity exists for the strands to form a duplex so no new DNAs will be formed.

c. The reaction tube with DNA #1 + DNA #2 has two DNA strands. In order for DNA polymerase to work these DNAs must form a region of double helical DNA - the two strands must have some complementary base sequences. They can pair with each other as follows:

```
    5' CTACTACGGATCGGG 3'
        3' TGCCTAGCCCTGACC 5'
```

In this configuration both strands can act as a template and as a primer. Each strand supplies a free 3' end to which DNA polymerase can attach new nucleotides whose sequence will be determined by complementarity with the template supplied by the other strand. Two new DNA molecules will be formed, each 5 nucleotides longer than the two original DNAs:

5' CTACTACGGATCGGGACTGG 3' and 3' GATGATGCCTAGCCCTGACC 5'

DNA sequences are usually written with the 5' end at the left, so the second of these DNA molecules could also be written as: 5' CCAGTCCCGATCCGTAGTAG 3'.

d. The reaction tube with DNA #3 is a special case. This single strand of DNA has two regions that have complementary base sequence so the DNA can form a so-called *hairpin loop* (problem 6-10). The two regions can base pair with each other as follows:

```
5' AGTAGCCAGTGGGG A A
        GGTCACCCC A   A
                    A A
```

Note that there is now a free 3' end to which DNA polymerase can add nucleotides as well as a template to guide the addition. The product will therefore be 5 nucleotides longer than the original:

5' AGTAGCCAGTGGGGAAAAACCCCACTGGCTACT 3'

It is also possible for two of these DNA molecules to pair as shown:

5' AGTAGCCAGTGGGGAAAAACCCCACTGG
3' GGTCACCCCAAAAAGGGGTGACCGATGA

The 5' adenines on the two strands (underlined) will not pair. Instead they will form a bubble in the middle of this double stranded molecule. There are now free 3' ends to which DNA polymerase can add nucleotides as well as templates to guide the addition. The product will be the same as that from the template with the hairpin loop.

Chapter 6　　Chromatin to Chromosomes

Synopsis:

This chapter describes the structure of eukaryotic chromosomes and how that structure affects function. The very long, linear DNA molecules are compacted with proteins in the chromosomes to fit into the nucleus. Several structures are essential for duplication, segregation, and stability. Replication origins are necessary for copying DNA during S phase; centromeres are necessary for attachment to spindle fibers and proper segregation during cell division; telomeres are necessary at the ends of the linear DNAs to maintain the integrity of the DNA molecule. Chromatin structure (packaging of DNA in the chromosomes) can have consequences for gene activity. Areas of normally packaged chromosome can become decompacted to allow for gene expression. Some regions of chromosomes, or entire chromosomes, are packaged in a different way that decreases gene activity as, for example, in heterochromatin or Barr bodies.

Key Terms:

exons sequences that are found both in a gene's DNA and in the corresponding mature *messenger RNA* (*mRNA*). See *introns*.

introns the DNA base sequences of a *gene* that are spliced out of the primary *transcript* and are therefore not found in the mature mRNA. See *exons*.

chromatin the generic term for any complex of *DNA* and *protein* found in a cell's nucleus.

histones small DNA-binding proteins with a preponderance of the basic, positively charged amino acids lysine and arginine. Histones are the fundamental protein components of *nucleosomes*.

nucleosome a rudimentary DNA packaging unit; composed of DNA wrapped around a *histone protein* core.

radial loop-scaffold model the model of looping and gathering of DNA by nonhistone proteins that results in high compaction of *chromosomes* at *mitosis*.

heterochromatin highly condensed chromosomal regions within which genes are usually transcriptionally inactive.

euchromatin a chromosomal region of cells that appears much lighter and less condensed when viewed under a light microscope. Contrast with *heterochromatin*.

Barr bodies inactive X chromosomes observable in interphase cells as darkly stained *heterochromatin* masses.

replicon (replication unit) the DNA running both ways from one *origin of replication* to the endpoints where it merges with DNA from adjoining *replication forks*.

telomerase an enzyme critical to the successful replication of *telomeres* at *chromosome* ends.

cohesin a multisubunit protein complex that associates with *sister chromatids* in eukaryotic cells and holds the chromatids together until *anaphase*; can be found at both the *centromere* and along the *chromosome* arms.

recombination the process by which offspring derive a combination of genes different from that of either parent; the generation of new allelic combinations. In higher organisms, this can occur by *crossing-over*.

Significant Elements:

After reading the chapter and thinking about the concepts you should be able to:

♦   Describe the essential elements of eukaryotic chromosomes.

♦   Predict the stability of artificially constructed chromosomes based on the components they contain.

♦   Analyze data on changes in chromatin compaction.

♦   Understand the role of chromosomal origins of replication.

♦   Explain why centromeres are necessary for proper segregation during mitosis and meiosis.

♦   Discuss the role of telomeres.

♦   Understand how chromatin packaging influences gene activity including nucleosomes, nonhistone scaffold proteins, euchromatin and heterochromatin.

♦   Explain X chromosome inactivation.

♦   In the process of recombination, understand how heteroduplex regions are formed and what effect they have on recombination outcomes.

♦   Work your way through the recombination process by drawing it out for yourself.

Problem Solving Tips:

♦   Put yourself in the position of being the researcher. When designing experiments consider the aim of the experiment, the concepts that apply to the problem, and think through experimental methods you know to find a relevant methodology.

Solutions to Problems:

Vocabulary

6-1.

i. 4; ii. 7; iii. 8; iv. 2; v. 3; vi. 5; vii. 1; viii. 6

Section 6.1 – Chromosomal DNA and Proteins

6-2.

Non-histone proteins, which make up ~1/2 the mass of proteins associated with DNA, are a very heterogeneous group of proteins. There are hundreds or even thousands of different kinds of proteins. Some of these proteins play a purely structural role, (e.g. scaffold proteins) while others are active in replication (DNA polymerase) and the processing of recombination (proteins in the synaptonemal complex). Still others are necessary for chromosome segregation (the motor proteins of the kinetochores). The largest class of non-histone proteins are those that foster or regulate transcription and RNA processing. In mammals there are 5,000-10,000 of these tissue specific transcription factors that are found in different tissues at different times in the life cycle. The distribution of the non-histone proteins along the chromosome is uneven. They are found in different amounts and in different proportions in different tissues. More nonhistone than histone proteins are required due to the wide range of roles they play in the cell, and the various nature in which they interact with DNA.

Section 6.2 – Chromosome Structure and Compaction

6-3.

In interphase the chromosomes are compacted 40-fold more than naked DNA and during metaphase the chromosomes are compacted 10,000 fold more than naked DNA.

6-4.

The core histones (H2A, H2B, H3 and H4) are the core of the most rudimentary DNA packaging unit, the nucleosome. It is around this protein core that DNA is wound, resulting in the first layer of compaction. The core is an octamer made up of 2 copies of each core histone. Roughly 160 bp of DNA wraps twice around the core, leading to a 7-fold compaction over naked DNA. About 40 bp forms the linker that connects one nucleosome to the next. Histone H1 lies outside the core, apparently associating with the DNA where it enters and leaves the core. Removal of H1 causes some DNA to unwrap from each nucleosome, but the core 140 bp of DNA stays intact. H1 is involved in the next level of compaction, formation of a 300 Å fiber.

6-5.

a. There are 3×10^9 bp in a haploid human genome. If each nucleosome has a spacing of 200 bp then 3×10^9 bp in a haploid human genome / 2×10^2 bp in a nucleosome = 1.5×10^7 nucleosomes to cover the DNA in a haploid genome. This estimate is high because not all parts of the genome are uniformly arranged into the most densely packed nucleosomes. The human genome is diploid, and after S phase each cell would have 2 chromatids for each chromosome, so

4 (1.5×10^7 nucleosomes) = 6×10^7 nucleosomes would be required per cell. Finally, each nucleosome contains two molecules of H2A, so cells would need roughly 1.2×10^8 molecules of H2A protein.

b. Histone proteins need to be synthesized during or just after S phase, when the chromosomes have just replicated. This is when there would be new "naked" DNA needing nucleosomes.

c. Each cell needs to make about 6×10^8 molecules of each type of histone during S phase of the cell cycle (see part a above). In human cells S phase generally lasts between 3 and 6 hours depending on the cell type. This is a lot of molecules of protein in a short period of time. Multiple copies of the histone genes mean more templates that the cells can transcribe simultaneously, allowing the more rapid production of histone proteins.

6-6.

Chromatin is the complex of DNA and proteins (histone and non-histone) which make up eukaryotic chromosomes. Evidently the nucleosome protects DNA from being digested with the micrococcal nuclease, so this enzyme preferentially attacks the DNA in chromatin somewhere in the linker DNA between nucleosomes. Thus, the pattern in lane A reflects the distribution of nucleosomes in chromatin - 200 bp is a single nucleosome, 400 bp is two nucleosomes, etc. If the nuclease treatment is short enough cleavage of the double-stranded the DNA will occur in some linker regions but not others, producing chromatin fragments with one or more nucleosomes as in lane A. Longer periods of nuclease treatment result in more cleavage - the enzyme will attack all the linker regions, so that all the chromatin will be reduced to units of single nucleosomes (lane B). Finally, if the treatment of the chromatin and nuclease is sufficiently long, then all the linker DNA will be digested, leaving core nucleosomes, each with about 160 bp of DNA as seen in lane C. These types of experiments were actually performed in the 1970s, and provided significant support for the emerging picture of the nucleosome.

6-7.

Histone H1 is located on the outside of the complex and "locks" the DNA to the core. This protein is thus able to interact with the H1 proteins from other nucleosomes, forming the center of the coil that is thought to form the 300Å fiber. The histone core is made up of 2 subunits each of H2A, H2B, H3 and H4. These eight proteins are coated with DNA and thus unable to interact with each other, so they are unable to participate in forming the 300 Å fibers.

6-8.

a. Knowing the amino acid sequences of the proteins associated the human CAF-1 (chromosome assembly factor) complex means that you can 'reverse translate' the protein sequences and predict the degenerate nucleotide sequences of the proteins. The entire yeast genome has been sequenced, so you can search for orthologous yeast genes. You expect the amino acid sequences, and therefore the DNA sequences, of these proteins to be very highly conserved. Alternatively, you can clone the yeast genes by using the predicted DNA sequences of the human CAF-1 genes to make degenerate oligonucleotide probes and probe a yeast genomic DNA library.

b. Why identify the yeast genes? You can experimentally manipulate the yeast much more easily! It is possible to make mutations of the CAF-1 proteins and carefully examine the effects on chromatin assembly in this model organism on a much faster time scale. It may be possible to extrapolate your findings to human chromosome assembly.

Section 6.3 – Heterochromatin and Euchromatin

6-9.

Using the cloned gene, mutate the codon coding for the acetylated lysine so that it codes for a similar, non-acetylated amino acid. Then, transform this mutated allele into yeast cells on an autonomous plasmid so that both the mutant and wild type genes are present. If the acetylation is important for function then these transformed cells will grow more slowly.

6-10.

a. 300 Å fiber;

b. DNA loops attached to a scaffold;

c. heterochromatin;

d. metaphase chromosomes.

6-11.

a. **1**; b. **0**; c. **1**; d. **1**; e. **3**; f. **0**.

6-12.

These twin sisters could still be monozygotic twins. They must both be carriers of the X-linked Duchenne muscular dystrophy (*Dmd*). In the affected twin, the X^{Dmd+} (wildtype) homolog was inactivated in the cells that are affected by muscular dystrophy (i.e. was on the X chromosome that became a Barr body). In the unaffected twin, the other X chromosome (X^{Dmd}) was inactivated in those same cells.

6-13.

Girls of genotype of $X^{CB}X^{cb}$ could have some patches of cells in the eye in which the X chromosome carrying the *CB* allele was inactivated and therefore those patches would be defective in color vision. Usually, enough cells have the *cb* allele inactivated and the *CB* allele active that there is sufficient color vision and therefore no phenotypic effect of the *cb* mutant cells.

6-14.

a. Heterozygous *Oo* female cats have tortoiseshell coats. In some patches of cells the chromosome with the *O* allele is inactivated so the coat is black as determined by the *o* allele. In other patches of cells the chromosome with the *o* allele is inactivated so the fur is orange since the *O* allele is still functioning. Crosses that could yield *Oo* females include *OO* x *o*Y (orange females x black males), *oo* x *O*Y (black females x orange males), *Oo* x *o*Y (tortoiseshell females x black males), and *Oo* x *O*Y (tortoiseshell females x orange males).

b. Male tortoiseshell cats could be XXY Klinefelter males who are heterozygous *Oo*. One of their X chromosomes would be inactivated in some patches of cells; the other X chromosome would be inactivated in other patches of cells, just as for the tortoiseshell females in part a.

c. Coat color in calico cats requires the action of another gene to produce white fur, but the white cannot be epistatic to the *orange* gene since the black and orange patches would not be visible. One possibility is that the *Oo* or *Oo*Y cats are also heterozygous for an X-linked white coat color gene. However, if this were the case, the white coat allele would have to be on either the X chromosome with *O* or that with *o*. These cats would be either white and black or white and orange. It turns out that an autosomal gene called the *white-spotting* or *piebald* gene causes the white spotting - a dominant allele of this gene causes white fur, but in heterozygotes this allele has variable expressivity so some patches have a color dictated by the functional alleles of the *orange* gene.

6-15.

a. All of the progeny will have mutant coat color since the wild-type allele is on the inactivated paternal X chromosome.

b. All of the progeny will have wild-type coat color since the mutant allele is on the inactivated paternal X chromosome.

c. To characterize alleles as recessive or dominant, you need to examine the phenotype of heterozygotes under conditions where both alleles are expressed. Here, the heterozygotes are all females whose phenotype was determined by the allele received by the mother.

d. In tortoiseshell cats the maternal X chromosome is inactivated in some embryonic cells and their descendants, whereas the paternal X chromosome is inactivated in other embryonic cells and their descendants. In marsupials, the paternal X chromosome is always inactivated, so all cells express the same allele.

6-16.

a. The chromosome that cannot express *Tsix* is more likely to express *Xist* and become the Barr body.

b. The *Tsix* transcript could hybridize with the *Xist* transcript (forming a double-stranded RNA) and prevent *Xist* function. Alternatively, *Tsix* transcription could somehow prevent *Xist* transcription.

c. We are still left with the problem of how the cell "decides" which one of the X chromosomes transcribes *Tsix* .

Section 6.4 –Transcription Requires Changes in Chromatin Structure and Nucleosome Position

6-17.

DNase I can only digest "open" DNA. This is DNA that is not bound by proteins like histones. Such DNase hypersensitive (DH) sites are found in the promoter regions of genes that are being transcribed or that are being prepared for transcription in a later step of cellular differentiation. Thus a hypersensitive site would suggest choice b.

6-18.

a. Studies of position effect variegation (PEV) show that methylation of a lysine in histone H3 marks the DNA for assembly into heterochromatin by signaling other proteins to interact with the DNA and further condense it into heterochromatin. In another example, the RNA produced by the

Xist gene on the X chromosome coats the DNA of the X chromosome that produced it. This leads to the methylation and partial deacetylation of histones H3 and H4. These histone modifications in conjunction with the binding of other protein factors produce inactive, condensed heterochromatic DNA leading to the formation of a Barr body.

b. Synthesis of the four basic histone proteins increases during S phase of the cell cycle to incorporate histones onto the newly replicated DNA. Special regulatory mechanisms tightly coordinate DNA and histone synthesis so that both occur at the appropriate time. The association of DNA with histones in the nucleosomes is the critical first step in packaging the 2 meters of DNA into the nucleus of a cell.

Section 6.5 – Replication of Eukaryotic Chromosomes

6-19.

At 50 nucleotides/second, DNA Polymerase (DNAP) could synthesize about 270kb in 3 hours. Since DNAP can synthesize DNA in both directions from an origin of replication, there could be up to 540kb of DNA between origins. Thus the minimum number of origins expected for a 3 billion base pair genome would be about 3 x 10^9 base pairs per genome / 5.4 x 10^5 base pairs per origin = 0.55 x 10^4 origins = 5500 origins of replication.

6-20.

a. In order to replicate the longest chromosome (66Mb) from one bidirectional origin of replication, 33 Mb would have to be copied along each replication fork during the 8 minute cycle (480 sec) = 33,000,000 bp replicated/480 sec = 68,750 bp/sec = ~69 kb/sec. Therefore, if a single origin of replication was used and replication took the entire 8 minutes of the cycle, the rate of polymerization would be 0.069 Mb/sec or 69 kb per second.

b. If bidirectional origins of replication occur every 7 kb, then only 3.5 kb would have to be replicated during the 8 min cell division cycle. The polymerization rate would be 3.5 kb/480 sec = 7.3 bp/sec, a _much_ more reasonable rate.

6-21.

a. Repeats of the sequence 5' TTAGGG 3' are found at the telomeres of human chromosomes.

b. Telomerase enables the ends of the chromosomes to be replicated; the enzyme provides the primer that would be otherwise be lacking for lagging strand replication. In the absence of the telomerase primer, the chromosomes would shorten each cycle of cell division. Shelterin protects the free ends of the chromosome from nuclease digestion and end-to-end fusions. When chromosomes are broken (for example by X-rays), the broken ends that form are not bound by shelterin. As a result, these chromosome fragments often become shorter due to nuclease digestion, and the broken fragments can fuse to each other out of order (for example, mistakenly connecting parts of nonhomologous chromosomes).

6-22.

a. If telomerase is unavailable, telomeres will become shorter at each cell division. Eventually cells will die when essential genes are removed. The absence of telomerase could have a major effect on the supply of stem cells that proliferate to renew tissues. The animals will age prematurely if the supply of stem cells is interrupted.

b. Most somatic cells are meant to have finite lifespans. Somatic cells that are not stem cells, and are not meant to proliferate indefinitely, do not express telomerase. If somatic cells inappropriately express telomerase, they might continue to divide when they should not. You will learn in Chapter 19 that immortality and overproliferation are two phenotypes of cancer cells. Thus, individuals whose somatic cells overexpress telomerase would be likely to develop cancers.

6-23.

In none of the cases (a-d) would chromosomes be expected to have exactly the same number of telomeric repeat sequences. The reason is that the telomerase enzyme does not copy the repeats that are already present, instead, it adds repeat units. The enzyme can add different numbers of repeating units to each different telomere depending on the number of translocation steps it undergoes.

6-24.

The new sequences that are added on to the end of this chromosome must be specific for the species which is adding them. Because the YAC was transformed into yeast, telomerase in the yeast cell added on the sequence specific for yeast.

Section 6.6 - Chromosome Segregation
6-25.

Shugoshin prevents Rec8 cleavage, and in the context of mitosis, this would mean that sister chromatids would not separate and move to opposite poles. The effect would be aneuploidy; both chromatids of each homolog would end up in one daughter cell or the other at random.

6.26.

a. The chromosomes shown at the left in the figure in the textbook are in prophase/metaphase of meiosis I; they are undergoing crossing over. At right, they are in anaphase of meiosis I. The light blue lines are sister chromatids of one homolog, and the dark blue lines are sister chromatids of the other homolog.

b. In the diagram below, cohesin complexes are indicated as red ovals. Along the arms, the only cohesin complexes shown are those distal to the recombination site (that is, further away from the centromere than the site of recombination). The cohesin complexes keep sister chromatids together by forming a "basket" of protein that surrounds both double helixes.

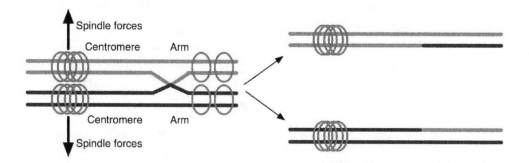

c. The bivalent at left in the diagram above is held together by cohesin complexes located distal to the recombination site. Cohesin proximal to the recombination site (that is, the chiasma) cannot hold the homologous chromosomes making up the bivalent together.

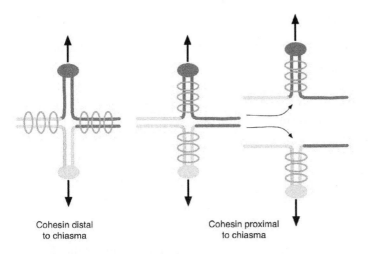

Cohesin distal
to chiasma

Cohesin proximal
to chiasma

d. Shugoshin protects the cohesin complexes at the centromere (but not those along the chromosome arms) from cleavage by separase enzyme during meiosis I. Note that the cohesin complexes at the centromere must remain intact throughout meiosis I because both sister chromatids need to move as a unit during this kind of division; it is only starting with anaphase of meiosis II that centromeric cohesin can be cleaved. In contrast, the cohesin complexes along the arms (particularly those distal to the chiasmata) must be cleaved at the start of anaphase of meiosis I so that the homologous chromosomes can segregate to opposite spindle poles.

6.27

a. The ends of chromosomes do not normally fuse together because they are protected by proteins called the shelterin complex.

b.

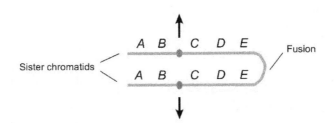

c. The fusion chromosome shown in part (b) above behaves as a bridge during mitosis because the centromeres are pulled to opposite poles. (Remember that these centromeres are those of sister chromatids that must be pulled to opposite poles during mitotic anaphase.)

d. The bridge is likely to break during anaphase, which means that each daughter cell will have a broken chromosome. This cleavage could occur anywhere in the "stretched" region between **the two** centromeres. During the following mitosis, the broken chromosomes will fuse and form a bridge again.

6.28.

a. Opening of chromatin near promoters to allow transcription involves histone acetylation; closing of chromatin to silence transcription or form heterochromatin (including Barr body formation) involves histone methylation and deacetylation.

b. Variant histones are required near the centromere for assembly of kinetochores.

Section 6.7 - Artificial Chromosomes

6.29.

a. Proper mitotic chromosome segregation would be disrupted by mutations in genes encoding (i) cohesin proteins, (ii) separase, (iii) kinetochore proteins, including the motor proteins that help chromosomes move on the spindle apparatus, and (v) components of the spindle checkpoint that makes the beginning of anaphase depend on the proper connections of spindle fibers and kinetochores. (vi) Mutations that alter the DNA comprising a centromere might also have similar effects in disrupting mitotic chromosome segregation.

b. In order to look for mutations that affect mitotic chromosome segregation, you need cells containing a YAC with a marker conferring a visible phenotype like colony color. Treat these yeast cells with a mutagen and look for colonies where some cells lost the YAC because of mitotic chromosome mis-segregation. You could also try to mutate the centromeric DNA of this YAC using in vitro mutagenesis. If the centromere were disrupted the YAC would not segregate properly and would be lost. Again, you could follow this loss if the YAC carried a genetic marker that resulted in a visible phenotype like colony color.

Section 6.8 - Chromosomal Recombination

6-30.

The coinfection of bacteria with c^+ and c bacteriophage allowed recombination to occur between the two genotypes of bacteriophage. How can a single progeny bacteriophage produce both c^+ and c progeny in the second round of infection? How can one bacteriophage with a single double stranded chromosome contain two kinds of genetic information? Remember that a key intermediate step in recombination is the formation of a heteroduplex region. Normally, the heteroduplex regions are corrected by DNA repair systems. However, in rare cases the heteroduplex is not corrected and a single bacteriophage particle can be generated with a chromosome that contains the mismatch. One strand of DNA would be c^+ and the other strand would be c. When such a bacteriophage infects a new bacterial host cell, DNA replication creates some molecules in which both strands are c^+ and other DNAs in which both strands are c.

As an aside, you might be wondering how you can actually isolate a single bacteriophage and look at its progeny. This will become clear in the next chapter, when methods for handling bacteriophage are explored in more detail.

6-31.

During strand invasion an enzyme similar to *E. coli* recA opens the nearby double helix and which allows the 3' end of the invading strand to search for a homologous sequence. If many short repeats are present in the double helix at the point where the invading strand is pairing, it is likely that the invading strand will not line up perfectly. This incorrect alignment can either generate extra repeats or eliminate some copies of the repeats.

6.32.

A mutant *spo11⁻* yeast strain will not be able to undergo recombination. Any event requiring recombination would not occur normally. In addition to not being able to reassort alleles on the same chromosome through crossing-over, the mutant strain would not be able to perform certain types of DNA repair.

Chapter 7   Gene Expression: The Flow of Genetic Information from DNA to RNA to Protein

Synopsis:

This chapter describes how the information in DNA is converted into usable machinery (proteins) in the cell via the processes of transcription and translation. This flow of information is part of the central dogma of genetics. You need to become very comfortable with using the terms transcription and translation <u>accurately</u>. In <u>transcription,</u> DNA information is converted into RNA information. In <u>translation,</u> RNA information is converted into protein information. Work on developing some mental pictures for yourself so you can see the process occurring when you speak the words. The three letter DNA code and the correspondence between DNA sequence and protein sequence is described in this chapter. Tie together your knowledge of transcription/translation and the genetic code. This chapter contains many new vocabulary terms. The best way to know you have a good grasp on the terms is use the terms while pretending you are describing transcription, translation and the genetic code to another person.

Begin to introduce more inquiry into your learning process. For example, think about the components involved in transcription, RNA processing, and translation. How could they be affected by alterations (mutations) in any one of the components? Start thinking about how we know what we know and what evidence supports a particular view of how a process occurs.

Key Terms:

transcription the conversion of *DNA*-encoded information to its *RNA*-encoded equivalent.

messenger RNA (mRNA) RNA that serves as a template for protein synthesis. See *genetic code.*

translation the process in which the *codons* carried by *mRNA* direct the synthesis of *polypeptides* from *amino acids* according to the *genetic code.* Compare with *transcription.*

genetic code the sequence of *nucleotides,* coded in triplets (*codons*) along the *mRNA,* that determines the sequence of *amino acids* in *protein* synthesis.

codon a nucleotide triplet that represents a particular *amino acid* to be inserted in a specific position in the growing amino acid chain during *translation.* Codons can be either in the *mRNA* or in the *DNA* from which the RNA is transcribed.

promoters DNA sequences near the beginning of *genes* that signal *RNA polymerase* where to begin transcription. Compare with *terminators.*

RNA polymerases enzymes that transcribe a DNA sequence into an RNA *transcript. Eukaryotes* have three types of RNA polymerases called pol I, pol II, and pol III that are responsible for transcribing different classes of genes.

introns the DNA base sequences of a *gene* that are spliced out of the primary *transcript* and are therefore not found in the mature mRNA. See *exons.*

exons sequences that are found both in a gene's DNA and in the corresponding mature *messenger RNA (mRNA)*. See *introns*.

RNA splicing a process that deletes *introns* and joins together successive *exons* to form a mature *mRNA* consisting of only exons.

alternative splicing the production of different mature *mRNAs* from the same *primary transcript* by joining different combinations of *exons*.

anticodons groups of three *nucleotides* on *transfer RNA (tRNA)* molecules that recognize codons on the mRNA by *complementary base-pairing* and *wobble*.

wobble the ability of the 5′ nucleotide of an anticodon to interact with more than one nucleotide at the 3′ end of codons; helps explain the *degeneracy* of the *genetic code*.

posttranslational modifications changes, such as cleavages that remove *amino acids* and additions of chemical constituents to specific amino acids, that occur to a *polypeptide* after *translation* has been completed.

silent mutations *mutations* without effects on *phenotype*; usually denotes *point mutations* that change one of the three bases in a *codon* but that do not change the identity of the specified *amino acid* because of the *degeneracy* of the *genetic code*.

missense mutations changes in the *nucleotide* sequence of a *gene* that change the identity of an *amino acid* in the *polypeptide* encoded by that gene.

conservative substitutions mutational changes that substitute an amino acid in a protein with a different amino acid with similar chemical properties. Compare with *nonconservative substitutions*.

nonconservative substitutions mutational changes that substitute an *amino acid* in a *protein* with a different amino acid that has different chemical properties. Compare with *conservative substitutions*.

nonsense mutations mutational changes in which a codon for an amino acid is altered to a premature *stop codon*, resulting in the formation of a *truncated protein*.

frameshift mutations *insertions* or *deletions* of base pairs that alter the grouping of *nucleotides* into *codons*. Refer to *reading frame*.

loss-of-function mutation a DNA *mutation* that reduces or abolishes the activity of a gene; most (but not all) loss-of-function alleles are *recessive*. Compare with *gain-of-function mutation*.

amorphic mutations changes that completely block the function of a *gene* (synonym for *null mutations*).

hypomorphic mutation a *loss-of-function mutation* that produces either less of a protein or a protein with very weak but detectable function. Compare with *hypermorphic mutation*.

haploinsufficiency a rare form of dominance in which an individual *heterozygous* for a *wild-type allele* and a *null* allele shows an abnormal *phenotype* because the level of gene activity is not enough to produce a normal phenotype.

gain-of-function mutations rare *mutations* that enhance a gene's function or confer a new activity on the gene's product.

hypermorphic mutation a *gain-of-function mutation* that generates either more protein than the *wild-type allele* or the same amount of a more efficient protein. If excess protein activity alters *phenotype*, the hypermorphic allele is dominant. Compare with *hypomorphic mutation*.

neomorphic mutations rare mutations that generate a novel *phenotype* due to production of a protein with a new function or due to *ectopic expression* of the protein.

dominant negative a mechanism of dominance in which some alleles of genes encode subunits of *multimeric proteins* that block the activity of the subunits produced by *wild-type alleles*.

reading frame the partitioning of groups of three *nucleotides* from a fixed starting point such that the sequential interpretation of each triplet generates the correct order of *amino acids* in the resulting *polypeptide* chain.

Significant Elements:

After reading the chapter and thinking about the concepts, you should be able to:

- Identify open reading frames in a DNA sequence.

- Assign 5' and 3' end designations to DNA or RNA sequences.

- Describe the parameters for transcription - describe the enzymes (RNA polymerase) and proteins that play a role and what information in the DNA (promoter and terminator sequence) is important for their ability to function.

- Identify the mRNA-like strand in the double-stranded DNA sequence either by knowing the sequence of the mRNA transcript or by looking for open reading frames.

- Describe the parameters for translation - describe the RNAs (rRNAs, tRNAs), proteins (aminoacyl synthetases) and RNA-protein complexes (ribosomes with the A, P and E sites) that are important and the information in the mRNA (ribosome binding site, start codon, stop codon) that is important for their ability to function.

- Understand that the nearly universal genetic code consists of 64 codons. Of these, 61 specify amino acids, while the other 3 (5' UAA, 5' UAG and 5' UGA) are nonsense or stop codons.

- Use a codon table to do a virtual translation of DNA into protein sequence and reverse translate protein into DNA sequence.

- Explain the steps in processing a eukaroytic primary transcript into an mRNA: addition of 5' methyl CAP, addition of 3' poly-A tail and splicing out of introns.

- Answer questions that require you to know the roles of the nucleic acids and proteins in transcription, translation, and RNA processing.

- Understand the ways that different types of mutations affect gene expression: silent mutations, missense mutations, nonsense mutations (and nonsense suppressors), frameshift mutations and mutations outside of coding sequences that alter signals required for transcription, processing of the mRNA or translation. Many types of mutations are classified by their effects on protein function.

- Understand and can explain the differences in gene expression between eukaryotes and prokaryotes.

Problem Solving Tips:

- The convention is to write DNA sequences with the top strand running 5' to 3' left to right.
- Transcription occurs in a 5' to 3' direction along the template DNA strand. The complementary strand of DNA is the mRNA-like strand. The mRNA-like DNA strand has the same polarity and sequence (with Ts instead of Us) as the mRNA.
- Ribonucleotides are added to a 3' end of the growing mRNA strand.
- Information in the 5' portion of a coding region of the mRNA will be information in the NH_2 terminal portion of the protein.
- There is mRNA sequence at the 5' and 3' ends of the transcript which is NOT translated into protein. These sequences are called the 5' and 3' untranslated regions (UTRs).
- By definition an open reading frame (ORF) is an RNA sequence with no stop (nonsense) codons in the adjacent groups of 3 nucleotides.

  If you are given an mRNA sequence, there are 3 possible reading frames to examine to see if they are open or closed (have an in-frame stop codon). Remember that the ribosome reads the mRNA from 5' to 3', so you check for ORFs by starting at the 5' end of the mRNA sequence. The first reading frame begins with the first nucleotide, the second frame begins with the second nucleotide and the third frame begins with the third nucleotide. When you begin with the fourth nucleotide you are back in the first reading frame.

  If you are given a DNA sequence to examine, there are 6 possible reading frames! Remember that the template strand of DNA is transcribed 3' to 5' to synthesize a complementary mRNA that is 5' to 3'. Use the complementary mRNA-like strand of DNA as a stand-in for the mRNA. Read the mRNA-like strand of DNA from its 5' end, checking the 3 possible reading frames. Then assume the other strand of DNA is the template, and repeat the process.

- Codons are found in mRNAs and anticodons are found in tRNAs. To avoid confusion, be consistent in how you write them. In the Study Guide the codons are written 5' to 3' and the anticodons are written 3' to 5'.

Solutions to Problems:

Vocabulary

7-1.

i. 5; **ii.** 10; **iii.** 8; **iv.** 12; **v.** 6; **vi.** 2; **vii.** 9; **viii.** 14; **ix.** 3; **x.** 13; **xi.** 1; **xii.** 7; **xiii.** 15; **xiv.** 11; **xv.** 4; **xvi.** 16.

Chapter 7

Section 7.1 - The Genetic Code

7-2.

a. **4**; b. **6**; c. **1**; d. **2**; e. **3**; f. **5**.

7-3.

a.   GU GU GU GU GU or UG UG UG UG UG.

b.   GU UG GU UG GU UG GU UG GU.

c.   If you start with the first base: GUG UGU GUG. If you start with the second base: UGU GUG UGU.

d.   GUG UGU GUG UGU GUG UGU GUG UGU. This is the result of reading the first 3 nucleotides then going back to the second nucleotide and reading a codon, etc. There are other possibilities, such as reading codons starting on 1, 2, 4, 5, etc. Overlapping codes will always give more coding information for the same number of bases compared to the non-overlapping code.

e.   GUGU GUGU or UGUG UGUG.

Section 7.2 - Transcription: From DNA to RNA

7-4.

In transcription, complementary base pairing with the template DNA strand is required to add the appropriate ribonucleotide to a growing RNA chain.

7.5.

DNA replication is a permanent event – the new daughter cells will each get only one copy of the DNA molecule. That one copy must serve as the template for all transcription and the template for further cell divisions. This is not true for transcription, and consequently there are several reasons why the higher level of error during transcription is tolerated:

(i) Transcription produces a transient product. mRNA molecules persist only for relatively short periods (the half life of a bacterial mRNA is typically only a few minutes, whereas those for eukaryotic mRNAs can vary from ~15 min to ~1 day), while DNA molecules must be maintained throughout and even beyond the life of the organism.

(ii) Cells contain multiple copies of each kind of mRNA. Even if a particular mRNA molecule contains critical errors that produce nonfunctional proteins, the cell has many other mRNA molecules transcribed from that same gene and the majority of them do not contain errors in critical locations.

(iii) Further, the degeneracy of the genetic code limits the effects of errors in transcription because many single errors will produce silent changes, and others will lead to conservative substitutions.

(iv) In most cases, portions of the primary RNA transcript produced by transcription will be spliced out of the molecule. For instance, only 0.6% of the dystrophin primary transcript will be present in the mature mRNA; the range for this value in different genes varies from 100% to 0.6%. Mistakes that are made in transcription of the untranslated regions (5' and 3' UTRs and introns) will have no effect on the amino acid sequence of the polypeptide.

(v) Lastly, the body produces much more protein than is actually required for most genes. Many disorders caused by lack of protein function (e.g. cystic fibrosis, muscular dystrophy, tyrosinase-negative albinism, hemophilia and other clotting disorders) are recessive. This means an individual with one nonfunctional, mutant allele and one normal, functional allele of these genes will produce only about one half the normal levels of functional protein. Yet these individuals have a completely normal phenotype. Therefore a small percentage of abnormal mRNA molecules that give rise to no protein (or perhaps even an abnormal protein) will not affect the phenotype of the individual.

7-6.

DNA sequences are generally written with the 5' to 3' strand on top and the 3' to 5' strand on bottom. If the protein coding sequence for gene F is read from left (N terminus) to right (C terminus), then top strand is the RNA-like strand which is read from 5' to 3', and the template strand must be the bottom strand of DNA. The template for gene G is the opposite since the coding sequence is read in the opposite direction (right to left). The template strand for gene G is the top strand. Note that this means the enzyme RNA polymerase moves from left-to-right along the DNA in transcribing gene F, and from right-to-left in transcribing gene G.

7-7.

The heavier lines in the figure below represent mRNAs from 2 different genes, I and II; two genes are portrayed to show that the results would be slightly different depending upon whether or not the gene has introns. In general the DNA strands form a double stranded DNA structure, except where their pairing is interrupted by the presence of the mRNA/DNA heteroduplex. Gene II pairs with the template strand of the DNA, forcing the other strand to loop out. Gene I has an intron which has been processed out of the mature mRNA. When the mRNA pairs with the template strand of DNA there is a loop-out of the DNA in the region corresponding to the intron.

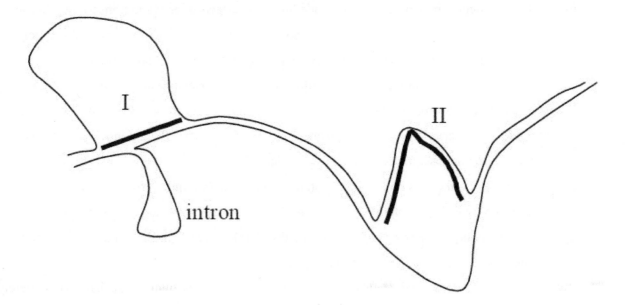

I

II

intron

Section 7.3 - Translation: From mRNA to protein

7-8.

In translation, complementary base pairing between the codon in the mRNA and the anticodon in the tRNA is responsible for aligning the tRNA that carries the appropriate amino acid to be added to the polypeptide chain.

7-9.

See Figure 7.11 for tRNA structure, 7.13 for codon/anticodon pairing, 7.16 for ribosome structure and 7.18 for translation. Assume that the complete gene sequence is shown. For part e only one codon is labeled. Part q is only present if this figure represents an mRNA from a eukaryotic cell. The following items are not found in this figure: a, d, g, i, j, n and t.

7-10.

a. This figure represents translation.

b. The next anticodon is 5' GUA which is complementary to the codon 5' UAC which codes for tyrosine. The tyrosine is added to the carboxy-terminal (C-terminal) end of the growing polypeptide chain. The protein will be 9 amino acids long when completed.

c. There are 4 other building blocks with known identities. The amino acid just placed on the carboxy-terminus of the growing polypeptide chain is tryptophan (anticodon of departing tRNA is 5' CCA which is complementary to the codon 5' UGG which codes for tryptophan). This would be the third amino acid from the protein's N terminus. The amino acid placed just after that (fourth from N-terminus) is proline, given the tRNA's anticodon of 5'GGG, corresponding to the codon 5' CCC. There is also an assumed building block with a known identity – the initiation codon (5' AUG) that starts off protein synthesis, placing the amino acid methionine at the amino-terminal (N) end of the protein. The final codon (5' UAA) is a stop condon, indicating termination of translation.

d. The first amino acid at the N terminus would be f-Met in a prokaryotic cell and Met in a eukaryotic cell. The mRNA would have a cap at its 5' end and a poly(A) tail at its 3' end in a eukaryotic cell but not in a prokaryotic cell. If the mRNA were sufficiently long, it might encode several proteins in a prokaryote but not in a eukaryote.

Section 7.4 – Differences in Gene Expression Between Eukaryotes and Prokaryotes

7-11.

Eukaryotic genes contain intervening sequences (introns) that do not code for proteins. Because they are spliced out of the primary transcript and thus are not included in the mature mRNA, introns do not have to contain open reading frames. In fact, introns almost always contain stop codons that would halt all possible reading frames. Thus, the reading frames of almost all eukaryotic genes are interrupted by introns that contain stop codons in that frame.

7-12.

a. The minimum length of the coding region is 477 amino acids x 3 bases/codon = 1431 base pairs (not counting the stop codon). The gene could be longer if it contained introns.

b. Look at both strands of this sequence for the open reading frame (remember that the given sequence is part of a protein-coding exon, so there must be an open reading frame). It occurs on the bottom strand, starting with the second base from the right (x = closed reading frames, o = open reading frames). The direction of the protein is N-terminal to C-terminal going from right to left in the coding sequence on the RNA-like strand (that is, the bottom strand of the DNA).

```
                                    xxx
        template strand     5' GTAAGTTAACTTTCGACTAGTCCAGGGT 3'
        mRNA-like strand    3' CATTCAATTGAAAGGTGATCAGGTCCCA 5'
                                                       xox

           mRNA          5' ACCCUGGACUAGUGGAAAGUUAACUUAC 3'
```

c. The amino acid sequence of this part of the mitotic spindle protein is: **N...Pro Trp Thr Ser Gly Lys Leu Thr Tyr...C**. Remember that the open reading frame begins with the second nucleotide. You cannot determine the amino acid corresponding to the A nucleotide at the 5' end of the mRNA because you don't know the first two nucleotides of the codon.

7-13.

First look at the sequence to determine where the Met Tyr Arg Gly Ala amino acids are encoded. The top strand clearly does not encode these amino acids. On the bottom strand, there are Met Tyr codons on the far right (reading 5' to 3') and Arg Gly Ala much farther down the same strand. Why aren't these codons adjacent? There could be an intron in the DNA sequence which is spliced out of the primary transcript. Thus, the mature mRNA would encode this short protein.

a. The bottom strand is the RNA-like strand, so the top strand is the template. The RNA polymerase moves 3' to 5' along the template.

b. The sequence of the processed nucleotides in the mature mRNA is shown below. The junction between exons is marked by a vertical line:

5' CCC AUG UAC A<u>G</u>|G GGG GCA UAG GGG 3'

The sequence of this mRNA contains nucleotides prior to the AUG initiation codon and subsequent to the UAG stop codon to emphasize that the mRNA does not begin and end with these codons: remember that mRNAs contain both 5' and 3'- untranslated regions (UTRs).

In fact, this problem has a simplified DNA sequence to allow the sequence to fit on the page and to facilitate your analysis of the sequence in a reasonable amount of time. If you look very carefully at the sequence, you can see that there are canonical splice donor and splice acceptor sequences at the borders between the intron and the two exons that flank it. However, the intron does not contain a canonical branch site. In reality, the shortest introns are about 50 bp long, instead of the 24 bp in the problem, and must contain branch sites.

c. A Thr residue at this position could occur if the G base on the bottom strand that just precedes the junction between the intron and the first exon (underlined in the answer to part b above) was mutated to a C. This base change would also alter the splice donor site, so splicing does not occur. The next codon after the ACG for Thr is a UAA stop codon, so the polypeptide encoded by the unspliced RNA is only three amino acids long.

7-14.

Mitochondria do not use the same genetic code! In yeast mitochondria, the codon 5' CUA 3' codes for Thr, not Leu as it does in yeast or human nuclear genes. If you want to ensure that the correct protein will be made by the yeast cell, you should mutate all the 5' CUA 3' codons in the mitochondrial gene to 5' ACN 3' before putting the gene into a chromosome in the yeast nucleus. This ensures that the cellular translation machinery will put a Thr at all positions it is required in the protein.

7-15.

a. The differences in transcription and translation prokaryotes (bacteria) and eukaryotes (humans) mean that the prokaryotic transcription and translation systems cannot produce a functional insulin protein from the human gene. For instance, the promoters for the human insulin gene may not work in *E. coli*, thus blocking transcription of the gene. One of the main problems is that the human insulin gene has introns which are transcribed into the primary transcript and then spliced out by the spliceosome. Bacterial cells do not have introns and thus have not evolved the machinery necessary to remove them from the RNA. Other eukaryotic post-transcriptional modifications such as addition of the 5'-cap are found in eukaryotes but are absent in prokaryotes. Also, the human insulin mRNA may not have sequences like the Shine-Delgarno box needed for efficient initiation of translation at the AUG. Finally, it is also possible correct folding of the polypeptide and other post translational modifications may not occur in the same ways in prokaryotic cells.

b.   To make these bacterial insulin factories, you would have to transform *E. coli* cells with a composite gene in which some parts would be from the human insulin gene and other parts from a highly expressed *E. coli* gene. The only parts of the human insulin gene that would be needed are the protein-coding sequences in the exons. These must be properly spliced together. The easiest way to get these sequences is to make a DNA copy of an insulin mRNA molecule (known as a cDNA). All of the DNA sequences controlling gene expression (promoter, Shine-Dalgarno sequence, transcription terminator) should come from an *E. coli* gene that is transcribed at very high levels.

7-16.

The order of these elements in the gene is: c; e; i; f; a; k; h; d; b; j; g.

7-17.

a.   All of these elements are in the RNA (that is, the terms are abbreviated) except the promoter (c) and the transcription terminator (g). These 2 are the only structures in this list that the RNA polymerase enzyme recognizes on the DNA. RNA processing and translation occur post-transcriptionally.

b.   a, e, f and i are found partly or completely in the first exon; a, h and k are found partly or completely in the intron (note that the splice donor site shown on the splicing figure includes nucleotides in both the upstream exon and the intron); and b, d, j and g are found partly or completely in the second exon.

7-18.

The diagram following the answer to part (q) summarizes how to approach all parts of this problem.

a. To calculate gene size, you simply add up all the exons and introns and ignore the 5'UTR and 3'UTR (because these are parts of exons): 119 + 532 + 337 + 1431 + 208 + 380 + 444 + 99 + 546 = 4096 bp.

b. To calculate the size of the primary transcript, you take the gene size (exons plus introns) = 4096 nucleotides = 4096 nt. Note that, in actuality the 5' cap and the poly-A tail at the 3' end are added very rapidly to the primary transcript, usually as it is being made prior to splicing, so some researchers consider that the primary transcript contains these modifications, as was just shown in the preceding figure. With this definition of primary transcript, you could thus add on 150 bases of poly-A tail at the 3' end: 4096 + 150 = 4246 bp. (You could also add plus one nucleotide to account for the 5' cap: 4096 + 150 + 1 = 4247 nt.

c. To calculate the size of the mature mRNA, you add up all the exons alone and add on 150 bases of poly-A tail (and possibly one nucleotide for the 5' cap): 119 + 337 + 208 + 444 + 546 + 150 (+1) = 1804 nt (1805 nt with the 5' cap).

d. To determine where the ATG initiation codon is located, compare the size of the 5' UTR to that of the first exon. Part or all of the first exon must be the 5' UTR. In this case, the 5' UTR (174 bp) is larger than the first exon (119 bp); the 5' UTR must therefore include the entire first exon plus an additional 55 bp (174-119 = 55). The second exon (337 bp) is larger than 55 bp, so the initiation codon must be in Exon 2. The first 55 bp of the second exon are thus the remainder of the 5' UTR, while (337-55 =) 282 bp of the second exon are coding sequence (that is, they correspond to the triplet codons in the mRNA). 282/3 = exactly 94 amino acids. Intron 2 is thus located in between codons.

e. You should now determine the extent of the 3' UTR in exactly the same way. In this problem, the 3' UTR is 715 bp. Exon 5 (the last exon) is 546 bp, so all of Exon 5 is 3' UTR, and the 3' UTR extends (715-546 =) 169 bp further into Exon 4. Exon 4 is more than 169 bp (it is 444 bp), so the stop codon must be in Exon 4. There is some semantic confusion about whether the 3' UTR contains the stop codon or not, but it is easiest to calculate things if you consider the 3' UTR to include the stop codon. Then the coding part of Exon 4 is (444-169 =) 275 bp.

f. No base pairs encode the 5' cap.

g. The promoter is upstream of the 5' UTR and so is not included in any of the DNA sequences listed in the problem.

h. Intron 4 [see part (e)].

i. Exon 4 contains the stop codon [see part (e)], and the codon preceding it encodes the final (C-terminal) amino acid.

j. The sequence encoding the poly-A tail does not exist in the gene (poly-A is added posttranscriptionally by poly-A polymerase).

k. We've already established that there are 282 bp of coding region in Exon 2 [see part (d)], and that this corresponds to 94 codons. This means that Exon 3 starts with the first nucleotide of a codon. There are 208 bp in Exon 3, which corresponds to 208/3 = 69.33 codons = 69 codons + one extra nucleotide. Therefore Intron 3 is placed between the 1st and 2nd nucleotide of the next codon. The coding region of Exon 4 is 275 bp [see part (e)], which corresponds to (275/3 =) 91.67 codons or 91 codons + 2 extra nucleotides. Therefore, the coding region of the gene is: 282 +208 + 275 = 765 bp. (Note: This assumes that the 3' UTR includes the stop codon and that the coding region does not include the stop codon.)

l. As explained in part (k): 94 (Exon 2) + 69 1/3 (Exon 3) + 91 2/3 (Exon 4) = 255 amino acids.

m. Intron 3 interrupts a codon [see part(k)].

n. Intron 2 is located between codons [see part(k)].

o. The sequence specifying poly-A addition is the sequence AAUAAA (or near variants of this), and this sequence occurs in the final exon of the gene (Exon 5) in the 3' UTR, and also in the primary transcript and mature mRNA. A ribonuclease cleaves the primary transcript about 20 nucleotides downstream (towards the 3' end) of this sequence, and poly-A polymerase then adds 150-200 A's.

p. As this is a normal (nonmutant) process, it could be explained by alternative splicing in which Exon 2 is connected either to Exon 4 or Exon 5, or Intron 2 is not removed at all. The 94 amino acids are those encoded by Exon 2.

q. We are assuming that, although this alternative splicing is a natural process, that this small protein has no function. Sometimes primary transcripts are spliced at low levels into alternative mRNAs with no functions; the unusual splice junctions are called "cryptic splice junctions". Assuming that this is a cryptic splice product, Intron 2 does not have codons, Exon 4 is out of frame with respect to Exon 2, and Exon 5 doesn't encode any ß2 lens crystallin protein. In any of these cases, the processed material would encode "junk" when spliced to the 2nd exon. The reason you would expect 20 amino acids of junk is because ~1/20th of the codons in the genetic code are stop codons, so you would run into a stop codon within 20 amino acids when junk is being translated if the sequence of DNA is random.

Section 7.5 – The Effect of Mutations on Gene Expression and Gene Function

7-19.

Nonsense or frameshift mutations that affect codons for amino acids near the C terminus are usually less severe than nonsense or frameshift mutations in codons for amino acids near the N terminus because less of the protein will be affected.

a. very severe effect as there will be no functional protein

b. probably mild effect if none of the last few amino acids are important for function

c. very severe effect as most of the amino acids in the protein will be incorrect

d. probably mild effect as only the last few amino acids will be affected

e. no effect, by definition a silent mutation maintains the same amino acid

f. mild to no effect as the replacement is with an amino acid with similar chemical properties

g. severe effect as the mutation is likely to destroy the protein's activity

h. could be severe if it affects the protein structure enough to hinder the action of the protein, or could be mild if the protein's function can tolerate the substitution

7.20

a. The deleted homolog has a known null activity allele for all the genes within the deletion (because the genes are not present at all). Therefore, if a mutant / deletion genotype has the same mutant phenotype as the mutant / mutant genotype, this suggests that the mutant allele has the same level of activity as an allele with known zero activity (the deletion). One limitation of this assumption is that some phenotypes have a threshold level of enzyme activity. In other words, the mutant phenotype is seen as long as the level of enzyme activity is below some critical threshold. Once the level of enzyme activity rises above this level, the phenotype becomes wild type. For example, imagine a situation where any individual has the mutant phenotype if the enzyme activity is <30%. Suppose allele *m* of an autosomal gene produces an enzyme with 20% of the activity as the enzyme encoded by the wild- type allele. Thus, an *m* /*m* individual would have 20% the enzyme activity of wild- type homozygotes, and an *m* /deletion heterozygote would have only 10% of normal enzyme activity. Because of the threshold, both of these individuals would have the same mutant phenotype, yet the *m* allele is clearly not null.

b. (i) Antibodies can be used to detect specific proteins present in *m* / *m* or *m* / deletion organisms. (ii) Molecular methods exist to detect mRNAs corresponding to particular genes. However, the inability to detect mRNA or protein does not necessarily mean that *m* is a null allele; it is always possible that protein and/or RNA is present, but below the levels of detection of these various techniques. Also, the presence of RNA or protein does not necessarily mean that the gene products retain function and that the allele is not null. (However, some geneticists use the strict definition for a null allele whereby no mRNA nor protein is made, whether it is apparently functional or not. The reason for this is that sometimes mutant RNAs or proteins could function in ways that are not apparent initially.) (iii) Finally, DNA sequence analysis of a mutant allele can often help to determine if the allele is likely to retain any function. All of these techniques will be discussed in detail in later Chapters. The bottom line is that it can be quite difficult to determine for certain whether or not an allele is null, especially if using the strict definition above.

7-21.

The size of the protein is 2532 amino acids. Thus the mRNA must be $2532 \times 3 = 7.6$ kb. To be detectable, any changes must be more than 1% of normal size or amount. The answers below are presented in the order of (i) mRNA size; (ii) mRNA amount; (iii) protein size; (iv) protein amount. A

'+' means there will be a >1% change, while a '-' means there will be no change. We assume in the answers below [excepting part (j)] that mutant mRNAs or proteins have normal stability in the cell, although this is not always true in practice.

a. − − − −. This is a nonconservative amino acid substitution changing the identity of only a single nucleotide in the mRNA and a single amino acid in the protein, so it will probably affect the ability of the protein to function normally, but it will not affect the size or amount of mRNA or protein.

b. − − − −. This is a conservative amino acid change, so it probably won't affect the function of the protein.

c. − − − −. This is a silent change, so it won't affect any detectable parameters.

d. − − + −. This is a nonsense mutation, so it won't affect mRNA size or amount, nor amount of protein. It will affect the size of the protein.

e. − − + − or +. Met1Arg could mean that no protein is made, as the ribosome can't initiate translation at an Arg codon. However, it is possible that a protein could be made if there is another downstream, in frame 5′ AUG codon that can be used to initiate translation. This second possibility would result in a smaller protein.

f. − + − +. A mutation in the promoter would most likely make it a weaker promoter, so RNA polymerase would bind less often. With less mRNA, less protein would be produced.

g. − − + −. This change would not be detectable in the mRNA, but it will cause a frameshift mutation in the protein which will obviously affect the size of the protein.

h. − − − −. A deletion of 3 bases (a codon) would remove only 1 amino acid / 2532 amino acids; this is a <1% change in size of the mRNA or protein.

i. + − + −. This mutation causes alternate splicing to occur, removing exon 19. Depending on the size of exon 19, this could easily have a >1% affect on the size of the mRNA and protein.

j. + + − +. Lack of a poly-A tail could make the mRNA noticeably smaller. It could also decrease the stability of the mRNA. If the mRNA is degraded faster then less protein will be translated.

k. − − + or − −. This substitution in the 5′ UTR could potentially affect mRNA localization or stability. It could have an affect on the amount of protein made if it affects ribosome binding, for example. Conversely, it may have absolutely no effect on the mRNA itself or how well the protein is translated.

l. − − − −. If this insertion is into an intron, then it should be spliced out of the primary transcript, producing a wild-type mature mRNA.

7-22.

a. Null mutants are those with no protein activity. (We are using the looser definition of null allele here, where nonfunctional gene product could be made.) The following changes could lead to loss of enzyme activity in the worst case scenarios: a (if this amino acid substitution blocks protein activity); b (if this amino acid substitution blocks protein activity); d (would destroy most of the protein activity); e (if there is no translation initiation); f (if promoter does not function); g (frameshift would alter most of the amino acid sequence of the protein); h (it is possible that the deletion of 1 amino acid blocks protein function or alters the tertiary or quaternary structure of the protein); i (will produce an altered protein that might be unable to function); j (could make the mRNA completely unstable); and k (losing exon 19 could inactivate the protein). In practice, mutations like j and k seem to cause less severe reductions in gene expression.

b. Any mutation that makes an altered protein with impaired function or lower levels of otherwise functional protein is likely to be recessive to wild type. Most null or hypomorphic alleles are in fact recessive, loss-of-function mutations. They are recessive because for most genes, homozygosity for the wild-type allele results in more than twice the amount of protein required for a wild-type phenotype. Loss of one of the two copies of the gene will thus not alter the wild-type phenotype. For this reason, any of the mutations in the list (except c and l) could be recessive. Those listed in the answer to part (a) are also the most likely to be recessive.

c. Any of the mutations, other than c and l, could potentially be dominant to wild type. For most of these, if the mutation was null or strongly hypomorphic there could be a dominant effect from haploinsufficiency, where one wild-type allele of the gene does not express enough gene product for a wild-type phenotype. This is true for any mutation that alters the protein product in size or amount. Any of the mutations that change the size of the protein, as well as a, b and h (which alter the protein to a lesser degree) could potentially have dominant negative or neomorphic dominant effects that would depend on the protein (for example, whether it is multimeric) and the exact consequences of the mutation. Finally, it is possible that a promoter mutation, as in f, could turn on a gene in the wrong tissue or at the wrong time, leading to a neomorphic allele due to ectopic expression. However, you should remember that most of the scenarios leading to dominant phenotypes are generally much more rare than recessive effects due to loss of function.

7-23.

Cross each of the reverted colonies to a wild-type haploid to generate a heterozygous (wild-type phenotype) diploid. Then sporulate the diploid and examine the phenotype of the spores. If the Met+

phenotype is due to a true reversion, then the cross was: *met- × met+ → met+ / met- → 2 met+ : 2 met-* . If there is an unlinked suppressor mutation in another gene, the suppressor (*su-*) and original *met-* mutation should assort from each other during meiosis: *met- su-* (phenotypically Met+) × *met+ su+* (wild type) → *met / met+ ; su- / su+* → 1 *met- su-* (Met+) : 1 *met - su+* (Met-) : 1 *met+ su-* (Met+) : 1 *met+ su+* (Met+) = 3 Met+ : 1 Met-. If the two genes are linked, you will still get the four classes but the proportions of the recombinant gametes (*met- su+* being the one you can detect as it is the only one with a Met- phenotype) will increase proportionate to the distance between the two genes. It is now possible to determine the DNA sequence of the entire yeast genome relatively inexpensively, so you could also sequence the genomes of the original met- strain and of the five apparent reversions to see whether the base pair responsible for the mutation is still present.

7-24.

a. The anticodon is complementary to the codon. The anticodon in this nonsense suppressor tRNA is 3' AUC 5'. Because the 5'-most nucleotide in the anticodon is C, the wobble rules predict that it can pair only with a 5' UAG 3' stop codon and not with any other triplet.

b. The wild-type *tRNA^{Gln}* recognizes either a 5' CAA 3' or a 5' CAG 3' codon. Only a single nucleotide was changed to turn the wild-type tRNA into the nonsense suppressor. The suppressor tRNA recognizes a 5' UAG 3' codon, so the wild-type tRNA must have recognized the 5' CAG 3' codon if only one base change occurred. The anticodon sequence in the wild-type tRNA is therefore 3' GUC 5'. The template strand employed to produce the tRNA is complementary to the tRNA sequence itself, so the sequence of the template strand of DNA for the wild- type *tRNA^{Gln}* gene is 5' CAG 3'.

c. In any wild-type cell of any species there is a minimum of one *tRNA^{Gln}* gene. The one tRNA it encodes has to be able to recognize both of the normal Gln codons, 5' CAA 3' and 5' CAG 3'. The wobble rules say that a tRNA with a 3' GUU 5' anticodon can recognize both Gln codons if the wobble U in the anticodon is modified to xm5s2U, so this would be the minimum *tRNA^{Gln}* gene number in any organism. However, B. adonis is a species that can harbor the Gln nonsense suppressing tRNA discussed in part (a). Therefore two *tRNA^{Gln}* genes must exist in a wild-type *B. adonis* cell. One would code for the *tRNA^{Gln}* (anticodon 3' GUC 5') that was changed into a nonsense suppressor, and the other gene would code for the *tRNA^{Gln}* (anticodon of 3' GUU 5') that recognizes both of the normal Gln codons.

7-25.

a. There is a progression of mutations from Pro (5'CCN, wild type) to Ser (5'UCN) to Trp (5'UGG, strain B) codons. The original wild-type proline codon must have been 5' CCG, so the sequence of the DNA in this region must have been:

5' CCG 3'

3' GGC 5'

b. The wild-type amino acid is Pro (proline). The amino acid at the same position in strain B is Trp (tryptophan). Although these are not the same amino acids, the phenotype of strain B is wild type. This means that Trp at position 5 is compatible with the function of the enzyme encoded by the gene. This fact implies that the change from Pro to Trp is a conservative substitution. The original mutation changed Pro to Ser (serine). This mutant is nonfunctional, so the Ser at position 5 is not compatible with enzyme function - it is a nonconservative substitution. Ser has an uncharged polar R group, so its chemical properties are likely to be very different than those of Pro.

c. Strain C does not have any detectable protein, so it is likely to be a nonsense mutation that stops translation after only a few amino acids have been added. One way in which thus could have happened is that the codon for Ser in the mutant (5' UCG) could have been changed by mutation to a 5' UAG. However, the nonsense mutation could also have occurred at other locations in the gene's coding region.

d. Strain C-1 is either a same-site revertant (5' UAG to sense codon) or a second site revertant (nonsense suppressing tRNA mutation). Because the reversion mutation does not map to the enzyme locus, it must be a nonsense suppressing tRNA.

7-26.

A missense suppressing tRNA has a mutation in its anticodon so that it recognizes a different codon and inserts an inappropriate amino acid. Problem 7-24 dealt with the change of the $tRNA^{Gly}$ anticodon from 3' GUC 5' to 3' AUC 5', making a nonsense suppressor tRNA. Imagine instead that the $tRNA^{Gln}$ anticodon had mutated to 3' GCC 5'. This mutant tRNA will respond to 5' CGG 3' codons, thus putting Gln into a protein in place of Arg. This is a missense suppressor.

a. Consider here the effect of the presence of a missense or nonsense tRNA on the normal proteins in a cell that are encoded by wild-type genes without missense or nonsense mutations. A missense suppressing tRNA has the potential to change the identity of a particular amino acid found in many places in many normal proteins. Using the example above of a missense suppressor that replaces Arg with Gln, most proteins have many Arg amino acids, so a missense suppressor could potentially substitute Gln for Arg at many sites in any single protein. In contrast, a nonsense suppressing mutation can only affect a single location in the expression of any wild-type gene (that is, the stop codon that terminates translation), making a normal protein longer. The longer protein will still have all of the amino acids comprising its normal counterpart. Together, these considerations mean that the presence of a missense suppressing tRNA has more likelihood of altering proteins synthesized in the cell than the presence of a nonsense suppressing tRNA.

b. In addition to the situation described above in which a mutation in a tRNA gene would change the anticodon to recognize a different codon, there are other possible ways to generate missense suppression, including: (i) a mutation in a tRNA gene in a region other than that encoding the anticodon itself, so that the wrong aminoacyl-tRNA synthetase would sometimes recognize the tRNA and charge it with the wrong amino acid; (ii) a mutation in an aminoacyl-tRNA synthetase gene, making an enzyme that would sometimes put the wrong amino acid on a tRNA; (iii) a mutation in a gene encoding either a ribosomal protein, a ribosomal RNA or a translation factor that would make the ribosome more error-prone, inserting the wrong amino acid in the polypeptide; (iv) a mutation in a gene encoding a subunit of RNA polymerase that would sometimes cause the enzyme to transcribe the sequence incorrectly.

7-27.

If a tRNA was suppressing +1 frameshift mutations, then it must have an anticodon that is complementary to 4 bases, instead of 3.

7-28.

Use the wobble rules to help solve this problem.

a. The nonsense codons that differ only at the 3' end are 5' UAG and 5' UAA. A tRNA with the anticodon 3' AUU 5' (U modified to xm5s2U) could recognize both of these nonsense codons because the U at the 5' end of the anticodon could pair with G or A at the 3' end of the nonsense codons.

b. This nonsense suppressing tRNA would suppress 5' UAA 3' and 5' UAG 3'.

c. This question asks which wild-type tRNAs could have their anticodons changed to 3' AUU 5' with a single nucleotide change. It is easier to answer this question from the perspective of the mRNA sequences. In other words, which sense codons could have mutated to become 5' UAA/G? These are: 5' CAA/G = Gln, 5' GAA/G = Glu, 5' AAA/G = Lys, 5' UCA/G = Ser, 5' UUA/G = Leu, 5' UAU/C = Tyr, and 5' UGG = Trp. Note that in the anticodons reacting with all of the codons above except the

Trp codon, a wobble U modified to xm5s2U would allow a single tRNA to recognize the codons that end with either A or G as the 3' base. A normal Trp tRNA could have a wobble U (an anticodon of 3' ACU 5'), but the wobble U would have to modified as xm5U so that the tRNA does not recognize a 5' UGA 3' stop codon; in other words, the anticodon of a normal Trp tRNA has to be specific for the codon 5' UGG.

7-29.

In the second bacterial species where the isolation of nonsense suppressors was not possible, there must be only a single *tRNA*^{Tyr} gene and a single *tRNA*^{Gln} gene. Thus, if either gene mutated to a nonsense suppressor, it would be lethal to the cell, as there would not be any tRNA that could put Tyr or Gln where they belong. In this scenario, the single *tRNA*^{Tyr} would have to have an anticodon of 3' AUG 5' to recognize the two Tyr codons of 5' UAU 3' and 5' UAC 3' based on the wobble rules. The single *tRNA*^{Gln} would have to have an anticodon of 3' GUU 5' (wobble U modified to xm5s2U) to recognize both 5' CAG 3' and 5' CAA 3' Gln codons.

7-30.

a. The mutant gene was a tRNA whose anticodon could recognize the stop codon 5' UAG 3'. Assuming that the nonsense suppressor tRNA was specific for that stop codon, the mutant anticodon sequence was 5' CUA 3' or 5' xm5UUA 3'.

b. Each M protein had a single amino acid change in its polypeptide sequence; the amino acid that the nonsense suppressor tRNA was charged with was inserted in place of the amino acid specified by the normal codon that was changed to UAG by the nonsense mutation. (Notes: (i) Even if the amino acid sequence is not identical to wild type, an M protein made from the mutant phages in the *su-* bacteria could still have wild-type function as long as the amino acid inserted by the nonsense suppressor tRNA into that specific location in the protein is compatible with the protein's function. (ii) Although the problem states that the particular mutants produce proteins with amino acid sequences different from wild type, some other M protein made from a phage with a different nonsense mutation could have a wild-type amino acid sequence if, by chance, the nonsense suppressor tRNA was charged with the amino acid specified by the original codon.)

Section 7.6 – How the Code was "Cracked"

7-31.

a. By comparing the two sequences, you can see that the 4th A from the 5' end of the wild-type sequence is deleted (-) in the mutant, and a G is inserted (+) just upstream of the "GCC" at the 3' end of the wild-type sequence. [See part (b) below.]

b. The amino acids in the wild-type and mutant proteins are shown below:

```
                        Lys  Ser  Pro  Ser  Leu  Asn  Ala
        wild-type:  5'  AAA  AGT  CCA  TCA  CTT  AAT  GCC
        3'
                            (-)                      (+)
        mutant:     5'  AAA  GTC  CAT  CAC  TTA  ATG  GCC
                    3'  Lys  Val  His  His  Leu  Met  Ala
```

The four bold amino acids between the − and + mutations other than Leu are different from wild-type.

c. Those four amino acids must not be in a crucial function domain of the protein (for example, they do not carry out catalysis), nor do they alter the overall structure of the protein significantly enough to affect its function.

7-32.

a. FC0 was a single-base insertion and FC7 was a single-base deletion nearby that restored the reading frame. A reversion of FC0 back to the wild-type sequence (deletion of the inserted base) could also have restored *rIIB*+ function.

b. The *rIIB*+ phage obtained by intragenic suppression is a double mutant (FC0 FC7) that has both a single-base insertion and a single-base deletion. In a coinfection, the double mutant *rIIB*+ can undergo recombination with the original wild-type *rIIB*+ strain – in the region between the FC0 and FC7 mutations – to generate *rIIB*- phage that are either FC0 or FC7. A true revertant cannot produce *rIIB*- progeny through recombination with wild-type *rIIB*+ phage because the true revertant and the wild-type have the same base pair sequence.

c. FC7 single mutants (*rIIB-*) produced by recombination between true wild types and FC0 FC7 double mutants have a property that distinguishes them from FC0 single mutants (*rIIB-*): Only FC7 mutants can recombine with FC0 to produce *rIIB+* phage.

d. To obtain many deletion mutations, several different intragenic suppressors of FC0 could have been obtained, including FC7; all of them are single-base deletions like FC7. Each would have been separated from FC0 by recombination with a true wild- type (*rIIB+*) strain, and the resulting *rIIB-* recombinants that are deletions distinguished from FC0 by their ability to recombine with FC0 to produce *rIIB+* phage. The resulting strains would be *rIIB-* phage with single deletion mutations. Multiple addition mutations (like FC0) could have been obtained by isolating suppressors of deletion mutants like FC7, recombining them away from FC7, etc. This process of isolating suppressors of suppressors of suppressors to obtain more and more mutations of opposite sign could go on ad infinitum.

7-33.

Glutamic acid can be encoded by either GAA or GAG. In sickle cell anemia this amino acid is changed to valine by a single base change. Valine is encoded by GUN with N representing any of the four bases. Therefore, the second base of the triplet was altered from A to U in the Hb^S allele. In Hb^C the glutamic acid codon (GAA or GAG) is changed to a lysine (AAA or AAG). The change here is in the first base of the codon. The mutation causing the Hb^C allele therefore precedes the Hb^S mutation in the sequence of β-globin gene when reading in the 5' - 3' direction that the RNA polymerase travels along the gene.

7-34.

a.   If the Asn6 (5' AAC) is changed to a Tyr residue, the nucleotide change is to a UAC. In protein B this means that the Gln (5' CAA) at position 3 becomes a Leu (5' CUA).

b.   Leu (5' CUA) at position 12 is changed to Pro (5' CCA). In protein B the Thr (5' ACU) at position 5 is still a Thr residue even though the codon is different (5' ACC).

c.   When Gln (5' CAA) at position 8 in protein B is changed to a Leu (5' CUA), the Lys codon (5' AAG) at position 15 in protein A is changed to a stop codon (5' UAG). This would cause the production of a truncated form of protein A only 14 amino acids long.

d.   This is a thought question that involves some speculation; the following are two reasonable possibilities. (1) As seen in parts a-c above, a mutation in the region of overlap has a high probability of causing alterations in both of the proteins simultaneously. Any change in this DNA sequence has the potential to affect two proteins instead of just one, and an organism would be less likely to tolerate mutations affecting the production of two proteins than mutations affecting the production of a single protein. There would thus be strong evolutionary selection against overlapping reading frames. (2) If a region of DNA evolved so as to encode a protein with a stable three-dimensional conformation, it is very unlikely that a stable protein could be produced by the sequence shifted by one nucleotide. This is because the alternate reading frame is likely to have a stop codon every 3 codons out of 64. This means that in reality, among the very few examples of overlapping reading frames that exist, either one or both of the proteins is very small, composed of only a few amino acids.

7-35.

Note that the nucleotide sequences below are written as mRNA sequences. From this you can easily convert to the DNA sequence of the gene. Remember that proflavin causes frameshift mutations (single base insertions and deletions) in the DNA. All mutagens work at the level of the DNA, even though the changes are often written at the level of the mRNA! Notice that there are several ambiguous bases in the wild-type sequence (any one of four bases possible is indicated by N; other amino acids are encoded by two different codons). Line up the invariant bases in the mutant with the wild-type and it is clear that a single base insertion occurred in the mutant. Knowing the amino acid sequence of the mutant and therefore the nucleotide sequence, all but one of the third base ambiguities in the wild type can be resolved. The mRNA sequence of the wild-type gene would be:

	Gly	Ala	Pro	Arg	Lys
wild-type mRNA:	5' GGN	GCN	CCN	AGA/G CGN	AAA/G
mutant mRNA:	5' GGN	CAU/C	CAA/G	GGN	AAA/G
	Gly	His	Gln	Gly	Lys

After comparing the wild type and mutant sequences you can see that the first nucleotide of the second codon was deleted to make the mutant sequence. The deduced DNA sequence of wild-type is:

5' GGN GCA CCA AGG AAA 3'

7-36.

a. As there are no AUGs in the RNA, polypeptides will be produced only at high Mg^{2+} concentrations. The codons in the RNA will be read as …UGU GUG UGU GUG… and so polypeptides with alternating Cys and Val amino acids will be made.

b. At low Mg2$^+$ concentrations, translation will start with AUG, and the RNA will be read as AUG CAU GCA UGC AUG …; polypeptides with repeats of Met-His- Ala-Cys will be synthesized. At high Mg2$^+$ concentrations, because translation can initiate anywhere on the RNA, the same polypeptides will be produced except they will not all begin with Met. (RNAs not read starting with AUG are read as UGC AUG CAU GCA… or GCA UGC AUG CUA…)

c. At low Mg2$^+$ concentrations, translation will start with AUG: AUG UAU GUA UGU… and thus polypeptides with the repeat Met-Tyr-Val-Cys will be made. At high Mg2$^+$ concentrations, translation can start anywhere on the RNA. This results only in polypeptides containing Met, Tyr, Val, and Cys in that order, but they will not all begin with Met. (RNAs that are not read starting with AUG are read as UGU AUG UAU GUA… or GUA UGU AUG UAU…)

7-37.

A nonsense mutation is a single nucleotide change that turns a sense codon (one coding for an amino acid) into one of the three stop codons. The change can occur at any of the three positions in the codon. The easiest way to identify such sense codons is to begin with each nonsense codon and systematically change each position to all other possible nucleotides. This gives nine different possible codons. Use the coding table to translate the resulting codons. Not all of these changes lead to sense codons – some of them will result in nonsense (STP) codons.

Stop Codon Change	UAA		UAG		UGA	
1st position	AAA	Lys	AAG	Lys	AGA	Arg
	CAA	Gln	CAG	Gln	CGA	Arg
	GAA	Glu	GAG	Glu	GGA	Gly
2nd position	UUA	Leu	UUG	Leu	UUA	Leu
	UCA	Ser	UCG	Ser	UCA	Ser
	UGA	STP	UGG	Trp	UAA	STP
3rd position	UAU	Tyr	UAA	STP	UGU	Cys
	UAC	Tyr	UAC	Tyr	UGC	Cys
	UAG	STP	UAU	Tyr	UGG	Trp

7-38.

a. Eight codons exist in RNAs made up of Us and Gs in random order: UUU, UUG, UGU, GUU UGG, GUG GGU, GGG.

b. The eight codons in part (a) correspond to six different amino acids: Phe, Leu, Val, Cys, Trp, and Gly.

c. The answers to part (a) and (b) are different because the genetic code is degenerate in that the same amino acid is specified by several different codons: UUU = Phe, UUG = Leu, UGU = Cys, GUU or GUG = Val, UGG = Trp, GGU and GGG = Gly.

d. The frequency of U is 3/4, and the frequency of G is 1/4. Therefore: $f(UUU) = (3/4)3 = 27/64$; $f(UUG) = f(UGU) = f(GUU) = 3/4 \times 3/4 \times 1/4 = 9/64$; $f(UGG) = f(GUG) = f(GGU) = 3/4 \times 1/4 \times 1/4 = 3/64$; $f(GGG) = (1/4)3 = 1/64$.

e. Phe (UUU) = 27/64; Leu (UUG) = 9/64; Cys (UGU) = 9/64; Val (GUU or GUG) = 9/64 + 3/64 = 12/64; Trp (UGG) = 3/64; Gly (GGU or GGG) = 3/64 + 1/64 = 4/64.

f. By doing this experiment, you would have been able to determine that UUU specifies Phe; that Val, Leu, and Cys are specified by codons composed of G+2U; and that Trp and Gly are specified by codons composed of 2G+U.

7-39.

a.   The protein would terminate after the His codon due to a nonsense mutation. The Trp codon (UGG) could have been changed to a either a UGA or a UAG codon. These stop codons result from changing the second or third base of the Trp codon to an A.

b.   Reverse translate the amino acid sequence: If you restrict the possibilities to mutations that substitute one base pair for another, there are four possible ways to generate a nonsense mutation from this sequence. (i) A UAG stop codon will result from a change of the second base of the Trp codon to A. (ii) If the third base of the Trp codon UGG changes to A, a UGA stop codon will result. (iii) If the Lys codon was AAA, and there is an A to T substitution at the first position, a UAA stop codon would be produced. (iv) If the Gly codon is GGA, a mutation of G to T at the first position will generate a UGA nonsense codon. There are many other changes that could cause the premature termination of the protein encoded by this sequence, for instance, the insertion or deletion of a single base pair causing a frameshift mutation. As just one example, if the Arg codon is CGU, a single base insertion in the DNA before or within this codon would lead to a UAA codon in the mRNA, with the U would come from the former Arg codon and AA from the Lys codon.

7-40.

The extra amino acids could come from an intron that is not spliced out due to a mutation in a splice site. The genomic DNA sequence in normal cells should contain this sequence. An alternative is that the extra amino acids could come from the insertion of DNA from some other part of the genome, such as the insertion of a small transposable element. In this case, the normal allele of the gene will not have this sequence. Note that the defect in this case could not be caused by a mutation that changes the stop codon at the end of the open reading frame to an amino-acid-specifying codon. If this were the case, the extra amino acids would be found at the C-terminus of the longer protein, not in the middle.

7-41.

Both strands of a double-helical DNA molecule are possible template strands. There are three possible reading frames on both the top and bottom strands. If a stop codon is found in a frame, then it is not an open reading frame (that is, the entire sequence cannot not code for a protein). Assume first that the bottom strand is the template strand, so that the top strand is the mRNA-like strand. Treat it as the equivalent to an mRNA, which means it would be translated in the 5' to the 3' direction and that you would substitute T for U to allow translation from the genetic code. Thus, the first potential reading frame begins with the first nucleotide, the second reading frame with the second nucleotide, etc. In the following sequence, an 'x' above the nucleotide means the reading frame is closed (that is, it contains a stop codon), while an 'o' means it is open. The stop codons in the top and bottom strands are shown in bold. Scan the sequence looking for stop codons (or their direct DNA equivalents: TAA, TAG and TGA). Repeat this process assuming the top strand of the DNA is the template strand and the bottom strand is the mRNA-like strand, with 3 possible reading frames beginning at the 5' end of the sequence. When you analyze this DNA sequence you find that the top strand has two open reading frames in the top strand (reading from 5' to 3' marked with an o above the first nucleotide of the open frame) and one closed reading frame (a stop codon in the frame marked with an x above the first nucleotide; these stop codons are shown in bold type). The bottom strand has one open reading frame while the other two frames are closed (reading 5' to 3').

```
        XOO
5' CTTACAGTTTAT TGA TACGGAGAAGG 3'
3' GAATGTCAAATAACTATGCCTCTTCC 5'
                          OXX
```

7-42.

a.   The physical map is based on the number of base pairs. In Figure 7.28a the physical map is represented by the red bar. On this map of the *trpA* gene in *E. coli* the distance between amino acids 1 and 10 will be the same as the distance between amino acids 51 and 60. The genetic map, shown in blue in this figure, is based on numbers of crossovers. If different regions in the gene (or genome) have different rates of crossing over, the genetic map will vary proportionally. Notice that amino acids 15 and 22 (21 nucleotides apart) are about the same genetic distance apart as amino acids 22 and 49 (81 nucleotides apart).

b.   Regions with a high rate of crossing over will have a proportionally larger genetic map relative to the physical map. Regions with a low crossover rate will appear smaller relative to the physical map. A comparison of the maps shown in Figure 7.28a, show that the N terminal 1/3 and the C terminal 1/2 of the gene have relatively high recombination rates, while the central portion of the gene has a lower rate of recombination.

7-43.

a. Yanofsky could have screened for *trp-* auxotrophs by growing wild-type bacteria in the presence of a mutagen, and then plating the culture to obtain single colonies on a plate containing minimal medium supplemented with tryptophan. Each colony on the plate would then be replica-plated onto a minimal medium plate; colonies that fail to grow on the replica plate are *trp-* auxotrophs.

b. The *trp-* auxotrophs include mutants in the gene for each enzyme in the tryptophan biosynthesis pathway. As the TrpA enzyme catalyzes the first step in tryptophan biosynthesis, the *trpA* - colonies produce all of the other enzymes in the pathway, and thus they are distinct from all the other *trp-* auxotrophs in that they are able to grow when supplemented with any downstream intermediate in the pathway.

7-44.

One aspect of the degeneracy of the genetic code is wobble: Due to unusual base pairing between the 5' base of the anticodon and the 3' base of the codon, a single tRNA species can bind to more than one codon. A further complication is that when the wobble base of the tRNA anticodon is either A or U, that base is modified enzymatically after transcription of the tRNA. In the case of wobble U, three different modifications are possible, and the particular modification dictates the base pairing ability of the anticodon. It is important to realize that the wobble base modifying enzymes recognize not just the anticodon sequence of a tRNA, but other aspects of tRNA structure (dictated by the tRNA base sequence) as well. This fact means that two different tRNAs transcribed from two different genes, both of which have the same anticodon and correspond to the same amino acid, can have their wobble bases modified differently.

a. As inosine (I) in the wobble position at the 5' end of the anticodon can pair with U, A, or C at the 3' end of the codon, anticodons with wobble base inosines must correspond to codons where 5″ XYU, 5″ XYA, or 5″ XYC all specify the same amino acid (X and Y are any two specific bases). By examining the genetic code table, you can see that those codons are: 5″ CGN (Arg), 5″ GGN (Gly), 5″ CCN (Pro), 5″ UCN (Ser), 5″ ACN (Thr), 5″ GCN (Ala), 5″ CUN (Leu), 5″ GUN (Val), and 5″ AUN (Ile) . Therefore, the anticodons that can have I as the wobble base are: 5' ICG, 5' ICC, 5' IGG, 5' IGA, 5' IGU, 5' IGC, 5' IAG, 5' IAC, and 5' IAU.

b. Remember that when U is in the Wobble position at the 5' end of the anticodon, it is modified in one of the three ways shown in Fig. 7.14. Any one type of tRNA (that is, a tRNA encoded by a single tRNA gene) with U in the wobble position is always modified in only one of these three ways (it is not the case that some molecules of one type of tRNA are modified in one way and other molecules of this type are modified in another way). Therefore, tRNAs with wobble U modified to xm5U are specific for codons whose 3' ends are G; tRNAs with wobble U modified to xm5s2U respond to codons whose 3' ends are A/G; and tRNAs with wobble U modified to xo5U will recognize codons with A/G/U (and rarely C) at the 3' ends. No matter how the wobble U at the 5' end of the anticodon is modified, it can always base pair with G at the 3' end of the codon. This fact means that the only anticodon sequence that could never be allowed to have a 5' U is 5' UUA, because whatever way this anticodon is modified, it would always base pair with the stop codon 5' UAG. Any other 5' UNN anticodon sequence could potentially be modified to xm5U so as to be specific for a single codon with a 3' base of G (5' NNG).

Certain 5' UNN codons can be modified to xm5U but not to xm5s2U and/or to xo5U. For example, 5' UAU anticodons in which the wobble U is modified either to xm5s2U or to xo5U would improperly recognize codons for both Met and Ile amino acids. However, tRNAs with 5' UAU anticodons modified to xm5U would be specific for Met as required by the genetic code. In a second example, 5' UAA codons could recognize only Leu codons if the wobble U was modified to xm5U or to xm5s2U, but if the wobble U was altered to xo5U, such a tRNA would mistakenly recognize both Phe and Leu codons.

c. As explained in part (b), xm5U can be the wobble base for all anticodons except for 5' UUA. A tRNA with a U converted to xm5s2U could recognize codons where the 3' nucleotide is A or G and the two specify the same amino acid. This includes all sense codons except 5' AUA, 5' AUG, and 5' UGG (and also excepts the stop codons 5' UAA, 5' UAG, and 5' UGA). Therefore, xm5s2U can be the wobble

base for all anticodons except for: 5″ UAU, 5″ UCA, and 5' UUA.

A tRNA with a U converted to xo5U could recognize only codons for which the

3' base could be any nucleotide and the codon would specify the same amino acid. This would include only the codons 5' CUN (Leu), 5' GUN (Val), 5' UCN (Ser), 5' CCN (Pro), 5' ACN (Thr), 5' GCN (Ala), 5' CGN (Arg), and 5' GGN (Gly). Therefore, the anticodons that would be able to have a xo5U as the wobble base are: 5' UAG, 5' UAC, 5' UGA, 5' UGG, 5' UGU, 5' UGC, 5' UCG, and 5' UCC.

d. All but one box of 4 codons in the genetic code table requires a minimum of 2 different anticodons to recognize all 4 codons in the box. Two possible scenarios for these two different anticodons include one anticodon with a wobble G for codons with 3″ base U or C, and a second anticodon with either a wobble xm5s2U for codons with 3″ base A or G or a wobble xo5U for codons with A, G, or U as the 3' base. Other scenarios involve one anticodon with a wobble I for codons with the 3' base U, C, or A, and a second anticodon with either a wobble C for codons with G as the 3' base or a wobble U modified in any of the 3 possible ways shown in Fig. 7.14. The exceptional box is the one with 5' UAN codons, as 5' UAA and 5' UAG are stop codons that do not base pair with anticodons. This box would require only one anticodon with a wobble G.

Therefore, as there are 16 boxes, the number of anticodons needed are $(16 \times 2) - 1$

$= 31$. Add one special tRNA for selenocysteine, and the minimal number of tRNAs required in humans is 32. Any of the scenarios above are possible for boxes in which all 4 codons are for the same amino acid. But only some of the scenarios would apply to boxes that contain codons for two amino acids. As an exercise, you should work out for yourself which combinations of two anticodons are possible for each such box.

7-45.

a. The mutant nucleotides are marked in red, and arrows indicate the sites of deletions or inversion breakpoints. (Inversions are 1800 rotations of a stretch of DNA sequence. For the time being, you should note that in the inverted region, the 5'-to-3' polarity of the DNA can only be maintained if the strands are flipped simultaneously with the sequence rotation.) The corresponding change to the amino acid sequence is shown below the RNA sequence.

```
wild type        5' AUG ACA CAU CGA GGG GUG GUA AAC CCU AAG
                    Met  Thr  His  Arg  Gly  Val  Val  Asn  Pro  Lys

mutant 1         5' AUG ACA CAU CCA GGG GUG GUA AAC CCU AAG
transversion                     Pro

                                        (G)
mutant 2         5' AUG ACA CAU CGA GGG UGG UAA ACC CUA AG
deletion                                    Trp  STOP

mutant 3         5' AUG ACG CAU CGA GGG GUG GUA AAC CCU AAG
transition          Thr (no change)

mutant 4         5' AUG ACA CAU CGA GGG GUU GGU AAA CCC UAA G
insertion                                Val  Gly  Lys  Pro  STOP

mutant 5         5' AUG ACA CAU UGA GGG GUG GUA AAC CCU AAG
transition                       STOP

mutant 6         5' AUG ACA UUU ACC ACC CCU CGA UGC CCU AAG
inversion                Phe  Thr  Thr  Pro  Arg  Cys  Pro  Lys
```

b. The frameshift mutations 2 and 4 (single base insertions and deletions) can be reverted with proflavin. Mutations 1, 3 and 5 are single nucleotide substitutions, either transitions (changes from one purine to the other or from one pyrimidine to the other) or transversions (changes a C-G base pair to a G-C base pair). EMS causes transitions, so it can revert mutations 3 and 5 (transition mutations) back to the original DNA sequences. Mutation 1 is a transversion, and EMS cannot change the G-C back to C-G. Often the term "reversion" is used in a more general sense, meaning simply a restoration of wild-type protein function rather than a change back to exactly the original DNA sequence. In this case, it is possible that another, non-wild-type amino acid at the mutant position will restore function. An EMS- induced transition in the mutant codon could give a functional protein. With this second meaning of "reversion", all three point mutations (1, 3, and 5) could potentially be reverted by EMS.

7-46.

Proflavin creates frameshift mutations. Thus the mutant protein is expected to have the normal amino acid sequence up until the point of the frameshift mutation (+1 insertion or -1 deletion). At the site of the frameshift mutation, the amino acid sequence of the mutant protein will change because the one of the other two reading frames in the mRNA is begin translated. A second equal (but opposite) frameshift in the gene would be expected to restore the correct frame and suppress the original mutation. This is how the intragenic suppressors located between the N terminus and the original mutation restore a functional polypeptide. Notice that the original mutant protein is shorter (110 amino acids) than the normal protein (157 amino acids). Thus the initial frameshift mutation changes the reading frame and there is a stop codon in this alternate reading frame. This stop codon terminates translation early and generates a shorter polypeptide. The second frameshift mutation of the opposite sign cannot restore function if it occurs after the premature stop codon. Because no suppressors can be identified after the original mutation (in other words, between the original mutation and the premature stop codon), we can predict that the stop codon is likely to be very close to the site of the original frameshift mutation. For example:

5'...GUG GCA AUA GAC...   Nonmutated sequence

5'...GUG GCA UAG AC....   Original frameshift mutation (-A)

5'...GUG GCA UAG AC....

In this example only an insertion in the blue region (just upstream of the U, between the U/A, or just downstream of the A) within three base pairs of the original deletion, could potentially restore the original, normal open reading frame.

7-47.

a. First, the mechanisms by which tRNA^{Pyl} and tRNA^{Sec} are charged with amino acids differ. A special Pyl tRNA synthetase exists to charge tRNA^{Pyl} with Pyl, but tRNA^{Sec} is recognized by a Ser tRNA synthetase that charges the tRNA with Ser; the Ser on the Ser-charged tRNA^{Sec} is subsequently modified to Sec enzymatically. Second, although both Sec and Pyl are encoded by nonsense (stop) codons, the way in which UGA is recognized as a Sec codon differs from the way in which UAG is used as a Pyl codon. For Sec incorporation, a special mRNA structure called the SECIS element, downstream of the UGA, prevents the ribosome from terminating translation. The tRNA^{Pyl} instead likely works like a nonsense suppressor mutant tRNA. In bacteria that incorporate Pyl into polypeptides, you might expect that for genes whose open reading frame terminates with UAG, some longer-than- normal protein would be made. Perhaps the cells can deal with these longer polypeptides if the amounts made are small, or perhaps evolution selects against the appearance of UAG codons at the end of the ORFs of genes where a longer-than- normal polypeptide product would be deleterious. Third, something about the structure of the tRNA^{Sec} and/or the SECIS element allows for unusual base-pairing of xm5U in the 5' position of the anticodon with A in the codon. The codon-anticodon interaction involving tRNA^{Pyl} does not require any non-canonical wobble.

b. The Pyl-charged tRNA^{Pyl} must get to the UAG at the ribosome before the ribosome stops translation and releases the mRNA. Also, as just described, both the Pyl incorporation mechanism and nonsense suppression could lead to the production of some longer-than-normal polypeptides.

Chapter 8   Mutation at the Molecular Level

Synopsis:

This chapter covers a lot of ground, but it's all about mutations. Mutations – changes in the base sequence of DNA – are the heart and soul of genetics. Mutations are the basis of genetic variation, the raw material for evolution, and the basic tool of genetic analysis. Now that you have been introduced to the structure of DNA and how the information in genes is used to produce specific proteins, you can understand the molecular nature of different kinds of mutations, how DNA damage or DNA replication errors can result in mutation, and how various repair mechanisms can prevent the damage or errors from causing mutation.

This chapter describes landmark experiments – particularly Beadle and Tatum's "one-gene-one-enzyme" study in *Neurospora* – that used mutations to reveal key insights into the nature of the gene,. In addition, this chapter introduces the idea that the reason mutations in genes affect an organism's phenotype is that most genes encode proteins.

As you review this chapter, be careful not to confuse the critical terms **complementation** and **supplementation**. These words sound similar, but their meanings are quite different.

Key Terms:

mutation – a change in the base pair sequence of DNA. In multicellular organisms, mutations can occur in any cell, but they are only heritable if they are passed through the gametes.

forward mutation and **reverse mutation** – mutation from a wild-type (normal) allele to a non-wild-type (mutant) allele is *forward* mutation. Changing a mutant base pair sequence back to the wild-type sequence is *reverse* mutation or **reversion**; the reverse mutants are called **revertants**.

base substitution (point mutation) – replacement of a nucleotide base by one of the other three bases; substitutions can be subdivided into **transitions** (one purine is substituted for the other purine, or one pyrimidine for the other pyrimidine) and **transversions** (a pyrimidine is replaced by a purine or *vice versa*).

deletion – removal of one or more base pairs of DNA.

insertion – addition of one or more base pairs of DNA.

somatic cells and **germline cells** – In animals, all of the body cells are *somatic cells* except for those that produce the gametes, which are the *germline cells*. Mutations can be inherited only if they occur in germline cells.

spontaneous mutation – changes in the base pair sequence that occur naturally in cells.

Spontaneous mutations are caused initially either by DNA damage due to by-products of metabolism or the environment, or by rare errors in the process of DNA replication. Regardless of their origin, mutations only become *fixed* in the DNA sequence after both strands of DNA are converted to the mutant sequence by DNA replication. The DNA-damaging processes include: **depurination** (removal of As or Gs from nucleotides); **deamination** (removal of amino groups from bases); **thymine dimerization** (joining together of adjacent Ts); and **oxidation** (for example, oxidized Gs pair with As). Mutation caused directly by errors in the process of DNA replication include incorporation of incorrect bases due to **base tautomerization** (a base in a rare form when the replication fork comes through); and **slipped mispairing** (pausing of DNA polymerase – **stuttering** – at short repeated sequences results in slippage of one of the two DNA strands and consequently either addition or deletion of repeat units).

mutagen – an agent that damages DNA and thereby promotes mutation. Mutagens include **base analogues** (molecules resembling nucleotides that can be incorporated into DNA); **X-rays** (radiation that makes double-strand breaks in DNA); **alkylating agents** (bases can be alkylated); and **intercalators** (molecules that insert between adjacent base pairs). The DNA damage caused by mutagens ultimately causes mutations either as a result of DNA replication with a damaged template, or of error-prone DNA repair.

unstable trinucleotide repeat – a region of DNA containing tandem base triplet repeats. DNA replication through the repeat region can result in mutation by slipped mispairing that increases or decreases the number of repeats. Diseases associated with unstable trinucleotide repeats (e.g., Huntington disease and fragile X syndrome) are usually due to alleles with increased repeat numbers.

base excision repair and **nucleotide excision repair** – DNA repair mechanisms in which a damaged base is removed by a specific enzyme (*base excision repair*), or an entire damaged nucleotide is removed (*nucleotide excision repair*). In both mechanisms, enzyme systems remove several nucleotides on either side of the originally damaged base, and DNA polymerases restore the missing nucleotides using the other (wild-type) DNA strand as a template for DNA synthesis.

double-strand break repair – Broken DNA initiates homologous recombination between sister or nonsister chromatids that results in rejoining of the broken DNA ends.

non-homologous end-joining (NHEJ) – a DNA repair mechanism where double-strand breaks are protected from degradation and brought together by proteins so that phosphodiester bonds may be formed by DNA ligase.

methyl-directed mismatch repair – correction of mismatched base pairs caused by DNA replication errors. Proteins recognize mismatched base pairs and remove the nucleotide in the mismatch from the newly synthesized (unmethylated) DNA strand; the new strand is repaired using the original template strand as a template for DNA synthesis.

unequal crossing-over – aberrant meiotic recombination between two similar, but different, DNA sequences (for example, two related genes) that are adjacent to each other on a chromosome and that misalign. The result can be gene *duplication*, gene *deletion*, or the formation of *hybrid genes*.

colony – a mound of bacteria growing on agar media in a Petri plate that all descend from a single bacterium. Assuming that no mutations occurred, all of the bacteria in the colony have the same genotype.

biochemical pathway – an ordered set of chemical reactions, each step of which is performed by a protein (an *enzyme*), through which an organism converts molecules it ingests or has made into different molecules that it needs.

auxotroph and **prototroph** – Bacteria that can grow on minimal medium (*prototrophs*) have no mutations in genes for biosynthetic enzymes; *auxotrophs* have a mutation in a gene encoding an enzyme required for biosynthesis of an essential molecule and thus cannot grow on minimal medium unless it is supplemented with that molecule or another compound that the auxotroph can use to synthesize it.

Ames test – an assay that determines whether or not a compound is a mutagen by testing its ability to revert auxotrophic bacteria to prototrophs.

complementation test – a genetic assay to determine whether or not two different recessive (to wild-type) loss-of-function mutations reside in the same gene. If an organism with the two mutant DNAs has a wild-type phenotype, the mutants **complement** one another; each mutant DNA provides the function that the other lacks, and so the two mutations must reside in different genes. If a mutant phenotype is observed (no complementation), then the two mutations must be in the same gene; neither mutant DNA supplies the function that the other lacks.

complementation group – a set of recessive (to wild-type) loss-of-function mutations that fail to complement each other because they are all mutant alleles of the same gene.

screen – large numbers of organisms are tested individually for a particular phenotype.

supplementation – addition of biosynthesis products (for example, amino acids) or intermediates in biosynthesis pathways to minimal media in order to support growth of auxotrophs

protein (also called a **polypeptide**) – a polymer of **amino acids** linked covalently by **peptide bonds**. The first amino acid in a protein is the **N terminus**, and the final amino acid added to the polypeptide is the **C terminus**. Proteins are important components of most cellular structures, and they constitute most of the enzymes that carry out cellular metabolism.

primary, **secondary**, **tertiary**, and **quaternary protein structure** – the sequence of amino acids in a polypeptide is its *primary structure*; some regions of polypeptides are locally ordered into α-helices or β-pleated sheets (*secondary structures*); the polypeptide chain as a whole folds into a characteristic three-dimensional shape (*tertiary structure*); often, separate polypeptides interact to form multisubunit structures (**multimers**) whose three-dimensional configuration is the *quaternary structure*.

Unifying Principles of Mutation and DNA Repair:

- **Mutation and DNA replication are intimately associated:**

    (1) Mutations can occur as mistakes in DNA replication.

    (2) If DNA is damaged, mutations can become fixed in the DNA sequence permanently if the damage is not reversed before the next round of DNA replication.

    (3) Because of reasons (1) and (2), the more rounds of DNA replication, the greater the chance that mutations can occur and become fixed in the DNA sequence.

    (4) Important DNA repair mechanisms involve DNA replication (see below). Such DNA repair pathways can cause a mutation to be fixed in the DNA sequence if they use the mutant base in a mismatched pair as the template.

- **DNA repair usually works in one of three general ways:**

    (1) Removal and resynthesis: A damaged or mispaired nucleotide is removed; that DNA strand is degraded on either side of that nucleotide to create a single-stranded gap; and finally DNA polymerase uses the complementary DNA strand as a template to synthesize a new DNA strand containing the correct base.

    (2) Homologous recombination: A double-strand break in a DNA molecule can initiate homologous recombination with a sister or nonsister chromatid, resulting in repair of the break during the process of recombination.

    (3) Non-homologous end-joining (NHEJ): A double-strand break in DNA can be repaired by proteins that simply bring the broken ends together so that DNA ligase can reform the phosphodiester bonds.

Complementation Tests in Diploid Organisms:

Complementation testing is a key technique in genetics whose purpose is to establish whether independently obtained mutations producing abnormal phenotypes are in the same gene or in different genes. A complementation test is quite simple: You simply cross the two mutant strains and then look at the phenotype of the F_1 progeny. If the F_1 display a mutant phenotype (no complementation), the parents have mutations in the same gene; if the F_1 are wild type, the parents harbour mutations in different genes and the two mutations complement each other.

It is critical to note that a complementation test can be interpreted in this way only if the two mutations result in a loss-of-function and are both recessive to the corresponding wild-type allele. The reason is that the test is asking whether the gamete from one parent can supply a function that the other gamete is lacking, and *vice versa*. For example, if the two mutations are in different genes, one parent could be written as *aa BB* and the other parent as *AA bb*. The F_1 progeny would be *Aa Bb*, and the F_1 phenotype would be wild type because one gamete supplies the function of gene *A* and the other the function of gene *B*. The two mutations complement each other. If instead the two mutations were in the same gene, the parents would have both been *aa* and the progeny would also have been *aa*; here the mutations fail to complement each other. When two different mutations fail to complement, the F_1 will have a mutant phenotype whose nature depends on the dominance relationship between the two alleles.

Scientists studying biological pathways often collect mutants for a particular trait (for example, flies with unusual eye colours) and then perform all pairwise complementation tests to determine which mutants are allelic. A **complementation group** is simply a collection of mutants that *fail to complement* one another in all pairwise crosses; all the members of a complementation group are simply different mutant alleles of the same gene.

Supplementation and the Dissection of Biochemical Pathways:

Beadle and Tatum asked whether **supplementation** of minimal media with any of the chemical intermediates in the arginine biosynthesis pathway could support growth of specific Arg⁻ auxotrophs that had previously been separated into complementation groups. It is important not to confuse supplementation with complementation. Supplementation asks at which point in a biochemical pathway a gene's protein product functions, while complementation defines which mutations are allelic. The results of these analyses are not necessarily synonymous. As just one example, two different mutations may affect a single step in a biochemical pathway, yet be in different complementation groups if the enzyme catalyzing that step is a multimer of different subunits.

Problem Solving:

Many of the problems in this chapter ask you to interpret data from complementation tests (*complementation matrices*) or from supplementation experiments.

Interpreting complementation matrices. A complementation matrix is simply a table that shows the results of all pairwise complementation tests. Usually, a "–" symbolizes no complementation, and a "+" means that the mutant pair complement. Analysis of complementatation matrices enables you to assign all of the mutants to *complementation groups*, and thereby figure out how many different genes are mutant among your collection of mutants. The simplest way to do this is to first look at all the boxes with a "–" in them; list all the mutants that *don't complement* each other. This process should sort the mutants into complementation groups (groups of alleles of different genes). Next, verify your list by looking at the boxes with "+"s in them. Make sure that all the mutants within each complementation group *do complement* those in other complementation groups. This should be the case if the data given are internally consistent. Make sure to notice any mutants that complement all of the other mutants; these represent complementation groups containing only one allele, and count as genes represented in your collection.

Interpreting supplementation experiments. If an auxotrophic mutant grows in the presence of an intermediate compound, the gene must encode an enzyme that functions at some step prior to the formation of that intermediate. Therefore, if there is a mutation early in the pathway, providing later intermediate compounds will allow growth because the subsequent enzymes are available. The blocked point has effectively been bypassed in these cases. If no growth is observed, the gene product functions subsequent to the formation of that intermediate compound. Remember that the final product is the compound on which all the mutants will grow.

Not all biochemical pathways display this simple linear pattern. For example, some pathways may branch, leading to the formation of more than one essential end product. Mutants affecting a step prior to the branch point will grow only if supplemented with all the end products, while those affecting a step after a branch point require supplementation only with the molecule at the end of that branch.

Solutions to Problems:

Vocabulary

8.1. i, **1, 2, 6**; ii, **2, 3**; iii, **4, 8**; iv, **5, 8**; v, **1, 2, 6**; vi, **4, 7**; vii, **5, 9.**

Section 8.1 - Mutations: Primary Tools of Genetic Analysis

8-2. We are told the trait in the pedigree is very rare. The trait is first seen in individual III-1 and shows a vertical pattern of inheritance between generations III and IV, suggesting a mutation that is dominant to the wild type. The mutant gene cannot be X-linked because male IV-1 inherits it from his father. Thus **the trait is autosomal dominant**, yet it is not seen in generations I and II.

It is possible that the mutant allele is incompletely penetrant. In this case one individual in generation I and one individual in generation II (either II-2 or II-3) have the mutant allele but do not display the trait.

A second possibility is that a mutation occurred in the germ line of either II-2 or II-3, producing a gamete with the dominant autosomal mutation. This gamete was then used to form III-1 (the *propositus* or *proband* – the person in a pedigree with the phenotype in question who is first investigated).

There are two potential ways to discriminate between these hypotheses. First, more information about this trait from a more extended family pedigree or from pedigrees of other families might indicate whether the trait is or is not completely penetrant. A pedigree where the trait appears suddenly in a generation, disappears in the next generation, and then reappears in a following generation would argue for incomplete penetrance. Second, if you could obtain DNA sequence information for the gene in question from II-2, II-3, and III-1, you could see if one of the alleles of the gene in the propositus has a mutation not found in his parents.

8-3. Each independently derived mutation will be caused by a different single base change. When you find a base that differs in only one of the sequences, that base is the mutation. Determine the wild-type sequence by finding the base that is present at that position in the other two sequences. The wild-type sequence is therefore:

5' ACC GTA G̲TC GAC T̲GG T̲A̲A ACT TTG CGC G 3'

8-4. Dominant mutations can be detected immediately in the heterozygous progeny who receive the mutant gamete (see problem 8-5). **Recessive mutations can only be detected when they are homozygous. To detect the appearance of new recessive alleles, you must perform a testcross with a recessive homozygote.** Testcrosses can be done in mice, where the researcher can control the mating, but it cannot be done in humans.

8-5. Of the achondroplasia births observed, 23/27 are due to new mutations because no family history of dwarfism exists. Achondroplasia is an autosomal dominant trait, so it will be expressed in the child that receives the mutant gamete. There were 120 000 births registered, so there were 240 000 parents in which the mutation could have occurred during meiosis, leading to a mutant gamete. **The mutation rate = 23 mutant gametes/240 000 gametes = 9.5×10^{-5}. This rate is somewhat higher than 2 to 12×10^{-6} mutations per gene per generation, which is the average mutation rate for humans.**

8-6. To ensure that the mutants you isolate are independent you should follow procedure #2. If you follow procedure #1, a mutation causing resistance to the phage could have arisen several generations before the time when you spread the culture; thus, several of the colonies you isolate could be descendants of the same cell and have the identical mutation. Different mutations in the same gene often give different information about the role of the gene product. Geneticists therefore generally strive to find many independent, different mutations in the same gene in order to understand as much about the gene as possible.

8-7. Kim's hypothesis is that the bacteriophages are able to induce resistance in ~1 in every 10^4 bacteria. If she is right, then several (~10 if there are 10^5 bacteria on each plate) of the colonies on each of the replica plates should contain resistant cells that will continue to grow after exposure to phage. **If Kim is corrct, resistant colonies will be distributed in random locations on the three replica plates**. Maria's hypothesis is that the resistant cells are already present in the population of cells they plated on the original (master) plate. If she is right then some of the colonies on the original plate (about 10 of them) should have already contained multiple resistant bacteria that will allow colonies to grow on the phage-treated replica plates. **If Maria is right, resistant colonies will appear at the same locations on all three of the replica plates (Figure 8.6b)**.

8-8. Since the mutation is not found in the somatic tissue (blood) from any of the parents in generation II, **the mutation must have occurred in the germ line of one of the parents. This parent must be II-2** since the two affected children had the same father but different mothers. However, mutations are rare, so how can III-1 and III-2 have exactly the same mutation? **The mutation must have occurred in the germ line of II-2 at a point before the formation of separate sperm.** In the male germ line, cells called spermatogonia divide mitotically to make many cells that will subsequently undergo meiosis (primary spermatocytes; see Figure 3.20). **It is likely that a mutation occurred in an early spermatogonial cell, leading to a large proportion of spermatocytes and therefore a large proportion of sperm in the testes that carry the same mutation. This pedigree suggests that the testes of II-2 exhibit germline mosaicism** - some of the spermatocytes carry the mutation while others do not.

Note that this inference is similar to the pattern seen in Hypothesis 2 of the Luria-Delbrück fluctuation test (Figure 8.5): **If a mutation occurs early in the growth of a bacterial colony (or in the mitotic division of the germ line), then many of the cells in the colony (or in the germ line) can have the mutation. Germline mosaicism in which a large proportion of the germ line carries a new mutation is likely to be rare because the mutation must occur early in the multiplication of the germ line. At this early stage there are fewer cells than later, so fewer chances exist for mutations to occur.**

8-9. Several equal aliquots of each of the 11 culture tubes could be spread on different Petri plates. If differences in the Petri plates are not a factor, every plate corresponding to a single one of the 11 culture tubes should contain approximately the same number of colonies.

8-10. Since the germ cells that produce human sperm undergo mitosis continually, the older the father, the more mutations, on average, each of his sperm contains. Recall that the fixation of mutation requires DNA replication (Figure 8.7). Human females, on the other hand, are born with all (or most) of the eggs that they are ever going to have, so maternal age is a much smaller factor in the accumulation of gene mutations. In addition, female germ cells underwent a far smaller number of mitoses than the germ cells of even a young, 20-year-old male. Because mutant alleles of a variety of genes are likely to promote autism, the correlation between autism and older fathers makes sense.

Section 8.2 – Molecular Mechanisms of Mutation

8-11. Without the Balancer X chromosome, X-ray-induced mutations on the irradiated X chromosome and the *Bar* mutation on the non-irradiated X chromosome could recombine in the germ line of the F_1 females. The experiment would be uninterpretable because Bar eyes would no longer serve as a marker for males that inherited no alleles from the irradiated X chromosome. Therefore, **the Balancer was crucial because, by preventing the appearance of recombinant X chromosomes in the gametes of the F_1 females, it enabled the absence of non-Bar-eyed F_2 males to signify that an irradiated X chromosome contained a lethal mutation** (that is, a mutation in an essential gene).

8-12. In all of these cases, a purine is replaced by the other purine, and a pyrimidine is replaced by the other pyrimidine; **all of these mutagens cause transitions**.

8-13.

a. *Essential* genes are those that produce a recessive lethal phenotype when mutant - if one such gene doesn't function because of a mutation, the animal does not live. H.J. Muller's control results showed that 0.3% of the females produced only wild-type (non-Bar) sons. Thus, these females had a recessive lethal mutation on the (non-irradiated) X chromosome with the *Bar* mutation. In other words, mutations in essential genes on the X chromosome occur at a rate of 3×10^{-3} mutations per gamete (3/1000 or 0.3%). The average spontaneous mutation rate for *Drosophila* genes is 3.5×10^{-6} mutations per gene per gamete. Therefore, 3×10^{-3} X-linked lethal mutations per gamete / 3.5×10^{-6} mutations per gene per gamete = **857 essential (lethal) X-linked genes**. This estimate depends on the accuracy of the estimate for the average mutation rate per gene in *Drosophila*.

b. The estimated 857 essential genes on the X chromosome / 2283 total genes on the X chromosome x 100 = **37.5% of the genes on the X chromosome are essential**. Although this is a rough figure, it matches fairly well to other estimates made with other techniques suggesting that only 1/4 - 1/3 of the genes in the *Drosophila* genome are essential. In other words, 66-75% of the genes in the genome could be disrupted by mutation and the flies could still survive.

c. Clearly the mutation rate has increased with exposure to X-rays, demonstrating that X-rays are mutagenic. Genetics became much easier to do because scientists could increase the chances they would find rare mutations. (H.J. Muller received a Nobel Prize for this finding.) You can calculate the average mutation rate per gene upon exposure to this dosage of X-rays if you use the answer to part *a* indicating the number of essential genes. There are 857 essential genes on the X   chromosome x (X-ray induced mutation rate/gamete) = 0.12 X-linked lethal mutations/gamete.   Thus **the X-ray induced mutation rate = 0.12/857 = 1.4 x 10^{-4}**. In other words, this high dosage of X-rays has **increased the mutation rate about 40-fold** over the spontaneous rate (1.4 x 10^{-4} / 3.5 x 10^{-6}).

8-14.

a. EMS induced new mutations in the *dumpy* gene in the sperm of the treated males. However, as shown in Figure 8.15, EMS-induced mutations are fixed in both strands of the DNA only after two rounds of DNA replication. **The DNA in the *dumpy* gene of a sperm just treated with EMS would have one DNA strand with the normal G and the other DNA strand with an ethylated G (G*)**. This sperm now fertilized a *dumpy* mutant egg. **After several rounds of DNA replication and mitosis, some cells will have the normal G:C base pair, while other cells will have a *dumpy* mutant A:T base pair**. An animal in which different cells have different genotypes is called a *mosaic* and will be described in more detail in other chapters. **The phenotype of the fly that grows from this fertilized egg would depend upon which particular cells in the body had the wild-type or mutant sequence of the *dumpy* DNA**. This fact explains why one wing might be short and the other long. **Whether or not the new dumpy mutation in the F$_1$ animals can be transmitted to future progeny depends on whether or not some of the cells in the germ line carried the mutant A:T base pair.**

b. If the progeny of the second cross have short wings, then the germline cells of their F$_1$ male parent carried the mutant A:T base pair. Many rounds of DNA replication are involved in producing the male germ line from the zygote. Therefore, **these progeny are not mosaics because they have received an A:T base pair from their F$_1$ parent in which both DNA strands are mutant; these progeny will have two short wings.**

8-15. A perfect reversion is a very rare event, even when induced by two-way mutagens. Such a reversion demands one particular change in the exact same base pair that was originally mutated (Figure 8.5b). These kinds of reversion events can normally be seen only in experimental organisms like bacteria or bacteriophage where it is possible to examine so many individuals that rare events can be detected.

a. Figure 8.15 shows how the base analogue 5-bromouracil (5-BU) can cause a T:A to C:G substitution. 5-BU can sometimes behave like thymine and sometimes like cytosine. In the figure, 5-BU behaves like T (because it base pairs with A), but then shifts to a state where it behaves like C, so that during replication, DNA polymerase will incorporate a G in the newly forming strand. **5-BU is a two-way mutagen**. A reversion can occur if 5-BU is incorporated into DNA in the C-like state; the DNA will then have a 5-BU:G base pair. If the 5-BU shifts into its alternative form during replication, it will act like a T, so the result will be a 5-BU:A base pair; following the next round of DNA replication, the result will be T:A.

b. **Hydroxylamine is a one-way mutagen** because it changes C to hydroxylated C (C* in the figure), and C* can only pair with A. This will yield a T:A pair after the next round of replication. Hydoxylamine cannot mutagenize this.

c. **Ethylmethane sulfonate (EMS) is a two-way mutagen** because it can modify either G or T. Figure 8.15 shows that ethylated G (G*) pairs with T, resulting in a G:C to A:T substitution. If EMS now ethylates T forming T* (this part is not shown in the figure), then the modified T will pair with G. This will result in an A:T to G:C substitution which is an exact reversion.

d. Nitrous acid changes C to U and also A to hypoxanthine. Figure 8.15 shows how this mutagen can cause both a C:G to T:A substitution as well as a reverse T:A to C:G substitution, making it a **two-way mutagen**.

e. **Proflavin is a two-way mutagen** because it can add a single base pair or delete a single base pair; the same base pair that was added can be deleted.

8-16. The mutagen induces mutations in somatic cells, not in gamete-producing cells in the germ line. These somatic cell mutations give rise to the tumour cells. When the tumour cells are injected into a new mouse, they will divide in an uncontrolled manner and cause a tumour to develop. **The somatic mutation that caused the original cell to become cancerous is not present in the germline cells of the mouse.** Thus, the cancer phenotype cannot be inherited in a Mendelian fashion.

8-17.

a. DNA in most organisms is not exposed to high levels of aflatoxin B_1. It is therefore unlikely that most cells would have evolved genes for enzymes that could directly remove the aflatoxin B_1 from guanine, or a glycosylase that could specifically remove the adduced guanine-aflatoxin B_1 base (as in base excision repair). **The nucleotide excision repair system is most likely to repair damage due to aflatoxin B_1.** This system would treat the adduct in a similar fashion to a thymine-thymine dimer, which is also a bulky group that distorts the double helix (review Figure 8.17). **It is also possible that the SOS-type error-prone repair system will repair aflatoxin B_1 damage.** Most other repair systems make less sense. Methyl-directed mismatch repair is unlikely because the mutagen works independently of DNA replication. Double-strand break repair is not involved because this mutagen does not produce double-strand breaks.

b. This new information changes the picture somewhat. Apurinic (AP) sites are intermediaries in base excision repair, so **AP endonuclease and other enzymes in the base excision repair system could remove the damage** (review Figure 8.16). A glycosylase would not be required because the adduct removes itself from the sugar. It is also known that **SOS repair systems can work at AP sites, adding any of the 4 bases at random** across from the AP site during DNA replication.

8-18.

a. **Yes; particular mutagens can revert only particular types of mutations. Proflavin, for example, can revert only single base insertions or deletions. The Ames test deals with this issue by testing potentially mutagenic compounds for their ability to revert *his⁻* strains that have different types of mutations at the molecular level.**

b. **A wild-type (*his⁺*) strain could be grown in the presence of a potentially mutagenic compound (plus rat liver enzymes) and then plated for single colonies on minimal medium + histidine. Replica-plating on minimal medium (without a histidine supplement) would identify colonies that are *his⁻*; they would fail to grow.**

c. **Identification of forward mutations as described in part *b* is through a *screen*, not a *selection*.** In the technique used to find forward mutations after exposure to the compound, both His⁺ and His⁻ colonies were allowed to grow, and they were "screened" by replica-plating for the His⁻ mutant phenotype. **Even though the forward mutation rate is higher than the reversion rate, this screening process is much more labour-intensive than the *selection* that is employed when testing for revertants.** In the selection for *his⁺* revertants, millions of bacteria can be spread on a single Petri plate containing minimal medium and only the rare revertants will form colonies, making them simple to identify and quantify even though the reversion rate is low.

8-19. Yes. The rat liver supernatant contains enzymes that convert substance X to a mutagen, and *his*⁺ revertants occur. Our livers contain similar enzymes that process various substances, converting them into other forms that cause mutation and could lead to cancer.

8-20.

a. As shown in Figure 8.8b, deamination of (nonmethylated) cytosine converts it to uracil. A base excision repair pathway, in which uracil glycosylase enzyme removes the uracil and a cytosine is replaced opposite the G on the other DNA strand, usually corrects the problem before DNA replication fixes it permanently in the DNA. **A reasonable hypothesis to explain the fact that methylated CpG dinucleotides are hotspots for point mutation would be that a thymine glycosylase enzyme does not exist in human cells, because unlike uracil, thymine is a normal component of DNA.** In reality however, thymine glycosylase enzymes *do* exist in humans, and they remove Ts from T-G base pairs caused by deamination of methylated cytosines. However, thymine glycoyslases are much less efficient enzymes than uracil glycosylases, and so errant Ts formed by deamination of 5–methylcytosines are less frequently repaired than Us, resulting in a high frequency of C-G to T-A transitions.

b. The frequency of each base is 1/4, and thus the expected frequency of CpG at a given location in the genome is the same as that of any particular dinucleotide: $1/4 \times 1/4 = $ **1/16 ≈ 6.25%.**

c. **Any CpG dinucleotides in the genome that are not important functionally would mutate to TpG over time.** Another interesting idea is that evolution may select against some CpG dinucleotides whose methylation could have deleterious consequences.

Section 8.3 - What Mutations Tell Us About Gene Structure

8-21. The formal difference between albinism and leucism is that the former affects only melanin formation or deposition, while the latter affects all skin pigments, not just melanin.

a. The progeny of two albinos will be either be **white (albino)** because the albino parents are both homozygous for recessive alleles of the same gene **or coloured** due to *complementation* (if the albino birds are homozygous for recessive alleles of different genes).

b. The progeny of two leucistic birds can be **either white** (if the leucistic birds are homozygous for recessive alleles of the same gene) **or coloured** (if the leucistic birds are homozygous for recessive alleles of different genes) due to *complementation*.

c.   The progeny of a mating between an albino bird and a leucistic bird will be **coloured** because the parents are necessarily homozygous for recessive alleles of different genes.

8-22. Do a complementation test by mating the two mice. If the mutations in each mouse are in the same gene, all the progeny will be mutant (albino). If the mutations causing albininsm in each mouse are in different genes, all the progeny will be wild type (the mutations will complement each other).

8-23.

a.   **Each complementation test involves taking pollen from a plant homozygous for one mutation and using it to fertilize ovules from a plant homozygous for another mutation. This creates plants heterozygous for the two mutations.** The diagonal (mutant 1 crossed with mutant 1, mutant 2 crossed with mutant 2, etc.) represents self-fertilization; a recessive mutation cannot complement itself. **A '-' indicates a lack of complementation and the resulting plants have serrated leaves. A '+' means that the two mutations complement each other, and so the resulting plant has wild-type leaves with smooth edges. The coloured boxes in the table represent crosses that were not done because the information is redundant** (that is, the same crosses had already been done in the opposite direction with the parents switched). For example, a cross with mutant 1 pollen and mutant 2 ovules will produce the same kinds of progeny as a cross with mutant 2 pollen and mutant 1 ovules.

b.   If a box has a '-' then the two mutants must be in the same complementation group or gene. If the box has a '+' the two mutations are in different complementation groups or genes. From the results given, mutation 1 is in the same complementation group as mutation 3 (-). Mutation 1 is in a different complementation group than mutation 2 (+). Therefore, mutation 2 must be in a different complementation group than mutation 3 (+). Mutation 1 is in a different complementation group than mutation 5 (+), which is also in a different group than mutation 6 (+). Mutation 2 and mutation 6 are in the same group (-). Mutations 3 and 4 are both in the same group as mutation 1 (both -). **The completed boxes are circled in the following diagram**.

	1	2	3	4	5	6
1	-	+	-	(-)	+	(+)
2		-	(+)	(+)	(+)	-
3			-	-	(+)	(+)
4				-	(+)	(+)
5					-	+
6						-

c.   There are **3 complementation groups or genes. One includes mutations 1, 3, and 4. A second group has mutations 2 and 6. The third consists only of mutation 5.**

8-24.

a. Assuming that the man and woman represented in the pedigree in <u>Figure 2.45c</u> each have a recessively-inherited form of albinism then **this is a complementation test**. In this example, **the two albinism-causing mutations are in different genes** (complement each other) and none of the children is albino. If the two mutations were in the same gene, then all of the children should be albino.

b. Complementation tests upon demand are not possible in humans. One way to tell if a trait can be caused by mutations in more than one gene (that is, the trait exhibits *locus heterogeneity*) is to **map the mutations in a number of independent families**. Mapping involves recombination analysis of the gene causing the mutant trait with other markers. If the mutations in different families map to different chromosomes or are far apart on the same chromosome, then they must be in different genes. If the mutations map close to each other on the same chromosome, they may or may not be in the same gene. For example, the two mutations could be in adjacent, closely-related genes such as the red and green photoreceptor genes shown in <u>Figure 8-30c</u>. In such a case, researchers can determine the DNA sequence of these closely-related genes in various mutant individuals to see if the mutations affects the same gene. All of these techniques will be described in detail in later chapters.

c. Again, as explained in part *b* above, you can try to **map the dominant mutations or analyze the DNA of candidate genes** you think might be involved in the conditions.

8-25.

a. The data shown is a complementation matrix. Analysis of the matrix (see suggestions at the beginning of this chapter's Solutions Manual) indicates that **there are two complementation groups and therefore two genes**.

b. **The complementation groups are (1, 4) and (2, 3, 5)**.

8-26. In this problem, rare recombination events in the region between different mutations in the *rosy* (*ry*) gene (the ry^{41} and ry^{564} alleles are mutations in distinct nucleotides) during meiosis in *Drosophila* females produce wild-type (ry^+) chromosomes in the progeny.

a. Diagram the cross:

$$Ly^+ \, ry^{41} \, Sb \, / \, Ly \, ry^{564} \, Sb^+ \, ♀ \times ry^{41} \, / \, ry^{41} \, ♂ \; \to \; 8 \; Ly \cdot ry^+ \, Sb \text{ and lots of } ry \text{ progeny}$$

Recombination events within the *rosy* gene, between the two *ry* mutations in the heterozygous female, generate the eight offspring with wild-type eyes. As shown in the following diagram, such a recombination event will produce one recombinant gamete with a wild-type *rosy* gene, thus giving a ry^+ phenotype in the progeny of this cross. The reciprocal recombinant gamete will be a double mutant, $ry^{41} \, ry^{564}$, which will yield *ry* progeny indistinguishable from the parental type *ry* progeny. The wing and bristle phenotypes of those eight recombinant offspring are a consequence of the order of the ry^{41} and ry^{564} alleles with respect to the flanking markers, the *Ly* and *Sb* genes. Try both orientations of the two *ry* mutations with respect to the flanking markers to see which order produces $Ly \, ry^+ \, Sb$ as the result of a crossover between the *rosy* mutations.

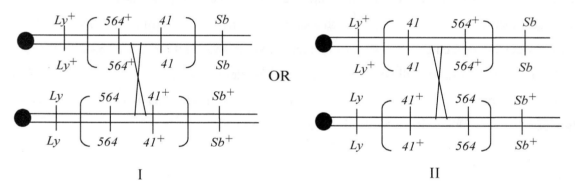

I   OR   II

Orientation II produces the $Ly \, ry^+ \, Sb$ recombinants obtained, so the order must be: $Ly \, [ry^{41} \, ry^{564}] \, Sb$. (The brackets around the two *ry* mutations shows that these are alleles of the same gene.)

b. We assume the $ry^{41} \, ry^{564}$ progeny are found in equal numbers to the ry^+ recombinants (even though we cannot discriminate them from the other *ry* progeny), so the **recombination frequency** = **(8 + 8) / 100 000 = 0.00016 = 0.016%. The distance between ry^{41} and ry^{564} = 0.016 m.u.**

Section 8.4 - What Mutations Tell Us About Gene Function

8-27. Designate the genes and alleles. The *W* gene product converts a colourless (white) pigment to green. The *G* gene product converts green to blue flowers; the mutant (nonfunctional) allele is *g*. Either of two gene products *B* or *L* can convert blue to purple flowers; *b* and *l* are the mutant alleles. Diagram the cross. Note that both parents are *WW*. All progeny will be *WW*, and it will not affect the array of phenotypes in the progeny. For this reason, it is not considered in this cross:

gg BB LL (green) x GG bb ll (blue) → F$_1$ GgBbLl (purple) → F$_2$:

$3/4$ *G–* x $3/4$ *B–* x $3/4$ *L–* = $27/64$ *G– B– L–* (purple);

$3/4$ *G–* x $1/4$ *bb* x $3/4$ *L–* = $9/64$ *G– bb L–* (purple);

$3/4$ *G–* x $3/4$ *B–* x $1/4$ *ll* = $9/64$ *G– B– ll* (purple);

$3/4$ *G–* x $1/4$ *bb* x $1/4$ *ll* = $3/64$ *G– bb ll* (blue);

$1/4$ *gg* x $3/4$ *B–* x $3/4$ *L–* = $9/64$ *gg B– L–* (green);

$1/4$ *gg* x $1/4$ *bb* x $3/4$ *L–* = $3/64$ *gg bb L–* (green);

$1/4$ *gg* x $3/4$ *B–* x $1/4$ *ll* = $3/64$ *gg B– ll* (green);

$1/4$ *gg* x $1/4$ *bb* $\times$ $1/4$ *ll* = $1/64$ *gg bb ll* (green)

The ratio is 45 purple : 16 green : 3 blue. You can see why the problem specified that the green parent was mutant in only a single gene, as *gg bb LL* or *gg BB ll* plants would still be green yet would yield a very different ratio of phenotypes in the F_2.

8-28.

a. Diagram the cross:

  orange x black $\rightarrow$ F_1 brown

The problem says that orange is caused by one autosomal recessive mutation and black is caused by another. This information implies that the two mutations are in different genes, and therefore the F_1 is doubly heterozygous. Thus, the cross is: *BB oo* (orange) x *bb OO* (black) $\rightarrow$ F_1 *Bb Oo* (brown) $\rightarrow$ F_2

And the underlying genotypic ratio of the F_2 is:

  9 *B– O–* : 3 *B– oo* : 3 *bb O–* : 1 *oo bb*.

The phenotypic ratio depends on the order of orange and black in the pathway to brown. If the pathway is orange $\rightarrow$ black $\rightarrow$ brown, with the O^+ gene product carrying out the conversion from orange to black and the B^+ gene product catalyzing the conversion from black to brown, **the F$_2$ would have 9 brown (*B– O–*), 3 black (*bb O–*), 4 orange (*B– oo* or *bb oo*).** In other words, *oo* (orange) would be epistatic to both alleles of gene *B*. **If the order were black $\rightarrow$ orange $\rightarrow$ brown,** with the O^+ gene product carrying out the conversion from black to orange and the B^+ gene product catalyzing the conversion from orange to brown, **the F$_2$ would have a 9 brown (*B– O–*): 3 orange (*bb O–*) : 4 black (*B– oo* or *bb oo*) ratio.** In this case, black (*oo*) is epistatic to both alleles of gene *B*.

b. If there are two pathways, one producing orange (requiring the O^+ gene product) and the other black (requiring the B^+ gene product), then there would be four different phenotypes in the F$_2$ generation: **9 brown (*B– O–*) : 3 black (*B– oo*) : 3 orange (*bb O–*) : 1 nonpigmented (*bb oo*).**

8-29.

a. Diagram the crosses:

1. blue x white → F$_1$ purple → F$_2$ 9 purple : 4 white : 3 blue

2. white x white → F$_1$ purple → F$_2$ 9 purple : 7 white

3. red x blue → F$_1$ purple → F$_2$ 9 purple : 3 red : 3 blue : 1 white

4. purple x purple → F$_1$ purple → F$_2$ 15 purple : 1 white

Two observations apply to the four crosses:

(1) All four crosses show modifications of the 9:3:3:1 ratios in the F$_2$, implying that 2 genes are controlling the colours.

(2) In all 4 crosses, the purple phenotype corresponds to the "*A– B–*" class.

Remember that the parents are pure-breeding.

Cross 1. *AA bb* (blue) x *aa BB* (white) → *Aa Bb* (purple) → 9 *A– B–* (purple) : 4 *aa – –* (white) : 3 *A– bb* (blue)

Cross 2. *AA bb* (white) x *aa BB* (white) → *Aa Bb* (purple) → 9 *A– B–* (purple) : 7 *aa – –* + *– – bb* (white)

Cross 3. *AA bb* (red) x *aa BB* (blue) → *Aa Bb* (purple) → 9 *A– B–* (purple) : 3 *A– bb* (red) : 3 *aa B–* (blue) : 1 *aa bb* (white)

Cross 4. *AA bb* (purple) x *aa BB* (purple) → *Aa Bb* (purple) → 15 *A– – – + – – B–* (purple) : 1 *aa bb* (white)

b. **The simplest biochemical pathways that could explain the data are diagrammed** as follows. In each case, the dominant alleles of genes *A* and *B* encode proteins (A and B, respectively) that perform the conversions indicated, and the recessive alleles are nonfunctional. Recall from Chapter 2 that in Cross 1, *bb* is epistatic to *A*; in Cross 2, gene *A* and gene *B* are complementary; in Cross 3, genes *A* and *B* work in independent pathways and so do not interact; in Cross 4, gene *A* and gene *B* are redundant.

1. colourless $\xrightarrow{A}$ blue $\xrightarrow{B}$ purple

2. colourless1 $\xrightarrow{A}$ colourless2 $\xrightarrow{B}$ purple *or* colourless $\xrightarrow{A,\ B}$ purple

3. colourless $\xrightarrow{A}$ red

   colourless $\xrightarrow{B}$ blue   (red pigment + blue pigment = purple)

4. colourless $\searrow^{A}$

   colourless $\nearrow_{B}$ purple

c. **Cross 2:** The results of this cross series are compatible with with two possible pathways. In one scenario, proteins A and B are separate enzymes that perform successive conversions. In a second pathway, proteins A and B are subunits of a single enzyme, and both subunits are required for the enzyme to function.

d. Assuming that "tightly linked" means that the distance between the A and B genes is 0 m.u. (no crossing-over occurs between the two genes), we can rewrite all four of the crosses as: $A\,b\,/$ $A\,b$ x $a\,B\,/\,a\,B \rightarrow F_1\,A\,b\,/\,a\,B$ (selfed) $\rightarrow$

    $1\,A\,b\,/\,A\,b : 2\,A\,b\,/\,a\,B : 1\,a\,B\,/\,a\,B.$

    The F_2 phenotypes for each cross are:

    Cross 1. 2 purple ($A\,b\,/\,a\,B$) : 1 blue ($A\,b\,/\,A\,b$) : 1 white ($a\,B\,/\,a\,B$)

    Cross 2. 2 purple ($A\,b\,/\,a\,B$) : 2 white ($A\,b\,/\,A\,b + a\,B\,/\,a\,B$)

    Cross 3. 2 purple ($A\,b\,/\,a\,B$) : 1 red ($A\,b\,/\,A\,b$) : 1 blue ($a\,B\,/\,a\,B$)

    Cross 4. all purple ($A\,b\,/\,a\,B + A\,b\,/\,A\,b + a\,B\,/\,a\,B$)

Note that if any recombination occurs between the two genes, then recombinant $a\,b$ gametes will be produced, allowing the emergence of white F_2 plants ($a\,b\,/\,a\,b$) in Crosses 3 and 4. The smaller the distance between genes A and B, the more the ratios will resemble those shown above. The greater the distance between the two genes, the more the ratios will resemble those in part a.

8-30. First, order the compounds from final product to first one in the pathway. The final compound is the one on which all of the mutants in the pathway will grow; you were told in the question that the final product is G, and you can see in the table that the data supports that idea. The compound before that (E in this example) is the one that allows all the mutants except one class to grow. Continue working toward the beginning of the pathway in this manner.

Chapter 8

Next, order the mutants. Again, you can do this by working backwards from the final product through the intermediates. Start by looking for the mutant that grows only when supplied with G; in this problem it is mutant 2. The mutation must be in the gene encoding the enzyme catalyzing the last step in the synthesis of compound G. Then look for the mutant that grows only when supplied with G or one other intermediate. Mutant 7 can grow only when supplied with intermediate E or with G. This verifies our earlier assignment of E as the intermediate that precedes G, and it also tells us that the gene in which mutation 7 is located encodes the enzyme that allows the synthesis of E. In this way, continue working back through the pathway to get the answer.

$$X \xrightarrow{6} F \xrightarrow{1} D \xrightarrow{5} A \xrightarrow{3} C \xrightarrow{4} B \xrightarrow{7} E \xrightarrow{2} G$$

8-31.

a. This problem is solved in the same manner as problem 8-30. The mutants all complement each other, meaning that each inactivates a different gene. Briefly, one mutant can grow only when supplemented with C, so C must be the final intermediate before thymine, etc. Mutant 21 cannot grow with any supplement other than thymine itself, so it must block the final step in the pathway (the conversion of C to thymine), etc. **The pathway is:**

$$X \xrightarrow{18} D \xrightarrow{14} B \xrightarrow{9} A \xrightarrow{10} C \xrightarrow{21} \text{thymine}$$

b. **Double mutant 9 and 10 accumulates B**; single mutant 9 would also accumulate B. In both cases, conversion of B to A is blocked by mutant 9, causing accumulation of B. The additional block of the conversion of A to C in the double mutant is inconsequential when no A is being made. By similar logic, **double mutant 10 and 14 accumulates D**. You can see the general rule here is that the mutant that acts first in the synthesis pathway dictates which compound accumulates.

8-32. To solve this problem involving a branched biosynthetic pathway, consider first only those mutants that are defective solely in biosynthesis of one amino acid. The mutants defective in only the proline pathway are those that grow when given proline in the media but not when given glutamine. Mutants 2, 6, and 1 are of this type. No intermediate exists that allows the growth of mutant 2, so the defect must be in the final enzyme that produces proline. Working backward from this point in the pathway, mutant 6 grows when supplied with intermediate A, so A is the final intermediate and mutant 6 is blocked in the step that leads to A. Mutant 1 grows when supplied with intermediates E or A, indicating that E is prior to A in the proline pathway.

Now conduct the same analysis for glutamine. Mutants 7 and 4 are only defective in glutamine biosynthesis. Mutant 4 grows only on glutamine, while mutant 7 grows when supplied with B or glutamine, indicating that mutant 7 is blocked in the production of B, and mutant 4 cannot convert intermediate B to glutamine.

Finally, look at the mutants that are defective in both glutamine <u>and</u> proline biosynthesis. Mutants 5 and 3 are of this type. Mutant 3 grows only if given intermediate C, so it must be blocked just prior to this step. Mutant 5 grows if given C or D, so it is blocked prior to the D intermediate. This represents the first part of the pathway that is used both in proline and glutamine biosynthesis.

Putting all of this information together, we have the following branching pathway:

$$X \xrightarrow{5} D \xrightarrow{3} C \begin{array}{c} \xrightarrow{7} B \xrightarrow{4} \text{glutamine} \\ \searrow_1 E \xrightarrow[6]{} A \xrightarrow[2]{} \text{proline} \end{array}$$

8-33.

a. This should be a **successful treatment** because the normal plasma contains both vWF and factor VIII. The **effect should be immediate** because both factors are present, **and prolonged** because vWF stabilizes factor VIII.

b. This **treatment should not be successful** because vWD plasma has neither vWF nor factor VIII.

c. This should be a **successful treatment** because the haemophilia A plasma contains vWF even though it does not have factor VIII. The **effect should be delayed** because the patient has no factor VIII and the added vWF will only stabilize factor VIII newly synthesized by blood cells in the patient, and this takes time. The **effect should also be prolonged** because vWF stabilizes factor VIII.

d. This should be a **successful treatment** because the normal blood contains both vWF and factor VIII. The **effect should be immediate** because both factors are present, **and prolonged** because factor VIII in the transfused plasma is already stabilized.

e. This **treatment will not be successful**. The vWD plasma has neither vWF nor factor VIII, and the patient cannot synthesize any factor VIII.

f. This **treatment should not be successful**. Neither the patient's blood nor the transfused plasma has any factor VIII.

g. This treatment **should be successful, but only after a delay** to allow the patient's blood cells to synthesize enough factor VIII that can be stabilized by the injected vWF. The **effects should be prolonged** because of the stabilization.

h. This **treatment should be unsuccessful** because no factor VIII can be made.

i. This treatment **should be successful immediately** because you are injecting factor VIII, but the **effects will be only very short term** because the injected factor VIII will be degraded in the absence of vWF.

j. This treatment **should be successful immediately, and the effects will be prolonged** because the patient's blood has vWF which can stabilize the injected factor VIII.

8-34. The data represent complementation experiments done at the biochemical level in the test tube. The results suggest that **there are 2 different X-linked genes that cause haemophila when mutant. Individuals 1 and 2 are mutant in one gene (call it gene A) and individuals 3 and 4 are mutant in the other gene (gene B).** Individuals 1 and 2 thus lack the function of one factor needed for clotting, while 3 and 4 lack a different factor. When the two kinds of blood complement (as in the mixture of blood from individuals 1 and 3), clotting occurs because the blood of each patient supplies the factor lacking in the other patient.

Several types of biochemical pathways involving possible functions of the products of these two genes are consistent with the data. The two genes could encode enzymes that sequentially convert a compound in the blood serum into an end-product that is required for clotting. Another of several possibilities is that one of the proteins (say A) is the substrate for a reaction catalyzed by enzyme B, and this reaction produces a needed clotting factor. The results exclude a pathway in which the product of one of these genes (say the A gene) is required for the synthesis of the protein encoded by the other gene (B). In such a case, the blood plasma of a patient mutant for gene A would have neither protein A nor protein B, so the mixture of mutant plasmas would have no source of compound B. (The plasmas are cell-free so new proteins could not be synthesized.)

As an interesting historical sidelight, the cited article in the *British Medical Journal* was published in the December 27th (Christmas) issue of 1952. The first patient whose blood could complement that of most other haemophiliacs in the test tube (thus indicating the existence of two different kinds of X-linked haemophilia) was a 5 year old boy whose family name was Christmas. Because of these facts, the rarer form of the disease, usually called haemophilia B, is still often called Christmas disease.

8-35.

a. **Two loci are needed**, one for the α-globin polypeptides and one for the β-globin polypeptides.

b. Assuming that both alleles of both genes are expressed as polypeptides at the same levels, then you would see 1 α1 : 1 α2 for the 2 forms of the haemoglobin α subunit and 1 β1 : 1 β2 for the forms of the β subunits. The α subunits will form the following sorts of dimers: 1 α1α1 : 2 α1α2 : 1 α2α2. The β subunits will assemble into dimers in the same way, giving a genotypic monohybrid ratio of: 1 β1β1 : 2 β1β2 : 1 β2β2. In order to figure out the types of hetero-tetramers and their frequencies, apply the product rule to the 2 monohybrid ratios: **1 α1α1 β1β1 : 2 α1α2 β1β1 : 1 α2α2 β1β1 : 2 α1α1 β1β2 : 4 α1α2 β1β2 : 2 α2α2 β1β2 : 1 α1α1 β2β2 : 2 α1α2 β2β2 : 1 α2α2 β2β2.**

8-36. The particular subset of supplements that will support growth of any specific Arg⁻ mutant is dictated by the order of the chemical reactions in the arginine biosynthesis pathway (Figure 8.25c). Only four different complementation groups are possible because the pathway consists of only four steps, each catalyzed by a unique enzyme encoded by a single gene. A particular Arg⁻ mutant will grow only on supplements that are pathway intermediates downstream of the blocked step in the pathway. The reason is that a mutant lacking the enzyme for that (blocked) step nevertheless contains the enzymes for all the upstream and downstream steps. The upstream enzymes and chemical intermediates are rendered irrelevant by the downstream block. However, the same is not true for the downstream enzymes and intermediates; if supplied an intermediate downstream of the blocked step, the downstream enyzmes present can use it to make arginine. Therefore, it is logical that the subsets of intermediates that are able to support arginine biosynthesis in any one mutant represent all of the intermediates downstream of the step catalyzed by the mutation.

The theoretical Arg⁻ mutants shown would not be found because in every case, the subsets of intermediates that support growth are not contiguous in the pathway. In other words, in each case, there is a pathway intermediate that fails to support growth which is located downstream in the arginine biosynthesis pathway of one that does support growth.

Section 8.5 – A Comprehensive Example: Mutations That Affect Vision

8-37. In unequal crossing-over, the homologous chromosomes align out of register according to DNA sequence similarity between related, but different genes (see the following diagram). **The result of crossing-over is a homologue with a duplication, β (δ/β), and a homologue with a deletion, β/δ.** The genes with a slash and enclosed in parentheses indicate hybrid genes.

As a point of interest not asked in the problem, these globin genes have differences even though they are very similar in DNA sequence. One of the more important differences between the δ and β genes is the time of expression. In these hybrid genes the regulatory region of the β gene may have been replaced with the regulatory information of the δ gene, or *vice versa*, so the hybrid gene may be expressed inappropriately (that is, during the wrong time in development). In addition, the polypeptides formed from the hybrid genes may affect the affinity of haemoglobin for oxygen in unpredictable ways.

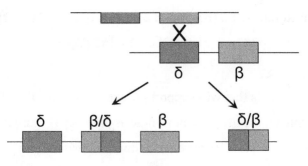

8-38.

a. The information in the problem is that most mammals, including New World primates, are dichromats
    (two kinds of photoreceptors), while Old World primates are trichromats (three kinds of
    photoreceptors). Primates diverged from mammals 65 million years ago (65 Myr), while Old World
    primates diverged from each other about 35 Myr ago. This information means that the final gene
    duplication event that led to different red and green photoreceptors most likely occurred in the lineage
    leading to the trichromatic Old World primates (like humans), but not in the lineage leading to the
    dichromatic New World primates (like marmosets). This interpretation dates the final gene duplication
    event to some time subsequent to 35 Myr. Since all mammals have rhodopsin plus at least two colour
    photoreceptors, you can also conclude that the two previous gene duplication events that led first to the
    blue gene and then to the green gene occurred some time prior to 65 Myr. **These conclusions can be
    summarized by annotating <u>Figure 8.30d</u> as shown in the following figure:**

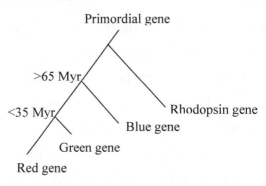

b. We assume here that only one allele for the autosomal receptor gene exists. For the X-linked receptor
    gene, any given female monkey will have two alleles while any male will only have one. **Males will be
    dichromats**, as they have only two kinds of photoreceptors: They are homozygous for the autosomal
    receptor gene but are hemizygous for the X-linked gene. However, **there will be 3 classes of males
    that see colours in different ways. Females can be dichromats** if they are homozygous for an allele
    of the X-linked gene, again there will be 3 classes. **Females can also be trichromats** if they are
    heterozygous for this gene, and there are 3 different combinations: 1-2, 1-3, and 2-3.

c. The fact that 95% of our receptors work best in low light conditions suggests that **early mammals were most active at night.** Natural selection would have favoured ancestors with the best night vision.

8-39.

a. Tetrachromats must have four different kinds of photoreceptor proteins. As shown in the following diagrams, men and women both have two copies of the autosomal blue photoreceptor gene (*darker blue rectangles*; one on each homologue). However, because the X chromosome has a red gene and green gene (*red* or *green rectangles*), **females have** an additional 2 X-linked photoreceptor gene copies and thus **a total of 6 photoreceptor genes, while males have only 4 photoreceptor genes. Males can become tetrachromats only if 1 of their blue photoreceptor genes is a mutant** that produces a photoreceptor with a different spectral sensitivity than the normal blue receptor (*light blue rectangle*). Females, on the other hand, can be tetrachromats if any one of their 6 photoreceptor gene copies make a receptor with altered spectral sensitivity (*light blue* or *yellow rectangles*). (This answer assumes that all of the retinal cells do not inactivate the same X chromosome.) **The chance that one of 6 genes will acquire such a mutation is obviously much higher than the chance that a single gene will do so.**

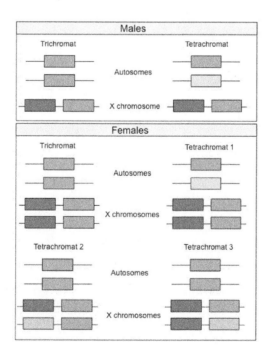

b. **A non-colourblind woman who has red-green colour blind sons will have X chromosomes like those of Tetrachromat 2 or 3 in the figure for part *a* above. The sons who inherit her X chromosome that lacks either a normal red or green photoreceptor gene will be colour blind.**

c. A rare XY male could be a tetrachromat if **he has 3 different photoreceptor genes on an X chromosome that was a product of unequal crossing-over between red and green genes** (Figure 8.31d): a red gene, a green gene, and a red/green hybrid that encodes a photoreceptor with a different spectral sensitivity than either the red protein or the green protein.

Chapter 9   Mutation at the Chromosomal Level

Synopsis:

Previous chapters mainly addressed point mutations – changes in single base pairs. This chapter is about different sorts of mutations that change the organization of entire chromosomes, or alter the number of chromosomes in each nucleus. These large-scale mutations can affect phenotype at the level of individual genes, but in addition they can affect meiosis, and thereby an organism's fertility and the genetic make-up of gametes it produces. Transposable elements – DNA segments that can move around the genome – are included in this chapter not only because their mobility can be considered to be a type of chromosomal reorganization, but also because transposable elements are a major cause of the other kinds of chromosomal rearrangements discussed in this chapter.

Key Terms:

deletion – a chromosomal mutation where a segment of DNA – sometimes a large region that contains several genes – is missing from the chromosome.

duplication – a chromosomal aberration where a segment of DNA (often large enough to contain many genes) is present twice on the chromosome. The two identical DNA segments are adjacent in **tandem duplications**, while the repeated segments are in different chromosomal locations in **nontandem duplications**.

inversion – a chromosomal aberration where a segment of the DNA is rotated 180° with respect to its normal orientation. To maintain the 5'-to-3' orientation of the chromosome strands, the Watson and Crick strands in the inverted region must also be flipped. An inversion is **pericentric** if the inverted region includes the centromere, and **paracentric** if the inverted region does not include the centromere.

reciprocal translocation – a chromosomal rearrangement where parts of two nonhomologous chromosomes switch places.

rearrangement breakpoints – the locations on rearranged chromosomes where the DNA was broken and then stitched back together (or recombined aberrantly). At rearrangement breakpoints, DNA sequences that would not normally be adjacent to each other are now juxtaposed.

gene dosage – the number of gene copies in a cell or organism. In a monoploid, the normal "dose" of single-copy genes is 1, while in a diploid, the normal "dose" is 2.

deletion loop – when homologous chromosomes pair during meiosis I in a deletion heterozygote, the structure formed by the segment of the nondeleted homologue that has no counterpart with which to pair on the deleted homologue.

inversion loop – When homologous chromosomes pair during meiosis I in an inversion heterozygote, a "loop" must form to allow the inverted and normal homologues to pair in the region of the inversion.

balanced gametes and **unbalanced gametes** – gametes with normal dosages of all genes are *balanced*; gametes with abnormal dosages of some genes – often due to deletions and/or duplications – are *unbalanced*. If the dosages of a sufficient number of genes are unbalanced, the zygotes formed from such gametes will not survive.

unequal crossing-over – aberrant crossovers between two homologues that misalign during meiosis I in a DNA region where two or more similar copies of a nucleotide sequence exist. When unequal crossing-over occurs, one recombinant chromosome loses copies of the repeated sequence, while the other recombinant chromosome gains copies.

crossover suppressor – describes a chromosome that contains an inversion and therefore in inversion heterozygotes prevents recovery of recombinant progeny for alleles within the inversion.

balancer chromosome – a chromosome made by researchers as an experimental tool that has numerous inversions preventing recovery of any recombinant chromosomes at all from a heterozygote. Commonly-used balancer chromosomes also carry a recessive lethal mutant (so that Balancer homozygotes do not survive) and a dominant phenotypic marker to distinguish the Balancer from the other chromosome in heterozygotes.

semisterility – a phenotype shared by heterozygotes for inversions or reciprocal translocations because a large fraction of the gametes they produce are genetically imbalanced.

pseudolinkage – the phenomenon where genes on two nonhomologous chromosomes behave as if they are linked because the organism is heterozygous for a reciprocal translocation. Pseudolinkage is observed for genes close to the translocation breakpoints because only one of three possible segregation patterns for the two chromosomes produces balanced gametes.

Robertsonian translocation – reciprocal exchange between two acrocentric chromosomes that results in a large metacentric compound chromosome and a small chromosome that is sometimes lost.

transposable elements (TEs) – segments of DNA that move from place to place in the genome by a process called **transposition**. Two classes of TEs exist: **DNA transposons** mobilize by a "cut-and-paste" mechanism that involves only DNA; **retrotransposon** mobilization is through transcription of the element into an RNA intermediate.

transposase – *trans*-acting protein encoded by DNA transposons that catalyzes their transposition by acting on the inverted repeats at the transposon ends. **Autonomous elements** are transposons with intact transposase genes; **nonautonomous elements** have mutant or deleted transposase genes but can mobilize nevertheless through the activity of transposase from autonomous elements in the same family.

euploid and **aneuploid** – Cells with complete sets of chromosome are *euploid*; if one or more chromosomes is missing from a set, or if extra chromosomes are present, the cells or organisms are *aneuploid*.

ploidy – describes the number of chromosome sets in a cell. **Monoploids** have one set, **diploids** have two sets, **polyploids** have more than two sets: **triploids** have three sets, **tetraploids** have four sets, etc.

monosomy and **trisomy** – forms of aneuploidy in diploids. In *monosomy*, an otherwise diploid cell is missing one chromosome, while in *trisomy*, an extra chromosome is present in addition to the two complete sets.

Turner syndrome and **Klinefelter syndrome** – abnormal human phenotypes due to X chromosome aneuploidy. Females who are XO have *Turner syndrome*; the phenotype includes unusually short stature and sterility due to lower than normal doses of X-linked genes. Males with more than one X chromosome (typically XXY) have *Klinefelter syndrome*; the phenotype includes unusually tall stature and sterility due to abnormally high X-linked gene dosages.

meiotic nondisjunction – the failure of homologues to separate during meiosis I, or the failure of sister chromatids to separate during meiosis II, resulting in aneuploid meiotic products.

Down syndrome – the phenotype in humans caused by chromosome 21 trisomy; sometimes called **trisomy 21**.

basic chromosome number (*n* or *x*) – the number of chromosomes that constitute a complete set.

autopolyploids – polyploids where all of the chromosome sets originated from the same species.

allopolyploids – usually sterile hybrids with complete chromosome sets from different, though related, species. **Amphidiploids** are fertile allopolyploids made by crossing two diploid species, and then doubling the chromosome number to generate homologous pairs.

gene family – a group of genes with similar base pair sequences and similar functions that derived from a single ancestral gene.

syntenic segments – regions of chromosomes in two different species where the genes and gene order are conserved.

Problem Solving:

As you approach the problems – keep several important general concepts in mind:

• Rearranged chromosomes can affect the functions of particular genes that are located at or near rearrangement breakpoints.

Chapter 9

- The rearrangement breakpoint can interrupt the gene and abolish its function (e.g., Figure 9.16), or connect parts of two genes together to make a *fusion* gene whose products may have novel functions (e.g., Figure 9.20).

  - The rearrangement breakpoint may put a gene in an environment that alters its expression. One possible scenario is that the rearrangement now juxtaposes a gene normally found in euchromatin to a position next to heterochromatin. The heterochromatin can spread, leading to *position-effect variegation* (review Chapter 11). Another possibility is that the coding region of the gene is placed nearby an enhancer for a different gene, causing misexpression. (The *Antennapedia* mutation in *Drosophila* that results in the development of a leg coming out of the fly's head is one example of this kind of event.

- Chromosomal rearrangements, and also changes in chromosome number such as aneuploidy, alter gene dosage. Decreased or increased dosage of some genes may have little or no obvious effects, but changes in the dosage of specific genes may alter phenotypes (e.g., Figure 9.13) or even in rare cases result in lethality. Almost always, rearrangements creating imbalances in the dosage of many genes causes lethality.

- Rearranged chromosomes, and also changes in ploidy, can affect the process of meiosis – the way chromosomes pair, cross over, and segregate into gametes. For this reason, when predicting the expected gametes from an individual who is heterozygous or homozygous for a chromosomal rearrangement (or from an individual with an unusual number of chromosomes), it is critical to diagram the pairing of homologous chromosomes at meiosis I. These diagrams will ensure that you understand the chromosome composition of the individual and the kinds of gametes this individual can produce.

  - Remember to trace out the meiotic products beginning from the centromere, because the chromosomes are pulled to the spindle poles by fibres that attach to the kinetochores that form at the centromeres. Keeping track of the centromeres is particularly important when considering heterozygotes for inversions and translocations.

  - Pay attention to whether or not the meiotic products are balanced (with one allele of each gene and one centromere). If the meiotic products are unbalanced either for many genes or for the centromere, then the progeny formed from them are usually inviable.

- **Deletions.** One sign of the presence of a deletion is the "uncovering" of recessive mutant alleles: That is, a heterozygote for the deletion may show a mutant phenotype that is normally recessive, if the non-deleted homologue carries a copy of the gene with the recessive allele and the deleted homologue has no copy of the same gene. Another indication of the presence of a deletion is the fact that in deletion heterozygotes, no recombination will be observed for genes in the deleted region, and the map distances for genes outside the deleted region will be reduced.

- **Inversions.** Severe reduction of recombination is also a sign that heterozygosity for an inversion may be involved. Single crossovers within the inversion loop lead to recombinant gametes that are unbalanced for genes outside the loop. Interestingly, all gametes have the expected amount of DNA for everything within the inversion loop. If the centromere is in the inversion (*pericentric*) then each meiotic product has a centromere. If the centromere is outside of the inversion loop (*paracentric*) then the meiotic products that result from a single crossover within the loop are unbalanced for the centromere as well as for some genes – one recombinant product will be *dicentric* while the other will be *acentric* (see Figure 9.18).

- **Reciprocal Translocations.** In a translocation heterozygote, only the products of the *alternate* segregation pattern are balanced, while the products of the *adjacent-1* and *adjacent-2* patterns are unbalanced (see Figure 9.21). This fact underlies two indications that an individual might be a translocation heterozygote. (1) *Semisterility* – less than half the gametes produced by a heterozygote for a reciprocal translocation will be balanced, so many zygotes formed from the gametes produced by this individual will be inviable. (2) *Pseudolinkage* – genes known normally to be on nonhomologous chromosomes will act as if they are genetically linked.

- **Changes in Ploidy.** The central ideas to consider in dealing with problems involving non-diploid, non-euploid chromosome numbers are that chromosome pairing is essential for proper chromosome segregation during meiosis I, and that pairing requires exactly two homologous chromosomes. If chromosomes cannot pair, they will missegregate and unbalanced gametes will result. One possible way to overcome this issue in non-diploid but euploid cases (either in nature or in experiments) is to disrupt cell division so as to create cells that now have two copies of each separate chromosome, creating polyploids. These two copies can now pair with each other and segregate properly.

Solutions to Problems:

Vocabulary

9.1. i. **4**; ii. **8**; iii. **6**; iv. **5**; v. **7**; vi. **3**; vii. **2**; viii. **1**.

Section 9.1 - Rearrangements of Chromosomal DNA

9-2.

a. *Deletion 1* removes the DNA homologous to Probe A and Probe B, while *Deletion 2* removes the DNA homologous to Probe B and Probe C.

Del1   Del2

b. Note that the order of the probes along the non-deleted chromosome (+) is telomere-A-B-C-centromere.

Del1   +

c. *Inv1* is a *pericentric* inversion. This means that one breakpoint of the inversion is in the middle of Probe A (as shown in the diagram in the text) while the other breakpoint of the inversion is on the other side of the centromere. This will have three effects: (i) Probe A will hybridize to two separate locations that will be located on different arms of the inverted chromosome. (ii) The centromere will shift location relative to its position in the normal (non-inverted) chromosome. Because the instructions say that the other breakpoint of the inversion is near the centromere, in this case the inversion will change the chromosome from a metacentric to a more acrocentric configuration. (iii) Probe B and Probe C will be found, along with part of Probe A, on the long arm of the chromosome in the order shown in the diagram that follows.

Inv1   +

d. In contrast with *Inv1*, *Inv2* is *paracentric*, meaning that both rearrangement breakpoints are found on the same side of the centromere and that the centromere stays in the same relative position on the chromosome as found in the normal homologue. The inversion moves Probe C away from the other two probes to a position closer to the centromere. (The problem stated that the other inversion breakpoint not shown in the figure is close to the centromere.)

e. See answer to part *d* above for a description of the hybridization of the three probes to the *Inv2* chromosome.

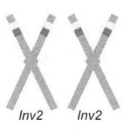

Section 9.2 – The Effects of Chromosomal Rearrangements

9-3.

a. (i) **No.** Loops will not be seen in a heterozygote for a reciprocal translocation. Instead, during prophase of meiosis I, a cruciform structure will form (see Figure 9.21b). (ii) **No.** Chromosomal bridges form consistently only during prophase of meiosis I in a heterozygote for a paracentric inversion (Figure 9.18b), not in a heterozygote for a reciprocal translocation..(iii) **No.** Same as answer to part (ii). (iv) **No,** The apparent suppression of recombination occurs only during meiosis in a heterozygote for an inversion, not in a heterozygote for a reciprocal translocation. (v) **Different chromosomes.** A reciprocal translocation involves two nonhomologous chromosomes.

b. (i) **Yes,** (Figure 9.17). (ii) **Yes, if recombination occurs within the inversion loop** (Figure 9.18b). (iii) **Yes, if recombination occurs within the inversion loop** (Figure 9.18b). (iv) **Yes.** (v) **Same side of a single centromere** (this is the definition of a paracentric inversion).

c. (i) **Yes.** A loop will form during meiosis I in a heterozygote for a duplication because the extra copy of the region cannot pair with any DNA sequences in the normal homologue. (ii) **No.** [See answer to part (a ii).] (iii) **No.** [See answer to part (a iii).] (iv) **No.** The apparent suppression of recombination occurs only during meiosis in a heterozygote for an inversion, not in a heterozygote for a tandem duplication. (v) **Same side of a single centromere.** Note that the duplicated region cannot include the centromere because the result would be a dicentric chromosome that could not be maintained when the cells divide.

d. (i) **No.** (ii) **No.** (iii) **No.** (iv) **No.** (v) **Different chromosomes.** [Same reasoning as for part *a*; a Robertsonian translocation is one subtype of reciprocal translocation.]

e. (i) **Yes**. (ii) **No**. (iii) **No**. (iv) **Yes**. (v) **Opposite sides of a single centromere**. Heterozygotes for pericentric inversions will behave similarly to heterozygotes for paracentric inversions as was described in part *b* with the following exceptions: Chromosome bridges and acentric chromosomes are formed consistently only during prophase of meiosis I in a heterozygote for a paracentric inversion, not for a pericentric inversion (Figure 9.18b). And by definition, in a pericentric inversion the centromere is within the inverted region, so the rearrangement breakpoints must be on opposite sides of the chromosome's centromere.

f. (i) **Yes**. See Figure 9.8 for a diagram of a deletion loop. (ii) **No**. (iii) **No**. (iv) **Yes**. The region of the normal chromosome that is removed in the deletion has nothing with which it can pair or recombine. Thus, no recombination occurs in the interval of the deletion during meiosis in a deletion heterozygote. (v) **Same side of a single centromere**. If the deletion breakpoints were on opposite sides of a chromosome's centromere, the resulting chromosome would be acentric and thus lost during cell division.

9-4.

a. Most deletions remove a large amount of DNA. No mechanism exists for restoring this DNA, so **reversion of this deletion is impossible**. In theory, a very small deletion of a single nucleotide, for example, could revert using a mutagen like proflavin.

b. This rearrangement could revert because all of the original information still exists in the genome. **Reversion within the duplication could occur fairly frequently** because there is a mechanism that generates revertants - they can occur as a result of **unequal crossing-over** in an individual homozygous for the duplication (**Figure 9.14**).

c. In theory, a pericentric inversion could revert because all of the information still exists in the genome. However, there is **no mechanism to ensure that the breaks will occur in the same locations as the original breaks that gave rise to the pericentric inversion, so the rate of reversion should be extremely low. One exception to this are inversions that result from intrachromosomal crossing-over between some sequence of DNA that is present at two locations on the same chromosome but in reversed order (Figure 9.3)**. A similar crossover in the inverted chromosome could regenerate the original gene order, and such crossovers could occur with substantial frequency.

d. **If the organism with the Robertsonian translocation has already lost the very small reciprocal chromosome generated in the process of translocation, then the translocation cannot be restored. If the small reciprocal chromosome still exists, then it is possible that the translocation could revert if it came about through crossing-over between repeated elements (Figure 9.3d).**

e. **For some types of transposable elements, the mechanism that allows the transposable element to jump into the gene can also allow the element to jump out again, often restoring the original DNA sequence of the gene (Figure 9.28b right). In these cases, the mutation will revert fairly frequently.** If this jumping mechanism is lost (for example, if the inverted repeat sequences at the ends of a DNA transposon were deleted), then these types of mutations revert very rarely.

9-5.

a. During meiosis in an inversion heterozygote, a loop of the inverted region is formed when the homologous genes align. In the following simplified drawing, each line represents both chromatids comprising each homologue. Note that the inversion is paracentric.

If a single crossover occurs within the inversion loop, a dicentric and an acentric chromosome are formed (see Figure 9.18b). **Cells containing these types of chromosomes are not viable, so the resulting allele combinations from such single crossovers are not recovered.** The four phenotypic classes of missing male offspring would be formed by single crossovers between the y and v or between the v and f genes in the female inversion heterozygote and therefore are not recovered.

b. **The y v f B^+ and y^+ f^+ v^+ B offspring are the result of single crossovers outside of the inversion loop, between the end of the inversion (just to the right of f on the preceding diagram) and the B gene. This region is approximately 16.7 m.u. long (19 recombinants out of 114 total progeny).**

c. **The y^+ v f^+ B^+ and y v^+ f B offspring would result from two crossovers within the inversion loop, one between the y and v genes and the other between the v and f genes.** You should note that these could be either 2-strand or 3-strand double crossovers, but they could not be 4-strand double crossovers.

9-6. The deletion data allows you to narrow down the region in which the genes lie. All of these deletions remove portions of polytene chromosome region 65 (which turns out to be on chromosome 3, a *Drosophila* autosome). Deletion A shows pseudodominace for javelin and henna, so all or part of both genes must lie within the deleted region— between A2-3 and D2-3. Deletion B, pseudodominant for henna, indicates that *henna* lies between C2-3 and E4-F1. Combining the results for deletions A and B, *henna* must lie between C2-3 and D2-3. Because deletion B is javelin$^+$, *javelin* must be located between A2-3 and C2-3 (the part of deletion A that is not removed in deletion B). Deletions C and D tell you that the *henna* gene cannot lie to the right of bands D2-3 on the figure in the text, delimiting *henna* to the interval between C2-3 and D2-3.

Inversions do not remove genes, they just relocate them. Therefore, if the inversion is made in a wild-type chromosome, the inverted homologue will have the wild-type alleles for all of the genes. Inversion B gives the expected result, and does not help locate either of the two genes. Inversion A, however, has a mutant javelin phenotype, indicating that there is a mutant allele of *javelin* on the inverted homologue. Thus, the *javelin* gene was broken by the inversion, so *javelin* is located in band 65A6. (This is consistent with the region containing *javelin* determined from the deletions above.) Very few *Drosophila* genes extend beyond one band, so we can assume that A6 is the location of *javelin*. In summary, **the *javelin* gene is in band 65A6 and the *henna* gene is between 65C2-3 and 65D2-3.**

9-7.

a. **Each fly has a chromosome containing a different deletion;** in a deletion heterozygote, half the number of sequence reads (relative to reads from elsewhere in the genome) are obtained for the deleted region. **The deletion breakpoints in Fly #1 are ~16.4 Mb and ~16.6 Mb, and in Fly #2 are ~16.45 Mb and ~16.55 Mb.** The breakpoints could be defined to the nucleotide by comparing the sequences of Fly #1 and Fly #2 in this region. **Sequence reads from Fly #1 will contain the deletion breakpoints; these reads will be present at half the frequency of reads elsewhere in the genome, and this particular juxtaposition of sequences will not be present in any sequence reads of Fly #2 or of a wild-type fly without any deletion. The same logic applies for sequence reads from Fly #2.**

b. At least part of the *st* gene must lie in the region of the chromosome deleted in both Fly #1 and Fly #2. That is, **part of the *st* gene must be in the region from 16.45 Mb – 16.55 Mb.**

c. **Yes,** some of the *st* gene could easily lie outside the region where the two deletions overlap; **deletion of even a small part of the gene could result in a loss-of-function *st* allele.**

d. Mapping using deletions is a **complementation** experiment. The deletion chromosome, if the deletion has removed the *st* gene, fails to complement the chromosome containing the *st*⁻ point mutation.

9-8. Each of the original strains is true breeding and shows the same recombination frequency of 21 m.u. between genes *a* and *b*. However, in the F$_1$ heterozygote genes *a* and *b* are only 1.5 m.u. apart. The only rearrangements that affect recombination frequency in this way in the heterozygote are deletions and inversions. There are two reasons why this cross cannot involve a deletion: (1) Both parental strains are homozygous (true breeding) and homozygous deletions are usually lethal; (2) In both parents, genes *a* and *b* are 21 m.u. apart, but if one parent were a deletion homozygote, the genes would be less than 21 m.u. apart.

This reduction of recombination between the 2 genes in the F_1 is therefore caused by an inversion. One parental strain has normal chromosomes and the other parental strain is homozygous for an inversion. There are 2 possibilities for the inverted region: (i) It includes almost all of the region between genes *a* and *b*, but does not include the genes themselves, or (ii) the inversion includes both genes and the DNA in between them.

Two other possibilities for the location of the inversion with respect to the genes can be ruled out. (iii) The inversion includes gene *a* and almost all of the DNA between the genes; and (iv) the inversion includes gene *b* and almost all of the DNA between the genes. These possibilities can be ruled out because in both cases the recombination frequency between *a* and *b* in the inversion homozygote would be much less than 21 m.u., as the inversion would bring the genes closer together.

In any case, the F_1 progeny are inversion heterozygotes. The inversion loop occupies either (i) almost all of the region between genes *a* and *b*, although the genes are not included in the loop, or (ii) the loop includes both genes and the DNA in between them. Any single crossovers within the inversion loop (the huge majority of crossovers between the genes) will result in inviable gametes. The few recombination events that occur between gene *a* and the inversion loop or between the inversion loop and gene *b* will result in balanced, viable, recombinant gametes in scenario (i), as will some of the double crossover events within the inversion loop in both scenarios (i) and (ii).

9-9. The genotype of the female is:

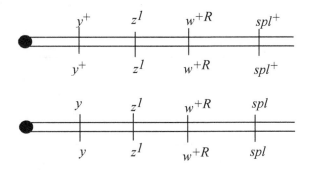

a. The remainder of the male progeny (76 671) are **the parental types, so they will be** $y^+ z^1 w^{+R} spl^+$ / **Y (zeste) and** $y z^1 w^{+R} spl$ / **Y (yellow zeste split).**

b. Classes A and B are a reciprocal pair of products. **They are the result of crossing-over anywhere between the *y* and *spl* genes** resulting in the reciprocal classes: $y^+ z^1 w^{+R} spl$ / Y (zeste split) and $y z^1 w^{+R} spl^+$ / Y (yellow zeste).

c. Remember that the w^{+R} allele is really a tandem duplication of the w^+ gene and that the zeste eye colour depends on having a mutant z^1 allele in a genome that also contains two or more copies of w^+. **Classes C and D are the result of mispairing and unequal crossing-over between the two copies of the w^+ gene.** The misalignment can occur in two different ways, as shown in the figure below. Misalignment I gives $y^+ z^1$ [3 copies w^+] spl (zeste split = same phenotype as class B) as one product and $y z^1$ [1 copy w^+] spl^+ (yellow wild-type eye = class C) as the reciprocal product. In misalignment II, the recombinant products are: $y^+ z^1$ [1 copy of w^+] spl (wild-type eyes split = class D) and $y z^1$ [3 copies of w^+] spl^+ (yellow zeste = same phenotype as class A). Each of these misalignments thus produces one class of recombinant products that results in a wild-type eye colour.

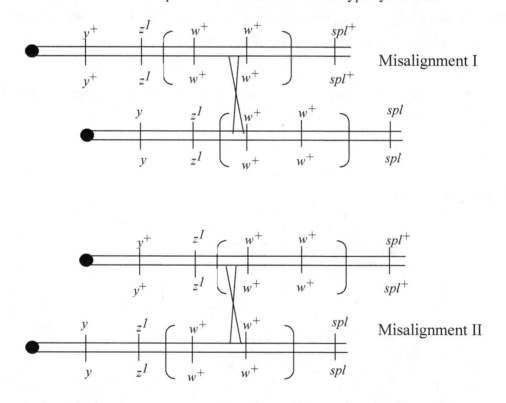

d. The **genetic distance between *y* and *spl*** = # recombinants between *y* and *spl* / total progeny = 2430 (class A) + 2394 (class B) + 23 (class C) + 22 (class D) / 81 540 = **6.0 m.u.** This recombination frequency includes all of the recombinants, because classes A and B contain the reciprocal events to classes D and C, respectively.

9-10. The data shows unexpectedly reduced recombination frequencies between certain pairs of genes in Bravo/X-ray and Bravo/Zorro heterozygotes. This reduction in recombination will be seen in both deletion heterozygotes and in inversion heterozygotes. You are told that the 3 strains have variant forms of the same chromosome, and that the number of bands in the polytene chromosomes is the same in all 3 strains. Thus, none of the strains is a deletion homozygote. The chromosomal rearrangements here must be inversions.

a. Recombination frequencies between genes in the Bravo/X-ray heterozygote are normal for *a-b* and *b-c* and *g-h* but are reduced for all other gene pairs. Thus, the inversion in the X-ray strain breaks between genes *c-d* and between genes *f-g* and inverts genes *d, e,* and *f.* The *c-d* and *f-g* intervals must still include some non-inverted DNA to allow recombination that produces viable gametes. Similarly, the genetic distance is reduced in the *b-c* and *f-g* intervals for Zorro, where the inversion end points are found, and minimal in those intervals completely within the inversion. **The order of the genes in X-ray is: *a-b-c-f-e-d-g-h*. The order of the genes in Zorro is: *a-b-f-e-d-c-g-h*.**

b. **The physical distance in the X-ray homozygotes between *c* and *d* is greater** than that found in the original Bravo homozygotes. The inversion occurred in this portion of the chromosome, so *c* and *d* are now separated by many more genes (all the inverted DNA).

c. **The physical distance between *d* and *e* in the X-ray homozygotes is the same** as that found in the original Bravo homozygotes because this interval is completely within the inverted segment. The relationship of *d* to *e* has not changed.

9-11.

a. **2, 4.** Inversion loops are seen during meiosis I only if the cells are heterozygous for an inversion.

b. **2, 4.** Single crossovers within the inversion loop in inversion heterozygotes generate genetically unbalanced chromosomes. The genetic imbalance involves deletions and duplications of regions outside the inversion loop. If the inversion is paracentric, then the recombinant products are also dicentric and acentric as well as imbalanced with respect to genes. Crossovers in inversion homozygotes do not cause genetic imbalance.

c. **2.** An acentric (and the reciprocal dicentric) fragment is produced from a single crossover within a paracentric inversion in an inversion heterozygote.

d. **1, 3.** In an inversion homozygote, crossovers within the inversion yield 4 viable, balanced gametes, all of which have the inverted gene order.

9-12.

a. Diagram the cross. Because the two genes are on different autosomes, they should assort independently:

$cn\ cn^+$; $st\ st^+$ x $cn\ cn$; $st\ st$ → 1/4 $cn\ cn$; $st\ st$ (white) : 1/4 $cn\ cn$; $st^+\ st$ (cinnabar) : 1/4 $cn^+\ cn$; st st (scarlet) : 1/4 cn^+cn; $st^+\ st$ (wild type).

b. The genes show pseudolinkage in this male. The $cn\ st$ and $cn^+\ st^+$ allele combinations seem to be linked. **This result suggests that the unusual male has a translocation between chromosome 2 and 3 with the mutant cn and st alleles either on the translocated chromosomes or on the normal chromosomes.** The figures below show two of the four possible genotypes for the unusual male fly. Both diagrams show the mutant alleles on the normal chromosomes, however, the mutant alleles of the genes could both be on the translocated chromosomes. Although both the cn and st genes may actually be on the same chromosome after the translocation (right-hand panel), this is not necessary. The pseudolinkage will be seen even if the 2 genes are still on separate chromosomes (left-hand panel). Also, remember that in the germline of male *Drosophila*, chromosomes do not recombine, so only parental-type progeny will be produced.

c. The wild-type F_1 females are translocation heterozygotes containing the cn^+ and st^+ alleles on the translocated chromosomes (they obtained the cn and st alleles from their non-translocated mother). The pairing in meiosis would be the same as shown for the male in part *b*, except that recombination can occur in the female. **A crossover either between cn and the translocation breakpoint or between st and the translocation breakpoint, followed by alternate segregation, produces gametes with the genotypes $cn\ st^+$ (cinnabar) and $cn^+\ st$ (scarlet).** These classes allow you to calculate the map distance between the st and cn genes in the translocation. The RF = 10 m.u. (See the diagram below).

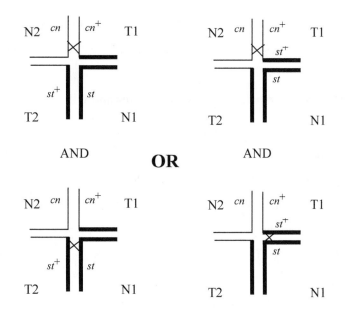

AND OR AND

9-13.

a. **1, 3, 5, and 6**. Translocation heterozygotes can produce gametes with any pairwise combination of N1, N2, T1, and T2.

b. **2 and 4**. Translocation heterozygotes cannot produce gametes with two copies of the same chromatid through any segregation pattern occurring during meiosis I (see Figure 9.21c).

c. **1 and 3**. These arise from alternate segregation, so they are balanced. You can also establish this point by noticing that the gametes in 1 and 3 have one copy of each region of both chromosomes.

d. **5 and 6**; these arise from adjacent-1 segregations. **2 and 4**; these arise from adjacent-2 segregations. Note that the adjacent-1 segregations are much more frequent than adjacent-2 segregations. The reason is that the adjacent-1 pattern represents a normal disjunction that occurs when homologous centromeres move to opposite spindle poles, while the adjacent-2 pattern is a form of nondisjunction that takes place as a result of the unusual cruciform structure that forms when the normal and translocated chromosomes pair during meiosis I.

9-14. Individuals that are homozygous for a translocation are fertile. However, **when insects that are translocation homozygotes mate with insects with normal chromosomes, the F_1 progeny will be translocation heterozygotes. The fertility of these F_1 individuals should be reduced by about 50% and half of their progeny will also have reduced fertility**. If the released insects are homozygous for several different translocations, then the fertility of the F_1 individuals should be reduced by a further 50% for each translocation for which they are heterozygous. For example, in an F_1 insect that was heterozygous for 3 different translocations (T1 - T3), only 1/8 of its gametes (1/2 balanced for T1 x 1/2 balanced for T2 x 1/2 balanced for T3 = 1/8 balanced gametes) would be balanced and give rise to progeny.

9-15. The semisterile F_1 progeny are translocation heterozygotes and will produce 1/2 fertile : 1/2 semisterile progeny from alternate segregation. Products of adjacent-1 or adjacent-2 segregations are unbalanced and therefore inviable - this is the basis of the semisterility. Because the only viable gametes are the result of alternate segregation, genes that are on the chromosomes involved in the translocation will not assortment independently. Instead, if the genes are located very close to the translocation breakpoints, only the parental classes will be viable, so the genes will display pseudolinkage. Genes that are on any other chromosome will assort independently of the translocation (i.e., such genes will assort independently from fertility/semisterility).

a. If the *yg* gene is on a different chromosome than those involved in the translocation, the traits [leaf colour (green vs. yellow-green) and fertility/semisterility (ears with no gaps vs. ears with gaps)] will assort independently. The product rule says you can cross-multiply the 2 monohybrid ratios: $1/2\ yg^+$ (normal green leaf colour): $1/2\ yg$ (yellow-green) and 1/2 fertile : 1/2 semisterile to give: **1/4 fertile yg^+ : 1/4 fertile yg : 1/4 semisterile yg^+ : 1/4 semisterile yg.**

b. If the translocation involved chromosome 9, the fate of the fertility and leaf colour phenotypes are connected – these phenotypes (and thus the genes) will show pseudolinkage. The original cross was: semisterile yg^+ x fertile $yg \rightarrow F_1$ semisterile x fertile yg. This means the normal, non-translocated chromosome 9 has the yg allele, while the translocated chromosome 9 has the yg^+ allele. Thus, the chromosomes of the heterozygous F_1 at meiosis I would look like:

(For simplicity, this figure shows only one chromatid per chromosome.) If the *yg* gene is close to the translocation breakpoint, no crossovers will occur between them in most meioses. Only the products of an alternate segregation are balanced and viable. **The progeny (after crossing with a fertile yg homozygote, and assuming no crossovers between yg and the translocation breakpoint) will be: 1/2 fertile yg (N1 + N2) : 1/2 semisterile yg^+ (T1 + T2).**

c. **The rare fertile *yg*⁺ and semisterile *yg* gametes result from recombination between the translocation chromosome and the homologous region on the normal chromosome with which it is paired, in the region between the *yg* gene and the translocation breakpoint.** After the recombination event, the N1+ N2 fertile gamete will contain yg^+ and the T1 + T2 semisterile gamete will contain yg.

The frequency of crossing-over, as represented by the rare fertile green and semisterile yellow-green progeny, will give you the genetic distance between the translocation breakpoint and the *yg* gene.

9-16.

a. A translocation heterozygote will make 2 types of gametes as a result of alternate segregation and 2 types of gametes as a result of adjacent-1 segregation in a 1:1:1:1 ratio (these two segregation patterns represent normal disjunction and are equally likely). The 2 products of alternate segregation are N1 + N2 and T1 + T2, both of which are balanced gametes. The two products of adjacent-1 segregation are N1 + T2 and N2 + T1, both of which are unbalanced gametes. When a translocation heterozygote is crossed to a homozygous normal individual, the unbalanced gametes from the translocation parent never give rise to viable progeny. However, if <u>both</u> parents of a cross are translocation heterozygotes (as is the case in self-fertilization), then it is possible for an unbalanced gamete from one parent to be fertilized by the reciprocally unbalanced gamete from the other parent. For example, a N1 + T2 gamete from one parent can fertilize an N2 + T1 gamete from the other parent, creating a zygote that is a balanced translocation heterozygote.

The following table summarizes all of the possible fertilizations in the cross of two translocation heterozygotes.

	N1 + N2	T1 + T2	N1 + T2	N2 + T1
N1 + N2	homozygous normal	translocation heterozygote	unbalanced, lethal	unbalanced, lethal

T1 + T2	translocation heterozygote	translocation homozygote	unbalanced, lethal	unbalanced, lethal
N1 + T2	unbalanced, lethal	unbalanced, lethal	unbalanced, lethal	translocation heterozygote
N2 + T1	unbalanced, lethal	unbalanced, lethal	translocation heterozygote	unbalanced, lethal

Thus, among the viable progeny you would expect a ratio of 2/6 fertile (homozygous normal + translocation homozygote) : 4/6 semisterile (translocation heterozygote) = **1/3 fertile : 2/3 semisterile**.

b. This problem involves the self-fertilization of a particular translocation heterozygote. Instead of producing 2/6 fertile : 4/6 semisterile progeny as in part *a*, this plant produced a ratio of 1/5 fertile : 4/5 semisterile. These numbers suggest that one out of the two fertile and viable classes in part *a* did not survive in this cross. Thus, one possible explanation for these results is that **the translocation homozygotes die because the translocation breakpoint interrupts an essential gene**. Alternatively, one of the four chromosomes involved in the translocation has a recessive lethal allele, so that homozygotes for this chromosome could not survive.

9-17. Remember that the Y chromosome pairs with the X chromosome during meiosis, so the N1 + N2 chromosomes in the male translocation heterozygote will be the autosome on which *Lyra* is normally found and the X chromosome, as shown on the figure below. (The chromosomes are drawn as bars, with a single bar representing both sister chromatids.)

This male can make only two kinds of genetically balanced gametes, which are the products of alternate segregation. (Remember as well that no recombination occurs in *Drosophila* males.) The T1 and T2 segregant has the Y chromosome and the autosome with the mutant *Lyra* allele. This gamete would fertilize an X-bearing egg, producing Lyra males (the *Lyra* allele is dominant). N1 and N2 would yield a gamete with the X chromosome and the autosome with *Lyra*$^+$. This gamete would produce wild-type females when fertilized with *Lyra*$^+$ gametes from the wild-type mother. **The progeny will be 1/2 Lyra males : 1/2 Lyra$^+$ females**.

9-18. A Robertsonian translocation (Figure 9.23) is a reciprocal translocation between two acrocentric non-homologous chromosomes. One chromosome breaks in the short arm near the centromere. The other chromosome must break in the long arm near the centromere. One translocated product has the long arm and centromere of the first chromosome joined to the long arm of the second chromosome. The other product of the translocation has the short arm of the first chromosome attached to the centromere and short arm of the second chromosome. This product is very small and does not contain many genes. This small product may eventually be lost during meiosis leaving just the large translocation product.

Based on the location and direction of primer A on chromosome 21, one translocation breakpoint must occur just to the right of the primer A arrow. Thus, the Robertsonian translocation between chromosome 21 and chromosome 14 must contain the entire long arm of chromosome 21 (21q), the chromosome 21 centromere, and a small amount of the short arm of chromosome 21. The rest of this translocation product must be the long arm of chromosome 14 (14q) excluding the chromosome 14 centromere. Thus, the chromosome 14 breakpoint must be just to the right of the centromere. This would generate the described Robertsonian translocation, and **primer pair A and 5** would be the best primer pair to produce a diagnostic PCR product. (Primer 6 would not be a good choice as it is too far away from the translocation breakpoint to produce a PCR product with primer A).

9-19.

a. If **breakpoints 1 and 2** were broken simultaneously, and the DNA between them lost when they were stitched back together, a deletion would result.

b. Primer A hybridizes to the bottom DNA strand of the chromosome at the top just upstream (5' to, or to the left in the diagram) of breakpoint 1. A primer that hybridizes with the top DNA strand of the same chromosome just upstream (5' to, or to the right in the diagram) of breakpoint 2, together with primer A, would amplify a 32 bp DNA fragment uniquely from a chromosome containing the deletion in part *a*. That primer sequence is:

5' GGTGCCCATGGATATT 3'

c. **Breakpoints 1 and 2** could yield an inversion if broken simultaneously, and the DNA between them inverted 180°, the strands flipped, and then included in the product when both breakpoints are stitched back together.

d.   As shown in the following diagram, primer* will hybridize with DNA in the inverted region, and when paired with primer A, will generate a PCR amplification product only from a template   containing the inversion. The sequence of primer* is: **5' TAGTTTCCCGGGACGT 3'.** Note that the primer drawn as a dotted line would work also, but the amplification product would be the shortest possible, not the longest possible. (Don't let it worry you that the base pairs within   the inversion appear to be upside-down; there's really no such thing as an upside-down base pair.   The inverted sequence is written this way to emphasize that its strands are flipped simultaneously   with its 180° rotation.)

e. **Breakpoints 1 and 3, or breakpoints 2 and 3** could yield a reciprocal translocation. You should note on the diagram that follows in part *f* that the translocated pieces must be put back together in the same orientation as shown in the figure. A translocated chromosome that includes primer A must also have the centromere of the chromosome at the top. For example, if the part of the bottom chromosome to the left of breakpoint 3 was rotated and then connected to the fragment to the left of breakpoint 1 (or to the left of breakpoint 2), the resulting chromosome would be dicentric.

f.   The diagram that follows shows that a single primer (primer**) will, together with primer A, PCR-amplify a DNA fragment from translocation 1/3 or translocation 2/3. The sequence of   primer** is: **5' TTAATTGGCCTAAAAG 3'.** As shown in the diagram, because each primer   hybridizes to a different chromosome, the primer pair cannot amplify a product from normal (nontranslocated) chromosomes.

Normal chromosomes

primer A

5' TCGATTCCGGAAAGCTTAGTTTCCCGGGACGTATTGCCAACCTAGGTAAGCGCCGAATATCCATGGGCACC 3'
3' AGCTAAGGCCTTTCGAATCAAAGGGCCCTGCATAACGGTTGGATCCATTCGCGGCTTATAGGTACCCGTGG 5'

    1   2

                5' GGCAATAGCCTAGGAACTTTTAGGCCAATTAA 3'
                3' CCGTTATCGGATCCTTGAAAATCCGGTTAATT 5'
                                3   primer **

Translocation with breakpoints 1 and 3

primer A

5' TCGATTCCGGAAAGCT CTTTTAGGCCAATTAA 3'
3' AGCTAAGGCCTTTCGA GAAAATCCGGTTAATT 5'
            13   primer **

Translocation with breakpoints 2 and 3

primer A

5' TCGATTCCGGAAAGCTTAGTTTCCCGGGACGTATTGCCAACCTAGGTAAGCGCCG CTTTTAGGCCAATTAA 3'
3' AGCTAAGGCCTTTCGAATCAAAGGGCCCTGCATAACGGTTGGATCCATTCGCGGC GAAAATCCGGTTAATT 5'

    1   23   primer **

g. **The translocation is not Robertsonian**. In Robertsonian translocations, one acrocentric chromosome breaks in the short arm, and the other in the long arm. The result of the translocation is a long, compound, metacentric chromosome made up of one long arm and most of a second long arm, and a tiny reciprocal translocation chromosome that sometimes can be lost (see Figure 9.22). Here, both acrocentric chromosomes were broken in their long arms. The pieces that result that contain a centromere would also necessarily have a short arm, so it would be impossible to generate a Robertsonian translocation in this way.

9-20. In all of the answers below, the assumptions are: (i) the organism is diploid; and (ii) because rearranged chromosomes are rare, the organism is heterozygous for the rearrangement in question. The 4 classes considered are deletions, duplications, inversions, and reciprocal translocations.

a. **Inversions and reciprocal translocations** are most likely to cause semisterility. Crossovers within inversion loops formed during meiosis in inversion heterozygotes can result in chromosomes with large deletions and sometimes also duplications (Figure 9.18). This result holds whether the inversion is paracentric or pericentric.

    Gametes formed by reciprocal translocation heterozygotes can be balanced only if translocated chromosomes segregate by chance during meiosis I according to the *alternate segregation pattern*. (That is, when the reciprocal translocation pair segregate together into one daughter cell, and the normal chromosome pair segregate together into the other daughter cell.) Because all four chromosomes participate together in homologous chromosome pairing during meiosis, alternate segregation occurs even less than half the time. The gametes formed by the *adjacent-1* and *adjacent-2* segregation patterns, which account for somewhat more than 50% of the gametes, are unbalanced and inviable. (See Figure 9.21b and c).

b. **Deletions** are most likely to be associated with lethality. A deletion can be lethal in a heterozygote if a single essential haploinsufficient gene is located within the deleted region; if the combined effect of having only one wild-type allele of several genes is lethal; or if the deletion uncovers a loss-of-function mutation in an essential gene on the homologous chromosome. Inversions, duplications, and reciprocal translocations can be lethal more rarely only if one of the rearrangement breakpoints falls within an essential gene.

c. **Deletions** cause the greatest vulnerability to mutation – both inherited mutations and new somatic mutations. If the deletion heterozygote has inherited, on the non-deleted homologue, a loss-of-function mutation in a gene missing from the deletion chromosome, the mutant phenotype (if any) associated with loss of that gene function is present. In addition, new random mutations in somatic cells on the non-deleted chromosome could, by chance, cause loss-of-function of a gene that is missing from the deletion chromosome. The descendant cells of that newly mutated cell will all contain the mutation, and they could have a mutant phenotype as a result. You will see in Chapter 16 that somatic loss-of-function mutations in particular genes called *tumour suppressors* are one cause of cancer. Therefore, deletion heterozygotes can be vulnerable to cancer if they inherit a deletion chromosome that is missing a tumour-suppressor gene.

d. **Deletions, inversions, and reciprocal translocations** most obviously alter genetic maps.

In deletion heterozygotes, the DNA region on the normal homologue that is missing in the deletion homologue cannot cross over because there is nothing for it to cross over with. This means that the genes on the normal homologue that are within the deletion cannot recombine, so the RF between any genes in that region will be zero (when measured in a deletion heterozygote). In addition, the genes flanking the deletion will have a shorter than normal genetic distance between them, because no crossing-over can take place in much of the DNA between them.

A different phenomenon takes place in inversion heterozygotes. Crossovers between the two homologues within the inverted region do take place, but those recombinant chromosomes are not recovered because they are unbalanced, containing deletions or duplications, and they can be acentric or dicentric (Figure 9.18). Thus, similar to what happens in deletion heterozygotes, the RFs between genes within the inversion are much reduced, and the RFs between genes that flank the inversion are reduced. (The genetic distances between genes within the inversion are not zero because certain kinds of DCOs can take place without producing unbalanced gametes.)

In reciprocal translocation heterozygotes, genes near the translocation breakpoints on nonhomologous chromosomes display a phenomenon called *pseudolinkage*. As only gametes resulting from the alternate segregation pattern produce viable progeny, the alleles of genes on the two chromosomes involved in the translocation appear to be linked (Figure 9.21c). Because of the way that the homologues pair during meiosis I (in a cruciform structure – see Figure 9.21b), the genes closet to the translocation breakpoint are the least likely to cross over, and so the pseudolinkage effect is strongest for these genes.

e. **Deletions** are most associated with haploinsufficiency. If a haploinsufficient gene is missing from the deleted chromosome, the haploinsufficient mutant phenotype will be apparent in a deletion heterozygote. (Other rearrangements could disrupt a haploinsufficient gene, but this is less likely as usually fewer genes are disrupted in inversions, translocations, or duplications than in deletions.)

f. **Deletions, duplications, reciprocal translocations, and inversions** are as an approximation equally likely to generate neomorphic mutations. The breakpoints of these arrangements could fuse the ORFs of two different genes, or fuse the promoter of one gene to the coding region of another gene.

g. **Duplications** are the most likely to generate hypermorphic mutations, as extra copies of a duplicated gene result in gene overexpression. However, deletions, inversions, and reciprocal translocations could more rarely result in a hypermorphic mutation by fusing a more highly active promoter to the coding region of a gene.

h. Crossover suppression is caused mainly by **deletions and inversions**. [See part *d*.]

i. **Reciprocal translocations and inversions** are most likely to cause aneuploidy in heterozygotes. Robertsonian translocations (Figure 9.23) can result in aneuploid gametes and progeny. Paracentric inversions can generate tiny chromosomes that could be lost (the acentric fragments in Figure 9.18b), and thereby aneuploid gametes and progeny. (Cells missing an acentric fragment would have one fewer chromosome than a normal cell.)

Section 9.3 – Transposable Genetic Elements

9-21. *Ds* is a defective transposable element that does not encode transposase. The *Ac* element is a complete, autonomous copy of the same transposon that encodes transposase. *Ds* can thus transpose (move around the genome) only in the presence of *Ac*. Chromosomal breakage at *Ds* insertion sites could be due to errors in the transposition mechanism catalyzed by the *Ac* transposase. A new insertion of *Ds* into a gene might yield a mutant allele that is unstable in the presence of *Ac* transposase (that is, the transposase could subsequently move *Ds* out of the location where it caused

the mutation). **Because *Ac* is complete and autonomous, it contains ends that can be recognized by the transposase. Thus, in different strains *Ac* has transposed itself into different chromosomal locations**.

9-22. As shown in Figure 9.30b, **if two copies of the same DNA transposon flank a gene, transposase can recognize the outermost inverted repeat of each transposon, and cut-and-paste the entire "composite" element, including the intervening gene.**

9-23.

a.   *P* elements are DNA transposons that rely on their inverted repeats for mobilization; the inverted repeats are the binding sites and substrates for the transposase enzyme. **If one of the inverted repeats is deleted, that *P* element cannot move. However, that deletion would not affect the ability of other *P* elements to move.** (That is, the contribution of the inverted repeats to the movement of a *P* element must be made in *cis*, not in *trans*.)

b.   The yellow intron (Figure 9.28) must be spliced out of the *P* element primary transcript in order to generate transposase mRNA; with the yellow intron remaining, the mRNA instead encodes a repressor of transposition. **A *P* element with a mutation that prevents splicing out of the yellow intron can move if somewhere else in the genome resides another *P* element that encodes transposase. A *P* element with such a mutation could in some cases affect the ability of other *P* elements to mobilize.** If the mutant transposase transcript simply retains the yellow intron, and thus produces repressor, the added repressor protein could inhibit – at least to some extent – the frequency of mobilization of other *P* elements in the genome. In addition, recall that the previously autonomous *P* element was a source of transposase. Depending on how many other autonomous *P* elements are present in the genome, the loss of the transposase from this one element could have a small or a large effect on the frequency of mobilization of nonautonomous *P* elements.

c.   **If the *P* element in part *b* had been the only autonomous *P* element in the genome, it would be immobile, as would be all other *P* elements in the genome.** Cells would no longer have any gene encoding transposase.

d.   *P* elements are normally mobile only in germline cells because only in the germ line is the yellow intron Figure 9.28 removed from the primary transcript; thus, transposase is made only in the germ line. **A mutant *P* element in which only the yellow intron was deleted could mobilize in somatic cells, because the primary transcript of this mutant *P* element would in essence have the yellow intron spliced out already. The mutation would enable the mutant *P* element to make transposase in somatic cells, so other *P* elements would also mobilize in the soma.** Obtaining a deletion that exactly removes the yellow intron would be an extremely rare event, but is by no means impossible.

9-24. The original *ct* mutant allele was caused by the insertion of the *gypsy* transposable element. The key to this problem is to understand that transposable element mobilization can sometimes be a "messy" process. For example, when DNA transposons like *P* elements are cut out of one location, normally the genomic DNA at that position is stitched back together without deleting any base pairs, a process called *precise excision*. However, occasionally some DNA at the site of the original *P* element insertion is deleted during the process of *P* element mobilization, a process called *imprecise excision*. This imprecise excision may delete nucleotide pairs in the gene, nucleotide pairs in the transposable element, or both. Sometimes imprecise excision even leaves parts of the transposable element at the original insertion site.

The stable *ct*⁺ revertants are likely to be precise excisions of DNA transposons in which the *gypsy* element has moved out of the gene completely, restoring the normal *ct*⁺ sequence. These revertants are stable because no transposable element DNA remains at the site of the original insertion. **The unstable *ct*⁺ revertants are likely to be cases in which the transposition process removed part, but not all, of the *gypsy* element while retaining the critical sequences in the *ct* gene.** In such revertants, the *ct* gene could still function normally. However, these revertants would be unstable because the *gypsy* sequence remaining would still be subject to the transposition mechanism. Imprecise excision of these remaining *gypsy* sequences could result in deletions or rearrangements of the *ct* gene, thus creating new, stronger *ct* mutant alleles.

The answer above assumes for simplicity that *gypsy* is a DNA transposon, but in fact, it is a retrotransposon. It turns out that the events resulting in stable and unstable revertants of the *ct*^{MR2} mutation are generally more complex than those just outlined. For example, several revertants are actually associated with the insertion of other transposable elements into the gene or even into the *gypsy* retrotransposon.

Section 9.4 – Aberrations in Chromosome Number: Aneuploidy

9-25.

a. **Bob is likely to have Down syndrome.** Each of his genomic ASO probes to loci on chromosome 21 hybridize with 150% the intensity as compared with the probes from his parents' genomes. (We are assuming here that, as suggested by the patterns in the parents Fred and Mary, *yellow* indicates one copy of the region, *orange* two copies, and *red* three copies.) The pattern of hybridization suggests that Bob has 3 alleles rather than the normal 2 alleles of each of these loci.

b. Bob inherited one chromosome 21 from one parent, and two chromosome 21s from the other parent due to nondisjunction (NDJ). Comparison of the alleles at each locus in the parents and in Bob reveals that Bob's TT alleles at loci 5, 7, and 9 could only have come from Mary, because Fred has no T alleles at any of these loci. This means that **the extra chromosome 21 inherited by Bob came from Mary's gamete**. Because Mary has only one T allele at each of loci 5, 7, and 9, the extra chromosome 21s are most likely sister chromatids that came **from NDJ at meiosis II** in one of Mary's secondary oocytes.

c. At locus 10, Bob inherited one C allele from Fred, and both G and C alleles from Mary given that the nondisjunction event occurred in Mary; in order for the sister chromatids to have different alleles at locus 10, a crossover must have occurred between loci 9 and 10 as shown in the following diagram.

Chapter 9

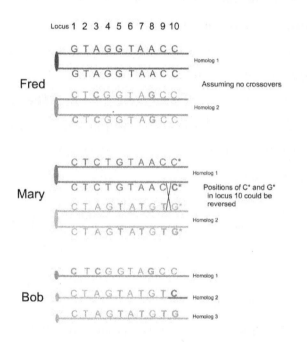

d. Without crossing-over, if the chromosome 21s in the *n* + 1 egg from Mary were due to NDJ at meiosis I, the expectation is that the two chromosome 21s would have different alleles at the loci that were heterozygous in Mary's genome, because they would be nonsister chromatids. On the other hand, if the two 21s were produced by NDJ at meiosis II, they would be expected to have identical alleles at heterozygous loci, because they are sister chromatids.

But now consider the fact that **the further a locus is from the centromere, the more likely a crossover between the centromere and that locus will occur in any given meiosis. Because these crossover events move alleles between nonsister chromatids, recombination can obscure whether NDJ occurred at meiosis I or meiosis II. One solution is to analyze loci close to the centromere. The shorter the distance of the centromere to the locus, the less probability exists that a crossover event could have taken place between them.** Also, as can be seen in the examples of loci 5,7, and 9, analysis of multiple loci can also be helpful. The TTs inherited by Bob at those three loci had to come from Mary, but they are unlikely to have resulted from nonsister chromatids and NDJ at meiosis I, as multiple crossovers within a small region of the chromosome would have been required to produce this pattern.

9-26.

a. **The key to this problem is to realize that uniparental disomy can occur only if two rare events take place, explaining why this phenomenon is so rare.** One homologous chromosome must somehow be lost, and the remaining one has to be duplicated. The following figure diagrams some of the several scenarios that can give rise to uniparental disomy. Paternal and maternal copies of the chromosome are in different shades of *blue*.

	Normal: No uniparental disomy	(i) Meiotic nondisjunction in both parents	(ii) Meiotic nondisjunction in one parent, then mitotic nondisjunction	(iii) Mitotic chromosome loss, then mitotic chromosome nondisjunction	(iv) Meiotic nondisjunction in one parent, then mitotic chromosome loss
Gametes		Disomic Nullisomic	Nullisomic		Disomic
Zygote				Loss ▼ Trisomic zygote	Trisomic zygote
Embryo			Duplication	Duplication	Loss

Normal	Uniparental disomy	Uniparental disomy	Uniparental disomy	Uniparental disomy

(i) Perhaps the most obvious mechanism for uniparental disomy is the fusion of a nullo gamete from one parent (the result of nondisjunction in either meiosis I or meiosis II in that parent), with a meiosis II nondisjunction gamete from the other parent (the mutant homologue must be the one that undergoes nondisjunction during meiosis II).

(ii) A second mechanism begins with the fusion of a nullo gamete from one parent (due to meiosis I or meiosis II nondisjunction) with a normal gamete carrying the mutant allele from the other parent. This generates a monosomic embryo, which then undergoes mitotic nondisjunction of the monosomic chromosome very early in development to create an individual homozygous for that chromosome.

(iii) A third possible mechanism begins with the formation of a normal heterozygous embryo. Very early in development, this embryo undergoes mitotic nondisjunction, leading to loss of the normal allele and retention of one homologue with the mutant allele. This loss of the normal homologue is then followed by a second mitotic nondisjunction event to generate a homozygous mutant genotype.

(iv) A fourth mechanism is fusion of a normal wild-type gamete from one parent with a gamete carrying 2 copies of the affected homologue (the result of nondisjunction in meiosis II). This would generate a trisomic embryo. Early in development, a mitotic nondisjunction or chromosome loss event would cause the loss of the normal allele, leaving the 2 mutant alleles.

There is no easy way to distinguish between these possibilities, because they all lead to the same result of uniparental disomy. In very rare cases, it might be possible to discriminate between these scenarios if the individual were a mosaic and you could find some cells with aneuploid chromosome complements predicted by one of the proposed mechanisms. (For example, in scenario (iv) you might see some somatic cells that are trisomic.)

b. **Girls with unaffected fathers that are affected by rare X-linked diseases could be produced by any of the mechanisms described in part *a*.** The mother must be a heterozygous carrier, and the father's chromosome is the one that must be lost. In mechanisms (i) and (iv), the nondisjunction producing the disomic gamete must occur during meiosis II in the mother, and the chromosome that is disomic must be the one with the recessive allele.

The transmission of rare recessive X-linked disorders from father to son could only be explained by mechanisms (i) and (iv) described in part *a*. For the son to be a male and also be affected, the son <u>must</u> inherit <u>both</u> his father's X and Y chromosomes. The maternal X chromosome must also be lost; this could occur by a meiotic nondisjunction event in the mother, or by a mitotic nondisjunction/chromosome loss event early in the development of an XXY zygote.

c. Another way in which a child could display a recessive trait if only one of the parents was a carrier involves mitotic recombination early in the development of a heterozygous embryo. The recombination event must occur between the mutant gene and the centromere. The zygote then forms from the recombination product that is homozygous for the mutant allele. To detect the occurrence of mitotic recombination, **you must examine several DNA markers along the chromosome arm containing the gene involved in the syndrome**. In particular, you want to compare markers close to the centromere with those near the telomere. **If the presence of the disease were due to mitotic recombination, then the person would be heterozygous for markers near the centromere but homozygous for those near the telomere. If uniparental disomy caused by any of the mechanisms described in part *a* was instead involved, the individual would be homozygous for all of the DNA markers** (assuming that the individual is not a mosaic).

9-27. Meiotic nondisjunction should give roughly equal numbers of autosomal monosomies and autosomal trisomies. In fact, the total number of monosomies would be expected to be greater, because chromosome loss produces only monosomies. The actual results are the opposite of these expectations. The much higher frequency of trisomies seen in the karyotypes of spontaneous abortions suggests that human embryos tolerate the genetic imbalance for 3 copies of a gene much better than one copy. Also, one copy of a chromosome will be lethal if that copy carries any lethal mutations. Monosomies usually arrest zygotic development so early that a pregnancy is not recognized, and thus they are not seen in karyotypic analysis of spontaneous abortions.

9-28. Both types of Turner's mosaics could arise from chromosome loss or from mitotic nondisjunction early in zygotic development. Chromosome loss would involve the loss of one of the X chromosomes early in development in an XX embryo (producing a mosaic with both 46, XX and 45, XO cells), or the loss of the Y chromosome in the XY embryo (yielding a mosaic with 46, XY and 45, XO cells). Mitotic nondisjunction in a normal XX embryo should produce an XXX daughter cell in addition to an XO, while mitotic nondisjunction in an XY embryo yields an XO and an XYY daughter cell. If the XXX or XYY daughter cells did not expand into large clones of cells during development, karyotype analysis would not be able to detect their presence. Note that for mitotic nondisjunction to have given rise to the described mosaic individuals, the nondisjunction event must have occurred after the first mitotic division so that there would be some XX or XY cells.

9-29. You have 3 marked 4th chromosomes: (i) $ci^+ ey$, (ii) $ci\ ey^+$, and (iii) $ci\ ey$. *Drosophila* can survive with 2 or 3 copies of the 4th chromosome, but not with 1 copy or 4 copies. You are looking for mutations which are defective in meiosis and cause an elevated level of nondisjunction.

a. **Mate potential meiotic mutants that are $ci^+ ey\ /\ ci\ ey^+$ with $ci\ ey\ /\ ci\ ey$ homozygotes. The normal segregants should be $ci^+ ey\ /\ ci\ ey$ (ey) and $ci\ ey^+\ /\ ci\ ey$ (ci). Nondisjunction in meiosis I will be seen as the rare $ci^+ ey\ /\ ci\ ey^+\ /\ ci\ ey$ (trisomic but phenotypically wild type) progeny.** Nullo-4 gametes without any copy of chromosome 4 would produce zygotes with only 1 copy of this chromosome, and such zygotes would not develop into viable progeny.

b. **The cross in part *a* will detect nondisjunction in meiosis I, but it will not distinguish meiosis II nondisjunction.**

c. Diagram the testcross: $ci^+ ey\ /\ ci\ ey^+\ /\ ci\ ey$ x $ci\ ey\ /\ ci\ ey \rightarrow$?
Remember that in a trisomic individual, two of the three copies of the chromosome pair normally at metaphase I of meiosis, while the third copy assorts randomly to one pole or the other. There are 3 different ways to pair the 4th chromosomes in the trisomic individual. The first option is: 1/3 ($ci^+ ey$ segregating from $ci\ ey^+$ with $ci\ ey$ assorting independently) = 1/6 probability of (1/2 $ci^+ ey\ /\ ci\ ey$: 1/2 $ci\ ey^+$) and 1/6 probability of (1/2 $ci^+ ey$: 1/2 $ci\ ey^+\ /\ ci\ ey$). The second option is: 1/3 ($ci^+ ey$ segregating from $ci\ ey$ with $ci\ ey^+$ assorting independently) = 1/6 probability of (1/2 $ci^+ ey\ /\ ci\ ey^+$: 1/2 $ci\ ey$) and 1/6 probability of (1/2 $ci^+ ey$: 1/2 $ci\ ey\ /\ ci\ ey^+$). The third option is: 1/3 ($ci\ ey^+$ segregating from $ci\ ey$ with $ci^+ ey$ assorting independently) = 1/6 probability of (1/2 $ci\ ey^+\ /\ ci^+ ey$: 1/2 $ci\ ey$) and 1/6 probability of (1/2 $ci\ ey^+$: 1/2 $ci\ ey\ /\ ci^+ ey$). Each option gives the following progeny phenotypes (which is the same as the gamete genotypes, as this is a testcross) in the following frequencies: option 1 = 2/12 $ci^+ ey$: 2/12 $ci\ ey^+$; option 2 = 1/12 wild type : 1/12 $ci\ ey$: 1/12 $ci\ ey^+$: 1/12 $ci^+ ey$; option 3 = same as option 2. The 3 options can be summed to give the final result: **1/3 $ci\ ey^+$: 1/3 $ci^+ ey$: 1/6 wild type : 1/6 $ci\ ey$.**

d. These compound 4th chromosomes (att4) can be used in crosses to assay potential mutants. For instance, cross a potential mutant that is $ci^+ ey\ /\ ci\ ey^+$ (as in part *a*) to a fly with attached 4th chromosomes that are not marked (that is, both are $ci^+\ ey^+$); that is, **potential meiotic mutants of genotype $ci^+\ ey\ /\ ci\ ey^+$ x att4 $ci^+\ ey^+\ /\ ci^+\ ey^+ \rightarrow$?** . In this cross, all of the normal progeny would have 3 copies of the 4th chromosome and would be phenotypically wild type. **Nondisjunction in meiosis II would be seen as unusual + ey progeny or ci + progeny.** This result would be obtained because half of the gametes in the att4-containing parent would have no copy of the 4th chromosome (nullo-4) as the att4 chromosome does not have a partner. The products of nondisjunction in meiosis II in the other parent would thus be $ci^+\ ey\ /\ ci^+\ ey$ (+ ey) or $ci\ ey^+\ /\ ci\ ey^+$ (ci +). **In this case, nondisjunction in meiosis I is not distinguishable** because the resulting progeny would be $ci^+\ ey\ /\ ci\ ey^+$ (wild type, like the normal progeny).

Another possible cross would be: **potential meiotic mutants that are $ci^+\ ey\ /\ ci\ ey^+$ x att4 $ci\ ey\ /\ ci\ ey \rightarrow$?** . (Here, the att4 chromosome would have mutant alleles of both genes.) In this cross, the normal progeny will be + ey and ci +. **Nondisjunction in meiosis I will give unusual wild-type progeny** ($ci^+\ ey\ /\ ci\ ey^+$ gametes from the potential mutant fertilizing nullo-4 gametes from the att4 parent). Nondisjunction in meiosis I or meiosis II would yield nullo-4 gametes from the potential mutant, so the progeny (which could only be formed with att4 $ci\ ey\ /\ ci\ ey$) would be phenotypically ci ey. **With this second cross you can screen for nondisjunction events both in meiosis I and meiosis II.**

9-30.

a. **The data shown refute the hypothesis that one "Down syndrome critical region" of chromosome 21 exists.** Individuals 1, 2, 3, and 6, for example, each have completely distinct chromosome 21 duplications, yet they all have one or more of the phenotypic abnormalities associated with Down syndrome.

b. **The data also do not support the idea that extra copies of different regions of chromosome 21 cause different aspects of the Down syndrome phenotype.** For example, individuals 1, 2, and 3 all have low IQ and short stature, yet their chromosome 21 duplications have no overlap. Similarly, individuals 5 and 6 share five different aspects of the Down syndrome phenotype, and yet their duplicated regions are completely distinct. Several additional observations of this nature that have recently been made similarly refute the hypothesis.

Prior to these recent findings, most researchers expected to find that extra doses of specific diseases would be more closely correlated with specific phenotypes. Scientists are still struggling to explain these new results. One possibility is that each Down syndrome phenotype is caused by overexpression of several different genes on chromosome 21. Another possibility is that the genetic backgrounds of individuals with trisomy 21 could affect phenotypes. That is, genes on chromosomes other than 21 could be required for expression of Down syndrome phenotypes, which would thus depend on the particular alleles of these genes present in the genome. Yet another possibility is that specific genes on chromosome 21 may not even be the main story. Recently, scientists have found that the extra chromosome 21 in people with Down syndrome affects the levels of expression of genes on every chromosome in the genome. It may be that the extra dosage of certain genes on chromosome 21 causes the global gene expression response, and these responses in turn are responsible for the Down syndrome phenotypes.

Section 9.5 – Variation in Number of Chromosome Sets: Euploidy

9-31.

a. **The x number in *Avena* is 7.** This represents the number of different chromosomes that make up one complete set.

b. **Sand oats are diploid ($2x = 14$); slender wild oats are tetraploid ($4x = 28$); cultivated oats are hexaploid ($6x = 42$).**

c. The number of the chromosomes in the gametes must be half of the number of chromosomes in the somatic cells of that species. **Sand oats: 7; slender wild oats: 14; cultivated oats: 21**.

9-32.

a. **15** ($= 2n + 1$). Note that $n = 7$ in this species.

b. **13** ($= 2n - 1$)

c. **21** ($= 3n = 3x$)

d. **28** ($= 4n = 4x$)

9-33.

a. **(i) aneuploid, (ii) monosomic for chromosome 5, (iii)** this will **probably be an embryonic lethal** because of genetic imbalance – this plant has probably evolved to require two alleles of at least some of the genes on chromosome 5.

b. **(i) aneuploid, (ii) trisomic for chromosomes 1 and 5, (iii)** this will **probably be an embryonic lethal** because of genetic imbalance – there are many genes where increased gene product is detrimental to the organism.

c. **(i) euploid, (ii) autotriploid, (iii) adults should be viable but they will essentially be infertile as they have an odd number of chromosome sets resulting in unbalanced gametes.**

d. **(i) euploid, (ii) autotetraploid, (iii) adults should be viable and fertile,** particularly if there is a mechanism that makes the chromosomes pair as bivalents or as quadrivalents. (See Problem 38 for a discussion of quadrivalents.)

9-34.

a. **(i) $5x = 45$ chromosomes, (ii) allopentaploid, (iii)** should be **sterile** - there are an odd number of chromosome sets so there is essentially no way to get an even distribution of chromosomes to the gametes during meiosis.

b. **(i) $4x = 36$ chromosomes, (ii) autotetraploid, (iii)** should be **fertile if the chromosomes could pair as bivalents or as quadrivalents**. (See Problem 38 for a discussion of quadrivalents.) The gametes should have half the number of chromosomes, so $n = 18$.

c. **(i) $3x = 27$ chromosomes, (ii) autotriploid, (iii)** should be **sterile** because there is an odd number of chromosome sets.

d. **(i) $4x = 36$ chromosomes, (ii) allotetraploid, specifically an amphidiploid, (iii)** should be **fertile** as the chromosomes in the two B genomes can pair with each other as bivalents and the chromosomes in the two D genomes can do the same, so $n = 18$.

e. **(i) $3x = 27$ chromosomes, (ii) allotriploid, (iii) infertile**; the chromosomes cannot pair at all.

f. **(i) $6x = 54$ chromosomes, (ii) allohexaploid, (iii)** should be **fertile** as each chromosome has a pairing partner of its own type, so $n = 27$.

9-35. Haploid plant cells in culture can be **treated with colchicine (a drug that interferes with formation of the spindle apparatus) to block mitosis (segregation of chromosomes) during cell division and create a daughter cell having the diploid content of chromosomes. Once the diploid resistant cell is obtained, it is grown into an embryoid. Proper hormonal treatments of the embryoid will yield a diploid plant.**

9-36. Only plants that are $F^A - F^B -$ will be resistant to all 3 races of pathogen. Because the chromosomes of same ancestral origin still pair, i.e. F^a pairs with F^A, and F^b pairs with F^B, the cross can be represented as a dihybrid cross between heterozygotes. This treats the resistance genes from the two ancestral species as independently assorting genes. You are doing a cross between parents that are heterozygous for 2 different genes. Thus, **9/16 of the progeny will have the F^A − F^B − genotypes, and these plants will be resistant to all three pathogens**.

9-37. This question is asking: What is the frequency of *A A* − − progeny when an *A A a a* tetraploid self-fertilizes? As shown in Figure 9.37, an *A A a a* tetraploid produces 3 different gamete types in the following ratio: 1 *A A*: 4 *A a*: 1 *a a*. The Punnett square that follows shows the types of fertilizations that could result and their relative frequencies. Note the 6 different fertilizations that give rise to *A A* − − progeny with two or more *A* alleles that would show the dominant phenotype (indicated here with *purple* shading).

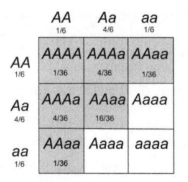

Therefore, the total frequency of *A A* − − progeny is 1/36 + 4/36 + 1/36 + 4/36 +16/36 + 1/36 = **27/36**.

9-38.

a. In an autotetraploid species, all four sets of chromosomes are from the same species. Normally these chromosomes pair two by two and form two bivalents. However, all four chromosomes are homologous, so this is not the only pairing option. Any one of the four chromosomes could pair with a second chromosome over part of its length, and with a third chromosome over the rest of its length. The remainder of the third chromosome would be available to pair with the fourth chromosome, making a quadrivalent. **The figure below shows one of the possible quadrivalent pairing configurations of the four chromosomes during meiosis I**. In the figure, each solid circle is a centromere. Each chromosome is drawn as a single line for simplicity, though of course in meiosis I each chromosome is actually composed of two sister chromatids.

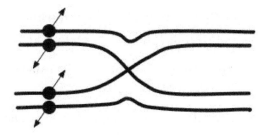

b. **To make euploid gametes, two of the chromosomes in the quadrivalent would have to go to one spindle pole during anaphase I, and the other two chromosomes to the other pole. The arrows in the diagram above show one way this can be done.** Paired centromeres (the two centromeres that are synapsed) will be connected to the spindle so that one centromere attaches to fibres from one spindle pole and the other centromere attaches to fibres from the other spindle pole. The pairing is usually ensured by molecular mechanisms at the centromeres that stabilize centromere/spindle fibre connections only when there is mechanical tension that pulls paired centromeres in opposite directions. In the two sets of paired centromeres shown above, two chromosomes will indeed go to one spindle pole and the other two chromosomes to the other spindle pole, thus giving euploid gametes.

c. An allopolyploid contains chromosome sets from two different, though related, species. Allopolyploids are usually sterile because the chromosomes from the two species cannot pair with each other. Effectively, the allopolyploid is haploid for each of two chromosome sets. Occasionally a fertile allopolyploid, or *amphidiploid*, arises when rare chromosomal doubling generates a homologue for each chromosome. (Or researchers can induce chromosome doubling purposely with the drug colchicine.) **As long as the two genomes in the amphidiploid are sufficiently different from each other, none of the chromosomes of one genome should be able to pair and synapse with chromosomes of the other genome. Thus, quadrivalents should not normally form in amphidiploids.** However, if the two species that formed the hybrid amphidiploid had diverged from each other only in the very recent evolutionary past, it is possible that some of these chromosomes would have retained sufficient sequence similarity to form quadrivalents.

9-39. Karyotype analysis is performed at metaphase of mitosis. The chromosomes are stained such that each different kind of chromosome has a characteristic banding pattern. Recall that allopolyploids contain chromosome sets from two different species; autopolyploids contain multiple chromosome sets from the same species. Thus, **the banding patterns of the homologues in the**

autopolyploids should be the same (for example, in an autotetraploid you would see four copies of each type of banding pattern), but the chromosomes of the different species that formed the allopolyploids would probably have different banding patterns (so in an allotetraploid you would see two copies of each type of banding pattern). Note that karyotype analysis allows you to determine the x number (the number of chromosomes in the basic set), because this will equal the number of different patterns you see. In turn, this allows you to determine the ploidy (the number of copies of the basic set), which is equal to the number of copies of each pattern.

9-40. It was of no importance whatsoever to either the viability or fertility of the hybrid *Raphnobrassica* that $x = 9$ in both cabbages and radishes. *Raphnobrassica* is an $n_1 + n_2 = 18$ amphidiploid with two complete chromosome sets – one from radish and one from cabbage. The 9 radish chromosomes are not homologues of the 9 cabbage chromosomes. **The reason that *Raphanobrassica* is fertile is the fact that plant breeders doubled the number of chromosomes with the drug colchicine.** The original F_1 hybrid which formed from the fertilization between gametes from the two species was sterile because the non-homologous chromosomes from radish and cabbage had no pairing partners. However, colchicine treatment doubled the number of chromosomes, producing 9 pairs of radish chromosomes and 9 pairs of cabbage chromosomes (total = 36 chromosomes). Because each radish chromosome has a radish homologue, and each cabbage chromosome has a cabbage homologue, the original x numbers of the two parental species made no difference to the fertility of *Raphnobrassica* after the chromosome doubling.

A hybrid plant will be viable if the gene products of both species can work together to produce a plant. However, as you have seen, the phenotype of such a viable plant is unpredictable.

9-41.

a. Triploids have 3 of each homologue, and during meiosis I, 2 of them migrate to one pole, and 1 of them goes to the opposite pole. Balanced gametes will be generated by triploid watermelons only if, in every case by chance, 2 of the 3 copies of each chromosome migrate to same pole during meiosis, and 1 copy of each migrates to the opposite pole. The balanced gametes that would be produced by this pattern would be two $2n$ gametes and two $1n$ gametes.

To obtain such gametes that are balanced for all 11 chromosomes, consider the fact that after the first set of homologues moves, the other 10 sets have to move in the same way. As there are two options every time – 2 up and 1 down, or 2 down and 1 up – the chance of any pair of homologues or the single homologue migrating the same way that the first one did is 1/2. Thus, when $x = 10$, meioses that produce balanced gametes (and the balanced gametes themselves) occur at a frequency of $1/2^{10}$.

b. The most obvious way to produce a viable seed would be by a fertilization between two balanced gametes; part *c* below shows that in terms of viability, it does not matter whether these balanced gametes are *n* or 2*n*. The frequency of such an event would be $1/2^{10} \times 1/2^{10} = 1/2^{20}$.

The above calculation is actually an underestimate of the probability of producing a viable seed. The reason is that viable seeds can also be produced not only by the union of balanced gametes, but also by fertilization events where both gametes are unbalanced, but in complementary ways. For example, one gamete might be $2n + 1 + 1 + 1$ with 3 copies of chromosomes 5, 10, and 11, and the other gamete is $2n - 1 - 1 - 1$, and lacks chromosomes 5, 10, and 11. Although it is true that one meiosis would produce both such gametes, and it is also true that watermelons can self-fertilize, fertilization with two such complementary gametes is extremely rare. The reason is interesting: Watermelons have separate male and female flowers, so pollen and eggs must be the products of different meioses.

c. **Viable seeds produced either by two balanced gametes could be 4*n* (tetraploid; 2*n* × 2*n*), 3*n* (triploid; 2*n* × *n*), or 2*n* (diploid; *n* × *n*).** Two unbalanced gametes could produce seed types listed above, and if each unbalanced gamete had 2 complete chromosome sets plus a complementary set of additional chromosomes, a pentaploid seed could be produced (at least in theory).

9-42.

a. In order for a hybrid to be viable, the gene products of both species have to work together in the context of single cells and the whole organism to build a functional animal. **The closer the two species are in evolutionary terms, the more similar their genes are, and the more likely it is that hybrids would be viable.**

b. **Viable hybrids will be fertile if the two species crossed are so closely related that they have the same monoploid number (*x*) of chromosomes, and that their chromosomes can behave as homologues during meiosis.**

You should note that the definition of the word "species" is inexact and controversial. Under some definitions, organisms whose matings can produce viable and fertile offspring of both sexes cannot be considered to be separate species and are instead regarded as sub-species. But many cases have been described in which hybrid offspring of one sex are fertile while those of these other sex are not, so the two parents would then be regarded as separate species. Other definitions of "species" are broad enough to categorize as separate species certain populations that can produce viable and fertile offspring of both sexes.

Section 9.6 – Genome Restructuring and Evolution

9-43. Heterozygotes for one reciprocal translocation are semisterile, while in homozygotes, fertility is unaffected. Once several translocations accumulate in a genome, that organism could no longer produce fertile progeny when mating with an organism that lacked the translocations. Thus, reciprocal translocations (T), once generated, would tend to accumulate in homozygotes. Populations of T/T and +/+ homozygotes would become reproductively isolated because the progeny within each population could reproduce freely while the progeny resulting from interbreeding could not.

9-44.

a. **Many blocks of genes in mostly conserved order are found on two different chromosomes.** For example, one such block is seen both on chromosomes Os08 and Os09. The majority of the genes in the *Oriza sativa* genome are duplicated in this way; the simplest explanation is that the whole genome duplicated in one event.

b. **The genome duplication may have originally resulted in tetraploid rice, but over time, the extra copy of the genome may have diverged, so that the four homologues were no longer similar enough to pair.**

c. **One ancestral chromosome's sequences are now found in rice chromosomes Os08 and Os09 [see part *a*]. A second ancestral chromosome's sequences are now found in chromosomes Os01 and Os05. The third remaining ancestral chromosome's sequences are now found in rice chromosomes Os11 and Os12.**

d. **Although most of chromosome Os12 consists of a duplication of sequences also found on Os11 (and therefore were derived from the same ancestral chromosome as explained in the answer to part *c*), part of Os12 consists of sequences that are duplicated in chromosome Os03 and were derived from a different ancestral chromosome.**

9-45.

a. Note that almost all of the *K. waltii* genes are homologous to a *S. cerevisiae* gene, which makes sense because the two species shared a common ancestor. The *K. waltii* genes that are shown in *dark purple* are homologous to two different genes in *S. cerevisiae*. For example, the left-most *K. waltii* gene in *dark purple* is homologous to both *S. cerevisiae* gene 206 on chromosome 4 and gene 233 on chromosome 12. Likewise, the other *dark purple* shaded *K. waltii* gene is homologous to both *S. cerevisiae* gene 201 on chromosome 4 and gene 238 on chromosome 12. Therefore, the *Scer* 4 gene 206 and *Scer* 12 gene 233 are the result of a duplication, so **the dark purple *K. waltii* genes have undergone a gene duplication event in *S. cerevisiae*.**

b. Both *S. cerevisiae* and *K. waltii* are descendants of a common ancestor. **At some time after the evolutionary lines for these two species separated, a portion of the *S. cerevisiae* genome was duplicated in a progenitor of *S. cerevisiae*. Over time, one copy was lost of many of the duplicated genes. Occasionally, both copies of a gene were retained**, probably because they had changed by mutation into genes with slightly different functions which were both valuable to the organism. This hypothesis explains both the presence of the duplicated genes in *S. cerevisiae* and the interleaving pattern of genes from *K. waltii* that are found in the same order on the two different *S. cerevisiae* chromosomes. The figure below diagrams the processes described. Individual genes are indicated with arrows.

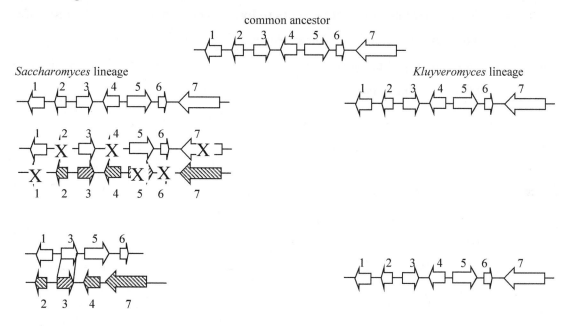

The duplication event that occurred in the *S. cerevisiae* lineage is represented by the appearance of new copies of these genes (hatched arrows). Some of the duplicated genes became lost as their nucleotide sequences diverged; probably they first became nonfunctional pseudogenes (shown with Xs) and then changed further so that any relationship to the ancestral gene was obscured. But in the cases of the genes marked in the problem as *dark purple*, the *S. cerevisiae* genome retained both copies of the duplicated gene.

9-46. You would focus your attention on the genes that are still duplicated in *S. cerevisiae* (the two genes in *dark purple*) and compare the sequences of both copies with that of K. *waltii*. From this information, you could infer the sequence of a gene ancestral to all three copies. The question you would attempt to answer is whether the two *S. cerevisiae* genes have diverged from the ancestral gene at similar rates, or whether one looks similar to the ancestral gene while the other has diverged much faster.

The sequence of the *K. waltii* gene would serve as a control. Because only one copy of the K. *waltii* gene exists, it likely fulfills a function similar to that of the ancestral gene and thus should have evolved from the ancestor at a (relatively slow) rate indicative of the degree of selection against changes that would disrupt this function.

9-47. A Robertsonian translocation that fused two acrocentric chromosomes in the great apes into a large metacentric chromosome appears to have given rise to human chromosome 2. This translocation must have occurred in the lineage leading to humans at some time since we last shared a common ancestor with any of the great apes. The small reciprocal product of the translocation must have been lost from the human genome.

Chapter 10   Prokaryotic Gene Regulation

Synopsis:

The genetic experiments of Jacob and Monod provided the first big ideas about how genes are turned on and off in response to changes in the cellular environment. A basic principle derived from these *lac* operon experiments is that proteins (*trans*-acting factors) bind to specific DNA sequences in genes to regulate transcription initiation. This binding can be influenced by small molecules that are present within cells or that enter cells from the external environment. Later genetic studies of the *trp* operon that led to discovery of the *trp* attenuator showed that bacteria regulate gene expression not only at the point of transcriptional initiation, but also during transcriptional elongation. Again, the function of the attenuator reflects the concentrations of small molecules, allowing the cells to respond to environmental conditions.

The *trp* attenuator is a sequence of RNA that can assume alternative configurations. More recently, scientists have discovered that RNA can mediate gene expression in many ways. *Cis*- acting RNA leader sequences can regulate not only transcription elongation as does the attenuator, but also the initiation of translation (*riboswitches*). Small *trans*-acting RNAs encoded in bacterial genomes also regulate translation initiation. Finally, *antisense RNAs* can influence either the transcription of a gene or the stability or the translation of the gene's RNA.

The work of Jacob and Monod also revealed another key idea: Genes in bacterial cells whose products cooperate in the same biochemical pathway are often clustered together in units called *operons*. The genes in the operon are expressed into a single, *multicistronic RNA*. This fact provides a means for the *coordinate regulation* of the genes in the operon: By controlling the transcription of the operon, the cell can regulate all of the genes comprising the operon simultaneously.

After you read Chapter 11, which describes the mechanisms that regulate genes in eukaryotic organisms, it will be interesting to compare and contrast what you learn in that chapter with the material in this chapter. You will see that some regulatory mechanisms are unique to prokaryotes, while some are found only in eukaryotes; nonetheless, many of the basic principles of gene regulation are shared by all organisms.

Key Terms:

gene expression – the process by which a gene's information is converted into RNA (transcription) and then, for protein-coding genes, into a polypeptide (translation).

RNA polymerase – the enzyme that transcribes a DNA sequence into an RNA transcript.

promoter – DNA sequences near (and usually upstream of) a gene's transcription start site to which RNA polymerase binds directly to initiate transcription.

ribosome binding site – region on prokaryotic mRNAs containing both an initiation codon and a *Shine-Dalgarno box*; ribosomes bind to these elements to start translation of protein-coding sequences on the mRNAs.

catabolic pathway – a metabolic pathway that breaks down complex molecules to produce smaller molecules (and often, energy). Lactose utilization, which breaks down lactose into glucose and galactose, is an example of a catabolic pathway. (See Figure 10.2).

anabolic pathway – a metabolic pathway that synthesizes a complex molecule from simpler ones. The genes of the *trp* operon encode enzymes that cooperate in the anabolic pathway that leads to the synthesis of the amino acid tryptophan.

transcription factor – a protein that binds DNA sequence-specifically and regulates transcription. In prokaryotes, two types of transcription factors exist: **positive regulators** activate transcription, and **negative regulators** (also called **repressors**) inhibit transcription.

inducible regulation – a mechanism of gene control where transcription occurs only in the presence of a molecule called an *inducer*. An **inducer** is a small molecule that binds to a positive regulator, altering the positive regulator's conformation so that it can bind DNA. Inducible regulation is particularly important for the regulation of catabolic pathways.

repressible regulation – a mechanism of gene control where transcription occurs only in the absence of a *corepressor*. In prokaryotes, a **corepressor** is a small molecule that binds to a repressor, thereby altering repressor conformation so that it can bind DNA. Repressible regulation is particularly important for the regulation of anabolic pathways.

induction – the process by which an inducer causes transcription of a gene or a set of genes.

operon – a unit of DNA composed of specific *structural genes* (encoding functional products), plus a *promoter* and an *operator*. These elements work in unison to regulate the coordinated response of expression of the structural genes to environmental changes.

allosteric protein – a protein that changes its conformation reversibly when bound to a specific *effector* molecule.

constitutive mutants – cause gene transcription to occur all the time in an unregulated manner; that is, regardless of environmental conditions.

effector – a small molecule that binds to an allosteric protein or to an RNA molecule and causes a conformational change. As examples, allolactose (an inducer), cAMP, and tryptophan (a corepressor) are both effectors.

in *trans* – describes the action of a protein or RNA that can bind to target sites on any DNA or RNA in the cell; a protein or RNA that acts in *trans* is said to be ***trans*-acting**. Molecules that act in *trans* diffuse throughout the cell to find their target sites.

in *cis* – describes the action of a DNA site or a region in an RNA molecule that acts only on the DNA or RNA to which it is connected physically; a DNA site or an RNA that acts in *cis* is said to be ***cis*-acting**.

domain – a discrete region of a protein that has a particular function. For example, the *lac* repressor polypeptide has a domain that binds to the *operator*, a domain that binds to the *inducer* allolactose, and a domain that allows polypeptides to associate into multimers.

catabolite repression – inhibition of the expression of genes or *operons* like the *lac* operon when glucose or another preferred catabolite is present.

RNA leader sequence – the 5' UTR of an mRNA; in prokaryotes, RNA leader sequences can act in *cis* to regulate transcription elongation or the transcript's translation.

hairpin loops (stem loops) – structures formed when a single strand of RNA folds back on itself because of complementary base-pairing between different regions in the same molecule.

attenuation – a type of gene regulation that responds to translation of an ORF in the RNA leader; the RNA leader is called the **attenuator**. When this ORF is translated efficiently, transcription of a gene or operon terminates in the RNA leader sequence before a complete mRNA transcript is made.

terminator – in prokaryotes, stem-loop structures that cause RNA polymerase to stop downstream transcription. Terminator formation in an RNA leader sequence (such as an attenuator or a riboswitch) can be prevented by formation of a different, competing stem-loop structure called an **antiterminator**.

riboswitch – an allosteric RNA leader that binds a small molecule *effector* to control gene expression.

RNA thermometer – an allosteric RNA leader that regulates translation in response to temperature through a stem-loop structure whose stability is temperature-dependent.

sRNAs – small RNA molecules that regulate translation in *trans* by base pairing with sites on mRNAs. This base-pairing of sRNA and mRNA can either hide or expose the ribosome binding site on the mRNA.

antisense RNAs – regulatory RNAs that are complementary in sequence to the mRNAs they regulate because they are transcribed using the opposite strand of DNA as a template. Antisense RNAs can block transcription or translation of their target mRNAs; the target mRNAs are sometimes called *sense RNAs*.

fusion gene – a gene constructed using recombinant DNA technology that is made up of parts of two or more different genes. For example, a fusion gene may contain the 5' regulatory region of one gene and the ORF of a different gene.

reporter gene – a fusion gene whose ORF encodes a protein that is easy to detect; expression of that protein "reports" activity of the fusion gene's promoter and also verifies that the fusion gene transcript was translated. (The term *reporter gene* also sometimes refers to the ORF of the fusion gene only.)

RNA-Seq (cDNA deep sequencing) – method for analysis of all of the transcripts made in an organism (the **transcriptome**) under a specific set of conditions. The data are obtained as approximately one billion sequence reads, each corresponding to an individual cDNA molecule. With current technology, each read is about 150 nt long.

quorum sensing – a communication system whereby bacteria sense their population density to regulate the transcription of particular genes.

Structures of Prokaryotic Genes and mRNAs:

Solving problems about the regulation of prokaryotic genes requires that you have a thorough knowledge of prokaryotic gene and mRNA structure. Be sure that you understand the functions of all of the parts of the typical operon and the mRNA in the diagram that follows. Critical to this diagram is the point that an operon's mRNA is *polycistronic*, meaning that it contains the ORFs for multiple *structural genes*. The expression of all of the structural genes in the operon can be coordinated by events that occur near the promoter and thus that affect the amount of the polycistronic mRNA. Even though they are on a single mRNA, these ORFs can be translated independently, because they each have a separate translation initiation signal [made up of a Shine-Dalgarno sequence and a ribosome binding site (RBS)].

Another important feature of prokaryotic gene expression is that transcription of the gene or operon and translation of the mRNA occur in the same space in the cell. Furthermore, translation can begin before the mRNA has been completely transcribed. These facts are central to phenomena like attenuation, where the structure of the 5'UTR (the upstream leader) of the operon mRNA can influence whether the rest of the operon will be transcribed.

RBS = <u>R</u>ibosome <u>b</u>inding <u>s</u>ite
UTR = <u>U</u>n<u>t</u>ranslated <u>r</u>egion

Fusion Genes and Reporter Genes:

Our understanding of prokaryotic gene structure has enabled scientists to cut and paste different parts of genes together – to make **fusion genes**. Such fusion genes are not only important experimental tools, but they also allow pharmaceutical companies to employ bacteria as factories to make clinically useful proteins. The fusion genes you saw in this chapter (Figure 10.25 and Figure 10.27a) contain the regulatory region of one gene, and the open reading frame (ORF) of a different gene. Such recombinant genes are sometimes called *transcriptional fusions* because transcription of an ORF is controlled by foreign regulatory sequences. If the regulatory region of the first gene is well-characterized and easy to manipulate, it can be used to make in bacterial cells large amounts of the protein encoded by the ORF.

Some fusion genes are **reporter genes**; the ORF of a reporter gene (e.g., *lacZ*) encodes a protein (e.g., β-galactosidase) for which there is a convenient assay. By monitoring reporter protein levels, researchers can assess the activity of the promoter and previously uncharacterized regulatory sequences that drive transcription of the reporter gene. The reporter can be used to test different base pairs in the putative regulatory elements for function through mutagenesis; to identify the *trans*-acting factors that bind the regulatory elements; or to test the transcriptional response of the regulatory region to various environmental factors.

Figure 10.26 shows the special case of a **"promoterless" reporter gene**. By incorporating this promoterless reporter gene into a transposon, researchers can isolate many strains in which the reporter is inserted into different, random positions in a bacterial genome. Reporter expression under a specific condition means that the reporter inserted adjacent to the regulatory region of a gene that responds to that stimulus.

In later chapters, you will see that reporter genes and other fusion genes are invaluable in studies of eukaryotic as well as prokaryotic organisms.

Protein/DNA Interactions:

Gene regulation involves *cis*-acting DNA elements and *trans*-acting factors that bind them. The following list clarifies key points how about transcription factors interact with DNA.

- In general, transcription factors bind to double-stranded DNA rather than single-stranded DNA; the DNA strands do not denature in order to bind transcription factors. Atoms at the edges of the base pairs (that are not involved in forming the hydrogen bonds between complementary base pairs) are available to form noncovalent bonds with atoms of the amino acid R groups within the DNA-binding domain of the transcription factor. Most of these interactions between amino acids and bases take place in the major groove of the DNA.

- The specificity of particular transcription factors for specific DNA sequences stems from the particular sequence of amino acids in the DNA-binding domain and the particular base pair sequence of the binding site. The sum of all of these attractive forces adds up the *affinity* of the transcription factor for the binding site.

- All transcription factors, no matter how high their affinity is for a site on DNA, are in *equilibrium* between bound and unbound states. How frequently a particular transcription factor is bound to a particular site on DNA depends on the affinity of the DNA-binding domain of the protein for that base pair sequence, and also on the concentrations of the protein and the DNA in the nucleus.

Problem Solving:

One of the most consistent themes in this chapter is that regulation of prokaryotic gene expression in response to the environment often occurs during the initiation of transcription and requires three different components: (1) a functional structural gene (e.g., $lacZ^+$); (2) intact *cis*-acting DNA sites [e.g., a promoter (P) and an operator (o)]; (3) functional *trans*-acting factor gene(s) (e.g., $lacI^+$).

Related concepts to keep in mind include:

- *cis* **and** *trans*: When analyzing a genotype to determine how particular genes will be expressed under specific environmental conditions, keep in mind the difference between *cis*-acting DNA sites and *trans*-acting factors. The promoter and operator are *cis*-acting sites at the 5' end of every operon; they function only with that operon – not with other genes or operons on unconnected DNA molecules. Transcription factors, on the other hand, are *trans*-acting proteins that can work on any operon in the cell; it does not matter whether the gene that encodes a *trans*-acting factor is on the same DNA molecule as the operon the factor regulates. The reason is that once it is made, the transcription factor protein can diffuse in the cell cytoplasm and find its binding site on any DNA molecule present there.

- **Prokaryotic promoters:** A prokaryotic promoter is simply a specific base pair sequence that attracts RNA polymerase to initiate transcription of a gene or operon. Amino acids that form the DNA-binding domain of RNA polymerase have an affinity for the particular base pair sequence in the promoter that is higher than the general affinity of RNA polymerase for binding DNA at random sequences.

- **Prokaryotic transcription factors can be positive regulators or negative regulators:** Positive regulators increase the affinity of RNA polymerase for the promoter. Positive factors do so because they bind DNA sites near the promoter, where the factors make contact with RNA polymerase. These contacts serve as attractive forces: A promoter with a positive regulator bound near it has a higher affinity for RNA polymerase than when the positive regulator is not bound there. Negative regulators can bind to DNA sites (operators) that overlap with the promoter and thus prevent RNA polymerase from binding there or from initiating transcription.

Solutions to Problems:

Vocabulary

10-1. i. **10**; ii. **8**; iii. **5**; iv. **2**; v. **7**; vi. **1**; vii. **9**; viii. **6**; ix. **3**; x. **4**.

Section 10.1 – The Elements of Prokaryotic Gene Expression

10-2. The first step of gene expression is the binding of RNA polymerase to the promoter. **If the main controls of gene expression acted later in transcription or in translation, the cells would sometimes waste energy making RNA that would not be utilized. Bacteria are clearly evolving under the constraint of conserving the energy they obtain from nutrients in their environments.**

10-3.

a. **i, ii, iii**. The first two, i and ii, reflect the rate at which the transcription of different operons is initiated. This rate will depend on the intrinsic affinity of the promoter of each operon for RNA polymerases - some promoters are stronger than others. (Although not in the list, the binding of sequence-specific DNA binding-proteins, like repressors or positive regulators, to DNA sequences near promoters also regulates levels of mRNAs). In addition, promoters are recognized by different RNA polymerases—some sigma factors may be needed for RNA polymerase to recognize some promoters and not others. Point iii indicates that the level to which an mRNA accumulates in the cell depends not only on its rate of transcription, but also on its rate of degradation. Different mRNAs can be degraded at different rates, due to differences in their structures that are recognized by various ribonucleases in the cell.

b. **iv, v, vi**. Point iv is quite interesting. In operons, the "distal" genes that are further from the promoter may be less efficiently transcribed, or transcribed later, than the "proximal" genes that are closer to the promoter. If the mRNA of the operon is long, it will take RNA polymerase some minutes to reach the distal genes. The RNA polymerase might sometimes fall off the DNA or encounter transcription termination signals before transcribing the distal genes. Since transcription and translation are coupled in bacteria, the transcription of distal genes might actually be regulated by the rate at which the proximal genes in the same mRNA are translated. Point v indicates that the efficiency of translational initiation for genes in the same operon can vary because of differences in Shine-Dalgarno sequences and because of differences in the way the various ribosome binding sites fold in three-dimensional space. Point vi is important because the amount of protein that accumulates in a cell is not only due to the rate it is translated, but also to the rate at which that protein is degraded.

10-4. The lack of *rho* function must be lethal for the cell, so ***rho* gene function is essential**. Conditional mutations are the only sort of mutation that can be isolated for essential genes. Given that the Rho protein is needed to terminate correctly the transcription of many genes and operons in the bacterial genome, it is not surprising that *rho* gene function is essential for survival.

Section 10.2 – Regulation of Transcription Initiation via DNA-Binding Proteins

10-5. Mutations in the promoter region can only act in *cis* to the structural genes immediately adjacent to this regulatory sequence. A promoter mutation in one operon will not affect the expression of a second, normal operon, in *trans*.

10-6.

Structure of the *hup* operon mRNA

Transcription begins with the first base at the 5' end of the mRNA shown above. RNA polymerase transcribes the template DNA strand until it reaches the transcription termination signal (TT). The transcription termination signal could be a hairpin loop (an intrinsic termination signal) near but not directly at the 3' end of the mRNA, or alternatively it could be a sequence near the 3' end of the mRNA that is bound by a protein factor like Rho (an extrinsic termination sequence).

Translation begins when a ribosome binds to the ribosome binding site (RBS) in the mRNA, which is made up of the Shine-Dalgarno sequence (SD) and, a short distance downstream, the initiation codon (AUG). The rectangles in different shades of *pink* represent the translated regions (open reading frames or ORFs) for each gene. Note that translation starts at three separate locations, one for each gene in the operon. In prokaryotes, the initiating amino acid is fMet. Translation terminates at a nonsense codon (Stop), leading to the release of the polypeptide and the dissociation of the ribosomal subunits.

Note that several regions in the mRNA are *not* translated. These include the sequences upstream of the first SD sequence, known as the 5' UTR (untranslated region), also called the *RNA leader sequence*. Other untranslated regions of the mRNA include the sequences between each ORF (the *intergenic regions*) and the sequences downstream of the last ORF (the 3' UTR) that include the transcription termination signal TT.

10-7. Statement (b) will be true. When a positive regulator is inactivated, the expression from the operon will be much reduced.

10-8.

a. When the gene encoding the DNA-binding protein has a loss-of-function mutation, the result is constitutive expression of the *emu* operon. Therefore, **the wild-type regulatory protein blocks transcription; in other words, it is a negative regulator of *emu* operon expression.** You can imagine, for example, that the DNA-binding protein could be a repressor like the Lac repressor.

You could similarly imagine that the regulatory site to which the DNA-binding protein binds is similar to the operator site in the Lac operon.

b. **Strain (i) will have inducible *emu1* and constitutive *emu2* expression, while strain (ii) will have inducible *emu1* and *emu2* expression.** In both strains, the Emu2 protein can be made only from the structural gene on the F' plasmid, while the Emu1 protein can only be made from the structural gene on the bacterial chromosome. Both strains should have enough Reg2 binding protein to repress transcription of *emu* operons on either the plasmid or the chromosome, because wild-type alleles of the *reg2* gene should be dominant to mutant loss-of-function alleles, and because binding proteins such as the Lac repressor work in *trans*.

In strain (i), the only functional *emu1*$^+$ gene (on the bacterial chromosome) is normally regulated (that is, it is inducible) because the *cis*-acting *reg1* DNA-binding site (operator) is intact and can interact with the Reg2 repressor. However, the F' plasmid, with the only functional *emu2*$^+$ gene, lacks a functional *reg1* operator. The Reg2 repressor cannot regulate the operon on the F' plasmid, so *emu1* expression is constitutive (the operon is transcribed all the time).

In strain (ii), the *emu* operons on both the F' plasmid and the bacterial chromosome have functioning *reg1*$^+$ operators. Binding of the Reg2 repressor protein to these operators makes the expression of both the *emu1* and *emu2* structural genes inducible.

c. **Strain (i) will have inducible *emu1* and *emu2* expression while strain (ii) will have inducible *emu1* and constitutive *emu2* expression.** In this case, both strains will have sufficient *trans*-acting Reg1 repressor. Strain (i) has functional operators on both the F' plasmid and the bacterial chromosome, while the only functional operator in strain (ii) is on the bacterial chromosome. Thus, the expression of *emu1*$^+$ from the operon on the bacterial chromosome will be normally inducible, while expression of *emu2*$^+$ from the operon on the F' plasmid will be constitutive because the Reg1 repressor cannot bind to the mutant operator.

10-9. When the λ phage infects a cell with an integrated λ phage (that is, the cell is a lysogen), the cI repressor protein is already present in the cytoplasm so can bind and repress the transcription of the genes on the incoming phage chromosome. Thus, the incoming phage is repressed and no progeny can be made. The non-lysogenic recipient cell has no cI repressor protein in the cytoplasm, so the incoming infecting phage goes into the lytic cycle, producing progeny phage.

10-10. These revertants of the constitutive expression of the *lac* operon could be changes in the base sequence of the operator site that compensate for the missense mutation in *lacI*. For

example, if an amino acid necessary for recognition of operator DNA is changed in the *lacI* mutant, a compensating mutation changing a recognition base in the operator could now allow the mutant LacI protein to recognize and bind to the mutant operator site. Note that this explanation depends on the fact that the original *lacI* mutation was a missense mutation changing the identity of a single amino acid. If the *lacI* mutation instead lead to more severe changes in the Lac repressor protein (for example, if the mutation was a nonsense or frameshift mutation early in the coding region), this scenario for suppressing the constitutive phenotype would not be possible.

10-11. The *lacZ* gene codes for the β-galactosidase enzyme. The *lacY* gene codes for a permease.

a. ***lacZ* is constitutive; *lacY* is constitutive**. The o^c mutation acts in *cis* on *lacZ*$^+$ and *lacY*$^+$; because the repressor cannot bind to the o^c site, the two genes are expressed at high levels whether or not the inducer allolactose is present.

b. ***lacZ* is constitutive; *lacY* is inducible**. The o^c mutation acts in *cis* on *lacZ*$^+$. Even in the presence of I^+, which works both in *cis* and in *trans*, *lacZ*$^+$ is constitutive because repressor made from the I^+ allele cannot bind the o^c operator. Expression of *lacY*$^+$ is inducible because it is downstream of a wild-type operator.

c. ***lacZ* is constitutive; *lacY* is inducible**. As in part *b*, *lacZ*$^+$ is constitutive because the o^c mutation acts in *cis* and cannot respond to I^+, while *lacY*$^+$ is inducible because it is downstream of a wild-type operator.

d. **no expression of *lacZ*; *lacY* is constitutive**. *lacZ*$^+$ cannot be transcribed without a functional promoter, and *lacY*$^+$ is constitutive because it is connected physically to o^c.

e. **no expression of *lacZ*; no expression of *lacY*.** I^S makes a *trans*-acting super-repressor that binds o^+ on both copies of the operon. The super-repressor cannot bind to the inducer allolactose, so expression of the structural genes cannot be induced.

10-12.

a. In the presence of glucose alone, **the repressor protein (LacI) is bound** to the operator because no inducer (allolactose) is present. Because glucose is present, the levels of cAMP are low, so the CRP protein cannot bind to its binding site adjacent to the operon's promoter.

b. In the presence of glucose + lactose, there will be **no proteins bound to the regulatory region** of the *lac* operon. Under this condition, the LacI repressor protein binds to the inducer allolactose and cannot bind to the operator. As in part *a*, the presence of glucose prevents the CRP protein from binding to the regulatory region because the levels of cAMP are low.

c. In the presence of lactose only, **the CRP-cAMP complex will bind to the promoter region** of the *lac* operon. The LacI repressor binds to the inducer rather than to the operator. In the absence of glucose, the activity of adenyl cyclase is high and thus the level of cAMP is high, allowing the CRP-cAMP complex to bind to its target site adjacent to the operon's promoter.

10-13.

a. Because one I^+ gene is present and both operons are o^+ P^+, both copies of the *lac* operon are inducible. Neither copy of the *lac* operon is transcribed in the first 10 minutes in the absence of lactose, because the LacI repressor is bound to the operators. Starting at 10 minutes when lactose is added as the sole carbon source, all three proteins will be induced because at least one wild-type structural gene is present to encode each protein and the LacI repressor can no longer bind to the operators.

b. The *lacZ*$^+$ and *lacY*$^+$ genes are constitutive (they are expressed even if lactose is absent) because they are physically connected to the *cis*-acting o^c mutation. On the other hand, *lacA*$^+$ is inducible because the only functional ($^+$) *lacA* gene copy is physically connected to o^+, and an I^+ gene is present.

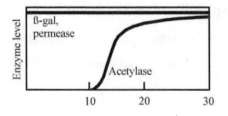

c. All three genes are off even in the presence of lactose because a functional copy of each is connected to a functional operator (o^+), and I^S makes a *trans*-acting super-repressor that prevents induction of either o^+ operon. (The super-repressor protein cannot bind to the inducer so it always binds to o^+ sites.)

and is mutant 7. The defective CRP-cAMP binding site (d) causes the same low levels of β-galactosidase expression with lactose or lactose + glucose because the CRP-cAMP complex cannot bind to the promoter region to increase expression. Thus mutant 1 or 2 contains a mutation in the CRP-cAMP binding site. The nonsense mutation in β-galactosidase (e) will result in no expression, so it is mutant 3 or 4. The nonsense mutation in the repressor gene (f) leads to constitutive expression of β-galactosidase, as in mutants 5 and 6. A defective *crp* gene (g) means the CRP-cAMP complex cannot form, so it cannot bind to the promoter region to augment gene expression; this phenotype is seen in mutants 1 and 2. To summarize, mutations 1 and 2 are the mutant CRP-cAMP binding site and the defective *crp* gene; mutations 3 and 4 are a super-repressor and a nonsense mutation in the β-galactosidase gene; mutations 5 and 6 are an operator deletion and the nonsense mutation in the repressor gene; and mutation 7 is an amber suppressor tRNA.

The next stage of the analysis involves understanding the results of the double mutant and merodiploid genotypes. An amber nonsense mutation of the *lacZ* gene would be suppressed by mutation 7 (amber suppressor tRNA) in the same cell. Therefore, mutant 3 contains the nonsense mutation in the β-galactosidase (*lacZ*) gene and mutant 4 must be a super-repressor mutation. Likewise, a nonsense mutation in the repressor gene would be suppressed by mutation 7 in the same cell, so mutant 5 is the mutant repressor gene and mutant 6 is the operator deletion. The defective *crp* gene can be distinguished from the defective CRP-cAMP binding site by the merodiploid genotypes presented (the genotypes with an F' plasmid in addition to the bacterial chromosome). In both merodiploids, the bacterial chromosome has a mutant gene for β-galactosidase, but all other parts of the *lac* operon expression system are wild type. The F' element has either a mutant CRP-cAMP binding site or a defective *crp* gene. In the latter case, the presence of the *trans*-acting wild-type crp^+ gene on the bacterial chromosome will result in normal regulation of the *lac* operon. However, if the mutation on the F' element is in the *cis*-acting CRP-cAMP binding site, the phenotype of the merodiploid will still be mutant. Thus, mutant 1 is the *crp* mutation and mutant 2 is the altered binding site. In summary: **a. 4; b. 6; c. 7; d. 2; e. 3; f. 5; g. 1.**

10-16.

a. **If you only screen for Lac$^+$ revertants, many of the revertants you find will be mutations in just the *lac* operon.** These could be compensating mutations in the *lac* operon's CRP-cAMP binding site (that is, mutations altering the binding site's sequence so that it can bind to mutant CRP-cAMP complexes) or mutations in the operon's promoter that would allow strong recognition by RNA polymerase even in the absence of the CRP-cAMP complex.

Demanding that the suppressor mutations yield both Mal⁺ and Lac⁺ phenotypes will limit the revertants you find to more general cases that affect all CRP-cAMP binding or activity. These could be second mutations in the CRP gene (such that a *crp* gene with the original mutation and the second mutation would now be functional), or mutations in genes that affect either CRP or cAMP production or the function of the CRP-cAMP complex.

You should note that the kinds of suppressors you isolate in either screen depend in large part on the kind of mutation in the *crp* gene you started with. The answers above assume that the *crp* gene had a missense mutation, so that mutant gene product would be made but has an altered amino acid sequence that would compromise some aspect of its function. If you started with a nonsense or frameshift mutant that could not make full-length CRP protein, the suppressors you find (excluding nonsense or frameshift suppressor mutations in tRNA genes) would have to bypass or circumvent the entire catabolite repression mechanisms. Very few ways can be envisioned to accomplish this kind of bypass.

b. **Most likely, the α-subunit of RNA polymerase interacts directly with the CRP protein.** If the original *crp* mutation was a missense mutation, then the gene could encode a full-length CRP protein that could no longer interact with the α subunit of RNA polymerase. If the gene encoding the α subunit had a compensating missense mutation, then the mutant CRP protein might be able to form contacts with the mutant RNA polymerase.

Much less likely is the hypothesis that the mutant RNA polymerase might recognize the promoters of the operons involved in metabolizing sugars more strongly than normal, so that positive control through the CRP-cAMP complex would no longer be needed for high levels of the expression of these operons. First, you know that promoter recognition is mostly mediated by the σ subunit of RNA polymerase rather than the α subunit. Second, a mutation that altered RNA polymerase's recognition of many promoters would likely be lethal to the cell.

10-17.

a. Mutations **i, iii, v, and vi** would all prevent the strain from utilizing lactose. (i) Deletion of *lacY* would prevent importation of lactose into the cell because Lac permease would be missing. (iii) A loss-of-function missense mutation in *lacZ* would abolish the ability of β-galactosidase to cleave lactose into galactose + glucose. (v) If the cell had a super-repressor mutation, transcription of the *lac* operon would not take place even if lactose was present in the medium because the super-repressor protein would always occupy the operator and could not be removed by it. (vi) By inverting the structural genes but not the regulatory region including the promoter, the structural genes could not be transcribed properly (the resultant message would be an RNA with the same sequence as the DNA's template strand, not the same sequence as the RNA-like strand, and the polarity would be incorrect).

b. The *lacY* deletion will be complemented by any other mutation that expresses the LacY (permease) protein. These will include **mutations ii, iii, and iv**. (In the strains with a Lac$^+$ phenotype, the *lacY$^+$* gene will be expressed from the operon on the plasmid, not from the operon on the bacterial chromosome.) Cells carrying plasmids with mutations v and vi will be Lac$^-$ in phenotype because the *lacY* genes on the plasmids could not be expressed as explained in part *a*, while the *lacY* gene on the bacterial chromosome has a *lacY* deletion.

c. First look for striking patterns that might indicate a specific mutation. For example, mutant 6 shows expression of *lacZ* when combined with any of the other mutations. Of the possible choices, mutation 6 could only be an o^c mutation. Strains containing mutation 5 and any of the mutations other than mutation 6 also have a very consistent pattern: *lacZ* is never expressed, except when combined with mutation 6 (the o^c mutation). Mutation 5 therefore shuts down the other copy of the operon in addition to its own copy, which can be explained by a super-repressor (I^s) mutation.

Looking at the remaining mutations, the inversion of the entire *lac* operon (iv) should not have an effect on expression and should not influence expression from other copies of the operon. Mutation 4 leads to inducible *lac* expression except when it is combined with mutation 5, the super-repressor. Thus, mutation 4 is equated with iv.

The inversion that does not include *lac I, P,* and *o* should not show expression because the regulatory region is now in the opposite orientation from the genes (see the answer to part *a*). This inversion should also not influence expression from the other mutant copy. Looking at the patterns for mutations 2 and 3, mutation 3 does not show expression except when combined with 4, so mutation 3 fits with this inversion.

By process of elimination, mutation 2 is a loss-of-function *lacZ* missense mutation. This conclusion makes sense because a cell with one operon containing this mutation can synthesize β-galactosidase only if the other operon has a *lacZ$^+$* gene that can be expressed.

To summarize: **mutation 1 is i; mutation 6 is ii; mutation 2 is iii; mutation 4 is iv; mutation 5 is v; and mutation 3 is vi.**

10-18.

a. **At its left end, the operator site begins at a position after the endpoint of deletion 1 and before the endpoint of deletion 5.** (The operator is intact in deletion 1 because the operon is still inducible, but part of the operator has been removed in deletion 5 because the operon is now constitutively expressed.) **The right endpoint of the operator cannot be determined by these data.**

b. **The deletions may have removed bases within the promoter that are necessary for the initiation of transcription.**

10-19.

a. **Mutations in either o_2 or o_3 alone have only small effects on Lac repressor binding.** Note on Figure 10.17 that one dimer in the Lac repressor tetramer can bind to *either o_2 or o_3*. If a *lac* operon had a mutation that disrupts one of these sites, the repressor still could bind to the either site. **A mutation in either element would have only a small effect on transcription of the operon** and would therefore be difficult to detect in screens for mutations that affect *lac* operon regulation.

b. **A mutagen that causes small insertions would produce an o^c mutant phenotype if the insertion disrupted the operator such that the Lac repressor could no longer bind to it efficiently.** There are two ways in which a small insertion could disrupt the operator sequence. First, the insertion could disrupt the specific base pair sequence at o_1 so that the repressor could not recognize it. A second way that an o^c mutant phenotype could be produced is if the insertion alters the spacing between binding sites. An insertion could change the spacing between the binding sites for the two Lac repressor monomers at o_1, or it could alter the spacing between the two operators (o_1 and o_2/o_3).

The reason spacing is important is that the Lac repressor is a tetrameric protein. A functional *lac* operator must have the four binding sites for the four subunits of the repressor protein on the same "face" of the DNA. (It takes 10.5 bp to achieve one full turn of the double-helix; binding sites that are multiples of ~11 bp apart will be on the same "face" of the DNA.) Two subunits of the tetramer bind to the two recognition sequences at the o_1 site, and the other two subunits of the tetramer bind to either the o_2 or o_3 site: the DNA in between the two operators must bend to allow simultaneous interactions with two sites. Small DNA insertions may change the way that the binding sites face one another.

c. **The o^C mutations described in part *b* that are caused by small insertions of DNA would most likely be insensitive to the I^S super-repressor protein, but *lac* operons with some such mutations might show some sensitivity to I^S depending on the nature and location of the particular DNA insertion.** ("Insensitive" here means that a double mutant strain with both an o^C mutation and an I^S super-repressor mutation would show high levels of constitutive expression of the *lac* operon. "Sensitive" means that the level of *lac* operon expression in the double mutant would be lower than in a strain with the o^C mutation alone; this low level would be seen in the presence or absence of lactose.)

An o^C mutation caused by disruption of the base pair sequence of the o_1 binding site, or alteration of the spacing between the monomer binding site at o_1, will be insensitive to an I^S super-repressor protein because the super-repressor would not be able to bind o_1, the site most critical for repression. The effect on super-repressor binding of an o^C mutation caused by altering the spacing between the two operators (o_1 and o_2/o_3) is more difficult to predict. LacI dimers might still be able to bind to the o_1 site, although the efficiency would be lower than normal because the full tetramer could not contact o_1 and o_2/o_3 simultaneously. In such cases, the level of *lac* operon expression would be reduced by the super-repressor; this expression level would be unaffected by the presence or absence of lactose because the super-repressor cannot bind to the inducer.

10-20. DNA-binding sites show rotational symmetry when they are bound by homodimers. Each monomer in the dimer has the same DNA-binding domain that recognizes the same base pair sequence. The two DNA-binding domains in the homodimer are positioned as mirror-images with respect to one another (see the chapter's opening figure), and so must be the base pair sequences that they bind.

The promoter is not rotationally symmetric because RNA polymerase is not a homodimer. It is instructive to ask why the promoter site cannot be rotationally symmetrical. The answer is that if this was the case, RNA polymerase would not "know" in which direction it should travel in order to transcribe the adjacent gene or operon.

Section 10.3 – RNA-Mediated Mechanisms of Gene Regulation

10-21. Attenuation, as in the *trp* operon, is unique to prokaryotes because it depends on translation of a nascent mRNA while the transcript is being elongated. **Transcription and translation occur simultaneously in prokaryotes, but this is not so in eukaryotes.** In eukaryotes, transcription occurs in the nucleus and transcripts are exported to the cytoplasm where they are translated.

10-22.

a. **At least three ribosomes** are required for the translation of *trpE* and *trpC* from one mRNA molecule. The fact that there is a full-length mRNA means that early in transcription one ribosome must have initiated translation of the leader and stalled at the tryptophan codons in the attenuator, resulting in antiterminator formation. A second ribosome must have bound to the ribosome binding site at the beginning of the *trpE* open reading frame, and a third ribosome must have bound to the ribosome binding site at the beginning of the *trpC* open reading frame.

b. If the two tryptophan codons in the leader were deleted, the terminator stem loop would form causing transcription termination. (With respect to Figure 10.21, the ribosome would translate the short open reading frame in the RNA leader rapidly, allowing the formation of the 3-4 stem-loop structure that terminates transcription.) **The transcription of the *trpE* and *trpC* genes would be rare** regardless of tryptophan concentration, because the level of full-length mRNA from the *trp* operon would be very low.

10-23. One open reading frame exists in this mRNA leader sequence, beginning with the first nucleotide. The predicted amino acid sequence is:

N Met Thr Arg Val Gln Phe Lys His His His His His His His Pro Asp C

Notice the 7 histidines in a row out of a total of 16 amino acids. Thus, if the cell is starving for histidine, the ribosomes will pause at the His codons (CAC or CAU) in the leader sequence because the tRNA^{His} molecules will not be completely charged with histidine. This ribosome pausing presumably allows the leader to fold up into an antiterminator configuration similar to that shown in Figure 10.21b for the *trp* operon. If the leader adopts this antiterminator configuration, RNA polymerase can complete transcription of the operon, giving maximal production of the polycistronic mRNA and maximal expression of the structural gene proteins which synthesize histidine.

10-24.

a. Since the promoter is deleted, transcription cannot occur and **there is no expression of either *trpE* or *trpC* under any conditions.**

b. The repressor cannot bind the operator, so transcription initiates constitutively. However, the attenuator is functional, so transcription often terminates prematurely (before RNA polymerase reaches the structural genes) when tryptophan is present. There will be **lower (but measurable) levels of expression of both *trpE* and *trpC* when tryptophan is present, and high levels of expression of both genes when there is no tryptophan.**

c. The repressor cannot bind tryptophan and thus cannot bind to the operator, so transcription of the structural genes is initiated constitutively. However, as in part *b*, the attenuator is normal so transcription often terminates prematurely when tryptophan is present. Thus, there will be **lower (but measurable) levels of expression of both *trpE* and *trpC* when tryptophan is present, and high levels of expression of both genes when there is no tryptophan.**

d. The repressor cannot bind to the operator, so expression of *trpC* and *trpE* is constitutive. The attenuator is nonfunctional, so the operon will always be transcribed at the maximal level. Thus, ***trpC* and *trpE* will show completely constitutive expression, with high levels of the gene products made whether or not tryptophan is present.**

e. The **expression of *trpC* is repressible by tryptophan** because the wild-type allele of this gene is controlled by a normal operator and because the repressor is *trans*-acting. When tryptophan is added to the medium, it will act as a corepressor that interacts with the repressor; the repressor/corepressor complex will bind to the operator and shut down transcription. The **expression of *trpE* is partially constitutive** (meaning that this gene is always transcribed, but the levels of expression are lower when tryptophan is present) because the *cis*-acting operator is defective but the attenuator is still functional.

f. The **expression of *trpC* is repressible by tryptophan** for the same reasons just described in part *e*. There will be **no expression of *trpE*** because one *trpE* gene has a null mutation while the wild-type *trpE⁺* gene is downstream of a defective *cis*-acting promoter.

g. Expression of ***trpE* is fully constitutive** ("on" at high levels all the time) because the *cis*-acting operator is defective and the *cis*-acting attenuator site is defective. ***trpC* expression is partially constitutive** (this gene is always transcribed, but the levels of expression are lower when tryptophan is present) because the *trpC⁺* gene is in *cis* with a defective operator and a functional attenuator.

10-25. To distinguish between the transcription interference and translation inhibition mechanisms for antisense RNA action, **you can test whether or not the antisense RNA can act in *trans* to inhibit expression of the gene it regulates; action in *trans* would rule out transcription interference.** Assuming that you have a method for detecting the protein product of the gene, a simple way to do this experiment would be to **use recombinant DNA technology to make a plasmid construct in which a strong bacterial promoter drives transcription of the antisense RNA.** You would then grow bacteria transformed with the plasmid under conditions where the gene product in question is normally expressed from the bacterial chromosome. **If the antisense RNA functions by interfering with sense transcription (in *cis*), then the antisense RNA from the plasmid should have no effect on the levels of the gene product. If the antisense RNA functions in *trans* by interfering with translation of the sense RNA, then bacteria containing the plasmid should synthesize little or no protein product.**

10-26.

a. Lac repressor: **protein; negative regulator; transcription initiation; in *trans*.**

b. *lac* operator: **DNA; negative regulator; transcription initiation; in *cis*.**

c. CRP: **protein; positive regulator; transcription initiation; in *trans*.**

d. CRP-binding site: **DNA; positive regulator; transcription initiation; in *cis*.**

e. Trp repressor: **protein; negative regulator; transcription initiation; in *trans*.**

f. charged tRNA^{Trp}: **RNA + small molecule; negative regulator; transcription elongation; in *trans*.**

g. *trp* operon antiterminator: **RNA; positive regulator; transcription elongation; in *cis*.**

h. riboswitch terminator: **RNA; negative regulator; transcription elongation; in *cis*.**

i. sRNA that blocks translation: **RNA; negative regulator; translation initiation; in *trans*.**

10-27.

a. *CsrA*: **protein; negative regulator; translation initiation; in *trans*. *CsrB*: RNA; positive regulator; translation initiation; in *trans*.**

b. **The CsrA/CsrB system is likely to respond to glucose levels. Target genes for glycogen synthesis (anabolic) could be induced by high glucose if a repressor of *CsrB* transcription cannot bind its operator when the repressor is bound to glucose. Target genes for glycogen breakdown (catabolic) could be repressed by high glucose if a positive regulator of *CsrB* transcription binds DNA only when it is not bound to glucose.**

You should note that the underlying logic for regulation of target genes is opposite to that governing the *lac* and *trp* operons. The *lac* operon is catabolic and induced by the substrate (allolactose), while the *trp* operon is anabolic and repressed by the synthesis product (tryptophan). The opposite is the case **for the genes targeted by the CsrA/CsrB system: An anabolic operon is induced by the substrate (glucose), while a catabolic operon is repressed** by the synthesis product (glucose). The reason for the reverse is the control by glucose rather than by glycogen. This makes biological sense because: (i) glycogen is a large molecule that cannot easily be imported into cells; (ii) the anabolic pathway generates glycogen as a means of storing excess glucose; and (iii) the catabolic pathway breaks down glycogen when glucose levels are low.

Section 10.4 – Discovering and Manipulating Bacterial Gene Regulatory Mechanisms
10-28.

a. **If the X-gal plates contained maltose, the colonies could be blue because transcription of the *lacZ* reporter would be induced. Plates without maltose would have white colonies.** (Note: these colonies are wild-type in the sense that all of the genes encoding regulators of the maltose-inducible operon are wild-type.)

b. In a blue colony, the reporter is transcribed in the absence of maltose. (Presumably, these colonies would also be blue in the presence of maltose.) Blue colonies could result either from a gain-of-function mutation in a gene encoding a positive regulator of *mal* operon expression, or from a loss-of-function mutation in a gene encoding a negative regulator of this operon. The wild-type regulator, whether positive or negative, would have to respond to the presence or absence of maltose.

If the mutant gene in this colony encodes a positive regulator of the maltose-inducible operon: (i) The wild-type protein encoded by this gene would be activated by maltose. In the likely case that the protein is a transcriptional regulator, the wild-type protein might bind DNA more efficiently in the presence of maltose. (ii) The mutation would result in a hypermorphic or neomorphic gain-of-function. (iii) The mutation would either increase the amount of the protein or alter the protein's amino acid sequence to make the protein work more efficiently or in a new way. For example, if the wild-type protein binds to DNA weakly in the absence of maltose, the mutation might result in more of the protein being produced; alternatively, mutant cells might produce normal amounts of a mutant protein that could bind DNA efficiently in the absence of maltose. The reporter gene would thus be expressed (the colony would be blue) even if maltose is not present.

If the mutant gene in a blue colony encodes a repressor of the maltose-inducible operon: (i) The wild-type protein encoded by this would function in the absence of maltose but not in its presence. In the most likely scenario, this protein would be a transcriptional repressor like the Lac repressor that could bind DNA in the absence, but not in the presence, of an inducer related to maltose. (ii) The mutation would be loss-of-function [either an amorph (null) or a

hypomorph]. (iii) The mutagen is not specified, so the mutation could be a nonsense mutation, a missense mutation in a key amino acid for protein function, a frameshift mutation near the start of the ORF, or a deletion of the gene. If the negative regulator function is missing, the reporter gene would be expressed (the colony would be blue) regardless of the presence of maltose.

c. **If the mutation is gain-of-function, transformation of mutant bacteria with a wild-type genomic library will not rescue the mutant phenotype (constitutive expression, seen as blue colonies on plates lacking maltose) to wild type (inducible expression, seen as white colonies on plates lacking maltose). However, transformation of a wild-type strain with a genomic library made from mutant genomic DNA would cause the mutant phenotype: A colony transformed with a plasmid containing the gain-of-function mutant gene would be blue in the absence of maltose.**

If the mutation is loss-of-function, the opposite results would be observed. Transformation of mutant bacteria with a wild-type genomic plasmid library would result in rescue of the mutant phenotype to wild type (in colonies transformed with a wild-type copy of the gene corresponding to the mutation), while transformation of mutant bacteria with a mutant genomic library would not – the genomic library would not contain a wild-type copy of the mutant gene.

10-29. The loss of LexA function leads to the new expression of many genes. **Therefore, the wild-type LexA protein acts as a negative regulator that shuts off the expression of these target genes.** One possible model is that the LexA protein is a repressor that binds to the operators of target genes or operons. However, given the information in the problem, LexA could also suppress target gene expression in other ways, for example by preventing translation of target gene/operon mRNAs.

It turns out that LexA is indeed a repressor that turns off target gene transcription by binding to an operator sequence. The mechanism by which DNA damage induces expression of the target genes is very interesting. In the presence of DNA damage, another protein called RecA interacts with LexA in a fashion that causes the LexA protein to cleave itself, disrupting LexA's DNA-binding domain. LexA can no longer bind to operators, so target gene/operon expression is induced.

This system becomes even more interesting when you consider that among the genes targeted by LexA are the genes encoding proteins that participate in the SOS system of DNA repair (described in Chapter 8). When DNA damage occurs, LexA is inactivated, leading to induction of the genes encoding these SOS system enzymes. These enzymes are now synthesized and the DNA damage can be corrected. Because the SOS system is error-prone, cells need to repress the synthesis of these enzymes if the DNA is not damaged; this is the function of the LexA repressor.

10-30. Fuse the *lacZ* coding sequences to the promoter and regulatory elements of one of the motility genes whose expression was increased during cell growth in poor carbon sources. Then introduce this fusion gene into a *lacZ⁻ E. coli* strain. This bacterial strain will make high levels of ß-galactosidase in media containing poor carbon sources, but lower levels in media with rich carbon sources. **Next, mutagenize this strain and look for mutants in which *lacZ* expression does not increase under poor growth conditions.** Such mutants can be assayed with a ß-galactosidase substrate like X-Gal that changes colour when cleaved. Mutant cells would not produce ß-galactosidase and so could not cleave X-Gal and would give rise to white colonies on Petri plates that were made with poor carbon source medium. The cells which do produce ß-galactosidase will cleave the X-Gal and give rise to blue colonies on the same plates.

The above experiment would allow you to isolate mutants in genes involved in the foraging response. **You would next have to identify the gene that was altered in each mutant strain.** One approach would be to map the genes; this procedure would be much easier if you mutagenized the cells with a transposon and then identified the transposon insertion site with inverse PCR. Another approach would be to "rescue" the mutant phenotype by transforming mutant cells with a plasmid library containing random fragments of the bacterial genome and looking for transformants that now give rise to blue colonies on poor carbon source Petri plates.

10-31.

a. **The plasmid diagrammed below** also contains an origin of replication and a drug resistance gene that are not shown. The *lac* operon regulatory region must contain the operon's promoter, operator, CRP-cAMP binding site, and the ribosome binding site. Note that the *lac* regulatory region must be followed by sequences encoding MBP, DDDDK, and erythropoietin (EPO) in that order because the N-terminus of the fusion protein is the N-terminus of MBP, while the C-terminus of the fusion protein is the C-terminus of EPO.

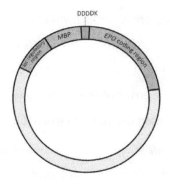

b. The ribosome binding site is in the *lac* regulatory sequences **(ii).**

c. In order for the plasmid to encode the desired fusion protein, MBP, DDDDK, and the EPO coding region must all be in frame with one another: **(i, iii, iv).**

d. The EPO coding sequences should come from a **cDNA** because bacterial genes do not have introns and therefore bacteria cannot splice eukaryotic RNAs that contain introns.

e. Based on the information given in the text, the most logical choices here would be to use either **lactose or allolactose** as the inducers to "turn on" expression of the fusion gene. In actuality, these compounds are metabolized (cleaved by β-galactosidase) so quickly that the induction would only be temporary. Genetic engineers can instead use a compound called isopropyl β-D-1-thiogalactopyranoside (IPTG) as the inducer for fusion genes under the control of the *lac* operon regulatory region. This compound is a molecular mimic of allolactose, so it can bind in the same way to the Lac repressor, but it is not cleaved at all by β-galactosidase. **The inducer should be added to the culture after the population has reached high density** because the fusion protein may be harmful to the bacterial cells. If the inducer was added too early, the culture might stop growing so that too few cells would be available, and too little fusion protein could be produced.

f. As its name implies, the maltose binding protein (MBP) binds tightly to the sugar maltose. **The fusion protein could be purified by passing an extract from MBP-DDDDK-EPO-expressing bacteria over a column containing maltose molecules coupled covalently to an insoluble resin.** You would then wash off proteins that are not bound tightly to the column, leaving the fusion proteins on the resin.

g. **You would add enterokinase enzyme to the column in part *f* that has bound MBP-DDDDK-EPO.** This enzyme cleaves polypeptides just after (C-terminal to) DDDDK. Thus after cleavage, N MBP-DDDDK C will remain bound to the column through the association of MBP with maltose, while EPO freed of MBP and DDDDK will elute from the column and can be collected.

10-32. Genes transcribed in response to osmolarity changes are likely to include genes transcribed in response to other stresses like heat shock as well as genes that are turned on specifically in response to the osmolarity change. Compare RNA-Seq data from bacteria grown under high and low osmolarity with bacteria grown in normal temperatures and in heat-shock conditions. **RNAs present specifically in the heat-shocked culture and also specifically in either high or low osmolarity conditions are likely to be general stress response genes.** (*Note*: In this usage, "present specifically" does not necessarily mean that no transcripts of the gene are seen in a particular condition, but instead the proportion of "reads" from the total mRNA would be significantly higher under one condition or the other. It will also be interesting to look at the RNA-Seq data to see if the expression of any genes is turned down in one condition versus the other.)

10-33.

a. There are **19 genes** depicted in Figure 10.29; one gene in *light blue* just upstream of *modA* is clearly shown but is unnamed. The average gene density is **1 gene per 1000 bp**, which is **characteristic of bacterial genomes. The figure depicts 5 multicistronic operons**; however, if you counted each "singleton" gene as a separate operon, you could say that 10 operons exist in this region [or even 11 as discussed in part *e* below].

b. No transcripts were found for the gene *t2110*, but the RNA-Seq analysis was performed under a single environmental condition; **under different conditions, it is possible that *t2110* transcripts could be detected.** In databases, *t2110* is curated as a "hypothetical gene" because it has a long ORF, but it has never been demonstrated that the polypeptide encoded by this ORF is ever made in cells.

c. Premature termination of transcription due to regulation by an attenuator or a riboswitch could be detected as **fewer sequence reads at the end of an operon that at the beginning. The *hutUH* operon may be regulated this way.** Note on Figure 10.29 that RNA-Seq detects significantly more reads for *hutU* than for *hutH*.

d. Antisense transcription would be detected as **sequence reads in both directions in a region of the genome.** (You would see some reads represented in *green* and some reads in *purple* in a particular position of the DNA sequence.) No such examples are seen in the figure.

e. The **figure shows more reads of the *galM* sequence than reads of the *galETK* genes**. This is unexpected because *galM* is furthest from the promoter; if anything, you would expect RNA polymerase to terminate transcription before it reached *galM*. This finding suggests that *galM* might be a single gene controlled by its own promoter rather than part of the same operon with *galETK*.

f. **No.** What is recorded by RNA-Seq is the relative number of transcripts corresponding to different genes. Translational regulation would not be apparent in the data.

10-34. (i) The sRNA sequences should not contain any ORFs. (ii) In many cases, sRNAs could be excluded as being fragments of a larger mRNA because the same RNA-Seq experiment may not reveal any nearby transcripts in the same orientation. (iii) The reverse complement of the sRNA sequence should exist in the sense strand of one or more mRNAs, specifically in the 5' UTR.

Section 10.5 – A Comprehensive Example: Control of Bioluminescence by Quorum Sensing

10-35. Using RNA-Seq analysis, the transcriptome of *V. fischeri* growing at high density and making light could be compared with that of non-bioluminescent *V. fischeri* growing at low density. The *luxICDABE* operon would be identified as a transcript present at much higher levels in bioluminescent bacteria than in those not making light. However, *luxR* would not be identified as it is transcribed at the same levels in *V. fischeri* under both low and high density conditions.

10-36. The key to solving this problem is to remember that loss-of-function mutations in the same gene do not complement (−), while mutations in different genes do complement (+). In addition, mutations that inactivate an entire operon will fail to complement mutations in single genes within that operon. The complementation matrix is shown in the following diagram. Along the diagonal, recall that mutations cannot complement themselves.

	1	2	3	4	5	6	7	8	9
1									
2	−								
3	+	+							
4	+	+	+						
5	+	+	+	+					
6	+	+	+	+	−				
7	+	+	+	+	−	−			
8	−	−	−	−	+	+	+		
9	−	−	−	−	+	+	+	−	

You can use this complementation matrix to sort the 9 bioluminescence mutants into four complementation groups: group I = 1, 2, 8, 9; group II = 3, 8, 9; group III = 4, 8, 9; group IV = 5, 6, 7. **These complementation results are unusual compared with those you saw in Chapter 8 in that mutants 8 and 9 are members of three distinct complementation groups. The reason is that the mutations in strains 8 and 9 prevent expression of the entire *luxICDABE* operon. In contrast, the mutants that define the three individual complementation groups each affect only one of the genes in the operon: Mutants 1 and 2 are *luxA⁻*, mutant 3 is *luxB⁻*, and mutant 4 is *luxI⁻*. Note that mutants 8 and 9 are not included in complementation group IV (mutants 5, 6, 7) because the group IV mutants are *luxR⁻*, and the *luxR* gene is not part of the *luxICDABE* operon.**

10-37.

a. **The *luxR* gene is transcribed at low levels** – not high enough to make the amount of *lacZ* transcript required for blue colonies.

b. **The *luxICDABE* operon is transcribed at low levels without autoinducer.**

c. **Transcription of *luxR* is not controlled by autoinducer;** Figure 10.32 does not indicate any way in which this could occur.

d. **LuxR bound to autoinducer activates transcription of the *luxICDABE* operon. The *luxI* gene encodes Synthase, which makes more autoinducer. The operon needed to be transcribed and translated in order to make enough autoinducer to produce enough *lacZ* transcript for the colonies to turn blue.**

e. ***luxR* transcription is constitutive but at a low level.**

10-38. Molecules that mimic the ligand for the quorum-sensing receptor would repress *V. cholera* toxin expression and could potentially be used as drugs to prevent cholera symptoms.

Chapter 11   Eukaryotic Gene Regulation

Synopsis:

As with prokaryotic genes, important steps in the regulation of eukaryotic genes occur at the level of transcription initiation. Because eukaryotic chromosomes are not naked DNA, but instead are protein/DNA complexes called chromatin, eukaryotic transcriptional activators and repressors function differently than those of prokaryotes. In multicellular eukaryotes, the multiplicity of diverse differentiated cell types requires that the control regions of the genes interact with many more transcription factors than is the case with the control regions of genes in prokaryotes. A fascinating feature of the control of eukaryotic transcription initiation discussed in this chapter is the existence of epigenetic phenomena such as *genomic imprinting* in which patterns of specific histone modifications and cytosine methylation in DNA that modulate gene expression can be inherited both through cell division and also through the gametes. (Interestingly, although it was not presented in Chapter 10, imprinting exists also in bacteria, but through adenine methylation.) The existence of epigenetic phenomena has many implications for both inheritance and evolution, and the study of events such as genomic imprinting is therefore an extremely active area of research.

Gene expression in eukaryotes is not regulated only at the level of transcriptional initiation, but also at subsequent steps. The housing of DNA in a nucleus precludes certain prokaryotic post-initiation control mechanisms like transcription attenuation that depend on transcription and translation occurring in a single cellular compartment. Nonetheless, some post-transcriptional gene control mechanisms that are of great importance in eukaryotes are either not available to prokaryotes or are employed in different ways. This chapter focuses on two such mechanisms. One is the ability of RNA-binding proteins to determine patterns of alternative splicing, thus allowing primary transcripts to be processed into different mature mRNAs. Surprisingly, the control of alternative splicing plays a key role in determining the sex of *Drosophila*. A second post-transcriptional mechanism described in the chapter concerns the existence of several classes of small RNA molecules that affect the stability and translation of eukaryotic mRNAs.

Key Terms:

promoter – a DNA sequence near the transcription start site that attracts RNA polymerase to the gene. Eukaryotic pol II promoters bind RNA polymerase indirectly, and contain a **TATA box**, a sequence of roughly seven nucleotides which are all As and Ts.

basal factors – transcription factors that bind the promoter, such as TATA-box binding protein (TBP), and their associated proteins, such as TBP-associated factors (TAFs); together, these proteins form a *basal factor complex* that attracts RNA polymerase to the promoter.

enhancer – a *cis*-acting DNA element that regulates transcription of one or more genes and that may be located thousands of base pairs distant from the promoter. Enhancers contain binding sites for transcription factors and are responsible for the spatiotemporal specificity of transcription.

activators and **repressors** – eukaryotic transcription factors that bind sites within enhancers. *Activators* are positively-acting factors that either stabilize the basal factor complex at the promoter, or recruit **coactivators**, which are proteins that displace nucleosomes from the promoter. *Repressors* are negatively-acting factors that recruit **corepressors**, which are proteins that either disrupt the basal factor complex at the promoter, or close chromatin at the promoter.

indirect repressors – proteins that prevent transcription of a gene by inhibiting the function of an activator rather than by binding to DNA.

GFP (green fluorescent protein) – a jellyfish protein used as a reporter protein by researchers; when activated by UV light, GFP glows in live cells.

insulators – DNA sites that bind proteins in order to organize chromosomes into loops; an enhancer can interact only with promoters in the same loop.

DNA methylation – in vertebrates, the addition of a methyl group to the cytosine base in a CpG sequence (5' CG 3') to form 5-methylcytosine.

CpG island – a *cis*-acting transcriptional regulatory element found upstream of some eukaryotic genes and that is rich in CpG sequences; the activity of the CpG island depends on the extent of cytosine methylation within it. Nonmethylated CpG islands bind activators, while methylated CpG islands exclude activator binding and may bind repressors.

epigenetic phenomenon – a heritable (directly through cell division or through gametes) change in gene expression not caused by a mutation in the gene's base pair sequence.

genomic imprinting – epigenetic phenomena due to methylation of transcriptional regulatory elements and particular histone modifications, where the maternal or paternal origin of an allele affects its expression in the progeny. **Imprinted alleles** are transcriptionally silenced.

miRNAs (micro-RNAs) and **siRNAs (small interfering RNAs)** – small *trans*-acting RNAs that regulate the stability or translation of specific mRNA targets through complementary base-pairing. miRNAs are produced by processing of long primary transcripts (*pri-miRNAs*), while siRNAs are produced by the processing of double-stranded RNAs. A given mature miRNA or siRNA binds a protein complex called **RISC (RNA-induced silencing complex)**, and guides it to the target mRNA.

piRNAs (Piwi-interacting RNAs) – small *trans*-acting RNAs that guide complexes containing *Piwi proteins* to transposable elements (TEs) or to TE transcripts. piRNAs are important for limiting the mobilization and transposition of TEs.

RNA interference – a research technique for reducing or turning off gene expression that exploits the siRNA pathway. Double-stranded RNA (dsRNA) corresponding to the base-pair sequence of a gene is introduced into a cell or organism. Enzymes in the cell or organism process the dsRNA into functional siRNA, which then guides the RISC to the target gene's mRNA, leading to degradation of that mRNA.

Structures of Eukaryotic Genes and mRNAs:

To think about gene regulation, you must be clear about the component parts of eukaryotic genes and mRNAs. In the figure below, note the following: (1) An enhancer can be thousands of base pairs away from the promoter. Most often, as shown in the figure, enhancers are located upstream of the promoter, but enhancers are sometimes found downstream of the entire transcriptional unit or even in the introns of the gene. (2) A gene is typically flanked by insulators if that gene's enhancer(s) do not activate expression of other genes also. (3) The start and stop codons can be in any exons; in other words, several exons can be devoted to the 5' UTR and/or the 3' UTR.

Eukaryotic vs. Prokaryotic Gene Regulation:

Eukaryotes	Prokaryotes
• **Promoters** bind basal factor complex, which attracts RNA polymerase	• **Promoters** bind RNA polymerase directly
• **Enhancers** determine temporal and spatial specificity of transcription	• **Operators** and **σ factors** control transcriptional response to environment
• **Insulators** organize genomic DNA to control enhancer/promoter interactions	• Neither **enhancers** nor **insulators** exist
• **Activators** bind enhancers and either stabilize the interaction of the basal complex with the promoter, or recruit **coactivators** that clear the promoter of nucleosomes	• **Activators** bind DNA near promoters and interact directly with RNA polymerase to stabilize the interaction between RNA polymerase and the promoter
• **Repressors** bind enhancers and recruit **corepressors** that either destabilize the interaction of RNA polymerase with the basal complex, or recruit nucleosomes to the promoter	• **Repressors** bind the operator and either inhibit RNA polymerase binding to the promoter, or prevent RNA polymerase from initiating transcription; **corepressors** are effectors that bind repressors and alter their conformation so that they can bind DNA
• **Alternate RNA splicing** can generate different proteins from a single gene and can be regulated by cell type-specific splicing factors	• **No RNA splicing** occurs
• Small RNAs (**miRNAs, siRNA, piRNAs**) control stability or translation of mRNA targets through complementary base-pairing	• **sRNAs** regulate translation of mRNA targets through complementary base-pairing
• **Transcription and translation occur in different cellular compartments;** mechanisms such as attenuation cannot occur	• **Transcription and translation of the same mRNA can occur simultaneously,** allowing mechanisms such as attenuation to exist

Chapter 11

Fusion Genes in Eukaryotes and Prokaryotes:

In Chapter 10, you were introduced to the idea that scientists employ recombinant DNA technology to make gene fusions. These gene fusions are useful for studying the regulation of gene expression and are also valuable for producing protein drugs in bacteria. Because the regulatory elements of prokaryotic and eukaryotic genes are somewhat different, gene fusions have different structures in bacteria and eukaryotes. The diagrams that follow summarize these differences and also show two kinds of eukaryotic fusion genes that you will encounter in later chapters. In these diagrams, P = promoter; o = operator; coloured boxes are DNA sequences from different genes; arrows indicate transcription start sites.

Two kinds of reporter genes, *lacZ* (encoding β-galactosidase) and *GFP* (encoding jellyfish green fluorescent protein) can be used both in prokaryotes and eukaryotes. Historically, *lacZ* was used first. The *lacZ* gene product can be detected in living bacterial colonies, but eukaryotic cells have to be killed in order to detect β-galactosidase. A major advantage of GFP as a reporter protein is the ability to detect GFP in living cells of both prokaryotes and eukaryotes.

Prokaryotes

• Reporter fusion to analyze regulatory elements

• Fusion to produce large amounts of Protein X

• Promoterless reporter inserted randomly in genome to identify regulatory elements and thereby genes with specific regulation

Eukaryotes

• Reporter fusion to study enhancer properties

• Fusion to produce large amounts of Protein X

• Enhancerless reporter inserted in genome randomly to identify enhancers and thereby genes with specific expression patterns

• In frame fusion of ORFs generates tagged hybrid protein

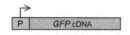

Problem Solving:

The problems in this chapter are mostly straightforward, but they require you to synthesize material from earlier chapters in the book – particularly information about chromatin (Chapter 6) and gene expression (Chapter 7). Keep in mind the structure of a eukaryotic gene and how it compares with a prokaryotic operon, and the other differences between prokaryotic and eukaryotic gene expression outlined on previous pages of this study guide.

Solutions to Problems:

Vocabulary

11-1. i. **7**; ii. **6**; iii. **4**; iv. **2**; v. **9**; vi. **8**; vii. **10**; viii. **1**; ix. **3**; x. **5**.

Section 11.1 – Overview of Eukaryotic Gene Regulation

11-2.

a. differential splicing: RNA splicing of any kind occurs in **eukaryotes** only

b. positive regulation: occurs in **both prokaryotes and eukaryotes**; *positive regulators* in prokaryotes, and *activators* in eukaryotes

c. chromatin compaction: only **eukaryotes** have chromatin

d. attenuation of transcription through translation of the RNA leader: **prokaryotes** only. Transcripts are translated during transcription elongation only in prokaryotes; in eukaryotes, transcription in the nucleus is physically separated from translation in the cytoplasm.

e. negative regulation: occurs in **both prokaryotes and eukaryotes** through *repressors*

f. translational regulation by small RNAs: occurs in **both prokaryotes and eukaryotes**; in prokaryotes through sRNAs, and through miRNAs and siRNAs in eukaryotes

11-3. Events that can affect the type or amount of active protein produced in a eukaryotic cell **include: transcript processing (including alternate splicing of the RNA), export of mRNA from the nucleus, stability of the mRNA, changes in the efficiency of translation (including regulation by miRNAs), stability of the protein product, chemical modification of the gene products, and localization of the protein product in specific organelles.**

Section 11.2 – Control of Transcription Initiation

11-4.

a. tRNAs: **pol III**

b. mRNAs: **pol II**

c. rRNAs: **pol I**

d. miRNAs: **pol II**

11-5.

a. **(i)** To identify a gene's enhancer(s), fuse the reporter to **(z)**, fragments of genomic DNA around the gene. A genomic fragment that includes an enhancer will cause GFP expression in at least some of the tissues in which the endogenous gene is normally expressed in mice. (The particular pattern of reporter expression observed will depend upon how many enhancers the endogenous gene contains and how many of these enhancers were fused to the reporter gene.) **(ii)** To express GFP tissue- specifically, fuse the reporter to **(y)**, a known kidney-specific enhancer. GFP will be expressed in the kidney. An alternative answer is **(z)**, fragments of genomic DNA surrounding a gene. This approach will work if the gene is known to be expressed tissue-specifically; one or more fragments of the DNA in the vicinity of the gene are likely to contain an enhancer that determines this tissue-specific expression. **(iii)** To identify genes expressed in neurons, fuse the reporter to **(x)**, random mouse genome sequences. Those that contain enhancers active in neurons will cause GFP expression in neurons; these enhancers can be used to identify the genes that they control normally**.**

b. As one example of ectopic expression, assume that the gene of interest is not expressed in the kidneys normally. If you fused the mouse gene to **(y)**, a known kidney-specific enhancer, the gene should then be ectopically expressed in the kidneys. This approach should work with any characterized enhancer because you could then predict where the fusion gene will be expressed. You might want to express a gene ectopically to determine whether a mutant phenotype will result; the nature of that phenotype can sometimes reveal information about the gene's normal function.

11-6. First, let's number the different parts of the regulatory region so that we can refer to them:

Maximal levels of transcription occur when both an enhancer and a promoter are present. Without a promoter, no transcription occurs; with only a promoter (and no enhancer), only low (basal) levels of transcription will occur. **The promoter must be located in fragment 5** because reporters with at least fragment 5 produce basal levels of GFP, and reporters without fragment 5 produce no GFP. This localization is expected because promoters generally are found very close to the start of transcription. **The enhancer must be in fragment 3** because reporters with at least fragment 3 + fragment 5 have maximal levels of GFP. Note that in this example, as in most cases, the enhancer and the promoter are not located adjacent to each other.

11-7. Constitutive expression of the galactose genes in yeast will be observed if GAL4 binding to UAS_G cannot be prevented. Therefore, **a *GAL80* mutation in which the protein is either not made, or is made but cannot bind GAL4 protein, will prevent indirect repression of the galactose genes and lead to constitutive synthesis. A *GAL4* mutation that prevents GAL4 protein from binding GAL80 protein would also lead to constitutive expression of the galactose genes.**

11-8.

a. As yeast is a eukaryote, the expectation is that **each gene would be transcribed individually.** Eukaryotic mRNAs are monocistronic.

b. **If the three genes (*GAL7*, *GAL10*, and *GAL1*) were somehow co-transcribed in a single mRNA, analysis of their ORFs in the genomic DNA should indicate that all three genes are transcribed from the same template strand – in the same direction.** In fact, *GAL1* is transcribed from a different template strand than are *GAL7* and *GAL10*, so it would be impossible for a single transcript to contain all three coding sequences.

To test if *GAL10* and *GAL7* are co-transcribed, generate cDNAs made from yeast cells that express both genes (for example, wild-type yeast cells grown in the presence of galactose or a strain containing a null mutation in *GAL80* that expresses *GAL7* and *GAL10* constitutively). Only if the two genes are co-transcribed will they be present on a single cDNA. You could establish this point by performing "deep sequencing" (RNA-Seq) on the cDNAs from this cell. Another way to answer this question is to perform PCR on the cDNA library (not on genomic DNA) from these cells using the primer pair shown above (*red arrows*). If the two genes were co-transcribed you would see a PCR product. However, because *GAL7* and *GAL10* are actually expressed from different transcripts, you would not find any cDNAs containing the coding sequences for both of these genes by either method.

c. A yeast genomic DNA construct could be made containing the *GAL10* and *GAL1* genes, in which the *GAL10* ORF is replaced by coding sequences for RFP, and the *GAL1* ORF is replaced by GFP coding sequences. The construct could be introduced into yeast in an autonomously replicating plasmid vector in a procedure similar to bacterial transformation. As the UAS$_G$ is located in the genomic DNA between the two divergent promoters, yeast cells containing the plasmid should express both GFP and RFP; these yeast colonies will glow either green or red when exposed to the appropriate wavelength of light. Yeast transformed with a similar genomic DNA construct but with the UAS$_G$ deleted should express neither GFP nor RFP.

In order to determine which sites are important for activation of transcription from the *GAL10* and *GAL1* promoters, a series of constructs with deletions or mutations in individual GAL4 binding sites within the UAS$_G$ could be made. A construct lacking a particular GAL4 binding site may fail to express RFP only (transcription not activated from the *GAL10* promoter), fail to express GFP only (transcription not activated from the *GAL1* promoter), fail to express both RFP and GFP (the mutant UAS$_G$ activate neither the *GAL10* nor the *GAL1* promoter), or continue to express both RFP and GFP (both the *GAL10* and *GAL1* promoters can be activated without that particular GAL4 binding site).

11-9.

a. If Id were a repressor, it would likely bind DNA at the same site on an enhancer as MyoD, or at an overlapping site. Id would inhibit MyoD function indirectly by competing for enhancer binding. Id could also function directly as a repressor by recruiting a

corepressor to the enhancer. The answer to part *b* of this problem below discusses other scenarios by which Id could function indirectly as a repressor even if it does not bind to an enhancer.

b. **As an indirect repressor, Id could bind to MyoD's activation domain (quenching), or it could form inactive Id/MyoD heterodimers (heterodimerization, also called titration). Another possibility is that Id could interact with MyoD in the cytoplasm and prevent MyoD from entering the nucleus (sequestration).**

c. **If hypothesis *a* were the case, Id ought to have a DNA-binding domain that would be recognizable in the amino acid sequence. If the heterodimerization/titration sub-hypothesis in *b* were the case, Id would have the same dimerization domain as MyoD.** The quenching and cytoplasmic sequestration hypotheses would be more difficult to discern from the Id amino acid sequence.

11-10. Let gene *A* encode transcription factor 1 and gene *B* encode transcription factor 2.

a. If both transcription factors are required for expression (complementary gene action), only the *A– B–* genotype will produce blue flowers. Diagram the cross:

Aa Bb x *Aa Bb* → 9/16 *A– B–* (blue) : 3/16 *A– bb* (white) : 3/16 *aa B–* (white) : 1/16 *aa bb* (white) = **9/16 blue : 7/16 white flowered plants**.

b. If either transcription factor is sufficient for blue colour (redundant gene action), then three of the four genotypic classes from a dihybrid cross will produce blue flowers: 9/16 *A– B–* (blue) : 3/16 *A– bb* (blue) : 3/16 *aa B–* (blue) : 1/16 *aa bb* (white) = **15/16 blue : 1/16 white flowers**.

11-11.

a. **In addition to *GFP* coding sequences, a gene construct that would express GFP in *Drosophila* needs to have a promoter, an enhancer, a transcription start site, a 5' UTR, and a transcription termination sequence within a 3' UTR.** The promoter, transcription start site, and 5' UTR need to be directly upstream of the coding region and in that order; the enhancer can be upstream of the promoter or downstream of the 3' UTR; the transcription termination sequences and 3' UTR are directly downstream of the coding sequences. Wing- specific expression would be achieved with a wing-specific enhancer.

b. **The "enhancerless" gene integrated in a different genomic location in each strain. GFP is expressed only if the construct integrated near an enhancer; the tissue and temporal specificity of that enhancer dictates the GFP expression pattern.** Reporter gene constructs like this are called *enhancer traps*; they can be used to identify genes expressed in particular cell types and/or at specific times during development when the constructs integrate near the enhancers for such genes.

11-12. You would start with a *Drosophila* strain from part *b* of Problem 11 in which the "enhancerless" GFP reporter is expressed in a tissue-specific pattern suggesting that it has integrated near an enhancer. **You would fuse wild-type *Drosophila* genomic DNA fragments from the region near the integration site to the same enhancerless promoter–*GFP* construct. You would then transform the various constructs into the genome of wild-type flies, and look for animals expressing GFP in the same tissue-specific pattern.** In this way, you could find a genomic fragment that contains the putative enhancer.

Remember that an enhancer should function upstream or downstream of a promoter, in either orientation. To verify that the genomic fragment indeed contains an enhancer, you should thus make recombinant DNA constructs in which the DNA fragment is again added to the promoter-GFP construct, but the location and orientation of the fragment relative to the coding sequence should be varied. After transformation into flies, GFP expression should again occur in the same tissue-specific pattern. Similarly, you could make constructs that include subfragments of the genomic piece in order to determine the precise boundaries of the enhancer within the original fragment.

11-13.

a. **In order to block enhancer function, an insulator needs to be located *between* an enhancer and a promoter.** Insulators prevent the expression of a given gene to be affected by enhancers associated with other genes that are located on the other side of the insulator.

b. **To identify insulators, you could make an enhancer-containing construct like the one in Figure 11.15, and insert random genomic sequences between the enhancer and the promoter driving *RFP* expression. Flies transformed with the construct will express GFP, but not RFP, if the DNA fragment contains an insulator.**

11-14.

a. The target genes of Myc-Max and Mad-Max are the same, but Myc-Max heterodimers are activators, while Mad-Max heterodimers are repressors. The implication is that in order to drive the cell cycle forward, Myc competes with Mad for Max binding. Myc expression at the G_0-to-S transition means that **target genes with enhancers that bind Myc-Max and Mad-Max would**

drive the cell cycle forward. These target genes would be repressed in the resting state (during G_0) when the *mad* gene is expressed, but they would be transcribed when the *mad* gene is turned on just before S phase. The target genes could encode proteins needed for the cell to progress into S phase and then into other phases of cell division.

b.

c. **Expression of Mad during G_0 keeps genes repressed that would otherwise advance the cell cycle. When Myc is expressed, it competes with Mad for Max binding, and the target genes that advance the cell cycle to S phase are activated instead of repressed.** As the cell gets closer to the transition between G_0 and S, the *mad* gene would presumably no longer be expressed and the Mad protein in the cell would be degraded and disappear. This latter property would act as an autocatalytic switch so that once a cell begins the transition, the decision to divide would become irreversible.

d. As will be explained in Chapter 16, Myc is a proto-oncogene; that is, a normal gene whose product promotes cell proliferation. **Cancer-causing mutations in Myc would be gain-of-function alleles** that in some way caused Myc to be overactive (hypermorphic). The more Myc function present in the cell, the more likely that the cell will proliferate in the out-of-control fashion typical of tumour cells.

11-15.

a. **Prokaryotic repressors, like the Lac repressor, directly block RNA polymerase from binding the promoter and/or block the movement of RNA polymerase bound at the promoter to the transcription start site** (see Figure 10.4b). **Eukaryotic repressors recruit corepressor proteins that either close chromatin or prevent pol II from binding the promoter** (see Figure 11.9).

b. **Prokaryotic activators, like CAP, attract RNA polymerase to the promoter by touching the polymerase directly. Eukaryotic activators bind coactivators that displace nucleosomes resulting in open chromatin, or recruit RNA pol II to the promoter through interactions with other proteins such as those in the Mediator complex** (see Figure 11.6).

11-16. The UAS_G-*lacZ* construct is a reporter gene that "reports" the interaction between the protein of interest (the "bait") and a protein encoded by a cDNA (the "prey"). The Gal4 DNA-binding domain brings the bait protein to UAS_G. If a prey cDNA encodes a protein that interacts with the bait protein, the Gal4 activation domain will also be recruited to UAS_G. The two fusion proteins bound together constitute a complete activator – a DNA-binding domain and an activation domain. Expression of β-galactosidase will signal the presence of a prey protein that interacts with the bait protein:

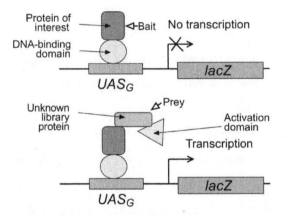

To identify proteins that interact with a protein of interest (the bait), you would take yeast cells previously transformed with the reporter plasmid (UAS_G-*lacZ*) and the bait plasmid (encoding the fusion between the protein of interest and the GAL4 DNA-binding domain) and now transform these cells with a prey cDNA library (in which each clone can express a fusion between the protein encoded by the cDNA and the activation domain of Gal4). Each yeast colony will contain a different prey plasmid from the library.

If the bait and the prey proteins interact with each other, the activation domain will be brought to UAS_G and *lacZ* will be expressed. Colonies that express β-galactosidase will be blue

on X-gal indicator plates. The prey plasmid can be purified and its cDNA identified, allowing you to find a protein that interacts with the protein of interest.

Section 11.3 – Chromatin Structure and Epigenetic Effects

11-17. Remember that Prader-Willi syndrome is caused by a mutation in an autosomal <u>maternally</u> imprinted gene. In order to answer this question, you must be able to figure out the genotype of the original affected parent. Remember that all individuals have only one transcriptionally active allele of this gene, and that is the allele they inherited from their father.

a. **True.** An affected male has a mutant allele of the gene that he inherited from his father and an imprinted (transcriptionally silenced) and presumably normal allele of the gene that he inherited from his mother. In the affected male's gametes, somatic imprints are removed and sex-specific ones are applied. As this gene is maternally imprinted, neither allele is imprinted in his germline. Therefore, half of his sperm will have the non-imprinted normal allele and the other half will have the non-imprinted mutant allele. All of his children will receive an inactivated (presumably wild-type) allele of this maternally imprinted gene from their mother and so half of his sons and half of his daughters will be affected.

b. **True.** See part *a*.

c. **False.** An affected female has a mutant allele of the gene that she inherited from her father and an imprinted (transcriptionally silenced) and presumably normal allele of the gene that she inherited from her mother. In the affected female's gametes, somatic imprints are removed and sex-specific ones are applied. As this gene is maternally imprinted, both of her alleles are imprinted, meaning that this gene is transcriptionally silenced in all of her eggs. Therefore, half of her eggs will have the imprinted normal allele and the other half will have the imprinted mutant allele. All of her children will receive an active (presumably wild-type) allele of this maternally imprinted gene from their father, so none of her children (whether sons or daughters) will be affected.

d. **False.** See part *c*.

11-18. Draw out the pedigree, including the information given in the problem. In the diagram that follows, the alleles of the maternally imprinted *IGF-2R* gene are *60K* and *50K*, while {} represents an allele that is transcriptionally inactivated (imprinted).

a. Both of Joan's alleles will be imprinted in her gametes, so Jill and Bill Jr. each express the allele they received from Bill Sr. Therefore, **Bill Sr.'s genotype is *50K/{60K}***. With this information, nothing further can be said about **Joan's genotype (*60K/{?}*)**, and there is no way of telling which of Joan's alleles Jill and Bill Jr. received.

b. Bill Sr.'s complete genotype and the further information about Pat and Tim are presented in the pedigree below.

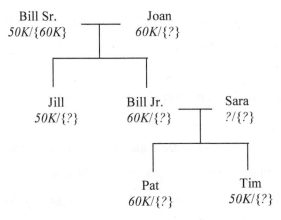

As in part *a* for Joan, both of Sara's alleles will be imprinted in her gametes. Therefore, Pat and Tim express the transcriptionally active alleles they received from Bill Jr. Because Tim's phenotype is 50K, Bill Jr. must be heterozygous *60K/{50K}*, with his imprinted *{50K}* allele having come from Joan. Therefore, **Joan's genotype is *60K/{50K}* and Bill Sr.'s genotype is *50K/{60K}***.

11-19. It may be helpful to refer to Figure 11.20a, which shows a typical pedigree diagram for a phenotype controlled by a paternally imprinted autosomal gene.

a. **No.** The alleles of the gene are not expressed in the germ cells of male I-2. The gene is paternally imprinted, and sex-specific imprints are applied in the germline. Therefore, by the end of meiosis, both alleles of this gene are imprinted (transcriptionally inactivated).

b. **No.** The allele of the gene from male I-2 will not be expressed in the somatic cells of II-2. The gene copy inherited from her father was turned off in his germ cells, so the somatic cells arising after fertilization will contain an inactive copy from I-2.

c. **Yes.** The allele of the gene from male I-2 will be expressed in the germ cells of II-2. The somatic cell imprinting inherited from I-2 (I-2 allele inactivated) is erased during gametogenesis, and sex-specific imprints applied. A female will not inactivate either of her alleles of this gene in any of her eggs, so both alleles of this gene will be active in the germ cells of II-2.

d. **No.** The allele of the gene from male I-2 will not be expressed in the somatic cells of II-3. The allele inherited from I-2 is imprinted, so the son's somatic cells will not express that allele.

e. **No.** The allele of the gene from male I-2 will not be expressed in the germ cells of II-3. The imprinting from I-2 is erased during gametogenesis, but the male will re-imprint both alleles of the gene in his germ cells.

f. **Yes.** The allele of the gene from male I-2 (should it be the one inherited) would be expressed in the somatic cells of III-1. The grandson (III-1) would have inherited the non-imprinted allele of the gene from his mother (II-2), so the allele from I-2 is expressed in the somatic cells of III-1.

g. **No.** The allele of the gene from male I-2 (should it be the one inherited) would not be expressed in the germ cells of III-1. Male III-1 will have imprinted both alleles of this gene in his germ cells.

11-20.

a. *Gene A* **is not imprinted**; whether the AKR strain was the female or male parent, half the sequence reads were from the AKR allele, meaning that the *Gene A* alleles from the AKR and PWD strains were expressed equally in the fetus. *Gene B* is **maternally imprinted**: When the female parent is AKR, no sequence reads are obtained from the AKR alleles of *Gene B*, indicating that the *Gene B* allele inherited from AKR is not transcribed; when the AKR is male parent (and PWD is the female parent), all of the sequence reads are from the AKR allele of *Gene B*, indicating that the PWD allele is inactive. *Gene C* is **paternally imprinted**: When the female parent is AKR, all of the sequence reads from *Gene C* are from the AKR allele (no transcripts from the PWD allele of *Gene C* are detected); when the male parent is AKR, none of the sequence reads of *Gene C* are from the AKR allele.

b. **Reciprocal crosses are important to determine if a gene is imprinted as opposed to having a mutation that prevents its expression irrespective of which parent the allele came from.**

c. A diagram of the cross looks like this:

$$\female\ A^{AKR}\ B^{AKR}\ C^{AKR}\ /\ A^{PWD}\ B^{PWD}\ C^{PWD}\ \times\ \male\ A^{PWD}\ B^{PWD}\ C^{PWD}\ /\ A^{PWD}\ B^{PWD}\ C^{PWD}$$

At each gene (A, B, and C), the progeny of this cross could be heterozygous AKR/PWD, or homozygous PWD/PWD. We determined in part a that *Gene A* is not imprinted, that *Gene B* is maternally imprinted, and that *Gene C* is paternally imprinted.

If a progeny mouse is heterozygous (AKR/PWD) for any one of the genes, the expected expression patterns are as shown in the diagram below at left. The key insight is that in the progeny, the AKR alleles come from the female parent and the PWD alleles from the male parent. If a progeny mouse is homozygous (PWD/PWD) for any one of the genes, that mouse will have no AKR alleles so the percentage of mRNA reads that are AKR-specific will be zero.

11-21. As shown in the diagram below, **an insulator that controls imprinting could be located between separate placenta and fetal heart enhancers, such that the insulator is between the placenta enhancer and the promoter**, but not between the heart enhancer and promoter. In this configuration, imprinting could be tissue-specific: The gene could be maternally imprinted in the placenta but not the fetal heart.

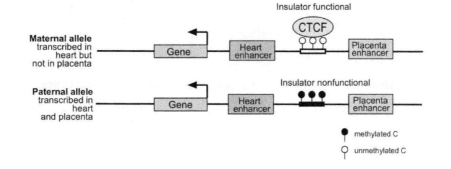

11-22. An antibody that binds only to DNA containing 5-methylcytosine could be used to identify genomic DNA fragments that are sex-specifically methylated; these fragments could include regulatory sequences of imprinted genes. The procedure you would use is similar to that outlined in Figure 11.17, but you would start with genomic DNA rather than chromatin. **You would make separate genomic DNA preparations from male and female cells. You would then fragment the DNA and incubate it with the antibody; the antibody would immunoprecipitate (IP) DNA fragments only if they are methylated. You would then sequence the IPed fragments and determine if any sequences are recovered only from male or only from female cells. You would then query the genome sequence to determine if these sex-specifically methylated sequences are near or within genes. Finally, you would use RNA-Seq to verify whether those genes are imprinted.** Allele differences in the copies of the gene inherited from each parent would allow you to determine if the transcripts from the gene in the progeny correspond only to one parental allele.

Section 11.4 – Regulation After Transcription

11-23. Experiments to determine whether or not the 5' UTR or the 3' UTR of *hunchback* regulate its translation would involve making transgene constructs and introducing them into the fly. You will learn the details of transforming transgenes into the *Drosophila* genome in Chapter 17, but assume for now that engineered DNAs can in fact be integrated into fly chromosomes.

You could perform three kinds of experiments. **(1) You could replace the 5' UTR or 3' UTR of a cloned copy of the *hunchback* gene with the corresponding part of another gene. (2) You could alter the base pair sequences of 5' UTR or 3' UTR of the cloned copy of the *hunchback* gene.** In either case, you would ask whether the manipulated *hunchback* gene you put into the fly genome could rescue the phenotype associated with *hunchback* loss-of-function mutations.

A third approach relies on the fact that the translational regulation of *hunchback* affects the distribution of the Hunchback protein. As you will learn in Chapter 17, although the *hunchback* mRNA is initially found everywhere in the embryo, the Hunchback protein is present only in the anterior half of the embryo. (A protein called Nanos prevents Hunchback translation in the posterior half of the embryo.) **(3) You could thus attach the 5' UTR or 3' UTR of *hunchback* to a reporter gene like *GFP*. If these UTR sequences regulate translation, you might see GFP fluorescence only in the anterior part of the embryo.**

11-24.

a. A single eukaryotic gene can give rise to several different types of mRNA molecules through **alternate splicing of the primary transcript**. In addition, some genes have **multiple promoters**, and so different transcription start sites can also generate different transcripts.

b. A single mRNA species can produce proteins with different activities through **posttranslational protein processing (e.g., cleavage of a zymogen) or posttranslational protein modifications (e.g., phosphorylation or ubiquitination).**

11-25. The protein may be posttranslationally modified only in fat cells (or in all cells except for fat cells) so that it is only active in fat cells. Alternatively, the protein may need a cofactor to be activated, and this cofactor is present only in fat cells.

11-26.

a. **Raise an antibody to the Argonaute-like protein, and use it to purify complexes between this protein and RNAs that exist within human cells. To do this, you would first isolate RNA-protein complexes from cells and try to stabilize these complexes by crosslinking them covalently with a reagent like formaldehyde. You would then immunoprecipitate (IP) the complexes containing the Argonaute-like protein using the antibody you prepared. After removing the proteins in these complexes with proteases, you would convert the IPed RNAs into cDNAs using reverse transcriptase. You would then sequence the cDNAs recovered and compare the sequences to those of known human miRNAs.**

b. In a mouse that lacks the Argonaute-like protein, any mRNAs that it down-regulates would be more abundant than in a wild-type mouse. You would thus **perform an RNA-Seq analysis comparing the mRNAs of the mutant mouse and its most closely related wild-type counterpart. You would then look for mRNAs that are overrepresented in the mutant relative to the wild-type transcriptome.**

11-27.

a. Transcription, processing of the primary transcript, and export of the mature mRNA to the cytoplasm take place before translation, but these events should only take a few minutes rather than 6 hours (1/4 of a day). Let's assume that all of these processes take about the same time for the interesting gene mRNA and the *GFP* mRNA. Therefore, **the difference in time between the first detection of the mRNA of the interesting gene and the GFP protein could be the result of some kind of translational regulation.** For example, translation of the mRNA could depend on a factor that is present in mouse embryos only starting at day 8.75. **A plausible alternative explanation is that the delay is caused by different sensitivities in detecting mRNA versus protein.** In other words, a lot of GFP protein has to accumulate before fluorescence is detectable.

The difference between the disappearance times of the mRNA and the GFP protein can be explained in at least two ways. First, **it is possible that GFP protein is more stable than the mRNA, so the protein remains in the cells for several days longer than the mRNA.** A second scenario involves the fact that the mRNA expressing GFP is not identical to the mRNA for the endogenous gene of interest. **It is thus also possible that *GFP* mRNAs are more stable than those of the interesting gene.**

b. **GFP protein expression should more accurately indicate the onset of gene activation than the cessation of gene activity.** Presumably, the *cis*-acting DNA elements controlling the transcription and translation of the *GFP* reporter gene allow reporter expression to be turned "on" and "off" with the same schedule as the transcription of the interesting gene. However, as explained in part *a* above, if mRNA or protein stability for the two genes differs, then GFP detection may cease sooner, or continue longer, than the activity of the protein product of the gene of interest. The data presented in the problem indeed indicate that the timing of GFP fluorescence aligns closer to the start than to the cessation of gene transcription. However, the investigator also needs to remember that the observation of GFP fluorescence lags the appearance of gene transcripts by a few hours.

11-28.

a. **The gene construct should express both a sense and an antisense RNA corresponding to the *gene X* ORF** (indicated as "*Gene X*" in the diagram below). The idea is that the bacteria should make double-stranded (ds) RNA. When nematodes (worms) eat the bacteria, enzymes in the worms will process the dsRNA into an siRNA, and this will lead to the degradation of the target gene's mRNA.

b. To determine if *gene X* mRNAs have been degraded by siRNA, **purify mRNAs from worms that have and have not eaten bacteria transformed with the *gene X* construct and use the two samples to make cDNAs. Using a primer pair within *gene X* and the cDNAs as the template, try to PCR-amplify a product. If the *gene X* mRNAs have been degraded by siRNA, you will be able to detect a product only from the worms that have <u>not</u> eaten the transformed bacteria. Alternatively, you could analyze the cDNAs by RNA-Seq and determine if *gene X* mRNAs are missing from the sample obtained from animals that have eaten the transformed bacteria.**

If you know that null mutants in *gene X* cause a particular phenotype, another way to test if *gene X* expression is obliterated (or at least is greatly reduced) is simply to examine the worms that have eaten the bacteria transformed with the construct and ask whether these animals show the mutant phenotype. In general, scientists would not perform this kind of experiment because the purpose of doing RNA interference is usually to ask whether knockdowns of *gene X* cause some unknown phenotype. (That is, these experiments would be done only in cases where null or hypomorphic mutations in the gene were not available.)

c. **Sometimes siRNAs affect expression of genes other than those intended. So-called "off-target effects" occur when some of the siRNA sequences are at least partially complementary to other genes.** This problem can be overcome at least in part by choosing carefully the sequences in the *gene X* construct shown in the answer to part *a*. You would select those sequences within *gene X* that have the least similarity to sequences anywhere else in the worm genome.

Section 11.5 – A Comprehensive Example: Sex Determination in *Drosophila*

11-29.

a. **Mutation of the Tra- or Tra2-binding site that prevents Tra or Tra2 binding but does not alter key Fru-M amino acids** would result in Fru-M expression in females. Even though these proteins are present in females, they could not associate with the *fru* primary transcript so the male-specific mRNA encoding Fru-M would be obtained.

b. **A construct in which a *fru-M* cDNA is downstream of the *fru* promoter** would express Fru-M in females. In effect, the primary transcript of this construct is already spliced into the male-specific pattern.

11-30.

a. **Null mutations in the *Sxl* gene are of no consequence to XY males, but are lethal to homozygous XX females.** Males do not normally express *Sxl*. The reason that the absence of Sxl kills XX animals (females) rather than transforming them into males is that the dosage compensation pathway (which equalizes the transcriptional activity of X-linked genes in males and females) is downstream of *Sxl*. Sxl protein in normal XX females leads to reduction in the transcription of X-linked genes. In contrast, the X-linked genes of XX flies that lack Sxl are over-expressed and this is lethal.

   Constitutively active *Sxl* alleles are transcribed in both XY and XX flies. As XX flies express Sxl anyway, **constitutively active Sxl would have no effect in females, but males (XY) would die.** In XY flies with a constitutively active allele, Sxl protein would reduce the amount of X-linked gene expression to about half of what it would be in normal XY flies; the result is lethality.

b. **As explained in part *a*, the lethal effects of *Sxl* mutations are all about dosage compensation.**

c. **Null alleles of *tra* transform XX flies (females) into morphological and behavioural males.** Without Tra protein, Dsx-M is produced instead of Dsx-F, and Fru-M is made instead of Fru-F. These male flies are sterile because they lack the Y chromosome and thus the Y-chromosome genes that contribute to male fertility.

   Constitutively active *tra* alleles transform XY flies (males) into morphological and behavioural females because Dsx-F and Fru-F would be expressed instead of Dsx-M and Fru-M.

d. XX animals with null *tra* alleles develop as males but they are sterile since **they do not have a Y chromosome which carries genes needed for male fertility in *Drosophila*.**

e. The *tra* mutants survive whereas the *Sxl* mutants do not because *Sxl* **controls dosage compensation, while *tra* does not;** the *tra* gene controls morphological sex and behaviour. In parts *a* and *b*, you learned that the sex-specific lethality associated with *Sxl* mutants reflects aberrations in dosage compensation.

f. As Tra-2 is required for Tra function, **the effects of *tra-2* loss-of-function would be equivalent to *tra* loss-of-function:** XX flies are transformed into morphological and behavioural males (that are sterile because of the absence of the Y chromosome), whereas XY flies would be normal males.

g. XX animals without Tra function would be transformed into morphological and behavioural males (see part *c*). **As the tra⁻ XX males express Fru-M, they would display male sexual behaviour and would try to mate with females. XY animals, on the other hand, would be normal males.**

11-31.

a. Because Sxl protein in made only in females and because MSL-2 is made only in males, the Sxl protein must repress translation of the *msl-2* mRNA from the proper (fourth) AUG. One way in which this could be accomplished is if Sxl instead promotes translation initiation from one of the wrong (out-of-frame) AUGs. **A reasonable model would be that Sxl binds the 5' UTR of *msl-2* mRNA near one of the three upstream AUGs, promoting its usage by the ribosome.** In fact, Sxl binds near the third AUG and promotes translational initiation at this site. The ribosome is then inhibited from scanning the mRNA for the correct downstream (fourth) AUG, and MSL-2 protein will not be made in females.

b. **Sxl protein is only made in females (XX), so the Sxl protein will bind to the *msl-2* mRNA in females but not in males.** It makes sense for *msl-2* translation to be inhibited only in females, as MSL-2 protein promotes dosage compensation by doubling the level of X-linked gene expression in males.

c. *Sxl* **loss-of-function is lethal to XX animals due to the failure to repress MSL-2 expression in the absence of Sxl:** Both X chromosomes will be improperly hypertranscribed in such XX animals. *Sxl* **gain-of-function alleles that are constitutively active are lethal to XY animals because Sxl will inhibit MSL-2 expression.** Because MSL-2 is not made, dosage compensation does not take place: The X chromosome in these animals will not be hypertranscribed (relative to the X chromosomes in XX females) as it should be.

d. **Loss of *msl-2* gene function would have no effect on females (XX) at all** because Sxl normally inhibits *msl-2* expression so that dosage compensation does not occur. **Without *msl-2* expression, males (XY) would die because they do not dosage compensate.** (That is, the X chromosome will not be hypertranscribed and will thus not produce the correct amount of X-linked gene products.)

Chapter 12   Variation and Selection in Populations

Synopsis:

The science of **population genetics** aims to describe how the frequencies of alleles, genotypes, and phenotypes change over the course of generations in populations of organisms. This goal may seem on the surface to be purely academic, but in reality population genetics provides essential tools for understanding evolution and even the history of humanity. The insights of population genetics have important practical implications ranging from forensics (DNA fingerprinting) to the control of bacterial pathogens and insect pests.

The starting point for population genetics is the **Hardy-Weinberg law**. At the beginning of the 20th century, these two investigators realized independently that under conditions in which a new generation is formed by the union of gametes randomly obtained from a very large pool of gametes produced by the previous generation, the allele frequencies, genotype frequencies, and phenotypic frequencies would remain constant. If these conditions are met, the population will remain in an equilibrium whose genotypic frequencies are described by the equation $p^2 + 2pq + q^2 = 1$ (if the population has two alleles of an autosomal locus whose allele frequencies are p and q). The Hardy-Weinberg law approximates the behaviour of many anonymous loci in human populations; these loci can thus be used in forensics because scientists can predict the probability that a random person's genotype at these loci will match that of a crime scene sample.

The genetic compositions of populations do and must change over time, indicating that the assumptions behind the Hardy-Weinberg equilibrium do not hold for any locus over the long term in actual populations. This chapter delves into two of the most important phenomena causing deviations from the idealized populations envisioned by Hardy and Weinberg. The first of these concerns the fact that real populations are not infinite in size. The smaller the population, the more important is **genetic drift** – changes in allele frequencies due to random sampling errors in choosing the gametes that happen to form the next generation. Allele frequencies can thus change rapidly in small populations. The second major reason real populations do not always obey the Hardy-Weinberg law is that some variants at some loci affect the organism's **fitness**: In other words, some mutations are not neutral, but instead confer selective advantages or disadvantages to individuals in the population. The effects of a mutation on fitness depend on the genotype and on the environment. As a result, some deleterious mutations such as the mutation causing sickle-cell anaemia can be maintained in certain populations if heterozygotes have a higher fitness than either class of homozygotes in a given environmental condition (such as tropical conditions in which the malaria parasite is frequently encountered).

For many traits, multiple genes, the environment, and chance events all contribute to the determination of phenotype. Such traits are called **multifactorial, quantitative,** or **complex traits**, and the extent to which any individual in a population displays the trait is called that individual's *trait value* or *phenotype value*. The contribution of genes (as opposed to the environment and chance) to a complex trait phenotype is called the **heritability** of that trait. Scientists can estimate heritability by comparing the trait values of parents, their progeny, and the population as a whole. Another way to measure heritability in humans is to compare the differences in the trait values of monozygotic (MZ) and dizygotic (DZ) twins. Heritability has practical implications, as a phenotype can change (evolve) as a result of genome mutation only to the extent that genes control the trait.

Key Terms:

population genetics – study of the transmission of genetic variation between generations in *populations*.

population – a group of individuals of the same species living in the same time and place.

gene pool – the sum total of all the alleles of all genetic loci carried in all members of a population. In a population of a diploid organism, the gene pool contains $2N$ copies of a locus, where N is the number of individuals in the population.

monomorphic vs. polymorphic locus – If a locus is *monomorphic*, only one allele of the locus exists in the population; when more than one variant exists in the population, the locus is *polymorphic*.

genotype frequency – proportion of all the individuals in a population who have a particular genotype.

phenotype frequency – proportion of all the individuals in a population who have a particular phenotype.

allele frequency – proportion of all the copies of a locus in a population that are of a given allele type.

Hardy-Weinberg equilibrium (HWE) – a condition in which allele frequencies, genotype frequencies, and phenotype frequencies remain constant between generations due to the random union at fertilization of *selectively neutral* alleles obtained from the gene pool of a very large population.

Hardy-Weinberg (H-W) proportions – the genotype frequencies for a given locus observed at Hardy-Weinberg equilibrium. If two alleles of the locus exist in a population, the H-W proportions are p^2 for homozygotes of allele A, $2pq$ for Aa heterozygotes, and q^2 for aa homozygotes, where p is the allele frequency of A and q is the frequency of the a allele.

match probability – the chance that a random individual from a population will have the same genotype as a particular chosen genotype.

Monte Carlo simulation – a method of modelling the effects of sampling error during a multi-event process, using a computer program that employs a random-number generator to choose an outcome for each event.

genetic drift – changes in allele frequencies between generations over time as a consequence of sampling error in the choice of gametes. The effects of genetic drift become significant even in the short term when population sizes are small.

allele extinction – the loss of an allele from a population.

allele fixation – When only one allele remains in a population (that is, when the locus becomes *monomorphic*), that allele is said to be *fixed*.

founder effect – a process that occurs when a few individuals leave a large population to establish a new, geographically isolated population. Due to random sampling error, the allele frequencies in the new population may differ considerably from those in the original population. If the new population is small, *genetic drift* may alter allele frequencies rapidly in the new population.

population bottleneck – a process that occurs when a catastrophe reduces a large population to a much smaller one. Like *founder effects*, allele frequencies before and after the catastrophe may change rapidly, and if it is small, the residual population will be subject to *genetic drift*.

migration – the movement of individuals from one population into a different population. Migrants from the first population can introduce new variants into the second population.

natural selection – the process by which nature progressively eliminates individuals with lower *fitness* and chooses individuals of higher *fitness* to survive and reproduce.

fitness – an individual's relative ability to survive (*viability*) and transmit its genes (*reproductive success*) to the next generation.

neutral/deleterious/beneficial mutations – *Neutral mutations* have no advantage or disadvantage from the point of view of natural selection; *deleterious mutations* confer a selective disadvantage; *beneficial mutations* confer a selective advantage.

molecular clock – *Neutral mutations* accumulate in genomes at a relatively constant rate over evolutionary time, so the number of such differences in the genomes of two species indicates when the two species last had a common ancestor.

balancing selection/heterozygote advantage – Any process that maintains polymorphisms in a population is called a *balancing selection*. One such process is *heterozygote advantage*, where heterozygous individuals have higher fitness than individuals of either homozygous genotype.

complex traits – phenotypes that can be influenced by many factors, including multiple genes, the environment, and chance events.

quantitative traits – complex traits where the phenotype can be measured numerically. The numbers assigned to different degrees of trait expression are called **phenotypic values** or **trait values**.

normal distribution – a set of data points that scatter around a central *mean* (average) without left or right bias; an equal number of data points fall below and above the mean. Normally distributed data can be represented by a *bell curve* graph in which the *x*-axis is the phenotypic value and the *y*-

axis is the number of individuals in the population who show a particular phenotypic value. The phenotypic values of quantitative traits are often normally distributed.

total phenotype variance (V_P) – describes the variation in phenotypic values for a given trait in a specific population. The number V_P is calculated as the average squared difference between each individual's phenotypic value and the mean phenotypic value. On a bell curve, the lower the value of V_P, the narrower the curve will be relative to the peak. Furthermore, because both genes and the environment influence complex traits, $V_P = V_E + V_G$ (see below).

environmental variance (V_E) – describes the fraction of the total phenotype variance (V_P) that is due to differences in environment (including chance) as opposed to genetic differences. Researchers can determine a numerical value for V_E experimentally by measuring V_P among a population of genetically identical individuals in a variable environment because under these conditions, $V_P = V_E$.

genetic variance (V_G) – describes the fraction of the total phenotype variance V_P that is due to differences in genes as opposed to environmental influences. Researchers can estimate a numerical value for V_G in an experiment where genetically different individuals inhabit a constant environment because under these conditions, $V_P = V_G$.

components of genetic variance (V_A, V_D, V_I) – Genetic variance has three components: (i) *additive effects* (V_A) of the contributions of different alleles to the trait value; (ii) the effects of *dominance interactions* (V_D) between different alleles of a single gene; and (iii) the effects of *gene interactions* (V_I) between alleles of different genes). Thus, $V_G = V_A + V_D + V_I$.

heritability – the fraction of total phenotypic variability of a trait due to genetic differences. **Broad-sense heritability (H^2)** accounts for all three components of V (V_A, V_D, and V_I), so $H^2 = V_G/V_P$. **Narrow-sense heritability (h^2)** accounts only for the additive component (V_A) of genetic variance, so $h^2 = V_A/V_P$. When heritability (whether h^2 or H^2) = 0, all of the observed variation in phenotypic values (V_P) is due to environmental influences (V_E); when heritability = 1, all observed phenotypic variation for a specific trait in the population is due to genetic differences—V_A (when h^2 is measured) or V_G (when H^2 is measured).

genetic relatedness – the average fraction of all alleles that two individuals share because they inherited them from a common ancestor. For example, the genetic relatedness of siblings is 0.5, of an uncle and a nephew is 0.25, and of first cousins 0.125.

midparent value – for a given trait, the mean phenotypic value for the two parents.

line of correlation – a straight line (the *best-fit line*) that relates the midparent values to the trait values of their progeny. The slope of the line of correlation (the *correlation coefficient*) is the narrow-sense heritability of the trait (h^2).

concordance – for discrete traits, the fraction of individuals that share the trait.

cross-fostering – In heritability studies with animals, parents and progeny are sometimes mixed randomly to minimize the effects of environmental differences (parental care) on trait values.

truncation selection – selective breeding where only individuals with particular trait values become the parents of the following generation. The difference in average trait value between the selected parents and the original population is called the *selection differential* (S), and the *response to selection* (R) is the difference in the average trait value of the offspring and the original population. R/S is called the *realized heritability*, which is the same as the narrow-sense heritability (h^2) if the phenotypic values are normally distributed. Because $R = h^2 S$, selective breeding makes sense as a way to alter average trait values only if the heritability of the trait is high.

Problem Solving:

Using the Hardy-Weinberg equation: $p^2 + 2pq + q^2 = 1$ is the starting point for most population genetics analyses. p and q represent the allele frequencies (for a locus with 2 alleles), while p^2, $2pq$, and q^2 are the genotype frequencies at equilibrium. For any value of either p or q, only one set of values for p^2, $2pq$, and q^2 would allow the population to be at equilibrium for the locus in question (Figure 12.4). If a population has such a set of values for these genotype frequencies, then the gametes that produce the next generation can be envisioned to be infinitely large pools consisting of the two alleles present at their respective allelic frequencies, and gametes from these pools are obtained and unite at random. This idea is reflected in the fact that the Hardy-

Weinberg equation can also be written as $(p + q)^2 = 1$, and that the population can be represented by the Punnett square shown in Figure 12.3.

You should note several special cases in using the Hardy-Weinberg equilibrium:

Random mating leads to equilibrium in one generation: For autosomal loci, if you start with a population that is not at equilibrium, random mating within the population will cause the population to reach equilibrium in one generation, assuming that the other Hardy-Weinberg assumptions are also met.

X-linked genes: For the population to be at equilibrium, p and q must be the same in males and females. This condition occurs for X-linked genes when the genotype frequencies in females are p^2, $2pq$, and q^2 while those in males are simply p and q. Note in Figure 12.5 that if a starting population has different X-linked allele frequencies in the males and females, it will take several generations of random mating to reach equilibrium.

Genes with more than two alleles: You would simply write an equation in which you would square the sum of all the allele frequencies: $(p + q + r + \ldots)^2$. Thus, in the case of a locus with three alleles, the equilibrium frequencies would be: $p^2 (A^1A^1) + q^2 (A^2A^2) + r^2 (A^3A^3) + 2pq (A^1A^2) + 2pr (A^1A^3) + 2qr (A^2A^3) = 1$.

Estimating allele frequencies from the frequency of a recessive homozygous genotype: In the cases of genetic diseases associated with homozygosity for a recessive allele, scientists often use the frequency of diseased individuals to estimate the frequency of the normal and mutant alleles in the population. If the population was at equilibrium, then $q = \sqrt{q^2}$, where q^2 is the proportion of individuals in the population showing the disease phenotype. Although the population cannot truly be in HWE if the fitness of one genotype is impaired, the equilibrium values nonetheless provide reasonably accurate estimates of the allelic and genotypic frequencies if the disease allele is rare.

When the population is not at HWE, then one of the Hardy-Weinberg assumptions must not hold for the particular locus in the particular population in question. The two most important exceptions are **genetic drift** (of high significance in small populations) and cases in which the **fitness** of all genotypes is not the same. Although some equations provided in the text can guide quantitative examinations of these issues, in general the questions at the end of the chapter probe your qualitative understanding of the underlying phenomena.

Heritability:

Heritability is defined as the fraction of phenotypic variance of a trait that is due to genetic variation, as opposed to the environment or chance (V_G/V_P). Heritability may be estimated experimentally in a number of different ways. One way is by comparing the phenotypes of parents and their progeny. Another way is by comparing the phenotypes of monozygotic (MZ) and dizygotic (DZ) twins.

Heritability is measured as the "correlation coefficient" between the mean trait values of genetically related individuals relative to the entire population. When those individuals do not share all alleles of all of their genes (for example, when comparing parents and their children), what is measured is **narrow-sense heritability (h^2)**, where $h^2 = V_A/V_P$. Because the effects of dominance interactions (V_D) and gene interactions (V_I) are randomized in this case, only the variation due to the additive contributions of alleles of a gene (V_A) is measured. **Broad-sense heritability (H^2)** is measured when correlating the mean trait values of individuals with identical genomes (for example, identical twins). In this case, all three components of V_G contribute to the correlation observed, and so $H^2 = V_G / V_P$. When h^2 (or H^2) = 0, all of the observed variation in phenotypic values (V_P) is due to environmental influences (V_E); when h^2 (or H^2) = 1, all observed phenotypic variation for a specific trait in the population is due to genetic differences V_A (or V_G).

For comparisons of parents and progeny, heritability can be estimated as the slope (**correlation coefficient**) of the best-fit line (the **line of correlation**) through a *scatter plot* of the trait values of the parents and their progeny (Figure 12.22). The more closely offspring resemble their parents, the closer the slope of the line is to 1; the more dissimilar the trait values of parents and offspring, the more the slope of the line moves towards 0. For a given data set, computer programs available on the internet will calculate this line and its slope for you. One simple explanation for how the *best-fit line* is calculated can be found here: http://www.mathisfun.com/data/correlation.html

Heritability can also be estimated using the correlation in trait values of MZ and DZ twins. For a particular trait, H^2 = 2[**correlation coefficient (MZ) – correlation coefficient (DZ)**].

Solutions to Problems:

Vocabulary

12-1. i. **13**; ii. **12**; iii. **8**; iv. **7**; v. **10**; vi. **1**; vii. **9**; viii. **2**; ix. **4**; x. **6**; xi. **15**; xii. **14**; xiii. **3**; xiv. **5**; xv. **11**.

Section 12.1 – The Hardy-Weinberg Law: Predicting Genetic Variation in "Ideal" Populations
12-2.

a. Calculate genotype frequencies:

G^GG^G = 120 / 200 = **0.6**; G^GG^B = 60 / 200 = **0.3**; G^BG^B = 20 / 200 = **0.1**.

b. The allele frequencies can be determined in two different ways. One way is to use the genotype frequencies in part *a*: Frequency of G^G = 0.6 + 1/2 (0.3) = **0.75**; frequency of G^B = 0.1 + 1/2 (0.3) = **0.25**.

Another method is to total all alleles within each genotype:

G^GG^G = 120 individuals with 2 G^G alleles = 240 G^G alleles

$G^G G^B$ = 60 individuals with one G^G allele = 60 G^G alleles

$G^G G^B$ = 60 individuals with one G^B allele = 60 G^B alleles

$G^B G^B$ = 20 individuals with two G^B alleles = 40 G^B alleles

There are (240 + 60) = 300 G^G alleles/400 total alleles so the frequency of G^G (p) = 0.75. There are (60 + 40) = 100 G^B alleles/400 total alleles so the frequency of G^B (q) = 0.25.

c. **For alleles at HWE, the expected frequency of $G^G G^G$ is p^2 = $(0.75)^2$ = 0.5625; the expected frequency of $G^G G^B$ is 2pq= 2(0.75)(0.25) = 0.375; the expected frequency of $G^B G^B$ is q^2 = $(0.25)^2$ = 0.0625.** Note that $p^2 + 2pq + q^2$ = 0.5625 + 0.375 + 0.0625 = 1.

12-3. For each population, determine the allele frequencies (p and q) using the observed genotype frequencies, and then use the Hardy-Weinberg equation ($p^2 + 2pq + q^2$ = 1) to determine if the genotype frequencies predicted for the next generation remain the same as those in the original population.

a. The frequency of A = 0.25 + 1/2 (0.5) = 0.5; the frequency of a = 0.25 + 1/2 (0.5) = 0.5. The predicted frequencies of genotypes in the next generation are AA [p^2 = $(0.5)^2$ = 0.25]; Aa [2pq = 2(0.5)(0.5) = 0.5]; aa [q^2 = $(0.5)^2$ = 0.25]. Because these genotype frequencies predicted by the Hardy-Weinberg equilibrium are the same as those of the original population, **population A is at equilibrium**.

b. The frequency of A = 0.1 + 1/2 (0.74) = 0.47; the frequency of a = 0.16 + 1/2 (0.74) = 0.53. The predicted frequencies of genotypes in the next generation are AA [p^2 = $(0.47)^2$ = 0.221]; Aa [2pq = 2(0.47)(0.53) = 0.498]; aa [q^2 = $(0.53)^2$ = 0.281]. These frequencies are not the same as the original genotype frequencies, so **population B is NOT at equilibrium**

c. The frequency of A = 0.64 + (1/2)(0.27) = 0.775; the frequency of a = (1/2)(0.27) + 0.09 = 0.225. The HWE frequencies are: AA = $(0.775)^2$ = 0.60; Aa = 2(0.775) (0.225) = 0.35; aa = $(0.225)^2$ = 0.05. **Population C is not at equilibrium**.

d. The frequency of $A = 0.46 + (1/2)(0.50) = 0.71$; the frequency of $a = (1/2)(0.50) + 0.04 = 0.29$. The HWE frequencies are: $AA = (0.71)^2 = 0.50$; $Aa = 2(0.71)(0.29) = 0.41$; $aa = (0.29)^2 = 0.08$. **Population D is not at equilibrium**.

e. The frequency of $A = 0.81 + (1/2)(0.18) = 0.9$; the frequency of $a = (1/2)(0.18) + (0.01) = 0.1$. The HWE frequencies are: $AA = (0.9)^2 = 0.81$; $Aa = 2(0.9)(0.1) = 0.18$; $aa = (0.1)^2 = 0.01$. **Population E is at equilibrium**; the original genotype frequencies are the same as those predicted for the next generation by the Hardy-Weinberg equation.

12-4.

a. There are 60 D^+/D^+ flies with normal wings and 90 D/D^+ flies with Delta wings. The frequencies of these two genotypes are $60/150 = 0.4$ D^+/D^+ and $90/150 = 0.6$ D/D^+. The allele frequency for $D = 0$ D/D homozygotes $+ (1/2)(0.6) = $ **0.3**; the allele frequency for $D^+ = 0.4 + (1/2)(0.6) = $ **0.7**.

b. The following frequencies of F_1 zygotes will be produced: 0.49 $D^+/D^+ + 0.42$ $D/D^+ + 0.09$ $D/D = 1$. The homozygous D/D zygotes do not live, so the viable progeny are $0.49 + 0.42 = 0.91$, or 91% of the original zygotes. If there are 160 viable adults in the F_1 generation, then there must have been $160 / 0.91 = $ **176 F_1 zygotes**.

c. The simplest way to answer this question is to realize that, given the answer to part b, 176 F_1 zygotes existed to produce 160 viable adults. Also as noted in part b above, the viable progeny (91% of the F_1 zygotes) are 0.49 $D^+/D^+ + 0.42$ $D/D^+ = 0.91$. Thus, $(0.49)(176) = 86$ D^+/D^+ and $(0.42)(176) = 74$ D/D^+.

Another way to answer this question is to normalize the equation 0.49 $D^+/D^+ + 0.42$ $D/D^+ = 0.91$ to equal 1 before you can calculate expected numbers of each type of progeny out of 160 total. That is, 0.49 $D^+/D^+ / 0.91 = 0.54$ $D^+/D^+ = $ proportion of the viable offspring with the D^+/D^+ genotype, and 0.42 $D/D^+ / 0.91 = 0.46$ $D/D^+ = $ proportion of the viable offspring with the

D / D^+ genotype. Thus, the expected numbers of viable individuals with these genotypes are: $0.54\ D^+/ D^+$ x $160 = \textbf{86}\ \boldsymbol{D^+/ D^+}$ and $0.46\ D / D^+$ x $160 = \textbf{74}\ \boldsymbol{D / D^+}$.

d. **No.** The lethality of the D / D genotype means **that there are genotype-dependent differences in fitness, violating one of the basic tenets of the Hardy-Weinberg equilibrium**. Therefore, this population will never achieve equilibrium for this locus.

12-5.

a. The frequency of $M = 0.5 + (1/2)(0.2) = 0.6$; the frequency of $N = 0.3 + (1/2)(0.2) = 0.4$. The expected genotype frequencies in the next generation are calculated using these allele frequencies and the equation $p^2 + 2pq + q^2 = 1 \rightarrow 0.36\ MM + 0.48\ MN + 0.16\ NN = 1$. These Hardy-Weinberg genotype frequencies are not the same as the genotype frequencies of the initial population, therefore **the initial population is not at equilibrium.**

b. As calculated in part a, **the genotype frequencies in the F_1 will be: 0.36 MM + 0.48 MN + 0.16 NN = 1**. From these values, the **allele frequencies in the F_1 generation** can be calculated: $M = 0.36 + (1/2)(0.48) = \textbf{0.6}$ and $N = 0.16 + (1/2)(0.48) = \textbf{0.4}$.

c. **In the next (F_2) generation, the allele and genotype frequencies will remain the same as in part b, [M = 0.6; N = 0.4; MM = 0.36; MN = 0.48; NN = 0.16].** HWE for this autosomal locus is reached after one generation of random mating, so the allele and genotype frequencies do not change subsequently.

12-6.

a. First, recalculate the distribution of genotypes as fractions of the total by dividing each by the total number (= 1480):

$Q^F Q^F R^C R^C$	0.137
$Q^F Q^G R^C R^C$	0.068
$Q^G Q^G R^C R^C$	0.068

$Q^F Q^F R^C R^D$ 0.251

$Q^F Q^G R^C R^D$ 0.126

$Q^G Q^G R^C R^D$ 0.126

$Q^F Q^F R^D R^D$ 0.112

$Q^F Q^G R^D R^D$ 0.056

$Q^G Q^G R^D R^D$ 0.056

Next, calculate the allele frequencies for the Q and R genes separately. In this population, the frequencies of the Q gene are 0.5 $Q^F Q^F$ + 0.25 $Q^F Q^G$ + 0.25 $Q^G Q^G$ = 1. The allele frequencies are Q^F = 0.625 and Q^G = 0.375. The genotype frequencies in the next generation expected by the Hardy-Weinberg equilibrium are therefore 0.39 $Q^F Q^F$ + 0.47 $Q^F Q^G$ + 0.14 $Q^G Q^G$ = 1. **The population is <u>not</u> at equilibrium for the Q gene.**

The genotype frequencies for the R gene in this population are 0.273 $R^C R^C$ + 0.503 $R^C R^D$ + 0.224 $R^D R^D$ = 1. The R^C allele frequency = 0.52 and the R^D allele frequency = 0.48. The expected genotype frequencies in the next generation (Hardy-Weinberg equilibrium) are 0.27 $R^C R^C$ + 0.5 $R^C R^D$ + 0.23 $R^D R^D$ = 1. In this case, the observed genotype frequencies are very close to the Hardy-Weinberg genotype frequencies, so **the population <u>is</u> at equilibrium for the R gene.** Note that the same population is at HWE for one gene (R) but not for a different gene (Q).

b. The fraction of the population that will be $Q^F Q^F$ in the next generation is the expected genotype frequency in part a: **0.39 for the $Q^F Q^F$ genotype.**

c. The fraction that will be $R^C R^C$ **in the next generation** will again be the expected frequency calculated in part a based on the allele frequency: **0.27.**

d. This probability is <u>not</u> influenced by allele frequencies calculated in part a above. Instead, this is a standard probability question starting with parents of specific genotypes as discussed in Chapter 2. This cross is $Q^F Q^G R^C R^D$ x $Q^F Q^F R^C R^D$. The probability is the product of the individual probabilities for each of the genes. One parent is heterozygous for the Q gene and the other is homozygous, so there is a 1/2 chance of a $Q^F Q^G$ child. Both parents are heterozygous for the R gene, so there is a 1/4 chance that the child will be homozygous $R^D R^D$. There is a 1/2 chance that the child will be male. The overall probability is $(1/2)(1/4)(1/2) =$ **1/16 that the child will be a $Q^F Q^G R^D R^D$ male.**

12-7. If a population is at Hardy-Weinberg equilibrium, then the allele frequency p is squared to give the genotype frequency p^2. Thus, **each different allele frequency of p has a different p^2 value and a different set of genotype frequencies at equilibrium; frequencies can differ between populations, but so long as they remain constant within a population, they are at equilibrium** (see Figure 12.4).

12-8. The 3:1 ratio is seen when <u>two heterozygous individuals</u> are crossed. This ratio is <u>not relevant</u> for a <u>population</u> where the crosses are of many different sorts – some will be homozygous dominant x homozygous dominant, others homozygous dominant x heterozygous, some homozygous dominant x homozygous recessive, some heterozygous x homozygous recessive, and others homozygous recessive x homozygous recessive. **The ratio of wild-type : mutant progeny in the population will depend on specific allele frequencies in that population.**

As you will see in a later section of this chapter, the idea that a dominant allele will automatically increase in frequency is also false for another reason: If a dominant allele has a deleterious effect on the fitness of an individual carrying it, the allele frequency would instead tend to decrease each generation. The term "dominance" by itself does not predict the allele's effect on fitness or its frequency in the population.

12-9.

a. The frequencies of the genotypes in the sailor population are: $MM = 324/400 = 0.81$, $MN = 72/400 = 0.18$, and $NN = 4/400 = 0.01$. **The frequency of the N allele $= 0.01 + (1/2)(0.18) = 0.1$.**

b. In order to calculate the allele and genotype frequencies in the children, you must calculate the allele frequencies of each original population and then combine them in the correct proportions. From part *a*, in the sailor population the frequency of $N = 0.1$, so the frequency of $M = 0.9$. In the Polynesian population, the allele frequencies are $N = 0.94$ and $M = 0.06$. When these two populations mix randomly, then 40% of the *M* and *N* alleles will come from the sailor population (400/1000) and the remaining 60% will be provided by the Polynesians. Therefore, the frequency of *N* in the mixed population $= (0.4)(0.1) + (0.6)(0.94) = 0.04 + 0.564 = 0.604$. The frequency of *M* in the mixed population $= (0.4)(0.9) + (0.6)(0.06) = 0.36 + 0.036 = 0.396$. The genotype frequencies in the next generation will be: $(0.604)^2$ *NN* $+ 2 (0.604) (0.396)$ *MN* $+ (0.396)^2$ *MM* $= 0.365$ *NN* $+ 0.478$ *MN* $+ 0.157$ *MM* $= 1$. If there are 1000 children, then **478 children would be expected to have the MN blood type (i.e. 1000 x 0.478 *MN*).**

c. The observed genotype frequencies in the children are 100/1000 *NN* + 850/1000 *MN* + 50/1000 *MM* $= 0.1$ *NN* $+ 0.85$ *MN* $+ 0.05$ *MM*. The allele frequencies among the children are $N = 0.1 + (1/2)(0.85) = 0.525$ and $M = 0.05 + (1/2)(0.85) = 0.475$.

12-10.

a. If a population is at Hardy-Weinberg equilibrium, then the allele frequency is the square root of the frequency of the homozygous genotype ($\sqrt{q^2} = q$). If 1/250 000 people are affected by the autosomal recessive disorder alkaptonuria, then the genotype frequency of the recessive homozygote (q^2) $= 4$ x 10^{-6}. Therefore $q = \sqrt{4 \times 10^{-6}} = 0.002$.

b. Remember that the population is at Hardy-Weinberg equilibrium, that $q = 0.002$, and *p* (frequency of the normal allele) $= 0.998$. Therefore **the frequency of carriers (heterozygotes) = 2 (0.998) (0.002) = 0.004 = 4 x 10^{-3}. The ratio of carriers / affected individuals = (4 x 10^{-3}) / (4 x 10^{-6}) = 1000:1.**

c. If the unaffected woman has an affected child then she must be a carrier, as was the father of the child. The woman has remarried. If her new husband is not a carrier and is unaffected, she can never have an affected child. However, if the new husband is a carrier or is himself affected, then she can have an affected child. The total probability of an affected child is the sum of each of these individual probabilities. **The probability that she will have an affected child by this marriage** = [(0.004 probability that her new husband is a carrier) x (0.5 probability that he passes on his mutant allele) x (0.5 probability that she passes on her mutant allele)] + [(4 x 10^{-6} probability that her new husband is affected) x (1 probability that he passes on a mutant allele) x (0.5 probability that she passes on her mutant allele)] = [0.001] + [2 x 10^{-6}] = 0.001002 = **0.001**. As you can see, the probability that her second husband is affected is insignificant. Therefore, the probability that this woman will have an affected child with her second husband depends only on the frequency of heterozygotes in the population.

d. **No – if one of the genotypes is selected against, then the frequencies of p and q will change each generation.** The population will never reach equilibrium (see <u>Problem 12-4</u> and <u>Figure 12.12</u>).

12-11.

a. If a gene has three alleles then $p + q + r = 1$. The genotype frequencies of a population at Hardy-Weinberg equilibrium would therefore be represented by the binomial expansion of the allele frequencies: $(p + q + r)^2 = (1)^2 = p^2 + 2pq + q^2 + 2pr + r^2 + 2qr = 1$. As discussed in the Problem Solving section at the beginning of this chapter, a Punnett square will give the same genotype frequencies:

	p	q	r
p	p^2	pq	pr
q	pq	q^2	qr
r	pr	qr	r^2

b. In the Armenian population, the allele frequencies are $I^A = 0.36$, $I^B = 0.104$, and $i = 0.536$. If the population is at Hardy-Weinberg equilibrium, then the binomial expansion of these allele frequencies gives: 0.130 I^AI^A + 0.075 I^AI^B + 0.011 I^BI^B + 0.111 I^Bi + 0.287 ii + 0.386 I^Ai = 1.

Therefore, the frequencies of the four blood types in this population are **0.516 A** (0.130 I^AI^A + 0.386 I^Ai), **0.122 B** (0.011 I^BI^B + 0.111 I^Bi), **0.075 AB** (0.075 I^AI^B), **and 0.287 O** (0.287 ii).

12-12.

a. When considering an X-linked gene, women have two alleles. Therefore, the **allele and genotype frequencies in women are** calculated exactly as we have been doing for autosomal loci: $p + q = 1$ **and** $p^2 + 2pq + q^2 = 1$. However, men are hemizygous (they have only one allele for genes on the X chromosome), so the **men's genotype frequencies are the same as the allele frequencies:** $p + q = 1$.

b. If 1/10 000 males is a haemophiliac, then the allele frequency of the mutant allele (q) = 1 x 10^{-4}. Therefore, the frequency of affected females = q^2 = 1 x 10^{-8}. If there are 1 x 10^8 (one hundred million) women in the United States, then **only one of them should be afflicted with haemophilia**. (Note that we assume here that only females homozygous for the mutant haemophilia allele are true haemophiliacs. However, as discussed in Chapter 3, rare heterozygous females show some symptoms of haemophilia.)

12-13.

a. Remember that colour blindness is an X-linked recessive trait, so boys are hemizygous. Using the data from the boys only, the allele frequency for C = **8324/9049 = 0.92** and for c = **725/9049 = 0.08**.

b. If the population is at Hardy-Weinberg equilibrium, then the girls should have the same allele frequencies as the boys. The genotype frequency of colour blindness (cc) in the girls = 40/9072 = 0.0044; if the girls are at equilibrium, then the allele frequency of c = $\sqrt{0.0044}$ = 0.066. This does not equal 0.08 (from part a).

Alternatively, if the population is at equilibrium, then the allele frequency of c in the boys should accurately predict the genotype frequencies in the girls. Thus, c^2 should represent the frequency of colour blind girls: $(0.08)^2 = 0.0064$, but this value does <u>not</u> equal the cc genotype frequency of 0.0044.

Therefore, given the information provided to this point, **this sample does not demonstrate Hardy-Weinberg equilibrium for the colour blindness gene.**

c. Based on this new information the frequency of the c^p/ c^p genotype in girls $= 3/9072 = 3.3 \times 10^{-4}$ and **the frequency of $c^p = \sqrt{3.3 \times 10^{-4}} = 0.018$.** The frequency of the c^d/ c^d genotype in the girls $= 37/9072 = 0.0041$, and **the frequency of $c^d = \sqrt{0.0041} = 0.064$.** The **frequency of the C allele is $1 - (0.018 + 0.064) = 0.918$.**

d. The genotype frequencies among the boys must be the same as the allele frequencies in the girls calculated in part c. **Thus in the boys, $C = 0.918$ (normal vision), $c^d = 0.064$ (colour blind), and $c^p = 0.018$ (colour blind). In the girls, the genotype frequencies are: $C/ C = 0.843$ (normal vision), $C/ c^d = 0.118$ (normal vision), $C/ c^p = 0.033$ (normal vision), $c^p/ c^p = 3.3 \times 10^{-4}$ (colour blind), $c^d/ c^d = 0.004$ (colour blind), and $c^d/ c^p = 0.002$ (normal vision).**

e. These new results make it much more likely that **the population is in fact at equilibrium. As seen in part c, the allele frequency of C is the same in boys and girls and the allele frequency of c in the boys is the same as the total frequencies of $c^d + c^p$ in girls.** Likewise, the frequencies of genotypes with normal vision (0.918 predicted in boys versus 0.92 observed in boys, and 0.996 predicted in girls versus 0.996 observed in girls) and with colour blind vision (0.082 predicted in the boys versus 0.08 observed, and 0.004 predicted in the girls versus 0.004 observed) fit the expectations of Hardy-Weinberg equilibrium.

12-14.

a. **The frequency of allele A^F is calculated in the following way:**

   Population 1:

$38\ A^F A^F \times 2 = 76\ A^F$ alleles

$44\ A^F A^S \times 1 = \underline{44\ A^F}$ alleles

$120\ A^F$ alleles in Population 1

$120\ A^F$ alleles / 200 total A alleles = **0.6.**

Population 2:

$80\ A^F A^S \times 1 = 80\ A^F$ alleles

$80\ A^F$ alleles / 200 total A alleles = **0.4.**

b. For Population 1, the allele frequencies are $p = 0.6$ and $q = 0.4$. Genotype frequencies when the population is at equilibrium are:

$$p^2 = (0.6)^2 = 0.36$$
$$2pq = 2(0.6)(0.4) = 0.48$$
$$q^2 = (0.4)^2 = 0.16$$

For Population 1, which consists of 100 individuals, the equilibrium distribution of genotypes would be 36 $A^F A^F$, 48 $A^F A^S$, and 16 $A^S A^S$ lizards. **Population 1 appears to be at equilibrium.** (Sampling error and small population size could lead to slight variation from the expected frequencies.)

For Population 2, the allele frequency p for the A^F allele was calculated in part a to be 0.4, so the allele frequency q for the A^S allele is 0.6. Genotype frequencies for a population at equilibrium would be:

$$p^2 = (0.4)^2 = 0.16$$
$$2pq = 2(0.6)(0.4) = 0.48$$
$$q^2 = (0.6)^2 = 0.36$$

Population 2 is <u>not</u> at equilibrium for variants of gene A.

c. The combination of the two populations of lizards results in one population with the following allele frequencies:

A^F alleles

$A^F A^F$ (Pop 1)	38×2	76
$A^F A^S$ (Pop 1)	44×1	44
$A^F A^S$ (Pop 2)	80×1	80
		200

A^S alleles

$A^F A^S$ (Pop 1)	44×1	44
$A^F A^S$ (Pop 2)	80×1	80
$A^S A^S$ (Pop 1)	18×2	36
$A^S A^S$ (Pop 2)	20×2	40
		200

The allele frequencies in the new population are 200/400, or 0.5, for both p and q.

The genotype frequencies in the next generation will therefore be:

$$p^2 = (0.5)^2 = 0.25$$
$$2pq = 2(0.5)(0.5) = 0.50$$
$$q^2 = (0.5)^2 = 0.25$$

12-15.

a. **AA male $\times$ AA female:** The frequency of matings within the population in which an AA male (genotype frequency p^2) will mate with an AA female (genotype frequency also p^2) with be $p^2 \times p^2 = p^4$.

b. **aa male $\times$ aa female:** $q^2 \times q^2 = q^4$.

c. **Aa male $\times$ Aa female:** $2pq \times 2pq = 4p^2q^2$).

d. **AA homozygote $\times$ aa homozygote:** There are two mutually exclusive ways in which an AA homozygote could mate with an aa homozygote. In the first, the AA homozygote is a male and the *aa* homozygote is a female; in the other, the sexes are reversed. Because these are mutually exclusive events, their individual probabilities must be summed to yield the desired probability. Thus, $(p^2 \times q^2) + (q^2 \times p^2) = 2p^2q^2$.

e. **AA homozygote × Aa heterozygote:** Again, two mutually exclusive events must be summed. These are: $(p^2 \times 2pq) + (2pq \times p^2) = 4p^3q$.

f. ***aa* homozygote × Aa heterozygote:** Again, two mutually exclusive events must be summed. These are: $(q^2 \times 2pq) + (2pq \times q^2) = 4pq^3$.

g. **Yes,** the six possibilities listed do account for all possible matings. You could demonstrate this in at least two ways. First, you could set up a Punnett square showing the possible matings between males and females of all possible genotypes:

♀↓ ♂→	AA (p^2)	Aa ($2pq$)	aa (q^2)
AA (p^2)	AA ♂ × AA ♀ $(p^2)^2 = p^4$	Aa ♂ × AA ♀ $2pq(p^2) = 2p^3q$	aa ♂ × AA ♀ $(q^2)(p^2) = p^2q^2$
Aa ($2pq$)	AA ♂ × Aa ♀ $(p^2)(2pq) = 2p^3q$	Aa ♂ × Aa ♀ $(2pq)^2 = 4p^2q^2$	aa ♂ × Aa ♀ $(q^2)(2pq) = 2pq^3$
aa (q^2)	AA ♂ × aa ♀ $(p^2)(q^2) = p^2q^2$	Aa ♂ × aa ♀ $2pq(q^2) = 2pq^3$	aa ♂ × aa ♀ $(q^2)^2 = q^4$

The Punnett square above shows that the 9 possible matings resolve into 6 combinations, all of which have been accounted for in parts *a-f*.

A second method is to use numbers to verify that the 6 types of matings account for all possibilities. If we set $p = 0.2$, then $q = 0.8$. $AA = (0.2)^2 = 0.04$, $Aa = 2(0.2)(0.8) = 0.32$, and $Aa = (0.8)^2 = 0.64$. These three genotypic frequencies of course sum to 1.0 because they account for the three possible genotypes. Now we can figure out the probabilities of the 6 mating combinations using the equations determined in parts *a-f* and show that they account for all the mating possibilities because the probabilities also sum to 1.0:

$$AA \times AA = p^4 = (0.2)^4 = \qquad 0.0016$$

$$aa \times aa = q^4 = (0.8)^4 = \qquad 0.4096$$

$$Aa \times Aa = 4p^2q^2 = 4(0.2)^2(0.8)^2 = \quad 0.1024$$

$$AA \times aa = 2p^2q^2 = 2(0.2)^2(0.8)^2 = \quad 0.0512$$

$$AA \times Aa = 4p^3q = 4(0.2)^3(0.8) = \qquad 0.0256$$

$$aa \times Aa = 4pq^3 = 4(0.2)(0.8)^3 = \qquad \underline{0.4096}$$

$$1.0000$$

h. **The probability for the mating of two individuals of the same genotype is simply the product of their genotype frequencies. The probability for the mating of two individuals of different genotypes must be 2 times the product of their genotype frequencies** because there are two ways such individuals can mate (males of one genotype with females of the other genotype, and *vice versa*).

i. $AA \; \male \times AA \; \female = (p^2)(p^2) = p^4$. **[Same as part *a*.]**

$AA \; \male \times Aa \; \female = (p^2)(2pq) = 2p^3q$

$AA \; \male \times aa \; \female = (p^2)(q^2) = p^2q^2$

12-16.

a. The number of nontasters (*tt*) in the population is 1707 - 1326 = 381 individuals. If the population is at HWE, then $q^2 = 381/1707 = 0.223$ and $q = \sqrt{0.223} = 0.472$. $p = 1 - q = 1 - 0.472 = 0.528$.

b. The genotype frequencies are: $TT = p^2 = (0.528)^2 = 0.279$. $Tt = 2pq = 2(0.528)(0.472) = 0.498$. $tt = q^2 = (0.472)^2 = 0.223$. [The genotype frequency of *tt* is also given by the fraction of nontasters in the population = 381/1707 as described in part *a*.]

c. **Nontaster $\times$ nontaster matings** $= (q^2)(q^2) = q^4 = (0.472)^4 = 0.050$.

d. **Taster** (both homozygotes and heterozygotes) $\times$ **nontaster matings** $= 2(p^2 + 2pq)(q^2) = 2(0.279 + 0.498)(0.223) = 0.347$. Note from the answer to Problem 15 part *h* that you must multiply the product of the two genotype frequencies by 2 to account for the fact that matings between taster males and nontaster females are mutually exclusive of matings between nontaster males and taster females.

e. **Taster ♂ (both homozygotes and heterozygotes) × nontaster ♀ matings = $(p^2 + 2pq)(q^2)$ = (0.279 + 0.498)(0.223) = 0.173.**

f. Two types of taster ♂ × nontaster ♀ matings exist. These are TT ♂ × tt ♀ and Tt ♂ × tt ♀. The fraction of all possible matings that are TT ♂ × tt ♀ is $(p^2)(q^2)$ = (0.279)(0.223) = 0.062. The fraction of all possible matings that are Tt ♂ × tt ♀ is $(2pq)(q^2)$ = (0.498)(0.223) = 0.111. The fraction of all possible matings that are between taster males and nontaster females = 0.062 + 0.111 = 0.173 [see also the answer to part e].

Of all the matings between taster males and nontaster females, 0.062/0.173 = 0.358 are TT ♂ × tt ♀. None of the progeny of these matings will be nontasters. Of all the matings between taster males and nontaster females, 0.111/0.173 = 0.642 are Tt ♂ × tt ♀. From these matings, half of the progeny will be tt nontasters. Thus, **among all the progeny produced by all matings between a taster male and a nontaster female, the proportion of nontasters will be (0.5)(0.642) = 0.321.**

g. **Taster (both homozygotes and heterozygotes) × taster (both homozygotes and heterozygotes) matings = $(p^2 + 2pq)(p^2 + 2pq)$ = (0.279 + 0.498)(0.279 + 0.498) = 0.604.** You can check your work by showing that the sum of the answers to parts c, d, and g [nontaster × nontaster, taster × nontaster, and taster × taster] = 0.050 + 0.347 + 0.604 = 1 (after accounting for rounding error).

12-17.

a. Note that the gene for pattern baldness we are considering is autosomal; it is NOT sex-linked. Because the baldness mutation is dominant in men, bald men could be either AA or Aa. The nonbald men must be aa. The genotype frequency of aa (the nonbald men) = 1 – 0.51 = 0.49. If the population is at HWE, then $q^2 = 0.49$ and $q = \sqrt{0.49} = 0.7$ (frequency of the a allele for normal hair). $p = 1 - q = 0.3$ (frequency of the A allele for baldness).

b. If the population is at HWE, the frequency for the baldness allele must be the same in males and females, so $p = 0.3$.

c. Because the baldness allele is recessive in women, **the percentage of women in the population with pattern baldness will be $p^2 = (0.3)^2 = 0.09 = 9\%$.**

d. The bald men are 51% (0.51) of the total men. The fraction of nonbald women will be $1 - 0.09 = 0.91$ of all women. **The proportion of all random matings that should be between a bald man and a nonbald woman is $(0.51)(0.91) = 0.464 = 46.4\%$.**

e. The bald men are both AA homozygotes and Aa heterozygotes. The frequency of the AA homozygotes $= p^2 = (0.3)^2 = 0.09$. The frequency of the Aa heterozygotes is $2pq = 2(0.3)(0.7) = 0.42$. **The fraction of the total bald men who are Aa heterozygotes $= (0.42)/(0.09 + 0.42) = 0.824 = 82.4\%$.**

f. If a nonbald couple has a bald son, then the man must be aa and the woman must be Aa (because the A allele for baldness is recessive in women). From this type of mating, half the progeny of either sex are Aa and half are aa. **Thus, the chance that the next son of this couple will be bald is 0.5.**

g. The woman is bald and therefore must be AA. Her daughter will be $A-$, with the unknown allele being either A or a. Because nothing is known about the father, and assuming that the mating is random, the chance that the unknown allele will be A (and therefore **the chance that the daughter will be bald) is simply the allele frequency of the A allele in the population $= p = 0.3$.**

Section 12.2 – What Causes Allele Frequencies to Change in Real Populations?

12-18. On Tristan de Cunha in the 1960s, the frequency of the retinitis pigmentosa phenotype was $4/240 = 0.017$, whereas the frequency of this trait in Britain (from where the settlers of this island originated) is $\sim 1/6000 = 0.00017$, about 100-fold higher. **The high incidence of retinitis pigmentosa**

on **Tristan de Cunha is likely due to three components all related to the history of the population and its small size. The first component was a founder effect:** at least one of the 15 original colonists in 1814 must have carried an allele for this condition, even though this allele was rare in Britain. **The second component was a population bottleneck** that occurred in 1885 when most of the males on the island were lost in a shipwreck. **The third component was genetic drift** due to the fact that the population on Tristan de Cunha always remained small.

The problem did not specify the nature of the allele causing retinitis pigmentosa. Some forms of this disease are known to be autosomal dominant, others are autosomal recessive, and yet others are sex-linked recessive. It turns out that the form on Tristan de Cunha is autosomal recessive. We can thus estimate the frequencies of the disease-causing allele in Britain and Tristan de Cunha during the 1960s by taking the square root of the frequencies of the affected individuals in these populations. For Britain, $q = \sqrt{0.00017} = 0.013 = 1.3\%$; for Tristan de Cunha, $q = \sqrt{0.017} = 0.13 = 13\%$.

12-19. If the deleterious effects of an allele (call it a) are completely recessive, the relative fitness values of the three genotypes will be $w_{AA} = w_{Aa} = 1$, while $1 \geq w_{aa} \geq 0$. Under such conditions, Δq, the decrease in the frequency of the deleterious allele a in one generation, will itself decrease over time. The lower the frequency of the a allele, the lower will be the frequency of aa homozygotes, and thus the less chance exists that natural selection can lower the frequency of the allele in the next generation. **In a very large population,** these facts mean that **natural selection alone can never cause extinction of the deleterious recessive allele; its frequency will decrease exponentially over successive generations, but will never reach a value of 0** (see Figure 12.12). **In a small population, genetic drift will eventually eliminate deleterious alleles** because a substantial chance exists that simply through random sampling error, the gametes used to form the next generation will not include the deleterious allele once its frequency is reduced by natural selection (see Figure 12.13).

12-20.

a. When $p = 0.5$ and $N = 100\,000$, the confidence interval for p in the next generation is **0.5 ± 0.0022.**

b. When $p = 0.5$ and $N = 10$, the confidence interval for p in the next generation is **0.5 ± 0.22.**

c. **The results of parts *a* and *b* demonstrate the mathematical basis for the effects of population bottlenecks on genetic drift.** If the population is large, then in the next generation, it is highly unlikely that the allele frequency will change substantially. In the example given, in part *a*, where $p = 0.5$ and $N = 100\,000$, the chance is 95% that in the next generation, p will be between 0.4978 and 0.5022. But under the conditions of part *b*, where the allele frequency is also 0.5 but $N = 10$, the chance is 95% that p in the next generation will be between 0.28 and 0.72. Thus, if a catastrophe occurs to lower the population size drastically, the chances are high that the allele frequency will begin to fluctuate dramatically. The equation provided in this problem allowed mathematicians to perform the Monte Carlo modelling shown in Figure 12.8.

12-21.

a. The allele frequency of $b = \sqrt{0.25} = 0.5$, so the allele frequency of $B = 0.5$.

b. To calculate Δq, first determine q in both generations. For all three tanks, $q = 0.5$ (see part *a*). For tank 1, q in the next generation $(q') = \sqrt{0.16} = 0.4$. Therefore, **Δq for tank 1 is $q' - q = 0.4 - 0.5 = -0.1$.** The same calculations are carried out for the other two tanks: **q for all tanks = 0.5; q' for tank 2 = 0.5 so $\Delta q = 0$; q' for tank 3 = 0.55 and $\Delta q = 0.05$.** These calculations are summarized in the table that follows:

	Tank 1	Tank 2	Tank 3
q in Generation 1	0.5	0.5	0.5
q in the next generation	$\sqrt{0.16} = 0.4$	$\sqrt{0.25} = 0.5$	$\sqrt{0.30} = 0.55$
b. Δq	-0.1	0.0	0.05
c. w_{Bb}	1.0	1.0	1.0
d. w_{bb}	<1.0	1.0	>1.0

c. **If the fitness of the *BB* genotype = 1.0 ($w_{BB} = 1.0$) and the *b* allele is totally recessive, then the fitness of the *Bb* genotype (w_{Bb}) = 1.0** also (see row c. in the table above). (This conclusion assumes that the effects of the alleles of the *B*/*b* gene on fitness are determined exclusively through the size of the tail.)

d. In all three tanks, the original frequency of the *b* allele (q) = 0.5. **In tank 1** the frequency of *b* in the progeny (q') = 0.4, so the frequency of the *bb* (small tail) males has decreased. Therefore, the fitness of the small-tailed males decreased, so $\mathbf{w}_{bb}$ **<1.0. In tank 2,** q' = 0.5 (the *b* allele frequency remained the same), so $\mathbf{w}_{bb}$ **= 1.0. In tank 3,** q' = 0.55 (the *b* allele frequency increased), so $\mathbf{w}_{bb}$ **>1.0.** We can come to the same conclusion in a more mathematical way by using Equation 12.6 to estimate the relative fitness of the *bb* genotype given that we concluded in part *c* that $w_{BB} = w_{Bb} = 1$.

12-22. The equilibrium frequency of the fava bean sensitivity allele (q_e) of the *G6PD* gene will be higher in the tropical regions of Africa in which malaria is endemic, compared with countries in North America in which malaria is absent. The major factors affecting the equilibrium frequency are the relative fitness values of individuals of the three genotypes (homozygotes for the normal allele, heterozygotes, and homozygotes for the fava bean sensitivity allele). If a heterozygote advantage exists, then the fitness of the heterozygotes is higher than that of either homozygote; if the relative fitnesses of the homozygotes are known, then the equilibrium frequency (q_e) can be estimated from Equation 12.8.

The basis of the phenomenon conferring (in malaria endemic regions) fitness advantage to individuals heterozygous for normal and fava bean sensitivity alleles of the *G6PD* gene is similar to the reason that the sickle-cell allele of the *Hbβ* gene is maintained at high frequency in the same areas of the globe. The malaria parasite reproduces in red blood cells, so if these cells are "sick", then the parasite cannot grow as well. It should be said that fava beans are not the only trigger for haemolytic crises in individuals homozygous for the sensitivity allele, as other foods, chemicals, and various diseases also induce haemolysis in such people.

12-23.

a. The affected genotype dies before reproductive age. Therefore, the **fitness value $w_{CF^- CF^-} = 0$ for** the affected genotype. Carriers have no fitness advantage relative to individuals with unaffected genotypes, so for both of these the fitness values $w_{CF^+ CF^+}$ **and $w_{CF^+ CF^-} = 1$.**

b. **The average fitness at birth of the population with respect to the cystic fibrosis trait is**

$$\overline{w} = p^2\, w_{CF^+ CF^+} + 2pq\, {}_{CF^+ CF^-} + q^2\, w_{CF^- CF^-} = (0.96)^2 \times 1.0 + 2\,(0.96)\,(0.04) \times 1.0 + (0.04)^2 \times 0 = \mathbf{0.9984.}$$ (see Equation 12.4a).

To calculate Δq using Equation 12.6:

$p = 0.96$, $q = 0.04$, $w_{CF^+ CF^+} = w_{CF^+ CF^-} = 1$, $w_{CF^- CF^-} = 0$, $\overline{w} = 0.9984$. After substituting these values, $\Delta q = \mathbf{-1.54 \times 10^{-3}}$.

c. This problem can be solved using Equation 12.8:

Here, $q_e = 0.04$, $w_{CF^+ CF^-} = \mathbf{1.0}$ (because this genotype is presumed to be the most fit), and

$w_{CF^- CF^-} = \mathbf{0}$. After plugging in these values, $0.4 = \{(w_{CF^+ CF^+} - 1) / [(0 - 1) + (w_{CF^+ CF^+} - 1)]\}$,

so $0.4 = (w_{CF^+ CF^+} - 1) / (w_{CF^+ CF^+} - 2)$, and $w_{CF^+ CF^+} = \mathbf{0.958.}$

d. Interestingly, one recent study suggests the hypothesis that **CF^+/CF^- heterozygotes may be better able to survive outbreaks of cholera**. This phenomenon is conceivable because people with cholera have diarrhea that pumps water and chloride ions out of the small intestine. The CFTR protein encoded by the CF gene is a chloride ion channel. CF^+/CF^- heterozygotes thus lose less water than CF^+/CF^+ individuals when infected with cholera. Theoretically, the heterozygotes are therefore less likely to die of dehydration.

12-24.

a. Convert the genotypes to frequencies: $60/150\ t^+/t^+ = 0.4\ t^+/t^+$, and $90/150\ t^+/t = 0.6\ t^+/t$. The **allele frequencies are: $t^+ = 0.4 + (1/2)(0.6) = 0.7$ and $t = (1/2)(0.6) = 0.3$.**

b. First determine the frequencies of the three genotypes if all lived, then remove the inviable mice from your calculations and normalize the genotype frequencies in order to calculate the allele frequencies. The expected genotype frequencies of the zygotes in the next generation are: $0.49\ t^+/$ $t^+ + 0.42\ t^+/t + 0.09\ t/t = 1$. However, the t/t zygotes die, so the remaining genotype frequencies are: $0.49\ t^+/t^+ + 0.42\ t^+/t = 0.91$. When this equation is normalized (that is, when both sides are divided by 0.91 to make the equation equal 1), it becomes $0.538\ t^+/t^+ + 0.462\ t^+/$ $t = 1$. If 200 progeny mice are scored, the expected values are **108 wild-type mice and 92 short-tailed mice**.

c. Pop 1 has 64 members and the genotype frequencies are $0.25\ t^+/t^+$ and $0.75\ t^+/t$. Thus the allele frequencies are $t^+ = 0.625$ and $t = 0.375$. Pop 2 has 84 members and the genotype frequencies are $0.571\ t^+/t^+$ and $0.429\ t^+/t$. The allele frequencies here are $t^+ = 0.785$ and $t = 0.215$. If the populations interbreed randomly, then the Pop 1 parents will provide $64/148 = 0.432$ of the alleles (gametes) found in the next generation, and Pop 2 will provide 0.568 or 56.8% of the alleles. Therefore, the combined gamete frequencies are: $t^+ = (0.432)(0.625) + (0.568)(0.785) = 0.716$ and $t = (0.432)(0.375) + (0.568)(0.215) = 0.284$. The genotype frequencies in the next generation will be $(0.716)^2\ t^+/t^+ + 2(0.716)(0.284)\ t^+/t + (0.284)^2\ t/t = 0.513\ t^+/t^+ + 0.407\ t^+/t + 0.081\ t/t = 1$. Of course, the t/t zygotes die (see part b above), so the normalized genotype frequencies of the two viable genotypes are **0.558 t^+/t^+ and 0.442 t/t**. {$0.558 = (0.716)^2 /$ $[(0.716)^2 + 2(0.716)(0.284)]$, while $0.442 = [2(0.716)(0.284)]/[(0.716)^2 + 2(0.716)(0.284)]$}.

12-25.

a. If the population size $N = 100\ 000$, then the number of total alleles for an autosomal locus $= 2N = 200\ 000$. **If a new mutation occurs at this locus, its original allele frequency p will be $1/200\ 000 = 5 \times 10^{-6}$.**

b. If the population size $N = 10$, then the number of total alleles for an autosomal locus $= 2N = 20$. **If a new mutation occurs at this locus, its original allele frequency p will be $1/20 = 0.05$.**

c. **The new mutant allele has a much higher probability of going to fixation by chance with genetic drift in the small population with $N = 10$.** In the small population, the new allele has a

0.05 probability of being fixed eventually in the population, while there is a 0.95 probability that it will be lost. In the large population, the new allele has a 0.000005 probability of being fixed eventually in the population, while the probability that it will be lost is $1 - 0.000005 = 0.999995$. Note that even if a new mutation occurs in a small population, the chances are still considerably higher that it will be lost than that it will eventually go to fixation.

12-26.

a. **A_1 corresponds to the *blue* line.** The beneficial effects of the A_1 allele on fitness are recessive, so natural selection favours homozygotes for this allele but not heterozygotes. The effects of selection will be observed only after many generations when the allele frequency increases by drift sufficiently for homozygotes to be formed. **B_1 corresponds to the *red* line.** In this scenario, the beneficial effects of the B_1 allele on fitness are dominant, and the B_1 allele has an immediate strong selective advantage relative to the alternative B_2 allele. **C_1 corresponds to the *green* line.** In this scenario, the beneficial effects of the C_1 allele on fitness are dominant and thus immediate, but the fitness advantage of the C_1 allele is only marginally higher than that of the alternative C_2 allele.

b. **Both the B_1 allele (*red*) and the C_1 allele (*green*) have dominant beneficial effects, but the B_1 allele's fitness relative to the alternative B_2 allele is much higher than the C_1 allele's fitness relative to its alternative C_2 allele.** Thus, the frequency of the B_1 allele in the population will increase over the generations at a faster rate than will the frequency of the C_1 allele.

c. **Because the beneficial effects of the A_1 allele on fitness are recessive, only $A_1 A_1$ homozygotes will have a selective advantage.** When the frequency of the A_1 allele is low, few individuals in the population will be $A_1 A_1$ homozygotes. Many generations must elapse before the frequency of the A_1 allele becomes sufficiently high (through genetic drift) so that any such $A_1 A_1$ homozygotes can be generated. In contrast, the fitness of individuals with even a single copy of B_1 or C_1 is higher than those individuals lacking B_1 or C_1, so natural selection will immediately favour an increase in the frequency of these alleles.

d. **(i) In a small population, the operation of genetic drift means that some likelihood exists that the alleles in question would become extinct before they would become fixed.** This is particularly true for the *blue* line, because natural selection would favour increases in the frequency of A_1 only when $A_1 A_1$ homozygotes were present. Because of genetic drift, it is highly likely that a newly-formed A_1 allele would be lost before homozygotes are formed. In the cases of the B_1 and C_1 alleles with dominant beneficial effects, it is still possible that newly-formed alleles would be lost from the population by genetic drift despite the fitness advantages conferred by one dose of the alleles.

(ii) Because of genetic drift in a small population, the curves would no longer be smooth and predictable. Instead, they would be jagged and their trajectories would be unpredictable, as seen in Figure 12.13.

12-27.

a. Diagram the cross:

$vg^+ vg^+$ x $vg\ vg$ → F_1 $vg^+ vg$ → F_2 1/4 $vg^+ vg^+$: 1/2 $vg^+ vg$: 1/4 $vg\ vg$ (3 wild type : 1 vestigial). If the vestigial F_2 flies are selected against, then the remaining F_2 genotypes are 1/3 $vg^+ vg^+$ and 2/3 $vg^+ vg$. Therefore, **the genotype frequencies in the F_2 are 0.33 $vg^+ vg^+$ and 0.67 $vg^+ vg$; the allele frequencies in the F_2 for vg^+ = 0.33 + (1/2)(0.67) = 0.67 (p) and for vg = (1/2)(0.67) = 0.33 (q).**

b. The expected **genotype frequencies in the F_3 progeny are $[p^2 = (0.67)^2 = 0.449\ vg^+ vg^+]$ + $[2pq = (2)(0.67)(0.33) = 0.442\ vg^+ vg]$ + $[q^2 = (0.33)^2 = 0.109\ vg\ vg]$ = 1, or 0.891 wild type and 0.109 vestigial.**

c. If the F_3 vestigial flies are selected against, then the altered F_3 genotypic ratio becomes 0.449 $vg^+ vg^+$ + 0.442 $vg^+ vg$ = 0.891. In order to calculate allele frequencies this equation must be normalized (see Problem 12-24b), becoming 0.504 $vg^+ vg^+$ + 0.496 $vg^+ vg$ = 1. The F_3 allele frequencies: $vg^+ = 0.504 + (1/2)(0.496) = 0.752$ and $vg = (1/2)(0.496) = 0.248$. The genotype

frequencies in the F_4 generation will be: $0.566 \; vg^+ \, vg^+ + 0.373 \; vg^+ \, vg + 0.062 \; vg \, vg = 1$.

Therefore, the **F_4 allele frequencies are $vg^+ = 0.566 + (1/2)(0.373) = 0.753$ and $vg = 0.062 +$**

$(1/2)(0.373) = **0.247**$.

d. **If all of the F_4 flies are allowed to mate at random,** then there is no selection and **the**

population will be at Hardy-Weinberg equilibrium. Therefore, the F_5 genotype and allele

frequencies will be the same as those in the F_4 generation in part c above: **$0.566 \; vg^+ \, vg^+ + 0.373$**

$vg^+ \, vg + 0.062 \; vg \, vg = 1$; $vg^+ = 0.753$ and $vg = 0.247$.

Section 12.3 – Heritability: Genetic Versus Environmental Influences on Complex Traits

12-28.

a. **Genetically identical dandelions ($V_G = 0$) grown in the controlled environment of a**

greenhouse (*green* curve in the following diagram) will vary in phenotype less than either

genetically identical plants grown in a variable environment (Figure 12.20a; *blue* curve) or

genetically different plants grown in a constant environment (Figure 12.20b; *red* curve). In

the figure that follows, V_G is larger than V_E, indicating that the heritability of this trait in this

population is high. Different traits in different populations may have different heritabilities. If the

heritability was low, the *red* curve in the figure could instead be narrower than the *blue* curve.

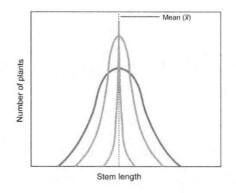

b. The phenotypic variance is not zero ($V_P > 0$) because **even in the greenhouse, the environment is not perfectly uniform;** different plants will experience slightly different microenvironments **and chance events might occur (including spontaneous mutations during the growth phases of the plants) that influence stem development and growth.**

c. To refine the estimate of V_G obtained from the *red* curve in Figure 12.20b [or the *red* curve in the diagram in part *a*], **subtract from this estimate the variance observed in the experiment described in part *a*,** depicted as the *green* curve.

12-29.

a. **False.** When $H^2 = 1$, all phenotypic variation is due to genetic sources, and MZ twins are twice as similar phenotypically as are DZ twins. The reason is that MZ twins share twice as many alleles with each other (100%) as do DZ twins (50%). As H^2 decreases, pairs of MZ twins would increasingly show the same degree of phenotypic differences as would pairs of DZ twins (compare the graphs for 1.0 and 0.0 heritability in Figure 12.23b).

b. **Mostly true.** It is always the case that MZ twins will show very little phenotypic variation if broad-sense heritability is high (see Figure 12.23b); in fact, the phenotypic variability between DZ twins will always be higher than that of MZ twins unless $H^2 = 0$. However, when broad-sense heritability is high, the average degree of variation between DZ twins depends largely on the frequency of the trait in the population as a whole (see Figure 12.23b). If the trait is rare, then it is quite possible that one DZ twin could inherit a rare trait-determining allele that the other twin does not inherit, so the twins in a pair could vary considerably in phenotype. If the trait is common, differences between DZ twins will be less pronounced.

c. **False.** Broad-sense heritability can vary in different populations for two reasons. Remember that $H^2 = V_G / V_P = V_G / (V_G + V_E)$. Different environments in different countries could affect the total phenotypic variance (V_P) through alterations in V_E. Likewise, different gene pools in different countries could alter the total phenotypic variance through V_G.

12-30.

a. Genetic clones have identical alleles of all of their genes, like identical (monozygotic) twins. **All of the phenotypic variation observed in genetic clones is due to environmental effects.** For any specific trait, $V_G = 0$ and thus $V_P = V_E$.

b. Monozygotic (MZ) twins are genetically identical (their genetic relatedness = 1), while dizygotic (DZ) twins have half of their alleles in common (their genetic relatedness = 0.5). **All of the phenotypic differences observed in separately adopted MZ twins are due to environmental effects.** Thus in MZ twins reared apart, $V_P = V_E$ for a particular trait. Note, however, that the value of V_E obtained in such a study may underestimate the effect of the environment on this trait in the population as a whole. The reason is that the families who adopt each twin are likely more similar than two random families.

   Comparisons of MZ and DZ twins, both raised in the same family, can be used to estimate the broad-sense heritability ($H^2 = V_G / V_P$) of specific traits. For a given phenotype, H^2 is equal to the twice the difference in concordance between pairs of MZ and DZ twins for that trait.

c. **In studies of heritability of traits in animals, cross-fostering helps to randomize the effects of the environment among offspring of different parents.** Cross-fostering is useful because measurements of heritability based on the phenotypic similarity between parents and offspring assumes that all parents and offspring in the population experience the same environment.

12-31.

a. **According to this study, in this population height has the highest broad-sense heritability and weight has the lowest.**

   MZ twins raised either together or apart differ in height about equally, and this difference is less than half of that observed between DZ twins or siblings. These results indicate that the environment plays a less important role in determining height than do genetic sources. Even though it is high, the broad-sense heritability of the height phenotype must nonetheless be less than 1.0, because MZ twins do not all have identical heights. This latter conclusion also makes sense when noting in Figure 12.17 that average heights in several populations increased considerably during a short period in which nutrition was improved.

MZ twins reared together are much more similar in weight than MZ twins reared apart. This observation indicates that the environment plays a more important role in determining weight than it does in determining height. The exact degree of heritability in the broad sense is hard to estimate because the data for DZ twins and siblings are not discriminated into separate classes for those raised together or raised apart. If the large majority of the DZ twins and siblings were raised together (as might be expected), the data would imply that the contributions of genes and the environment to the phenotypic variance are roughly equal.

The broad-sense heritability of IQ as determined from this study is in between those for height and weight. MZ twins reared together are more similar to each other than MZ twins reared apart, indicating an important contribution of the environment. However, the differences between DZ twins or siblings are even more pronounced than those between MZ twins raised apart. Thus, both genes and environment affect IQ. In this study, the contribution of the environment is greater than it was in the case of height, while the contribution of genetic sources is greater than it was in the case of weight.

b. **Since the phenotypic changes occurred during a period of only 42 years, the rise in height and weight must be due to environmental effects.** (Forty-two years is much too short a time period for the gene pool of a large population to change significantly through mutation, random genetic drift, or a moderate amount of selection; it is also unlikely that migration during this time period altered the gene pool enough to account for these increases.) **These findings make sense with respect to the conclusions that can be drawn from part *a*.** Height increased by $(68.4 - 67.5)/67.5 \approx 1.3\%$, and weight increased by $(150.3 - 135.5)/135.5 \approx 11\%$. As height has high heritability in the broad sense, environmental factors would not be expected to alter the average trait value very much. Weight, however, has a low broad-sense heritability and so it makes sense that changes in the environment such as better nutrition could alter average weight to a greater extent.

12-32.

a. **Comparisons of the degree of similarity between MZ and DZ twins measure the proportion of variation due to genetic sources (broad-sense heritability) only if the range of environments experienced by each group is similar.**

b. **The concordance of phenotypes in MZ twins is a better indicator of broad-sense heritability than is the concordance of phenotypes in DZ twins, because in MZ twins, none of the differences in phenotypes can be due to genetic differences.** The advantage of looking at MZ twins is particularly large when looking at rare traits, where the concordance is 100% if the broad-sense heritability is 1.0 but the concordance is very low if the broad-sense heritability is near 0.0 (review the right-hand column of Figure 12.23b).

12-33.

a. **Founder effects** could explain the relatively high incidence of certain recessive disorders and the relatively low incidence of others. If present-day Finns descend almost exclusively from a small number of people, the alleles that those particular "founders" of the population introduced are the prevalent ones now. Furthermore, the frequency of alleles of various genes could change rapidly by genetic drift if the population remained small. In fact, studies have suggested that the founding population of Finland around 4000 years ago was as small as 3000 individuals, and that the population remained as low as 50 000 as late as the 12th century (about 900 years ago).

b. **Inbred populations like the Finns will have a smaller number of genes that may affect a given quantitative trait such as schizophrenia (these genes are known as quantitative trait loci), each of which makes a large contribution to the phenotype. The high trait values for the quantitative trait loci (QTLs) make them easier to identify. On the other hand, the paucity of variation in the Finnish population means that some phenotypes will not exist in** the population at all and cannot be studied. Another disadvantage is that some QTLs that help determine the trait in other populations cannot be found by examining Finns.

12-34. Heritability values for a rare trait depend on the frequency of the trait in the population, on the total amount of phenotypic variation in the population, and on environmental factors that could influence the trait. In addition, different populations of the same species may have different histories, leading to the presence of different genes influencing the trait.

12-35.

a. If n genes exist that each contribute equally to a complex trait, and each gene has two codominant (or incompletely dominant) alleles, **the number of different trait values is $2n + 1$.** For example, when $n = 1$, the genotypes AA, Aa, and aa each have different phenotypes. And when $n = 2$, the five different trait values are explained by the following genotypes: (1) $AA\ BB$; (2) $Aa\ BB = AA\ Bb$; (3) $Aa\ Bb = aa\ BB = AA\ bb$; (4) $Aa\ bb = aa\ Bb$; (5) $aa\ bb$.

b. From the examples given, the formula for determining the frequency of the extreme phenotypes in the F_2 of a cross is $(1/4)^n$, where $n =$ the number of genes that determine the phenotype. You can see that this formula makes sense if you consider the simplest case where $n = 1$. If the parental cross was between AA and aa, then the F_1 are Aa, and the progeny are $1/4\ AA : 1/2\ Aa : 1/4\ aa$. The genotypes AA and aa correspond to the extreme phenotypes. When progeny with the extreme phenotypes are each present at a frequency of $1/256$, then $(1/4)^n = 1/256$, and $n = 4$. Thus, **4 different genes control kernel colour;** the genotypes corresponding to the extreme phenotypes are $AA\ BB\ CC\ DD$ and $aa\ bb\ cc\ dd$.

12-36.

a. From Problem 35 part a, we know that $2n + 1 = 9$ different phenotypes will exist in the F_2. Remember that A', B', C', and D' each add 2 cm to leaf length, while A, B, C, and D add 4 cm each to leaf length. The alleles of all four genes have additive effects. The probability of each allele =

(1/2) and there are a total of 8 alleles controlling the phenotype. Therefore the probability of any single genotype is $(1/2)^8 = 1/256$. As in <u>Problem 35</u> part *b*, the maximum and minimum leaf lengths are the parental types: *A/A, B/B, C/C, D/D* (length = 32 cm) at a frequency of 1/256, and *A'/A', B'/B', C'/C', D'/D'* (length = 16 cm) at a frequency of 1/256.

The remaining 7 phenotypic classes correspond to genotypes with 1 prime and 7 non-prime alleles, 2 prime and 6 non-prime alleles, 3 prime and 5 non-prime alleles, etc. The trait values for each class are easy to determine simply by adding the contributions of each of the eight alleles. For example, for an F_2 with only one prime allele and seven non-prime alleles, the leaf length is 1(2 cm) + 7(4 cm) = 30 cm.

The frequency of each genotype is trickier to determine. The simplest, although quite time consuming, way to calculate the frequency of each phenotype is to set up the Punnett square of all possible genotypes. In this case, there are 16 different genotypes of gametes: *A' B' C' D', A B' C' D', A' B C' D', A' B' C D', A' B' C' D, A B C' D', A B' C D', A B' C' D, A' B C D', A' B C' D, A' B' C D, A' B C D, A B' C D, A B C' D, A B C D', A B C D*. **The frequencies and leaf lengths for all 9 phenotypic classes of progeny are: 16 cm (8 prime alleles), 1/256; 18 cm (7 prime alleles), 8/256; 20 cm (6 prime alleles), 28/256; 22 cm (5 prime alleles), 56/256; 24 cm (4 prime alleles), 70/256; 26 cm (3 prime alleles), 56/256; 28 cm (2 prime alleles), 28/256; 30 cm (1 prime allele), 8/256; and 32 cm (0 prime alleles or 8 non-prime alleles), 1/256.**

b. You can determine the genotypic frequencies for each gene using the Hardy-Weinberg equation: $p^2 + 2pq + q^2 = 1$. **For gene *A*, $p^2 = f(A/A) = (0.9)^2 = 0.81$; $2pq = f(A/A') = (2)(0.9)(0.1) = 0.18$; $q^2 = (A'/A') = (0.1)^2 = 0.01$. For gene *B*, $p^2 = f(B/B) = (0.9)^2 = 0.81$; $2pq = f(B/B') = (2)(0.9)(0.1) = 0.18$; $q^2 = (B'/B') = (0.1)^2 = 0.01$. For gene *C*, $p^2 = f(C/C) = (0.1)^2 = 0.01$; $2pq = f(C/C') = (2)(0.1)(0.9) = 0.18$; $q^2 = (C'/C') = (0.9)^2 = 0.81$. For gene *D*, $p^2 = f(D/D) = (0.5)^2 = 0.25$; $2pq = f(D/D') = (2)(0.5)(0.5) = 0.50$; $q^2 = (D'/D') = (0.5)^2 = 0.25$.**

c. The plants with leaves that are 32 cm long have the genotype *A/A, B/B, C/C, D/D*. Because the loci assort independently, you can find the frequency of plants with this genotype in the population described in part *b* by multiplying together the relevant genotype frequencies for each gene: $(0.81) \times (0.81) \times (0.01) \times (0.25) = \mathbf{0.0016}$.

12-37. Knowledge of the phenotypic variance and of the number of loci that influence the phenotype does not provide sufficient information to answer this question. Remember from Equation 12.15 that the response to selection (R) of a phenotypic trait is determined by the proportion of the phenotypic variance that is due to additive genetic variation (the narrow-sense heritability, h^2) and the strength of selection (S) according to the relationship $R = h^2 S$ (assuming that the distribution of the phenotype fits a normal bell-shaped curve). **The key parameters governing the response to selection are not the total phenotypic variance and the number of loci, but rather the narrow-sense heritability and the strength of selection.** These two sets of parameters are related but not identical. The additive genetic variation h^2 is only one component of the total phenotypic variation. Furthermore, a given narrow-sense heritability incorporates the complexities of different numbers of major and minor loci, but knowledge of the number and strength of the genes involved in their traits is insufficient to measure h^2.

   The information given in the problem does not allow you to determine the key parameters of h^2 and S that you would need to solve the problem. If you could estimate these parameters, Equation 12.15 clarifies that the trait with the highest narrow-sense heritability will evolve the fastest, all else being equal. If h^2 is the same for the two traits in question and the strength of selection is the same, then the response to selection will also be the same.

Chapter 13   Genome Evolution

Synopsis:

This chapter takes a look at the evolution of the information of life, combining some of our recent knowledge of the structure and function of nucleic acids and the organization of information in the genomes with fossil record and paleontological evidence. Much of the information is speculative and hypotheses are proposed that are thought-provoking. Genome analysis provides information that drives the development of new hypotheses in this field.

Key Terms:

diversification the evolution of many variants from one progenitor molecule.

natural selection in nature, the process that progressively eliminates individuals whose fitness is low and chooses individuals of high fitness to survive and become the parents of the next generation. Contrast with *artificial selection.*

metazoans multicellular animals that first appeared about 570 million years ago.

punctuated equilibrium the tendency of evolution to proceed through long periods of stasis (lack of change) followed by short periods of explosive change.

genetic drift a change in allele frequencies as a consequence of the randomness of inheritance from one generation to the next.

unequal crossing-over a change in DNA caused by out-of-register *recombination* during meosis in which one *homologous chromosome* ends up with a *duplication*, while the other homologue sustains a *deletion.*

pseudogene a nonfunctioning gene. The result of *duplication* and divergence events in which one copy of an originally functioning *gene* has undergone *mutations* such that it no longer has an intact *polypeptide* coding sequence.

phylogenetic tree a diagram composed of *nodes*, which represent the taxonomic units, and *branches*, which define the relationship of these units.

gene superfamily a large set of related genes that is divisible into smaller sets, or families, with the genes in each family being more closely related to each other than to other members of the larger superfamily. The single-gene or *multigene families* that compose a superfamily reside at different chromosomal locations. The families of genes encoding the globins and the *Hox* transcription factors are examples of gene superfamilies.

Significant Elements:

After reading the chapter and thinking about the concepts, you should be able to:

♦   discuss the merits of DNA and RNA as information carrying molecules

♦   distinguish between synonymous and non-synonymous changes in DNA sequence

♦   describe how duplications can occur

♦   derive a molecular clock value and understand how to use it

♦   think creatively

Problem Solving Tips:

♦ Synonymous base changes in DNA do not change the amino acid that is encoded. Non-synonymous base mutations will result in a different amino acid being present in the protein.

♦ Duplications can occur by unequal crossing-over between repeated sequences or transposition of DNA.

♦ Molecular clock rates can be established by dividing the number of base changes by the length of time when the two organisms diverged (according to fossil or paleontological evidence)

Solutions to Problems:

Vocabulary

13-1

.i. 4; **ii.**6; **iii.** 5; **iv.** 2; **v.** 1; **vi.**7; **vii.** 3.

Section 13.1 –The Origin and Evolution of Life on Earth

13-2.

The fact that the same genetic code directs the cellular basis of life in varied organisms supports the unity of life hypothesis

Section 13.2 – The Evolution of Genomes

13-3.

a. The rates of non-synonymous substitutions differ for these three genes because there is a different constraint on the function of each of the proteins. The function of the histones is very fixed in different organisms, so there is little room for variation, whereas growth hormone may have evolved to interact with other proteins that also have evolved. Explanation for β-globin

b. The rates of synonymous substitutions are more constant between different genes because these base changes do not affect function of the gene product.

13-4.

The immunoglobulin genes encode subunits of antibodies and a great diversity of antibodies is needed in the immune response. The changes that occur are therefore evolutionarily advantageous and would be maintained rather than being selected against.

13-5.

The maintenance at a relatively high level suggests that there is some benefit to the *CF* allele in the heterozygous state (heterozygous advantage). Recent evidence indicates that the allele may be somewhat protective against certain diseases. The *CF* allele may be similar to the sickle cell allele that protects heterozygous individuals against malaria.

13-6.

A single copy of a gene can be duplicated if it is surrounded by small repetitive sequences and these sequences misalign during meiosis and crossing-over occurs. The gene that lies between the misaligned sequences will be duplicated.

13-7.

Because the three color vision genes are cross-hybridizing, it is likely that they arose by duplication events and then diverged evolutionarily to function as different color receptors.

13-8.

In transposition, a copy is transposed to a new location in the genome and therefore can be found at a very different location than the original copy. Unequal crossing-over produces extra copies adjacent to the original copy.

13-9.

a. The *A* allele in humans and the *M* allele in mice are 600 base pairs different and mice and humans are 60 million years apart in evolutionary time. The clock rate we can derive from this information is that over 1 million years, 10 bp on average were changed. The *A* allele has 3000 base differences compared to *Xenopus* (*X* allele). Using the mouse-human numbers, we estimate that frogs and humans are 300 million years apart. That means that frogs and mice are separated evolutionarily by 240 million years.

b. Two duplications must have occurred to lead to alleles *B* and *C* in humans. Because the *C* allele has 300 bases different from *A* the *A* - *C* duplication occurred 30 million years ago and has undergone base changes over that time period. The *B* allele has fewer differences compared with *C* so was duplicated and evolved more recently than *C*. Using our clock rate, the *B* allele arose by duplication 1 million years ago.

c. The duplication of *B* resulted in a copy on a different chromosome (or far enough away on the same chromosome so that it is unlinked). The duplication could have been a transposition type of event. Because *C* is a tandem copy, it could have arisen by a misalignment of repeated sequences around the original copy followed by a crossing over.

13-10.

Chromosome mutations have the potential for much more dramatic effects. For example, regulatory regions of one gene get juxtaposed to regions of other genes; several genes can be lost by deletion.

13-11.

This aberrant phylogeny of the glucose-6-phosphate isomerase could indicate that this particular gene was introduced from a different species.

13-12.

The differences should affect many processes. The majority of the alterations should be effects on brain structure and function since the differences between humans and chimps are primarily in the cognitive functions. One way that many functions can be affected is by alterations in master regulatory genes (changing function or creating new regulators) that control the expression of many other genes.

Section 13.3–The Organization of Genomes

13-13.

a. exons; b. genes.

13-14.

a. In vertebrates there are four *HOX* gene family clusters compared with one cluster in *Drosophila*, for example. This fits well with the tetraploidization hypothesis since the two doublings should lead to four copies of the genes.

b. The variation within the four gene family clusters could be the result of duplications within the gene family in certain lineages.

13-15.

LINES or SINES can mediate genome rearrangements by unequal crossing-over between elements and they can contribute regulatory elements adjacent to a gene.

13-16.

The size of dinucleotide repeat sequences can change by unequal crossing-over between the repeated sequences within the element.

The answers for 16a. and 16b are in 13.17

a.   SINES or LINES.

b.   Centromeric satellite DNA; although we don't know the precise function, it appears to be needed for proper centromere function in higher eukaryotes.

13-17.

a. **2**; b. **4**; c. **1**; d. **3**

Chapter 14   Molecular Analysis of DNA

Synopsis:

This chapter introduces you to many of the recombinant DNA techniques that have provided a powerful new approach for studying the mechanisms of inheritance and functions of specific genes. Restriction enzymes, cloning DNA, making libraries, identifying clones of interest, DNA sequencing and PCR amplification are now just a part of the toolkit that all biologists (not just geneticists) use. These techniques will be referred to over and over throughout this textbook (and probably in your other biology courses as well) so it is worthwhile to get a solid understanding of these techniques from this chapter.

As you read about the various techniques and apply them to solve problems, try to keep in mind which techniques are done in solutions in test tubes (restriction enzyme digests, ligating fragments together, PCR, DNA sequencing, making cDNA) and which techniques involve analyzing or manipulating DNA in cells (transformations, screening libraries, preparing large amounts of cloned DNA, total genomic DNA or cellular RNA). This should help your understanding of the techniques and their uses. Hybridization of nucleic acids is central to many techniques but is often challenging to understand. The basis of hybridization is *complementarity* of bases in forming double stranded nucleic acids. A probe DNA or RNA molecule is used to locate a specific sequence (on a nitrocellulose or membrane based blot after electrophoresis in a gel, as a clone inside a cell, or in a chromosome squash) based on hybridization. A probe contains a recognizable radioactive or fluorescent tag that makes it possible to identify the place where the probe found a complementary sequence.

Key Terms:

recombinant DNA technology methodologies used by geneticists to cut, copy, and paste together DNA fragments from multiple sources; these methodologies allow researchers to bring together genetic material from different sources to create novel *sequences* not before seen in nature.

restriction enzymes proteins made by bacteria that recognize specific, short *nucleotide* sequences and cut DNA at those sites.

blunt end the 5′ or 3′ end of a double-stranded DNA molecule without *sticky ends*.

sticky end the result achieved after digestion by many *restriction enzymes* that break the *phosphodiester bonds* on the two strands of a double helix DNA molecule at slightly different locations. The resulting double-stranded DNA molecule has a single protruding strand at each end that is usually one to four bases in length.

electrophoresis a method of separating large molecules (such as DNA fragments or proteins) from a mixture of similar molecules. An electric current is passed through a medium containing the mixture, and each kind of molecule travels through the medium at a different rate, depending on its size and electrical charge. See *gel electrophoresis.*

vector a specialized DNA sequence that can enter a living cell, signal its presence to an investigator by conferring a detectable property on the host cell, and provide a means of replication for itself and the foreign DNA inserted into it. A vector must also possess distinguishing physical traits by which it can be purified away from the host cell's *genome.* See *cloning vector.*

plasmids minute circles of double-stranded DNA that can gain admission to and replicate in the cytoplasm of many kinds of bacterial cells, independently of the *bacterial chromosome.*

selectable markers antibiotic resistance genes and other *vector* genes that make it possible to pick out cells harbouring a particular DNA molecule.

genomic library a long-lived collection of *cellular clones*, containing copies of every DNA sequence in the whole *genome* inserted into a suitable *vector.*

cDNA library a large collection of cDNA clones that are representative of the *mRNAs* expressed by a particular cell type, tissue, organ, or organism.

polymerase chain reaction (PCR) a fast inexpensive method of replicating a DNA sequence once the sequence has been identified; based on a reiterative loop that amplifies the products of each previous round of *replication.*

hybridization the natural propensity of complementary single-stranded molecules of *DNA* or *RNA* to base-pair and form stable double helixes.

Significant Elements:

After reading the chapter and thinking about the concepts, you should be able to:

♦   Describe the essential steps in cloning.

♦   Describe the basic components and uses of different types of cloning vectors.

♦   Make a map of restriction enzyme sites.

♦   Read and interpret DNA sequencing gels and automated DNA sequencing results.

♦   Design PCR primers.

♦   Determine which technique(s) you must use to achieve a desired goal. There is often more than one way to reach a goal. However, there is usually one most efficient, preferred way to solve a problem.

♦   The technique used determines what is being examined and limits the interpretation of the data. For instance, probing a genomic library will give you a clone that is homologous to the probe, but this clone probably won't be transcribed and translated in *E. coli.* Probing a cDNA library will give you a clone which could be translated and transcribed in *E. coli.*

Problem Solving Tips:

Essential Steps in Cloning:

Cloning is basically a straightforward process that has lots of options and variations that can be used depending on what is desired. Basic components are insert DNA and vector. There are relatively few sources for the insert DNAs. However there are many, many types of vectors that have been developed for various purposes.

Types of insert DNA

- cDNAs contain only the regions of genes that are present in processed (spliced) transcripts synthesized in the cell from which they were isolated.

- Genomic DNAs are digested fragments of the genomic DNA of an organism, and so contain all of the DNA (genes and non-coding regions) from the cells.

Basic vector criteria

- Vectors must have an origin of replication so they can be replicated in the host organism, usually *E. coli.*

- Vectors must have a selectable marker(s) so you can determine that they are present in the host organism; the selectable marker is often an antibiotic resistance marker.

- Vectors also often have multiple cloning sites with known restriction sites and ways to detect the presence of an insert DNA after cloning. One example of an insert detection system is the β-galactosidase / X-gal detection system. Insertion of a fragment into the middle of the *lacZ* gene inactivates the gene. Cells carrying an insert within the *lacZ* gene are unable to cleave a lactose-like substrate (X-gal) and are phenotypically Lac⁻. They are recognized as white colonies while colonies that received intact copies of the vector (no insert interrupting the *lacZ* gene) can cleave the substrate, turning the cells blue (often referred to as blue-white screening).

Types of vectors/purpose of cloning

- Plasmid vectors accept small pieces of insert DNA (10 kb or less). Plasmid vectors may be used to amplify large amounts of specific DNA sequences. Specialized plasmid vectors called expression vectors allow transcription and translation of cloned genes; must be used with cDNA inserts (Genetics and Society, Recombinant DNA Technology and Pest-resistant Crops). Use your knowledge of the requirements for transcription and translation when considering if genes cloned into expression vectors will be expressed in the host cell.

- BAC vectors (bacterial artificial chromosomes) accept very large inserts of 300 kb.

Cloning

- After restriction enzyme digestion, mix insert and vector DNAs and ligate together sticky ends that have complementary overhanging single-stranded bases. It may be helpful to draw out the 5' and 3' ends generated (including the individual bases of the recognition site) when a double stranded DNA is cut by a restriction enzyme.

- Transform the ligation mix into the host cells, usually *E. coli*.
- Select for presence of vector (may also be able to isolate those vectors that you know have an insert).
- Grow up a large amount of the clone(s).

Identifying the desired clone

- Often you must identify a particular desired clone from a large variety of different inserts; this usually involves probing, or hybridization with a labeled DNA.

Other Techniques

- Gel electrophoresis separates DNA fragments according to their size.
- Blotting is the process of transferring the material in the gel to a nitrocellulose filter or a nylon membrane and covalently binding the material from the gel to the filter or membrane. A Southern blot has DNA on the membrane (a genomic Southern has genomic DNA), a Northern blot has mRNA on the membrane and a Western blot has protein on the membrane.
- Restriction mapping is part science and part art, like putting together a jigsaw puzzle. Use a pencil and an eraser. Be patient. The first step is usually ascertaining if you began with a linear or a circular piece of DNA. Usually this is gotten out of context - a plasmid clone is circular, for instance. Begin the map by examining a single digestion lane on the gel and determining the total size of the DNA (the sum of all the fragments) and the number of restriction sites for that enzyme (2 fragments when you digested a circular piece of DNA means there were 2 restriction sites; 2 fragments when you digested a linear piece of DNA means there was only 1 restriction site). Next, look at the double digestion lane. Determine which bands from the single digestion are left undigested in the double enzyme digestion. The fragments from the single enzyme digestion that disappear in the double digestion must have a restriction site for the second enzyme within them. Figure out which smaller fragments they have been broken into, then begin mixing and matching various combinations of bands until you find one that gives you an order that will give the correct pattern of bands when you digest the DNA with the second restriction enzyme alone. Make sure the final sites you put on a map are consistent with results from all digests.
- DNA sequencing provides the ultimate description of a cloned fragment of DNA. Make sure you can explain the Sanger sequencing method (dideoxy sequencing) to a friend.
- PCR rapidly purifies and amplifies a single DNA fragment from a complex mixture. In order to do PCR you must know something about the DNA sequence of 2 short stretches of the DNA to be amplified. The DNA fragment to be amplified is defined by a pair of oligonucleotide primers that are each complementary to one of the strands of the DNA template. These primers are extended

at their 3' ends. The size of the final product of the PCR reaction is determined by the distance between the 5' ends of the primer pair.

Solutions to Problems:

<u>Vocabulary</u>

14-1

i. 10; **ii.** 1; **iii.** 9; **iv.** 7; **v.** 6; **vi.** 2; **vii.** 8; **viii.** 3; **ix.** 5; **x.** 4.

<u>Section 14.1 – Sequence-Specific DNA Fragmentation</u>

14-2.

a. *Sau*3A recognition sites are 4 bases long and are expected to occur randomly every 4^4 or 256 bases. The human genome contains about 3×10^9 bases, one would expect $3 \times 10^9 / 256 = 1.2 \times 10^7$ or ~12,000,000 fragments.

b. *Bam*HI recognition sites are 6 bases long and would be expected every 4^6 or 4096 bases. $3 \times 10^9 / 4,100 = 7.3 \times 10^5$ or ~700,000 fragments are expected.

c. The *Sfi*I recognition site is 8 specific bases. The N indicates that any of the four bases is possible at that site and therefore does not enter into the calculations. Recognition sites would be expected every 4^8 or 65,536 bases; $3 \times 10^9 / 65,500 = 4.6 \times 10^4$ or ~46,000 fragments are expected.

14-3.

The rate at which a piece of DNA moves through a gel is dependent on the strength of the electric field, the gel composition, the charge density and the physical size of the molecule. When electrophoresing DNA the only variable is the size of the molecule - all the rest of the variables are the same for each molecule. Longer DNA molecules take up more volume and therefore bump into the gel matrix, slowing down the molecule's movement. Shorter molecules can easily slip through many pore sizes in the gel matrix.

14-4.

When you digest a circular DNA, one fragment indicates that the DNA has a single restriction site for the enzyme. Thus, *Bam*HI and *Eco*RI each cut the plasmid once. The double digest gives information about the relative positions of these two sites. The 2 restriction sites are at two different positions on the plasmid. The *Eco*RI site is 3 kb away from the *Bam*HI site and it is 6 kb around the rest of the circle back to the *Eco*RI.

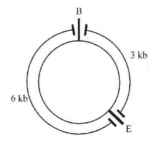

14-5.

a.   Remember the Problem Solving Tips at the beginning of this chapter! If there is one restriction site then digesting a circular molecule results in one fragment, while digesting a linear molecule generates two fragments. Digestion of a circular molecule will always result in one fewer restriction fragments than the digest of a linear molecule. Sample A is therefore the circular form of the bacteriophage DNA.

b.   The length of the linear molecule is determined by adding the lengths of the fragments from one digest. 5.0+3.0+2.0 kb = 10.0 kb. (This size is not realistic - λ DNA is, in fact, about 50 kb in length.)

c.   The circular form is the same length - 10.0 kb.

d.   Comparison of the circular and linear maps gives you information on which fragments contain the ends of the linear molecule. The 5.0 kb *Eco*RI fragment is present in the circular but not the linear digest so the 4.0 and 1.0 kb fragments must be joined in the circular map while they are at either end of the linear molecule. Begin drawing a picture of the molecule for yourself at this point. The same logic applies to the 2.7 kb *Bam*HI fragment – it is present in the circular but not the linear digest so the 2.2kb and 0.5 kb pieces must be at the ends of the linear molecule. If the 0.5 kb *Bam*HI fragment was at the end where the *Eco*RI 1.0 kb fragment is, the 1.0 kb *Eco*RI fragment would have been cut by *Bam*HI in the double digest. However, the 1.0 kb fragment is still in the double digest, so the 0.5 kb fragment must be within the 4.0 kb *Eco*RI fragment. The remaining *Eco*RI site is placed based on the double digests. The 2.0 kb *Eco*RI fragment is not cut by *Bam*HI but the 3.0 kb fragment is, so place the site within the 3.0 kb. Now double check that all the *Bam*HI+*Eco*RI fragment sizes are as seen in the different double digests.

14-6.

Plasmids are circular pieces of DNA, thus the *Eco*RI and *Sal*I digests indicate that there is one site for each of these enzymes. *Hind*III, in contrast, cuts the molecule at three sites. Draw a circle showing the three *Hind*III sites. In the *Sal*I+*Hind*III digest the 4.0 kb *Hind*III fragment is cut into 2.5 and 1.5 kb fragments. The *Sal*I site is therefore 1.5 kb from one end or the other in the 4.0 kb *Hind*III fragment. Similarly the *Eco*RI+*Hind*III double digest splits the 1.0 kb *Hind*III fragment into 0.6 and 0.4 kb fragments, but the orientation of the *Eco*RI site within the 1.0 kb *Hind*III is ambiguous. Try placing the *Eco*RI site in the two different positions in the 1 kb *Hind*III fragment. In each case see how this fits with the *Eco*RI+*Sal*I digestion results. The orientation that works places the 0.4 kb *Hind*III-*Eco*RI fragment adjacent to the 2.5 kb *Sal*I-*Hind*III fragment.

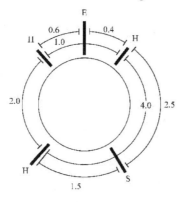

Section 14.2 – Cloning Fragments of DNA

14-7.

Selectable markers in vectors provide a means of determining which cells in the transformation mix take up the vector. These markers are often drug resistance genes so a drug can be added to the media and only those cells that have received and maintained the vector will grow.

14-8.

The study of genes often involves studying mutations in the genes and their associated phenotypes (or diseases). If you are interested in studying mutations and diseases then you want to focus on the protein-coding part of the genes. Eukaryotic genes are often very large. However the majority of this

DNA consists of intronic sequences which do not end up in the mRNA. For example the human dystrophin gene in humans is 2,500 kb (2.5 Mb). The gene has more than 80 introns which are spliced out to give an mRNA that is 14kb long. Therefore 2,486 kb of the dystrophin gene is introns! Thus, most of the DNA in eukaryotic genomic libraries does not code for proteins. It can be difficult to figure out which sequences of the genomic DNA are actually part of the mRNA so it can be difficult to figure out which gene sequences are important to the protein and which are unimportant. cDNA libraries, which are made from the mRNAs, allow you to ignore all of these intronic sequences. All eukaryotic mRNAs have polyA tails at their 3' end and this is used to make cDNAs. The process begins by isolating mRNAs from an organism or a tissue in an organism and then using polyT primer with reverse transcriptase.

In prokaryotes most of the DNA in the genome codes for mRNA – there is very little non-transcribed DNA. Prokaryotes also lack introns and in general the 5' and 3' UTRs are small, so most of the mRNA consists of coding sequences. It would also be difficult to make cDNA libraries in prokaryotes because there is no polyA tail nor any other common sequence between all mRNAs.

14-9.

First, work through the digestion and ligation of the DNA fragments and the vector. The vector is cut with *Bam*HI, leaving the following ends:

```
5' —G          GATCC—
3' —CCTAG          G—
```

The insert DNA is cut with *Mbo*I, leaving the following sticky ends:

```
5' —          GATC—
3' —CTAG          —
```

The ligation of an *Mbo*I fragment to a *Bam*HI sticky end will only occasionally create a sequence that can be digested by *Bam*HI. It depends on the exact base sequence at the ends of the *Mbo*I fragment. The 'X' in the sequence below indicates this ambiguity. In all cases the following sequence will be found: The sequences from the inserted *Mbo*I fragment are in bold.

```
5' —GGATCX—————XGATCC—
3' —CCTAGX —————XCTAGG—
```

a. 100% of the junctions can be digested with *Mbo*I

b. A junction that can be digested with *Bam*HI must have a C at the 3' end of the *Mbo*I recognition sequence. This would occur 1/4 or 25% of the time.

c. None of the junctions will be cleavable by *Xor*II.

d. The first five bases fit the recognition site for *Eco*RII. The final position must be a pyrimidine (C or T). There is a 1/2 chance that the junction will contain an *Eco*RII site

e. For the restriction site to be a *Bam*HI site in the human genome it must have had a G at the 5' end. This G was in the vector sequence in the clones created. The chance that the 5' end was NOT a G=3/4.

Section 14.3 – Genomic and cDNA Libraries

14-10.

a. The genomic library is based on the most inclusive and complex starting material, so it would consist of the greatest number of different clones.

b. All of these libraries would overlap each other to some extent. The genomic library contains all the DNA sequences, while the other libraries are made up of subsets of the genomic sequences. All cells express a common subset of genes (housekeeping genes). These genes would result in some overlap of clones, although the cDNA libraries will each contain some unique sequences. Although introns often have repeated DNA, the transcribed and translated portions of sequences are usually unique, so the library of unique genomic sequences will overlap with the cDNA libraries as well.

c. Genomic libraries are created from chromosomal DNA and repetitive sequences in the genomic DNA would have to be removed to create a unique DNA library. cDNA libraries are typically created from mRNA present in cells. Since genomic DNA libraries are created from all the DNA in the cell, genomic DNA libraries from either the liver or brain should be identical. However, cDNA libraries from liver and the brain should have some clones that are identical between them but they should also have clones that are entirely unique to each one as well as having clones that are derived from the same genes but represent splice variants.

14-11.

a. You need 4-5 genome equivalents to reach a 95% confidence level that you will find a particular unique DNA sequence.

b. The number of clones needed depends on the total size of the genome of your research organism and the average insert size in the vector. BAC inserts can be 500kb while plasmid vectors normally have inserts smaller than 15 kb. Divide the number of base pairs in the genome by the average insert size then multiply by five to get the number of clones in five genome equivalents.

14-12.

a. An intact copy of the whole gene would be on a fragment larger than 140 kbp and would therefore have to be cloned into a BAC vector.

b. The entire coding sequence of 9.7 kbp could be cloned into a plasmid vector (<15kbp) as a cDNA copy of the gene.

c. Exons are usually small enough, so exon 3 can be cloned into a plasmid vector (<15 kbp inserts).

14-13.

When the vector (pWR590) is digested with *Eco*RI you get one 2.4 kb fragment. When the vector is digested with *Mbo*I there are 3 fragments - 0.3, 0.5 and 1.6 kb.

The somatostatin insert was cloned into the vector at the *Eco*RI site. There is also an *Eco*RI site very near one end of the insert DNA. Therefore, after digestion of the recombinant plasmid with *Eco*RI, a small *Eco*RI insert fragment of 49 bp and the vector fragment of 2.4 kb will be generated.

Next, consider the *Mbo*I restriction pattern. The insert fragment contains an *Mbo*I site 5 bp from one end. The insert fragment could ligate into the vector in either of 2 possible orientations. In one orientation the *Mbo*I site in the insert is nearest the 700 bp *Mbo*I vector fragment, so digestion with *Mbo*I produces 705, 300, 500 and 944 (formed from the 900 bp vector fragment + the rest of the insert) bp fragments. In the other orientation, the *Mbo*I digest produces 905, 500, 300 and 744 bp fragments.

14-14.

Draw the recombinant plasmid to help you determine the fragment sizes before sketching the gel.

14-15.

a. The goal of a ligation is to generate clones which have attached one piece of frog DNA to one vector molecule. A ligation mixture consists of linear double stranded vector DNA with complementary *Eco*RI sticky ends at both ends and linear double stranded frog DNA with complementary *Eco*RI sticky ends at both ends. Ligase simply attaches a 3'OH (hydroxyl) group to a 5'P (phosphate). There are three different products that will occur in a ligation mix. (i) The desired ligation is vector/frog (intermolecular ligation). (ii) Ligase will also join vector/vector (intramolecular ligation which yields reconstituted vector molecules with no inserts) and (iii) frog/frog (intramolecular ligation, giving chains of insert DNA with no vector). In order to encourage the desired result you add more vector than insert – the vector DNA is easier to come by. This decreases the likelihood of chains of the insert DNA and increases the probability that any vector molecule that is ligated to an insert is only ligated to one insert molecule. However adding more vector increases the likelihood of reconstituted vector with NO inserts. To decrease the amount of reconstituted vector you treat the linear, digested vector with alkaline phosphatase. Alkaline phosphatase removes the 5'-phosphate groups on the linear DNA molecule – see * below. Remember that this represents the digested vector, so the DNA strands are contiguous except for the boxed area. This continuity is represented by the dashes at the ends of the lines. The boxed area represents the sticky ends created by EcoRI

After the treatment with alkaline phosphatase, ligase cannot join a hydroxyl group to the de-phosphorylated 5' ends. Therefore the 2 ends of the vector cannot be ligated to each other and this treated molecule will remain linear. If insert DNA is added then the ligase will join the 3'OH on the vector with the 5'P on the insert. In effect, this will ligate the left end of the top strand of the vector shown above to the insert. The left end of the bottom strand cannot be ligated to the insert leaving a nick in the bottom strand at this point. On the right end the bottom strand ligates to the insert and the top strand at the right end cannot ligate leaving another nick. The ligation mix is then transformed into *Escherichia coli*. These nicks in the phosphate backbone of the cloned DNA are repaired after the ligated DNA enters the cells.

Plasmid vectors are constructed so that they contain the *lacZ* gene with a restriction site right in the middle of the gene. If the vector reanneals to itself without inclusion of an insert, the *lacZ* gene will remain uninterrupted; if an insert has been cloned into the vector the *lacZ* gene will be interrupted. The ligation mix is transformed into *E. coli* cells such that about one cell out of 1,000 cells takes up a plasmid. The transformed cells are plated on media containing ampicillin. Only the cells with a plasmid will grow, thus removing the intramolecular ligation products that consist of inserts. The media also contains X-Gal. This is a substrate for the β-galactosidase protein that is coded for by the *lacZ* gene. The β-galactosidase enzyme cleaves X-Gal and produces a molecule that turns the cell blue. Those cells that took up an intact, re-circularized vector with no insert will produce β-galactosidase and form blue colonies. The bacterial cells that took up a vector + insert (clone) will not be able to produce functional β-galactosidase and will form white colonies.

     The ligation with the non-phosphorylated vector reanneals to itself at a high frequency, leading to 99/100 blue colonies. The phosphorylated vector formed 99/100 white colonies, showing that almost all of the vectors had an insert.

b. Yes, the suggestion was a good one. The dephosphorylation of the vector increased the number of clones (vector + insert) 100 fold.

c. The choice of whether to dephosphorylate the vector versus the insert DNA is based on an understanding of the mechanics of the bacterial transformation that is carried out after the ligation. If the vector is dephosphorylated, it cannot self-ligate. The insert can self-ligate. The self-ligated inserts do not have any vector DNA, so they do not have a bacterial origin of replication (ORI) nor do they have a gene encoding antibiotic resistance. Therefore, these recircularized DNA's will not allow the transformed bacteria to grow on the selective media. If the insert were dephosphorylated, it will not self-ligate, but the vector WILL self-ligate. The vector has the antibiotic resistance gene and ORI, so the "empty" vector will be propagated in *E. coli*, generating a high level of "background."

Section 14.4 – Hybridization

14-16.

Probes need to be at least 15 nucleotides to effectively anneal to DNA. In this experiment short probes are desirable, because the longer the probe the greater the degeneracy. Thus, this type of experiment is usually done with probes between about 15 and 18 nucleotides long. The design of degenerate probes is based on reverse translation, and there are a few considerations to keep in mind:(i) if you know the amino acid sequence of the protein in one species then you can make some guesses about the amino acid sequence of the corresponding gene in the second species. You hope that the amino acid sequence of a particular, small region of the protein will be identical in the two species. Since there are 20 different amino acids even one amino acid difference would make it hard to design a probe. If you knew the sequence of the protein from several bacterial species you could choose a very highly conserved region on which to base a probe. If the amino acids are identical in several different species then they might be identical in *Beneckea nigripulchritudo.* (ii) If you don't know anything about the amino acid sequence of the protein in other species of bacteria then you would find a region of 5 or 6 contiguous amino acids with low degeneracy - that is amino acids that are encoded by the lowest possible number of codons. The best choices are Met and Trp which are each encoded by only a single codon. Unfortunately, it is highly unlikely that a region of 5 or 6 amino acids would be composed solely of Met and Trp. The next best choices are Phe, Tyr, Cys, His, Gln, Asn, Lys, Asp, or Glu, which are each coded for by 2 codons. The worst choices would be Leu, Arg, and Ser (6 codons).(If you had a 5 amino acid region composed only of these three amino acids, then the number of different molecules in the degenerate probe would be $6^5 = 7776$).

14-17.

c, j, f (although f could be performed before c and j). These steps must be performed before the rest. The order for the rest of the steps is a, k, i, g, b, e, h,d.

Section 14.5 – The Polymerase Chain Reaciton

14-18.

a. The human genome sequence shows the sequence of the normal allele of PKU. You wish to know whether the PKU syndrome in this patient is caused by a mutation in the phenylalanine hydroxylase gene. You suspect that there might be such a mutation in this particular exon, so you will sequence the PCR product. If there is a mutation in this 1 kb exon, you want to know exactly what it is, how it affects the enzyme, and perhaps something about the history of this mutation in human populations. For example, if you compare the sequence in many patients and track where the patients are from, you might get an idea of where this mutation arose in time and geographical space. If you do not find a mutation in this 1 kb exon that changes the amino acid sequence of the enzyme, there might still be a mutation in a different exon.

b. One haploid human genome contains 3×10^9 bp. Therefore (3×10^9 bp/haploid genome) x (6.6×10^2 g/mole) x (mole/6.02×10^{23} bp- avagadro's constant= 3.3×10^{-12} g/haploid genome. In other words, one haploid genome weighs 3.3×10^{-12} g or 3.3 picograms. Each haploid genome will contain only one phenylalanine hydroxylase gene to be used as the template for the PCR reaction. You start the PCR reaction with 1 ng (1×10^{-9} g) of human DNA. Therefore (1×10^{-9} g DNA) x (1 haploid genome/3.3×10^{-12}g) x (1 template molecule/1 haploid genome) = 0.3×10^3 template molecules= 300 template molecules in 1 ng of DNA.

c.   You begin the PCR with 300 template molecules. If the PCR runs for 25 cycles then this number of molecules doubles exponentially 25 times. Therefore you will end up with 300 molecules x $2^{25} = 10^{10}$ or about 10 billion molecules. This result explains the power of PCR: you started with only 300 template molecules and end up with 10 billion copies of the region you are amplifying. In practice the yields are not quite as high because not all potential template molecules get amplified each cycle. However the amplification is still substantial. The PCR product is 1 kb long, so (10^{10} molecules of PCR product) x (10^3 bp/molecule of PCR product) x (mole/6.02×10^{23} bp) x (6.6×10^2 g/mole) = 1.1×10^{-8} g = 110 ng. You started with 1 ng of the whole genome and ended up with 110 ng of a 1 kb section of the genome after the PCR!

14-19.

 Primers have to be 5' to 3' and have the 3' end toward the center so DNA polymerase can extend into the sequence being amplified. Only set b. satisfies these criteria.

14-20.

a.   Both of the primers in set b in <u>problem 14-19</u> are 18 nucleotides long. If (i) human DNA is assumed to be a random sequence of equal proportions of A, G, C, and T (this is not entirely accurate, but it is close enough for this discussion), and (ii) no mismatches are allowed between the primer and the genomic template (again, this is not entirely accurate as seen in parts b and c below, but again, it is close enough) then the chance that one of the two primers will anneal to a random region of DNA that is not the targeted CFTR exon would be $(1/4)^{18}$, or about 1 chance in 7×10^{10}. In other words, an 18 base sequence will be present once in every 70 billion nucleotides. Since the human genome is 3 billion nucleotides long it is extremely unlikely that even one of the primers will anneal anywhere else than the desired target. The probability is much lower that <u>both</u> of the primers will anneal to other stretches of DNA that happen to be close enough together to allow the formation of a PCR product. This latter number is hard to calculate exactly because of the variation in the possible distance between the primers.

b. (i)The lower limit on the size of the primers is governed by two main factors. First, the PCR amplification must be specific, so the primers should be long enough to guarantee this specificity. As in part a, the chance probability of a 16 base sequence in random DNA is $(1/4)^{16}$, or 1 chance out of 4×10^9. Therefore, two 16 base pair primers allow a comfortable margin for specificity. More importantly the primers must anneal to the genomic DNA to be amplified. As discussed in Chapter 9, hydrogen bonding between 15 or 16 nucleotides of contiguous base pairs is required to allow DNA to remain double stranded. (ii) If the primers are too long, several potential problems arise. First, the longer the primers the more expensive they are to synthesize. Second, the longer the primers the more likely they are to anneal with each other, or for a single primer to anneal to itself and form a hairpin loop, and the less likely the primers are to anneal with the template. Third, and most importantly, if the primer is too long it can hybridize with DNA with which it is not perfectly matched. Internal mismatches are tolerated and hybridization can occur as long as there are enough surrounding base paired nucleotides, especially at the 3' end of the primer. Thus, longer primers might anneal to other regions of the genome than the region you actually want to amplify.

c. You would be more likely to obtain a PCR product if the mismatch were at the 5'-end. The 3'-end of a primer is its business end - that is where DNA polymerase adds additional nucleotides to the chain. Mismatches at the 3'-end would prevent DNA polymerase from adding any new nucleotides to the chain. (You might remember that some DNA polymerases have a 3'-to-5' exonuclease activity that could potentially remove the mismatch, now allowing further polymerization. This is true of *E. coli* DNA polymerase, but many of the DNA polymerases used in PCR come from thermophilic bacteria and these DNA polymerases do not have this exonuclease activity.) A mismatch at the 5'-end of the primer does not matter as long as there is enough base-pairing between the primer and genomic template to allow annealing.

d. Add the sequence 5'-GAATTC-3' to the 5'-end of both the forward and reverse primers.

14-21.

a. The *Eco*RI and the *Sal*I restrictions sites are both found in the pMore vector sequence shown in the problem. The *Eco*RI site is nearer the 5' end and the *Sal*I site is nearer the 3' end of the pMore sequence shown. This region of pMore is at the C-terminal end of the maltose binding protein (MBP). Therefore your cloning will insert the CFTR DNA sequence into the DNA sequence that codes for the C-terminal end of the MBP protein. In other words, the N-terminus of the fusion protein contains most of the MBP protein sequence. The MBP sequence ends at the 8th amino acid from the C-terminus of MBP where the *Eco*R1 site cuts the MBP DNA. The next part of the fusion protein contains the CFTR protein encoded by the PCR product. Note that the PCR amplifies the last protein coding exon of the CFTR gene. Therefore the C-terminal end of the fusion protein will contain the C-terminal end of CFTR. Remember that the N-to-C orientation of the CFTR protein must be the same as that of the fusion protein as a whole. Further details of the fusion protein will be discussed in part c below.

b. When you use two different restriction enzymes, the CFTR gene can only be inserted into the vector with the desired orientation yielding the fusion protein you described in part a. Thus the N-to-C orientation of the CFTR protein will be the same as the MBP protein. If the vector was only cut with *Eco*R1 and the PCR product had *Eco*R1 sites at both ends, then the PCR product could be inserted into the vector in two equally likely orientations, only one of which is the one you desire. A second advantage is that cutting with two enzymes minimizes unwanted products of the ligation in which ends of the same molecule come together.

c. There are many things to take into consideration here. First, you can use the set b PCR primers you designed in your answer to problem 14-20 in order to amplify the entire CFTR exon. Second, the CFTR exon does not have sites for *Eco*R1 and *Sal*I so you need to add nucleotides to the 5'-ends of the two primers that will contain appropriate sites for the two restriction enzymes. These sites cannot be exactly at the 5'-ends of the PCR primers – you must also add 5 more nucleotides beyond the restriction sites to enable the restriction enzymes to bind to their recognition sequences and digest the DNA. The sequence of these 5 nucleotides is not important. Third, the two parts of the fusion protein must end up being in frame. Because the PCR product encodes the C terminus of the fusion protein, there are fewer constraints on the identity of the additional nucleotides added to the second (backwards) primer. The answer below is just one of many possible solutions. The sequence of the critical part of the pMore vector is reproduced here. The dots at the left and right ends of this sequence represent the continuity of the DNA - this was a circular plasmid before the digestion.

```
5'...AGGATTTCAGAATTCGGATCCTCTAGAGTCGACCTGTAGGGCAA...3'
3'...TCCTAAAGTCTTAAGCCTAGGAGATCTCAGCTGGACATCCCGTT...5'
```

The vector is digested with *Eco*RI and *Sal*I to generate these sticky ends:

```
ArgIleSerGluPhe
5'...AGGATTTCAGTCG ACCTGTAGGGCAA...3'
3'...TCCTAAAGTCTTAA GGACATCCCGTT...5'
```

The PCR product using the set b primers is shown below. Remember that this PCR product contains the last protein coding exon of the CFTR gene. The left hand primer only has one open reading frame with the amino acid sequence shown below. The right hand primer contains the

DNA sequence coding for the last four amino acids at the C-terminal end of the CFTR protein, as shown in the problem. The stop codon (STP) is underlined. Therefore the amino acids are

```
       LeuArgSerGluPheSerGlu.....TrpAlaIleMet
5' GGCTAAGATCTGAATTTTCCGAG...TTGGGCAATAATGTAGCGC 3'
3' CCGATTCTAGACTTAAAAGGCTC...AACCCGTTATTACATCGCG 5'
```

Now you need to add an *Eco*R1 site to the 5' end of the left primer and a *Sal*I site to the 5' end of the right primer – the restriction sites are underlined below. These sites cannot be directly at the ends of the DNA sequence, so you need 5 random nucleotides added to each of the primers. Furthermore, you must maintain the continuity of the ORF (open reading frame) between the MBP and the CFTR proteins after the vector and insert are digested and ligated. Therefore two more nucleotides (note the two G:C pairs, italicized) were added to the left primer between the restriction site and the beginning of the CFTR ORF. Also, the region between the vector and the insert cannot have any in-frame stop codons. The PCR product using these primers is:

```
LeuArgSerGluPheSerGluTrpAlaIleMet
5'CCCCCGAATTCGGGCTAAGATCTGAATTTTCCGAG...TTGGGCAATAATGTAGCGCGTCGACCCCCC 3'
3'GGGGGCTTAAGCCCGATTCTAGACTTAAAAGGCTC...AACCCGTTATTACATCGCGCAGCTGGGGGG 5'
```

Upon digestion of the PCR product with *Eco*R1 and *Sal*I, you will get:

```
LeuArgSerGluPheSerGlu....TrpAlaIleMet
5' AATTCGGGCTAAGATCTGAATTTTCCGAG...TTGGGCAATAATGTAGCGCG3'
3'     GCCCGATTCTAGACTTAAAAGGCTC...AACCCGTTATTACATCGCGCAGCT 5'
```

Now you can ligate the vector and the PCR product yielding:

```
ArgIleSerGluPheGlyLeuArgSerGluPheSerGlu...…TrpAlaIleMetSTP
5'...AGGATTTCAGAATTCGGGCTAAGATCTGAATTTTCCGAG...TTGGGCAATAATGTAGCGCGTCGACCTGTAGGGCAA...3'
3'...TCCTAAAGTCTTAAGCCCGATTCTAGACTTAAAAGGCTC...AACCCGTTATTACATCGCGCAGCTGGACATCCCGTT...5'
```

The Gly (italicised) is the result of the adjustment to the PCR primer to ensure that the N-terminal part of the CFTR region was in frame with MBP. So in summary, the two PCR primers needed are:

5' CCCCCGAATTCGGGCTAAGATCTGAATTTTC 3' and

3' ACCCGTTATTACATCGCGCAGCTGGGGGG 5'

Again, there are many possible answers that have minor variations, but you must still go through all of these steps to make sure your PCR primers will work properly

d. The fusion protein contains almost all of MBP, so it should also bind to the amylose resin. The cloning described in part b removes only the last 7 amino acids from MBP. Make extracts of bacterial cells expressing the fusion protein and add these extracts to amylose resin. The fusion protein should stick on the resin while all the other bacterial proteins in the extract should not. You can wash the other bacterial proteins away leaving the fusion protein bound to the resin. To get the fusion protein off the resin you can add the sugar maltose. Maltose and amylase will compete for binding sites on the fusion protein. If maltose is in excess then it will "disconnect" the fusion protein from the resin, leaving a solution with purified fusion protein.

Section 14.6 – DNA Sequence Analysis

14-22.

Notice how many of these processes require the use of DNA polymerase, underlining why it is so important to learn how this enzyme works.

a. Enzyme-based; DNA ligase.

b. Enzyme-based; restriction enzymes.

c. Non-enzymatic; hybridization relies on complementary base pairing.

d. Enzyme-based; DNA polymerase.

e. Enzyme-based; reverse transcriptase for the first strand of cDNA and DNA polymerase for the complementary strand.

f. Enzyme-based; DNA polymerases from thermophilic bacteria (*E. coli* DNA polymerase would not be very effective for PCR because at each cycle, heat is applied to denature the DNA, and this heat would inactivate the *E. coli* enzyme. This is not true of DNA polymerases from bacteria that live in high temperature conditions).

14-23.

Assuming the DNA molecule to be sequenced is already in hand, the only enzyme you would need to sequence DNA is DNA polymerase (a).

14-24.

a. Reading the peaks from left-to-right (corresponding to the 5'-to-3' direction because DNA polymerase successively adds nucleotides to the 3' end) the sequence would be 5' TTTGCTTTGTGAGCGGATAACAA 3'.

b. The sequence written in part (a) is of the strand that is being newly synthesized in the sequencing reaction.

c. You know how to design the primer because: (1) You added the insert into the vector at a known location defined by a specific restriction enzyme; and (2) you know the sequence of the vector that flanks the position of the insert.

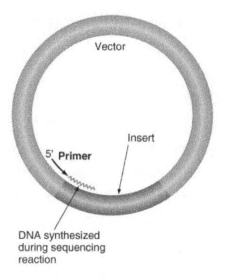

d. The smallest molecule synthesized in the sequencing reaction that contains dideoxy G would be:

    5' GCCTCGAATCGGGTACCTTTG* 3'

The asterisk indicates the dideoxy G, which must be at the 3' end because the chain terminates when this dideoxy nucleotide has been incorporated.

Chapter 15   Genome-Wide Analysis of Genetic Variation

Synopsis:

The genomes of any two humans differ from each other at more than 3 million nucleotides on average; it is these differences that make us individually distinct. This chapter describes the kinds of sequence variations that differentiate individual genomes, how we can detect this variation, and how we can use and interpret this information about genome variation. The analysis of genome variation has many practical purposes: from genotyping prospective parents, fetuses, or just-fertilized embryos; to the identification of tissues from individuals (DNA fingerprinting); to pinpointing the genes responsible for diseases; to understanding human history. As you read the chapter, you should be aware of the level of resolution afforded by different methods of analyzing individual genomes. Some techniques, particularly those based on the polymerase chain reaction (PCR), allow researchers to look at sequence differences (DNA polymorphisms) at just one or a handful of locations in the genome. Other methods, particularly those involving hybridization of probes to DNA microarrays, are suitable for looking at several million locations in the genome at one fell swoop, but these microarrays still sample less than 0.1% of all the 3 billion nucleotide pairs in the human haploid genome. Finally, due to spectacular advances in DNA sequencing technology, we can now begin to look at all the polymorphisms that distinguish individual genomes.

Key Terms:

locus a designated location on a *chromosome*. See α-*globin locus* and β-*globin locus.*

DNA polymorphisms two or more *alleles* at a *locus* detected with any method that directly distinguishes differences in DNA sequence. The sequence variations of a DNA polymorphism can occur at any position on a chromosome and may, or may not, have an effect on *phenotype*. See *polymorphisms.*

anonymous locus a designated position on a chromosome with no known function. See *locus*

marker an identifiable physical location on a *chromosome*, whose inheritance can be monitored. Markers can be expressed as regions of DNA (genes) or any segment of DNA with variant forms that can be followed.

single nucleotide polymorphism (SNP) a single *nucleotide* locus with two naturally existing *alleles* defined by a single base pair *substitution*. SNP loci are useful as DNA-based *markers* for formal genetic analysis.

inDels or DIPs genetic variants with short deletions and insertions; type of SNPs.

simple sequence repeat (SSR) a two- or three-base-long *SNP.*

copy number variant (CNV) a category of genetic variation arising from large regions of duplication or deletion, occurring with an overall frequency of less than 1 percent in a population. Compare with *copy number polymorphism.*

unequal crossing-over a change in DNA caused by out-of-register *recombination* during meosis in which one *homologous chromosome* ends up with a *duplication*, while the other homologue sustains a *deletion.*

polymerase chain reaction (PCR) a fast inexpensive method of replicating a DNA sequence once the sequence has been identified; based on a reiterative loop that amplifies the products of each previous round of *replication*.

DNA fingerprint the pattern produced by the simultaneous detection of *genotype* at a group of unlinked, highly *polymorphic* loci.

allele-specific oligonucleotides (ASOs) short *oligonucleotides* of 30–40 bases that hybridize to only one of the two alleles at a *SNP* locus under appropriate conditions.

DNA probe a purified fragment of DNA labelled with a radioactive isotope or a fluorescent dye and used to identify complementary sequences by means of *hybridization*.

positional cloning the process that enables researchers to obtain the clone of a gene without any prior knowledge of its protein product or function. It uses genetic and physical maps to locate *mutations* responsible for particular *phenotypes*.

Significant Elements:

After reading the chapter and thinking about the concepts, you should be able to:

♦ Recognize, describe and explain the effects of the four different types of DNA polymorphisms: SNPs, InDels (deletions/duplications/insertions into non-repeated loci), SSRs (simple sequence repeats, microsatellites and minisatellites), CNV/CNP (copy number variation/polymorphism).

♦ Explain the techniques used to detect the different polymorphisms.

♦ Distinguish different forms of a DNA marker and assign heterozygote and homozygote genotypes.

♦ Determine if a particular marker is informative for mapping a disease gene - is it linked and is it polymorphic in the family you are studying?

♦ Follow inheritance of a disease allele of a gene using a linked molecular marker.

♦ Determine the likelihood that a particular individual carries a disease allele based on the molecular marker data and the degree of linkage between the marker and the disease gene.

♦ Describe the steps in positional cloning from phenotype to gene clone.

♦ Describe steps for understanding the function of a gene (the phenotype affected) starting with a cloned gene.

♦ Interpret data for locating genes in a DNA sequence.

Problem Solving Tips:

Genotyping by PCR: The key point about the polymerase chain reaction is that the technique amplifies a specific region of the genome (usually less than 10 kb long) located between the 5' ends of two primers. These primers must be oriented so that their 5'-to-3' polarities point toward each other. This means that each primer uses a different DNA strand (Watson or Crick) as a template for DNA synthesis. To detect polymorphisms in the amplified region, you can either sequence the PCR product (for any polymorphism) or determine its size by gel electrophoresis (for Indel or SSR polymorphisms that alter the number of nucleotide pairs in the PCR product).

Genotyping by DNA microarrays: This method is generally used for analysis of SNP polymorphisms. For all the end-of-chapter problems based on this technique, each column represents an individual locus (that is, a specific nucleotide pair somewhere in the genome), and each row represents one of the four possible alleles of this SNP (that is, A, C, G, or T as read off of one strand of the chromosome). The other important aspect of microarray data concerns the intensity (color) of the signal for each of the four alleles in a column. White means that the allele in question is not found in the genomic DNA, orange means that the genome contains one copy of the relevant allele, and red indicates that the genome contains two copies of the relevant allele. For an autosomal gene in a diploid organism, you would expect to see that the total number of copies in each column is 2.

Whole-genome sequencing: Because this technology is evolving so rapidly, you should not concern yourself with understanding the nuts-and-bolts of the various methods. What is essential is to understand the concept of a read: a small snippet of sequence obtained ultimately from a single molecule of DNA. Reads are distinguished of course first by their actual DNA sequence. But the next critical piece of information concerns the number of reads of a particular sequence that was obtained in the experiment. For example, if an individual is a heterozygote for two alternative SNP alleles of a locus, then roughly equal numbers of reads corresponding to each allele should be observed. Finally, the diagram shown in Fig. 10.25 on p. 365 is critical; it shows you how to interpret whole-genome sequence information so as to find the polymorphisms responsible for a genetic disease.

Positional cloning: This procedure aims to locate the gene responsible for a genetic disease based on the gene's proximity to anonymous DNA polymorphisms (that are usually followed on microarrays). Positional cloning is in essence nothing more than recombination mapping: if the disease gene and the DNA polymorphism are close together, they will exhibit genetic linkage. Remember that gene mapping requires that at least one parent must be a double heterozygote for the two loci in question (in this case, one parent must be simultaneously heterozygous for the disease gene and for a particular DNA polymorphism). In determining recombination distances, you can only consider progeny from a cross in which the phase (that is, the haplotypes in the doubly heterozygous parent) is known or can be inferred with considerable certainty.

Finally, two numerical generalizations will be of value:

(i) on average, 1 map unit corresponds to 1 Mb of human DNA, and

(ii) on average, there is ~1 gene/100 kb of human DNA

Once the recombination frequency between the disease gene and polymorphism is determined, these numbers will allow you to approximate the physical distance between them and the number of candidate genes likely to be located in this interval. Because the genomic locations of the polymorphisms used for positional cloning are known, you can consult the human RefSeq database website to identify the candidate genes.

Allelic heterogeneity: In evaluating various candidate genes that might be responsible for a genetic disease (as identified either by positional cloning or by whole-genome sequencing), you need to be aware that many genetic conditions can be caused by a variety of different mutations within the disease gene; this is allelic heterogeneity. If the aberrant phenotype is recessive to wild type, you will see allelic heterogeneity as trans-heterozygosity: an affected person can have one mutant allele on one chromosome but a different mutant allele on the homologous chromosome.

Solutions to Problems:

Vocabulary

a.	DNA polymorphism	5.	a DNA sequence that occurs in two or more variant forms
b.	phase	3.	arrangement of alleles of two linked genes in a diploid
c.	informative cross	8.	allows identification of a gamete as recombinant or nonrecombinant
d.	ASO	6.	a short oligonucleotide that will hybridize to only one allele at a chosen SNP locus
e.	SNP	2.	two different nucleotides appear at the same position in genomic DNA from different individuals
f.	DNA fingerprinting	7.	detection of genotype at a number of unlinked highly polymorphic loci
g.	SSR	1.	DNA element composed of short tandemly repeated sequences
h.	locus	4.	location on a chromosome
i.	compound heterozygote	10.	individual with two different mutations in the same gene
j.	exome	9.	all exons in a genome

Section 15.1 – Variation Among Genomes

15-2.

When examining anonymous DNA markers you are looking directly at the DNA sequence of an individual. The terms dominant and recessive are usually used only when discussing the phenotype of an organism, so in one sense this question is meaningless. [Also, the majority of these anonymous DNA loci are not located in genes and so have no effect on the phenotype of the organism (Problem 11-4)]. However, geneticists often say that DNA markers are inherited in a codominant fashion to denote that both alleles can be seen in the DNA sequence and that the genotype of a heterozygote depends equally on both alleles. This use of the word "codominant" makes sense if you think of the phenotype being described as the DNA sequence of the marker locus (SNP), or the size of PCR product band on a gel (SSR).

15-3.

SNPs in protein coding regions are more likely to have a deleterious effect on the organism as they are more likely to affect protein function, so they are expected to be relatively rare. Also most SNPs are found in noncoding DNA simply because noncoding DNA in humans comprises a much greater proportion of the genome (98%) than coding DNA.

15-4.

a. The genome in a gamete is $\sim 3 \times 10^9$ bp long. This number times 1×10^{-8} base substitutions per bp per gamete yields ~30 base substitutions in the genome of a gamete. Because individuals are formed from two gametes (an egg and a sperm), your own genome should contain ~60 new base substitution mutations that were not found in the genomes of either of your parents.

b. Because these mutations were passed on to you, these *de novo* (new) mutations must have occurred in the germ lines of your parents. They could have happened during the mitotic divisions that increase the number of germ-line cells (that is, in the spermatogonia or oogonia), or during meiosis (in spermatocytes or oocytes). You should note that every time a cell divides provides an opportunity for mutations to accumulate.

c. The more rounds of cell division that take place before the production of sperm or eggs, the more mutations will be found in the gamete. Because more rounds of cell division are needed for the production of sperm than eggs, sperm should contain more base substitution mutations than eggs. (Because each gamete is the result of a single meiosis, most of these divisions are in the spermatogonial and oogonial cells.) The average rate of base substitutions at SNP loci mentioned in the problem (1×10^{-8} base substitutions per bp per gamete) is actually a composite of very different values for sperm and egg: The average rate of new base substitutions in sperm is actually considerably higher than that for eggs. Thus, most of the *de novo* mutations that are found in your genome but not in the genomes of either of your parents must have been obtained from the sperm. Recent research (as of 2014) suggests that this conclusion may be behind findings that the rate of autism and behavioral problems such as attention deficit disorder (ADD) is higher among the children of older fathers than younger fathers. The older the father, the more rounds of cell division took place before sperm are produced. (In testes, spermatogonial cells are continually dividing throughout adulthood.) Thus, the older the father, the more new mutations will appear in the sperm. (A good argument for younger males is to freeze and store their sperm!) In contrast, human females are born with a full complement of oocytes (or nearly so), so maternal age is not a factor in the number of base substitutions that accumulate in eggs. (Of course, older women are subject to increased rates of chromosome nondisjunction leading to Down syndrome among their children.)

15-5.

The regions in which Watson and Venter share the same SNPs imply that these two men must have shared a recent common ancestor (within several generations) from whom they derived these SNPs. The interspersion of such regions of shared SNPs with regions in which the two men do not share SNPs is the result of recombination. That is, the one particular chromosome from their recent common ancestor began to recombine with other homologous chromosomes that were different in the separate lineages leading to Watson or to Venter. These homologous chromosomes had different SNPs. Thus, the present-day chromosomes in Watson and Venter are pastiches of parts obtained from the common recent ancestor and parts obtained from other ancestors who were not common to the two men; recombination over generations has shuffled and reshuffled these different parts. You should understand that any comparison of the genomes of any two people alive today will also show patterns in which similar and nonsimilar SNPs will be interspersed. The more closely related the people, the longer will be the regions of SNP similarity. For people more distantly separated, like people from Africa versus those from Asia or Europe, the similarities will be harder to find, but they will still be present because humanity as a species is quite young.

15-6.

a. 3 billion – 50 million = 2.95 billion. The main point here is that the majority of nucleotides in the human genome are the same in all people.

b. The studies to date with thousands of human genomes will have already found most of the SNPs that are common in human populations (~50 million). But there are many more rare SNPs that will be found in just one or a very few people (for example, very recently occurring mutations). To find all the rare mutations in all the human genomes on earth, you would have to sequence the genomes of all present-day humans. It is interesting to consider why the human population has so many rare SNPs and not so many common SNPs. Remember that the accumulation of mutations depends on cell division, so each new individual can have dozens or more mutations not found in the genomes of his or her parents (see Problem 4). The total population of humans on the earth was historically very small, but starting with the Industrial Revolution in ~1750, there was a tremendous population explosion. Many new mutations would have been introduced into the species during this short time period, and these mutations would be rare because only a few people would share them (the person who first inherited a rare mutation would not have been able to engender many descendants given the few generations involved). In contrast, the mutations giving rise to common SNPs must have occurred many more generations in the past, but there are relatively few of such mutations because the population prior to 1750 was relatively so small.

c. The chance that any one bp is bi-allelic in the thousands of humans examined to date is $5 \times 10^7 / 3 \times 10^9 = 1.67 \times 10^{-2}$. The chance that another mutation happened at this same base pair would be $(1.67 \times 10^{-2})^2 = 2.79 \times 10^{-4}$. This number times $3 \times 10^9 = 8.37 \times 10^5$, or about 840,000 positions at which 3 different alleles might be found at any one nucleotide position in the human genome. For 4 alleles, this would be $(1.67 \times 10^{-2})^4 = 7.78 \times 10^{-8} \times 3 \times 10^9 = 2.3 \times 10^2 = 230$ positions. You can see that for the large majority of SNP loci, the human population has only two alternative alleles. The calculations above are only very rough approximations. They assume that all possible mutations that change one nucleotide pair to another are equally likely, but in fact transitions are about twice as likely as transversions because the mechanisms that generate transitions spontaneously are more prevalent. The calculations for 3 or 4 different alleles also do not account for the fact that if 2 or 3 alleles already exist in the population, then only a subset of possible mutations would change the base pair into a new allele. (For example, if A, C, and G alleles were already present in the population, then a pre-existing allele could only change to a T in order to make the SNP locus tetra-allelic.) These factors would tend to make tri- and tetra-allelic loci even less common in human genomes than the calculations above would indicate.

15-7.

a. SSRs are polymorphisms in which the alleles differ in the number of tandem repeats of a simple sequence less than about 10 bp long.

b. SSRs are likely generated by a mechanism of DNA polymerase stuttering (slipped mispairing of DNA strands) at repeated sequences during DNA replication.

c. CNVs are repeats of units longer than 10 bp. DNA polymerase stuttering is unlikely to generate these kinds of changes. Instead, it is thought that unequal crossing over between repeats is responsible for most changes in the number of CNV repeats. In contrast with the short repeat units of SSRs, the repeat units of CNVs are sufficiently long that they can mispair in prophase of meiosis I.

d. SNPs could potentially occur at any of the 3 billion bp in the human genome. SSRs could occur only at positions that already contain several repeats of a small DNA sequence. Thus, there are many fewer SSR loci than SNP loci.

15-8.

The figure that follows illustrates the answers to parts (a), (b), and (c). In all the red designations, the letter to the left of the arrow is the ancestral nucleotide and that to the right of the arrow is derived. The sequence in the common ancestor of all three species is at the top. For position #3, you don't know if the ancestral sequence was A or T. You do know that the mutation causing this polymorphism arose after the gorilla lineage split from the chimp/human lineage. Note that the data indicates considerable substructure to the human population. The G -> T mutation at position #4 occurred at one moment in time, and then among the descendants inheriting that mutation, a mutation at position #7 occurred.

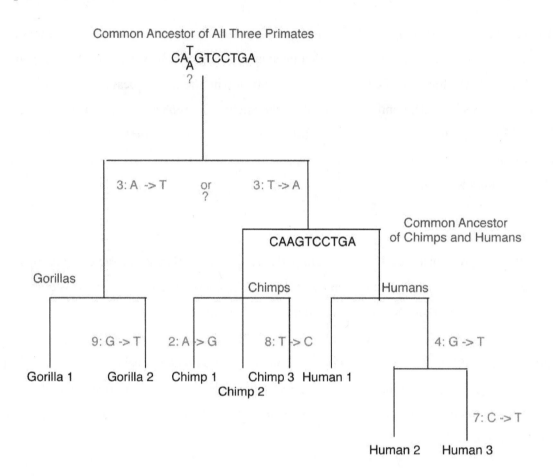

Section 15.2 – Genotyping a Known Disease-Causing Mutation

15-9.

a. The human genome sequence shows the sequence of the normal allele of PKU. You wish to know whether or not the PKU syndrome in this patient is caused by a mutation in the phenylalanine hydroxylase gene. You suspect that there might be such a mutation in this particular exon, so you will sequence the PCR product. If there is a mutation in this 1 kb exon, you want to know exactly what it is, how it affects the enzyme, and perhaps something about the history of this mutation in human populations. For example, if you compare the sequence in many patients and track where the patients are from, you might get an idea of where this mutation arose in time and geographical space. If you do not find a mutation in this 1 kb exon that changes the amino acid sequence of the enzyme, there might still be a mutation in a different exon.

b. One haploid human genome contains 3×10^9 bp. Therefore $(3 \times 10^9$ bp/haploid genome$) \times (6.6 \times 10^2$ g/mole$) \times ($mole$/6.02 \times 10^{23}$ bp$) = 3.3 \times 10^{-12}$ g/haploid genome. In other words, one haploid genome weighs 3.3×10^{-12} g or 3.3 picograms. Each haploid genome will contain only one phenylalanine hydroxylase gene to be used as the template for the PCR reaction. You start the PCR reaction with 1 ng (1×10^{-9} g) of human DNA. Therefore (1×10^{-9} g DNA) × (1 haploid genome/3.3 × 10^{-12} g) × (1 template molecule/1 haploid genome) = 0.3×10^3 template molecules = 300 template molecules in 1 ng of DNA.

c. You begin the PCR with 300 template molecules. If the PCR runs for 25 cycles then this number of molecules doubles exponentially 25 times. Therefore you will end up with 300 molecules × 225 = 10^{10} or about 10 billion molecules. This result explains the power of PCR: you started with only 300 template molecules and end up with 10 billion copies of the region you are amplifying. In practice the yields are not quite as high because not all potential template molecules get amplified each cycle. However the amplification is still substantial. The PCR product is 1 kb long, so (10^{10} molecules of PCR product) × (10^3 bp/molecule of PCR product) × (mole/6.02×10^{23} bp) × (6.6×10^2 g/mole) = 1.1 × 10^{-8} g = 110 ng. You started with 1 ng of the whole genome and ended up with 110 ng of a 1 kb section of the genome after the PCR!

15-10.

The two primers should flank the target sequence and should be oriented so that their 5'- to-3' orientations drawn as arrows should point to each other (with the 3' ends towards the center). This reflects the fact that DNA polymerase adds nucleotides sequentially to the 3'-ends of the primers. You want DNA polymerase to extend the primer into the sequence being amplified. Only set b satisfies these criteria.

15-11.

a. If human DNA were a random sequence of equal proportions of A, C, G and T (not entirely accurate, but close enough), then the chance that either primer would anneal to a random region of DNA would be (1/4)18, or about 1 chance in 7 x 10^{10}. In other words, any particular 18 base sequence would occur at random only once in every 70 billion nucleotides. As the human genome is 3 billion nucleotide pairs long, it is very unlikely that even one of the primers will anneal anywhere else except to the *CFTR* gene. The probability is even much lower that *both* primers would anneal to other random stretches of DNA that happen to be close enough together to allow the formation of a PCR product. (This probability is hard to calculate exactly because of the variation in the possible distance between the two primers.)

b. The lower limit on the size of the primers is governed by several factors. The most important is that the primers must anneal to the genomic DNA. Hydrogen bonding between 15 nucleotide pairs is ordinarily required to allow DNA to be double stranded stably. A second factor is that the primers need to be sufficiently long so that the PCR amplifies specifically only the target DNA. Using the same logic as we did in part (a), the chance that one primer of 16 nucleotides would anneal to random DNA is $(1/4)^{16}$ = one in 4 billion. As there are only 3 billion nucleotides in the human haploid genome, a 16 bp primer will likely hybridize to only one sequence in the human genome. A particular 15 bp primer will be present every $(1/4)^{15}$ bases, which is about 1 time every 1 billion bp. That means that a 15 bp primer sequence is likely to be in the 3- billion bp human genome 3 times. The chance that two such primers would anneal to random DNA close enough together for PCR amplification is extremely low. However, because a primer that is at least 16 bp primer is likely to hybridize to a unique genomic sequence, most researchers would view 16 bp as the lower limit. Interestingly (though not asked in the problem), very long PCR primers (more than 40 or so nucleotides) also create some problems. In particular, the longer primers might hybridize with genomic DNA sequences to which they are not perfectly matched. (Internal mismatches are tolerated and hybridization can occur as long as there are enough surrounding base-paired nucleotides, particularly at the 3' end of the primer. Thus, very long primers might amplify regions of the genome other than the target.

c. You would be more likely to obtain a PCR product if the mismatch were at the 5' end. The 3' end of the primer is the business end, where DNA polymerase adds additional nucleotides to the chain. But mismatches at the 3' end would prevent DNA polymerase from adding any new nucleotides. (This question is important because it means you can add nucleotides unrelated to the template to the 5' ends of PCR primers. In this way, for example, you could add a restriction enzyme recognition site to the ends of the PCR product to facilitate cloning.)

15-12.

a. If you see a double peak and this represents a mistake, much of the PCR product must have the same error. This scenario could occur only if the mistake happened early in the PCR amplification and was then copied over many PCR cycles.

b. It is more likely that a mistake would happen in a late round of PCR, because there are more molecules present and thus more chances for mistakes. Fortunately, the later these mistakes happen, the less likely you would be to see them because only a small proportion of the PCR product would have this mistake.

c. Basically, you would want to determine the person's genotype several times with independent PCR reactions. These mistakes are so rare that it is almost impossible that the same mistake would occur in multiple independent PCR reactions. You could not do multiple independent PCRs easily in preimplantation genotyping, because you would have to remove multiple single cells from the same ~8 cell embryo.

d. This exonuclease function would prevent the *P. furiosa* DNA polymerase from making as many mistakes in base incorporation as the *T. aquaticus* enzyme, so the PCR reaction would be more accurate and reliable.

15-13.

This problem requires you to remember that people are diploids and therefore have two copies of autosomal loci. They could be homozygotes for any of the three sequences in the table, or they could be heterozygotes for any two of the three sequences. If you were doing Sanger sequencing of PCR products, then for heterozygotes you would see double peaks where the two sequences in a heterozygote are different.

a. The three possible answers are thus:

CAAGTCCTGA/CAATTCCTGA (1/2) + CAATTCTTGA/CAATTCTTGA (3/3)

CAAGTCCTGA/CAAGTCCTGA (1/1) + CAATTCCTGA/CAATTCTTGA (2/3)

CAAGTCCTGA/CAATTCCTGA (1/2) + CAATTCCTGA/CAATTCTTGA (2/3)

Note that the sequence data from the 1/2 or 2/3 heterozygotes reveal both 10 nt haploid sequences unambiguously because there is only one double peak - only one variable nucleotide. Because there are no double peaks in the sequences from the homozygotes (1/1 or 3/3), the sequence traces for these individuals reveal both haploid sequences (which are of course identical) in their genomes.

b. If a person was (1/3), there are two differences and thus two double peaks. One possible solution is:

CAAGTCCTGA/CAATTCTTGA (1/3)

However, the gel trace is also compatible with:

CAAGTCTTGA/CAATTCCTGA (4/2)

where 4 is a new allele that is neither 1, 2 or 3. You could not distinguish these two possibilities using this methodology. You could not conclude that a person whose sequence trace is that produced by (1/3) is in fact (1/3), as they could instead be (4/2). Note that this issue would not exist if you examined the people's genotypes by single-molecule DNA sequencing because each sequence would be from a single chromosome, not a mixture of the two homologous chromosomes as is the case with PCR-amplified material.

15-14.

Huntington disease is late-onset dominant lethal disease. The disease is associated with the expansion of a CAG trinucleotide repeat in the *HD* gene. As stated in the text, normal individuals have up to 35 copies of the triplet. Individuals with repeat regions containing more than 35 repeats are susceptible to Huntington disease; all disease alleles with 42 or more repeats are completely penetrant. In general, greater numbers of repeats correlate with younger age of onset of the disease.

a. Individuals A, B, C and E all have one PCR band (one allele) that is much larger (between 270 and 380 nucleotides long) than the second allele (between 200 and 220 nucleotides long). It isn't possible to correlate these band sizes with trinucleotide repeat numbers because we don't know the position (relative to the repeats) of the unique sequences to which the PCR primers anneal. However these much larger bands must have more copies of the repeat than the smaller bands. The repeat region in individual B is the longest; so this person is likely to have the earliest onset of the disease.

b. Both PCR bands for individuals D and F are smaller, so they appear to have received *HD+* alleles from both of their parents. Thus they should not have the disease.

c. This problem can be solved only if the number of repeats in an allele is known. If we assume that the longest *HD+* allele shown in the figure (the smaller band in individual B) contains the maximum number of repeats for a non-disease-causing allele (35 repeats), then the 220 bp of this PCR product should include $35 \times 3 = 105$bp of CAG repeats, plus 70 bp between the 5' end of one PCR primer to the nearest CAG repeat. Therefore, $220 - 175 = 45$ bp will remain from the end of the CAG repeats to the 5' end of the second PCR primer. Note that the distance between the primers and the beginning and end of the SSR repeats is the same for all alleles.

15-15.

a. In the patient whose graph is shown on the top, the CAG repeat number in the *HD+* allele is approximately 15; the somatic cells of the patient on the bottom has about 20 CAG repeats in the *HD+* allele.

b. These results say a great deal about the mechanisms that give rise to mutant *HD* alleles. First, the repeat number varies among different sperm from the same individual, so these processes take place in germ-line cells during spermatogenesis. Second, it appears that the larger the original number of repeats in any *HD* allele, the more likely it is that the number of repeats in the sperm will vary and the greater the degree of potential variation. In the graph on the top, almost all of the sperm with the mutant *HD* allele have more than 62 repeats, some sperm have more than 120 repeats and the distribution is quite broad. The distribution of mutant sperm sizes in the graph on the bottom is tighter. In addition, note the fact that there is little if any variation in sperm size of the sperm containing an *HD+* allele. Third, it is interesting that the sperm mostly seem to accumulate more CAG repeats rather than lose CAG repeats - few if any sperm have less than the number of CAG repeats in the *HD* genes in somatic cells.

c. There is some probability that the number of CAG repeats can expand during spermatogenesis, even with lower numbers of CAG repeats. A man with an *HD* allele on the high side of normal (~30 CAG repeats) or in the gray area between 36 and 41 repeats (who may not show any symptoms), may produce sperm with more than 42 repeats. Note that these data predict that the unaffected father (but not the unaffected mother) of a Huntington disease patient should have an allele with between 30 and 42 repeats, because this particular repeat expansion occurs during spermatogenesis. Interestingly, in fragile X syndrome, another trinucleotide repeat disease, the expansion usually occurs during meiosis in the mother.

d. You would expect that each of the two blood cell samples would show a very tight distribution of CAG repeat numbers around the numbers seen in the normal and mutant *HD* alleles (15 and 62 for the patient at the top; 20 and 48 for the patient at the bottom). There should be very little variation in repeat number between different blood cells from the same person since the expansion in repeat number seems to be restricted to the germ line.

Section 15.3 – Sampling DNA Variation in a Genome

15-16.

The evidence could be used to show that the accused's pickup truck was at a specific location in the Arizona desert where the Palo Verde tree was growing. Presumably this location would be very close to where the corpse was discovered.

15-17.

In general, SNPs are bi-allelic and have only 2 alleles in human populations (see Problem 6 above). The SSRs used in CODIS have many alleles that vary in the number of repeating units. This means that the chance of any two people sharing the same set of alleles at 14 SNP loci is much higher than the chance they would share the same set of alleles at 14 SSR loci. The *Hardy-Weinberg equilibrium* allows you to calculate the probability that any two random people would share the same alleles of any polymorphism, as long as you know the frequency of that allele among all of the alleles in the population being studied. Of course, the lower the frequencies at which the alleles in the test subject are found in the population, the lower the probability that a random individual from the population will have exactly the same alleles. Because the CODIS loci are unlinked to each other (and therefore are inherited independently), you can multiply the low probabilities for a match with the alleles of each locus together, resulting in extremely low probabilities of a match with the alleles of all 14 CODIS loci. This is of course the basis of DNA fingerprinting.

b. Dogs and other domesticated animals have been highly inbred. This means that any two dogs would be much more likely to share the same alleles of any polymorphism than any two humans; moreover, the dogs would be much more likely to be homozygous at any given location. You would thus have to look through many more DNA sequences to find one that would vary between any two dogs.

15-18.

a. C-Tsar; E-Tsarina; ABDH-Daughters, G – Son (Tsarevitch), F- unrelated. There is no completely systematic way to do analyze these data, so eventually you will need to sort through the most likely alternatives and see which ones fit. The easiest place to start is with the males (C and G), one of whom must be Tsar Nicolas II and the other of whom must be Tsarevitch Alexei. Because G has two alleles for D3S1358, neither of which is found in A and B (who must be sisters because they share all alleles but one of all loci), G does not pass on any alleles to these daughters and so G must be the Tsarevitch rather than the Tsar. Once this determination is made, the rest of the analysis becomes straightforward. An alternative way to begin is to search for the unrelated individual, who must be F because she has at least one allele of each locus that is found in none of the other people.

b. B (12,12); C (11,12); E (9,11)

c. No, none of the daughters has identical alleles at all loci.

d. The sizes of the skeletons might reflect the ages of the daughters. Perhaps dental records exist might match the teeth of one or more of the skeletons.

e. All of the daughters are accounted for, so Anastasia must have been one of the skeletons.

f. $1/8 = 12.5\%$. (The Tsarina and Philip's grandmother should share $1/2$ of their alleles because they are sisters. There is a $1/2$ chance for Prince Philip's mother to inherit a common allele from Philip's grandmother, and a $1/2$ chance for Philip to inherit a common allele from his mother. $1/2 \times 1/2 \times 1/2 = 1/8$.)

g. $1/16 = 6.25\%$. Another factor of $1/2$ for the Tsarevitch to inherit a common allele from the Tsarina.

h. The Tsarina was Prince Phillip's great aunt.

15-19.

a. In this problem, you are not looking at individual sperm, but instead at semen, which contains millions of different sperm. If the man is heterozygous for two alleles of an SSR locus, about half of his sperm would have one allele and the remaining half the other allele.

b. The purple locus is on the X chromosome. Note that there is only one copy in the semen and one copy in individuals 1 and 4. These two people must be males. Individuals 2 and 3 have two copies of the purple locus, and thus 2 copies of the X chromosome; these two people are females.

c. The green locus is on the Y chromosome. There is one copy in the semen and in the somatic genomes of males. Individuals 2 and 3 don't have any green bands because they don't have a Y chromosome.

d. If any individual was the rapist, all the bands of all the colors should match the semen sample.

e. Note that individual 2 matches the rapist at 5 alleles out of 10 (one black, two red, and two orange). Individual 2 is likely to be the rapist's sister.

f. The bands are 200 and 212 bp long. Each primer for the PCR is 20 bp long; PCR requires two primers. The repeating unit is 4 bp. Thus, the 200 bp allele would have (200-40)= 160/4 = 40 repeats. The 212 allele would have 3 more repeats, or 43.

15-20.

a. The microarray hybridization technique is not very sensitive, so you need to generate enough fluorescently labeled probe to see any signals.

b. This question is basically asking you to draw the following:

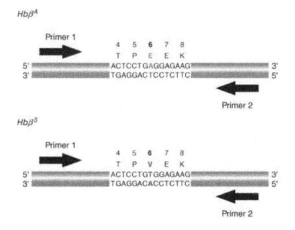

c. At 80°C, the hydrogen bonding between the two strands of DNA (one strand on the silicon chip and the other being the fluorescent probe) is disrupted by the heat, so the probe cannot bind to the DNA on the chip.

d. The incubation temperature affects the accuracy of annealing between complementary sequences. If the temperature is sufficiently low, then one mismatch will not affect the ability of the two strands of DNA to come together and stay together.

e. Embryos 2 and 3 are homozygous for the *A* allele (*AA*); embryos 1, 5, and 7 are *AS* heterozygotes, and individuals 4 and 6 are *SS* homozygotes. To avoid the possibility that the child would have sickle cell anemia, you would choose the *AA* homozygotes. If only a few embryos were available, you might also implant the *AS* heterozygotes (which are usually phenotypically normal except under exceptional circumstances like long exposure to low amounts of oxygen). You would not choose the *SS* homozygotes, as they would have sickle cell anemia if brought to term. In the early days of *in vitro* fertilization, physicians implanted several embryos into the uterus of the expectant mother. As the negative effects of multiple births became increasingly apparent, the number of implanted embryos has been reduced. As of this writing (2014), no more than two or three embryos are chosen in most cases of preimplantation genotyping.

15-21.

The two possible ASOs for the *HbβA* allele are:

5' CTGACTCCTGAGGAGAAGTCG 3' or 3' GACTGAGGACTCCTCTTCAGC 5'

The two possible ASOs for the *HbβS* allele are:

5' CTGACTCCTGTGGAGAAGTCG 3' or 3' GACTGAGGACACCTCTTCAGC 5'

15-22.

a. You would only need a single primer because the same adapter sequence was already added to both ends of the fragment prior to the PCR. The primer you would use for the PCR amplification step shown in the figure would correspond to this sequence as it is shown.

b. You would want to cut the DNA with a restriction enzyme that made sticky ends; this would make it very easy to add the adapter at the two ends. (The adapter would be made with one end being blunt and the other having the sticky end, as shown in the figure.) It would not matter if the sticky end had a 5'-overhang or a 3'-overhang. You would generally want to cut the DNA with an enzyme that recognized only a 4 bp recognition site. The reason here is mostly technical. PCR can only amplify regions of DNA less than 10 kb or so. So if you used an enzyme that recognized 6 bp or 8 bp, much or even most of the genomic DNA fragments would be too large for PCR amplification.

15-23.

a.   Dad: 1-AC 2-GG 3-AG 4-GT 5-CC 6-CG 7-AG 8-GT

Mom: 1-AA 2-CG 3-GG 4-AT 5-CC 6-CC 7-AG 8-TT

b. SNP locus 4 has alleles A, G, and T.

c. You know the whole sequence of the human genome. You designed the ASOs on the microarray with the benefit of this knowledge.

d. If the 8 loci are each about 10 Mb apart, SNP1 and SNP8 would be ~70 Mb apart. 70/191 = 37% of chromosome 4. The answer depends on the average value of 1 cM corresponding to 1 Mb in the human genome. This value masks a great deal of variation in the rate of recombination for a given length of DNA in different parts of the genome; the rate for any given region also varies between males and females.

Section 15.4 – Positional Cloning

15.24

a. The disease is dominant: the condition is rare and you see a vertical pattern of inheritance (the affected children have an affected father). The disease is also autosomal; it cannot be X-linked because there is father-to-son transmission. Note also that this cannot be X-linked for another reason: The males and females have two copies of the SNPs (assuming that these SNPs are syntenic with the disease gene).

b.   Affected son: 1-C 2-G 3-A 4-G 5-C 6-C 7-A 8-T

Affected daughter: 1-A 2-G 3-A 4-G 5-C 6-C 7-A 8-G

Unaffected son: 1-C 2-G 3-A 4-T 5-C 6-G 7-G 8-T

Unaffected daughter: 1-A 2-G 3-G 4-T 5-C 6-G 7-G 8-T

c. SNP2 and SNP5 are uninformative for linkage to the disease gene because the father is a homozygote for both SNPs. (Remember you can only follow linkage in a double heterozygote.)

d. SNP1 is unlinked because half the affected and half the unaffected have the A allele of SNP1, while the other half of the affected and the other half of the unaffected have the C allele. R = NR, so RF = 50%.

e and f. See the figure that follows. *Dark blue* and *light blue* indicate the two copies of chromosome 4 in the father. The chromosome has the dominant disease-causing allele *D*. The *light blue* chromosome has the normal recessive *d* allele. A recombination event in the father's germ line that gave rise to the affected son occurred somewhere between SNP7 and SNP8. The recombination event in the father giving rise to the unaffected son must be somewhere between SNP3 and SNP4. The disease gene must be between these two crossovers. The disease gene thus must be between SNP3 and SNP8; it must be to the left of SNP 4 and to the right of SNP7. The boxes that are crossed by the Xs signifying crossovers show the regions of uncertainty. The crossovers must occur within the boxes, but we don't know exactly where.

15.25

Yes, there is evidence of linkage. There are 2 informative matings (I-1 × I-2 and II-7 × II-8) which together yielded 11 progeny, only 1 of which (II-7) is recombinant. The estimated genetic distance is thus $1/11 \times 100 = 9.1$ map units. Note that I-1 produces parental types that are C + dominant disease allele and T + recessive (wild-type) allele. II-7 received a recombinant sperm that is T + dominant disease allele. This combination defines the parental types among the gametes that II-7 produces. Note also that the mating of II-1 × II-2 is uninformative, because neither parent is a double heterozygote.

b. The LOD score is based on the following calculations,:

Likelihood ratio: $[(1 - (1/11))^{10} \times (1/11)^{1}]/(1/2)^{11} = 71.7$

$LOD = \log_{10}(71.7) = 1.86$

This value means that it is 71.7 times more likely that the disease gene is linked to the SNP than that they are unlinked. This is pretty good evidence for linkage, but it would still not be accepted as definitive because the LOD score is below 3.

15.26

a. Matings W, Y and Z are not informative because neither parent is a double heterozygote. Mating X is informative because both parents are double heterozygotes and because all possible permutations of the gametes can be distinguished as parental or recombinant types.

b. It is likely that both A and B are SSRs rather than SNPs. Most SNPs are bi-allelic in human populations (see Problem 6c above), but the data show 4 different alleles of A and 4 alleles of B. One A allele is labeled "A5," implying that there might be 5 alleles or more in human populations, so SNP A would be definitely excluded if in fact an A4 allele existed in some person not shown.

15.27

Note that the disease is recessive. Thus, it for a mating to be informative, it must be the unaffected parent who could potentially be the double heterozygote.

a.

Locus 1 - No, neither parent is a double heterozygote.

Locus 2 - No, neither parent is a double heterozygote.

Locus 3 - Yes, but only in some cases. The mother would have to be a heterozygote for the disease gene. If the children were AC, you could not tell which allele they got from which parent, so these cases would be uninformative. Children who are AA or CC will be potentially informative whether they have the disease or not, because you would know what disease allele and what SNP allele they inherited from their mom.

(b): In terms of phase, such children are almost certainly inheriting the parental combination from their mother if the SNP is close to the disease gene (because it would be unlikely that these children would inherit a rare recombinant combination from both parents).

Locus 4 - Yes, if the mother is a heterozygote for the disease gene (and thus a double heterozygote). All of the children will be potentially informative because you can tell what alleles of the disease gene and the SNP locus they got from their mom. As for Locus 3, you could solve the phase problem if you knew that the SNP and disease gene were in fact closely linked. Because this is a consanguineous mating, the carrier mother would be most likely to have one chromosome with both the disease allele and the C allele of the SNP, as was true for both of the chromosomes in her affected partner.

15.28

a. It is clear that allele C is common to almost all of the individuals who have Huntington disease, so this allele is highly likely to be part of the same haplotype (that is, on the same chromosome) as the disease-causing allele.

b. Surprisingly, if you make no assumptions at all, then you can't say for certain that any people in the pedigree were formed from parental or recombinant gametes with respect to the *HD* gene and the G8 marker. The reason is that there are no cases in which the children, parents, and grandparents are all genotyped. You thus don't know the phase without making the assumption of linkage.

c. Looking first at the affected people in the pedigree who are genotyped at G8, all of them have the C allele. The simplest assumption is thus that they all received the parental configuration *HD* C that was present in I-1. Of the unaffected blood descendants of I-1 who could have inherited the *HD* allele from their affected parent, none have the C allele of G8 except for VI-5. It is possible that this woman could have received C from her unaffected father (in other words, V-3 is definitely AC and V-4 could have been AC as well). Thus, the most straightforward reading of this pedigree is that no one in this pedigree must have received a recombinant gamete from their affected parent (in terms of the *HD* gene and the G8 marker).

d. With no recombinants, the map distance would be 0 map units. But stated more accurately, you could only say that the map distance would be less than 1/47 x 100 = 2.1 cM. (*Note:* there are actually 47 people resulting from informative matings, not 46 as stated in the problem.)

e. Calculating the LOD score by the method outlined in the Tools of Genetics Box and the existence of 47 (rather than 46) progeny of informative matings:

Likelihood ratio = $[(1-0)^{47} \times 0^0] / (1/2)^{47} = 1.4 \times 10^{15}$

LOD = 15.14

It is 15 orders of magnitude more likely that *HD* and G8 are linked than that they are unlinked. This would be taken as absolutely conclusive evidence for linkage. (If you used the value of 46 informative matings given in the problem, then the likelihood ratio would be 7×10^{14} and the LOD score would be 14.85; still convincing evidence for linkage.)

15.29

a. It is possible that the SNP is tightly linked to the disease-causing mutation, but is not the mutation. You have simply not examined enough children to see any rare recombinants.

b. You could: (1) Determine whether or not the SNP locus is rare by asking whether it is found in databases of known SNPs. (2) Determine if the SNP is within a gene, and if so, is it likely to affect gene function (is it non-anonymous)? Possibly the base pair substitution results in a missense mutation affecting a conserved amino acid or a nonsense mutation. Perhaps the substitution disrupts a splicing junction. (3) Check other unrelated families, some with the disease and some without. Perhaps the same G base is always correlated with the disease. Maybe you would find that in all affected families, the gene in which this substitution occurs consistently has a non-anonymous SNP, even if the polymorphism in the family is not the T/G change noted in the problem. The same gene could harbor different mutations in different affected families in cases of allelic heterogeneity.

15.30

a. D is the dominant, disease-causing allele; d is the normal allele; $m1$, $m2$ and $m3$ are the SSR alleles. In each case, you first need to determine the phase of the disease gene alleles and the SSR alleles; in other words, you need to determine which disease gene alleles (D or d) and which SSR alleles ($m1$ or $m2$) are on the same chromosome as one another in the male parent. Second, given the RF of 10% between the two loci, and the knowledge of the SSR allele that the child inherited from the male parent (the *condition*), you need to use conditional probability to determine the chance that the child also inherited D. In the pedigree at the left, the male parent's chromosomes are $D\,m2\,/\,d\,m1$. He produces the following gametes at the frequencies shown in parentheses: $D\,m2$ (.45); $d\,m1$ (.45); $D\,m1$ (.05); and $d\,m2$ (.05). Child A inherited $m1$ from her father; this means that she inherited either $d\,m1$ or $D\,m1$. The 45:5 ratio (or 9:1 ratio) of $d\,m1$: $D\,m1$ gametes means that the probability is 10% that Child A inherited allele D (diseased). Child B inherited $m2$ from her father, meaning that she inherited either $D\,m2$ or $d\,m2$. The 9:1 ratio of $D\,m2$: $d\,m2$ gametes means that the chance is 90% that Child B is diseased (inherited allele D). In the middle pedigree, Child C inherited the $m2$ allele from her father. The probability that Child C is affected is not influenced by the fact that the first child was affected, so the calculation is the same as for child B; that is, the probability that Child C has the disease is also 90%. In the pedigree at the right, the phase of the alleles in the male parent is not known. However, we can use the information that the sibling of Child D is affected to determine the likelihood of one phase or the other. The brother of Child D inherited $D\,m1$ from his father. This means that the chance is 90% that the genotype of the father is $D\,m1\,/\,d\,m2$, and the chance is 10% that his genotype is $d\,m1\,/\,D\,m2$. Child D inherited $m2$ from his father. The probability that Child D inherited $m2\,D$ from his father is the weighted sum of the chances of inheriting this chromosome given each of the father's possible genotypes above. If the father's genotype is $D\,m1/\,d\,m2$, then using the same logic as we did above for Children A-C, there are 9 $d\,m2$ gametes produced for every 1 $D\,m2$ gamete made, and so the relative chance of $D\,m2$ is 10%. If the father's genotype is $d\,m1/\,D\,m2$, the relative chance of $D\,m2$ is 90%. Therefore, the chance that Child D has the disease (inherited $D\,m2$) is: $(0.9)(0.1) + (0.1)(0.9) = 0.09 + 0.09 = 0.18$, or 18%.

b. A human geneticist would not want to use an SSR marker 10 map units (cM) away to diagnose a gene because 10% of the time, the presence in a fetus of the SSR allele linked to the disease allele would lead to an incorrect diagnosis that the fetus is diseased when it was not. 10% of the time when the other SSR allele (usually on the same chromosome as the recessive, non-disease allele) is seen in the fetus, the fetus would actually be affected. Thus, 10% of the negatives would be false negatives, and 10% of the positives false positives.

15.31

a. The affected first child shows which marker allele is linked to the disease allele in each parent. The affected child got Dad's large allele and Mom's small allele. Note that the marker is in the *CFTR* gene, but is not the causative mutation. The fetus has Dad's small allele and Mom's small allele. The fetus is thus a carrier, but the chance the fetus will be affected is very close to 0%. It is possible that recombination could have occurred between the SSR and the disease mutation in the Mom, but this possibility is very low because the marker and SSR are so close together (both in the same gene). So the likelihood is greater than 0%, but not much greater.

b. The fetus will grow into a woman who is a carrier. Because this is a rare recessive trait, the chances are very low that any of her children would have cystic fibrosis, because they would not only have to get a mutant allele of *CFTR* from this woman (probability = 0.5), but they would also have to get a mutant allele of the *CFTR* gene from their father. The problem states that 3% of the population carries a mutant *CFTR* gene, and we furthermore assume that this man does not himself have cystic fibrosis. Thus, the mating that could produce a child with cystic fibrosis is *CF/CF+* × *CF/CF+*. We already know that the woman is a carrier (probability = 1), and the probability that any given man is *CF/CF+* is 0.03. The chance is 1/4 that any individual child produced from this mating would be *CF/CF* and have the disease. Thus, the probability that a child of this woman (and a man chosen at random from the population) would have cystic fibrosis is $1 \times 0.25 \times 0.03 = 0.0075 = 0.75\%$.

c. In contrast with the situation described in Problem 30 above, the chance of false positives or false negatives is very low in the scenario described here, so such a test would be quite accurate (though not 100% so). Because so many different mutations in *CFTR* could cause cystic fibrosis, doctors would not know what mutations to test for, whereas they would be able to follow the SSR marker and make accurate predictions about the fetus's disease status with high (but not perfect) confidence. You should note that in the future, when whole genome sequencing becomes more routine, you could potentially find all disease-causing mutations in the fetus's *CFTR* gene, so this indirect method would not be needed.

15.32

a. The drug should be effective in the G551D heterozygote, although likely less so than in a homozygote as there will be half as much protein in the heterozygote that can be made functional by the drug.

b. Younger patients have not built up as much mucus in their lungs as older ones, and it may be easier for the drug to get to the CFTR in the membrane. Furthermore, older patients likely already have some irreversible damage; the drug is not really designed to repair damaged tissue.

c. The researchers put compounds into the growth media of the cells homozygous for the G551D mutant and then looked under the microscope for cells that have beating cilia. This was in fact the approach that led to the development of ivacaftor. You should note that this approach cannot work in the case of patients who have no CFTR protein function (because they are homozygotes or *trans*-heterozygotes for null alleles). This technique depends upon the presence in the membrane of some mutant protein that could be made functional after binding of the drug. If no such protein is present, then this approach would not allow the formation of functional chloride ion channels.

15.33

a. The poly-A is added for two reasons: (i) To bind the single-stranded fragments of genomic DNA to the surface of the flowcell through the oligo-dT already present on the surface. (ii) Because the oligo-dT can act as a primer for DNA synthesis.

b. You need to remove the fluorescent tag at the end of each cycle so that you can detect reliably the color of the fluorescent tag of the nucleotide incorporated at the next cycle. Remember that this method ultimately will produce a movie for each template fragment showing successive flashes of color that indicate the sequence of the newly synthesized strand. You could not obtain such a movie if the fluorescent tag added each round remained at the same location.

c. The blocking group ensures that only one nucleotide will be added each cycle. If you did not remove the blocking group, then you could not add any more nucleotides to the growing chain so you could not sequence anything.

15.34

a. The researcher should look for possible cases of *trans*-heterozygosity; that is, look at genes to find whether both alleles are mutant but in different ways. In theory, the researcher would want to look at any such genes identified to see if the two mutations are likely to result in a loss of function, such as nonsense or frameshift mutations; and also to see if the two mutations affect highly conserved amino acids (if they are missense).

b. Unfortunately, it is hard to know what to look for in the whole genome outside of the coding regions. Maybe the patient has a mutation in an intergenic region or in an intron that affects the expression of a target gene, but how would the scientist be able to recognize it among the many polymorphisms that exist in the patient's whole genome? One possible approach is to focus the search on particularly well-conserved nucleotides, or those in the binding motifs known for certain transcription factors. Problem 35 below discusses how scientists might be able to determine whether a genetic condition results in quantitative changes in the expression of a particular gene in the tissues from a patient.

15.35

a. Using this kind of "deep sequencing" of mRNAs, researchers could attempt to find mRNAs whose levels change dramatically in the patient with respect to unaffected controls. This approach might be very useful if no mutations are found in the coding regions of genes, because mutations might affect the amount of expression of a gene. Scientists might also be able to detect changes in splicing patterns of a gene's transcript. But there are issues with this technique. How would you know which tissue to examine? If you don't choose the right one, then you might not find any changes in gene expression levels. (Sometimes the disease phenotype would suggest what tissue to look in.) The information from this approach would not be informative unless dramatic changes in the amounts of a specific mRNA were observed.

b. If major changes were observed in the size or amount of a protein in a patient, then the gene encoding that protein could be responsible for the disease. You might subsequently be able to detect changes in regulatory regions that cause aberrant expression of the gene, or nonsense or frameshift mutations in the coding region. You would not obtain any information from this method if the disease was caused by a missense mutation in the coding region because neither the amount or gross size of the protein would have changed. Note that one problem with this technique is that you can only look at one protein at a time, and you would need a specific antibody to examine the protein. So you would only use this technique if you regarded a particular gene as a very likely suspect for the disease gene.

15.36

a. Miller syndrome could be due to a dominant mutation if: (i) The trait was not completely penetrant, so that both of the parents had the mutant allele but did not express the trait; or (ii) There was a *de novo* mutation in the germ line of one of the parents that occurred in oogonia or spermatogonia, so that many oocytes (and then eggs) or spermatocytes (and then sperm) might have the same mutation. The mutation could not have happened late in germ line development (that is, during meiosis in oocytes or spermatocytes) because more than one child was affected. Part (b) explores the *de novo* mutation scenario in more detail.

b. *De novo* mutations in the germ line do in fact occur. For a large proportion of the gametes produced by a parent to carry the new mutation, the mutation would have had to occur relatively early in the mitotic proliferation of oogonia or spermatogonia. The earlier in the proliferation of the germ line, the fewer cells would have been present and thus the fewer chances for mutation to occur. This is why new mutations that occur in the germ line and that cause a large percentage of gametes to be mutant are extremely rare. Human geneticists always need to be aware of such possibilities, even if they might not be very likely.

c. Any place there is a color shift from a dark shade to a light shade or *vice versa*, a recombination event must have occurred during the meiosis in one of the parents that produced the gamete making one of the offspring. The *green arrow* added to the preceding figure shows the recombination event that occurred closest to the *DHOD* gene. This recombination event is seen because *DHOD* is in an Identical region (where the affected son and affected daughter share the same alleles from the mother and the same alleles from the father) to a Haploidentical Maternal region in which they share the same alleles as their mother but have different alleles from their father. Thus, at the site of the *green arrow,* a recombination event must have occurred during meiosis I in a primary spermatocyte found in the father's testis. We do not know from the way the data is displayed whether this recombination event happened during the meiosis leading to the sperm that made the son or the daughter.

d. The data reveal about 2× more crossovers than expected, but the actual numbers are still surprisingly close to expectations. The figure shows 8 crossovers on chromosome 16 and 10 crossovers on chromosome 17 among the 4 gametes that were used to make the two affected children. The two chromosomes are together about ~170 Mb, and thus 170 centiMorgans long. 1 cM means one crossover in 100 gametes, so you would expect about 170 crossovers in 100 gametes on chromosomes 16 and 17 together. In 4 gametes, this would be about ~7 expected crossovers, but the data show slightly more than twice this number (18).

e. You would simply compare the nucleotides in the parents' whole genomes with those in the children's, and look for *de novo* alterations. Then you divide the number of alterations in the two children by 4× the haploid genome size (because there are 4 haploid genomes in the two children). Interestingly, note that in many cases (depending on the actual arrangement of alleles), you can actually tell in which parent a particular mutation occurred. The data from this study revealed that the two children in this family each received on average 30 new mutations that occurred in the mother's germ line, and about 50 that occurred in the father's germ line. You would expect that the number of paternal *de novo* mutations would increase in the offspring of older fathers but not mothers, because the male germ line is always being propagated mitotically, and the more divisions, the more chance for mutations to occur (review Problem 4 above).

15.37

a and b. The conclusions are summarized in the following Table. All autosomal loci should have equal numbers of reads, 90% of which should be from the mother's genome and 10% from the fetus's genome. If the mother and the fetus were homozygotes for the same allele, there should be only one type of read representing that allele. If there are two or three types of reads (two or three alleles), the relative proportions depend on whether the alleles are shared by the mother and fetus. For a locus on the X chromosome, you would expect either the same situation as for autosomal loci (the same number of reads; 90% maternal, 10% fetal) if the fetus was an XX female, but there would be 5% fewer reads (of which 95% would be maternal and 5% fetal) if the fetus was an XY male with only 1 X chromosome. For a locus on the Y chromosome, the number of reads would only be 5% of the number of reads for an autosomal locus. (Obviously, these data have been much simplified relative to the actual results researchers would obtain from such a test.)

Locus	Sequences	# of Reads	Mother's Genome	Fetus's Genome	Autosomal X-linked Y-linked
1	α: TCTTTGGTAAACGCAAG	1000	α α	α α	autosomal
2	α: GTACCGGAGGCAGCCTC β: GTACCGGCGGCAGCCTC	500 500	α β	α β	autosomal
3	α: AGCCATTGCGGATCCGA β: AGCTATTGCGGTTCCGA	950 50	α α	α β	autosomal
4	α: GGGGCCTTATGATAAGG	50	– –	α –	Y-linked
5	α: CAGTTCCTGGAGTTGTA β: CAGTTCATGGAGTTGTA	550 450	α β	α α	autosomal
6	α: GCAGCCCGTGCTGTTAA β: GCAGCCCGTGCTGTCAA	500 450	α β	α –	X-linked
7	α: CACTCAGTCCTACGGAC β: CACTCGGTCCTACGGAC γ: CACTCAGTCCTAAGGAC	500 450 50	α β	α γ	autosomal

c. The fetus is clearly male as one of the loci (4) is Y-linked.

d. The 8th locus with 1500 reads suggests that there are additional copies of this region. Most likely, the 8th locus is also autosomal, and both the mother and the fetus have 3 copies of the locus instead of the normal 2. One possibility is that the locus is on chromosome 21, and both the mother and the fetus are trisomic for this chromosome (that is, both have Down syndrome). Alternatively, the locus could be on any autosome and both the mother and the fetus could be heterozygotes for the duplication.

15.38

a. The researchers would not have looked only for homozygous variants. Insofar as we know, Nic's parents are not close relatives, so it is entirely possible that Nic is a compound heterozygote (that is, Nic would have inherited two different mutations in the same gene, one from each unaffected parent).

b. (i) The mutation causing Nic's disease could have been a *de novo* dominant mutation that occurred in the germ line of one of his parents (so they would not be affected). (ii) It is also possible that the condition is dominant but the penetrance is low, so one of Nic's parents could have had the mutation but not have been affected. Fortunately for Nic, the doctor's original presumptions were correct. It would have been much harder to find the disease mutation if these other hypotheses had to have been considered.

c. You could accomplish this goal very simply using PCR. You would design primers that would amplify the region of the genome containing the causative mutation. You would then PCR-amplify this region from the genomes of Nic's two parents (say from a swab from their cheeks). If this mutation was not found in either genome, it must have occurred *de novo*. [This approach would also provide evidence that the causative mutation is X-linked and the condition is recessive if you see heterozygosity for the mutation in the mother's genome.]

15.39

a. If this is the first exon, it must contain the initiating ATG codon. Thus, the sequence of the protein product that can be deduced from the nucleotide sequence of the first exon is: N Met-Cys-Gly-Ala.... .

b. Individual 2 is a homozygote (because only one kind of sequence was found), for the allele

  5' CAACGCTTAGGATGTGAGGAGCCT 3'

c. The disease is caused by a dominant allele, because heterozygotes with one normal allele (found in RefSeq) and one abnormal allele have the condition.

d. Yes, the data show the existence of allelic heterogeneity. Among these four patients, different mutant alleles can cause the disease.

e. None of these individuals is a compound heterozygote (also called a *trans*heterozygote). (A compound heterozygote would have two different mutant alleles, but none of these individuals do.)

f. The data provide no evidence for locus heterogeneity in Brugada syndrome. You can explain the disease in all of the affected individuals by the existence of mutations in a single gene. Locus heterogeneity would mean that mutations in different genes could cause the syndrome. The data do not exclude this possibility (because other patients could exist who have the disease because of mutations in some other gene), but this hypothesis is not required to explain the data.

g. Individual 4 should be normal (that is, not affected by Brugada syndrome). One allele is the RefSeq allele. The other allele is a silent mutation (changing a TGC codon to a TGT codon, both for Cys).

h and i. Individual 1's mutation in the bottom allele changes GCC (Ala) to GAC (Asp). This is a missense mutation. This would be classified as a SNP because only one nucleotide pair is changed. The mutation causes a loss-of-function, but you cannot tell just from this mutation alone (see below). If this is a loss-of function mutation with dominant effects, the reason must be haploinsufficiency. This is probably a hypomorphic allele with less activity of the protein product because it is loss-of-function but some protein is likely produced (since all the amino acids are present except one that is changed). You could perhaps classify this as a null mutation instead of hypomorphic if the missense mutation resulted in a protein with no function. Individual 2 is homozygous for a nonsense mutation in the second codon. Again, this is a SNP because only one base pair is affected. This must be a null, loss-of-function allele because no protein is produced. The fact that individual 2 survives means that the gene cannot be essential. It would be of interest for a scientist to look hard at this person's electrocardiogram. It might be possible that heart function in this individual is affected more than in other patients with Brugada syndrome because he/she is a homozygote without any gene function. Individual 3 is a heterozygote for a frameshift mutation in which one nucleotide is lost from the reading frame. This mutation would be classified as a DIP, not a SNP. This would be a null mutation because the allele could not produce any normal protein. The gene is haploinsufficient, explaining why the heterozygote would have the condition. (This is why the mutation in individual 1 is likely to be loss-of-function as well; heterozygosity for at least one loss-of-function mutation produces the disease.) In individual 4, the allele that is not the RefSeq allele has a silent mutation (an anonymous SNP) as discussed in part (g) above.

j. Yes, the function of the gene is haploinsufficient. You know this to be the case because Individuals 2 and 3, who are heterozygotes for null alleles of the gene (in each person's genome, one allele is wild type, and one allele is null), have aberrant Brugada syndrome symptoms.

Chapter 16   The Genetics of Cancer

Synopsis:

This chapter presents a straightforward thesis: Cancers are genetic diseases caused by the accumulation in somatic cells of mutations in certain key genes; these mutations lead to uncontrolled proliferation and other phenotypes such as metastasis. The clinical properties of different cancers depend on which key genes have been changed by mutation and the nature of the cells that have accumulated these mutations. All cancers involve an insidious positive feedback pathway in which cell proliferation increases the chances that new mutations will occur, and these new mutations lead to increased rates of cell proliferation.

Researchers have identified two major classes of genes whose mutant alleles can contribute to cancer. **Proto-oncogenes** are genes whose products promote cell-cycle progression; dominant gain-of-function alleles of proto-oncogenes are called **oncogenes**. In contrast, **tumour-suppressor genes** encode products that either inhibit cell proliferation or that protect the genome from changes. Loss-of-function mutations in tumour-suppressor genes contribute to cancer by removing these important safeguards. It is critical to note that normal genomes contain wild-type alleles of both proto-oncogenes and tumour-suppressor genes, because the products of these genes are required both for cells to proliferate at the proper rate and for genomes to remain intact; it is mutations in these genes that promote cancer.

Recent advances in DNA sequencing technologies have led to the advent of one of the most hopeful trends in the fight against cancer: *personalized cancer treatment*. Clinicians can now determine the genome sequences of a patient's tumour cells and normal cells; comparisons of these genomic DNA sequences can help scientists pinpoint the particular critical mutations in proto-oncogenes and tumour-suppressor genes that contributed to the patient's particular cancer. Armed with this knowledge, physicians can sometimes prescribe treatments effective against that specific cancer. This strategy is imperfect, in part because the genomes of tumour cells are constantly accumulating new mutations. Personalized cancer genetics is nonetheless becoming increasingly powerful as researchers gain new information about the response of tumours with particular mutations to an increasing array of anti-cancer drugs.

Key Terms:

contact inhibition – the process by which normal cells stop dividing when they come into physical contact; normal cells cultured on Petri plates thus proliferate until they form a *monolayer* one cell thick at the bottom of the plate. Cancerous cells lose contact inhibition; in culture, tumour cells form piles called *transformed foci* that are many cells thick.

apoptosis/programmed cell death –When the genome of a normal cell becomes damaged past the point where it can be repaired, a genetically-directed program of cell death called *apoptosis* occurs, leading to the destruction of that cell. Cancerous cells often have lost their ability to undergo apoptosis, and this loss is dangerous because it allows cells with damaged genomes to proliferate.

autocrine stimulation – Most normal cells will not proliferate unless they receive the proper molecular signals from their environment. Cells that exhibit *autocrine stimulation* can instead divide in the absence of these external signals (that is, the tumour cells provide their own division-stimulating signals).

senescence *versus* immortality – Most normal somatic cells undergo *senescence* – an end to proliferation – after they have undergone a limited number of cell divisions; in contrast, many cancer cells continue to proliferate with no such limitation – they are *immortalized*. An important facet of immortalized cells is that they express the enzyme *telomerase*, whereas most normal somatic cells lack telomerase so their chromosomes lose DNA from the telomeres during each round of cell division.

genomic instability – describes the tendency of cancer cells to accumulate genomic changes at a rapid rate. These changes can include increased frequencies of point mutations, chromosomal rearrangements, aneuploidy, and even polyploidy.

angiogenesis – a process whereby tumours stimulate the growth of blood vessels into the tumour so that the cancerous cells can be supplied with oxygen and nutrients.

metastasis/malignancy – a property of cancerous cells that allows them to escape into the bloodstream and thus to start secondary tumours in other parts of the body.

immune surveillance – describes the ability of a person's immune system to identify newly-formed cancer cells and to destroy them. The cells in successful tumours accumulate mutations that somehow allow them to evade this normal process of immune surveillance.

tumour progression – the process by which pre-cancerous and cancerous cells progressively accumulate (through mutation) additional properties that make the cancers increasingly invasive and malignant.

growth factors – molecules that promote or inhibit cell proliferation; those that promote cell division are **mitogens**. Those mitogens that are produced by one cell type but act on other cell types are called *hormones*.

growth factor receptors – molecules embedded in the membranes of receptive cells that are targeted by growth factors. The binding of a growth factor to a growth factor receptor at the surface of a cell initiates a **signal transduction pathway/cascade** that eventually influences the activity of transcription factors within the cell's nucleus. These transcription factors regulate the transcription of genes whose products either promote or inhibit cell division.

signal transducers – molecules that act as intermediaries within signal transduction pathways to transmit the signal (the binding of a growth factor to a growth factor receptor at the cell surface) to the effectors of the pathway (the transcription factors that regulate the expression of genes whose products are involved in cell division).

cyclin-dependent kinases (CDKs) – the key enzymes that drive cell-cycle progression. CDKs generally consist of two subunits: One subunit is a *kinase*, an enzyme that phosphorylates (adds phosphate groups to) other proteins. The other subunit is a *cyclin*, a polypeptide whose abundance varies with stages of the cell cycle and which functions as a specificity factor to direct the kinase to phosphorylate particular protein substrates.

checkpoint – a molecular pathway that prevents cell-cycle progression until necessary preconditions have been fulfilled. For example, the *G_1-to-S checkpoint* prevents cells from replicating their chromosomes until any DNA damage has been repaired.

gene amplification – a type of *genomic instability* in which the number of copies of particular chromosomal regions is increased. Gene amplification can result either in *homogeneously staining regions* (*HSRs*) in which the additional copies are positioned in tandem with respect to each other at one location in the genome, or in multiple *double minutes*, small chromosome-like bodies lacking centromeres and telomeres. Gene amplification is particularly important to tumour progression if the region now found in additional copies includes a *proto-oncogene*.

oncogene/proto-oncogene – An *oncogene* is a cancer-inducing, gain-of-function mutant in a *proto-oncogene*, which is a normal gene whose product promotes cell cycle progression.

tumour-suppressor gene – A *tumour-suppressor gene* encodes a product that impedes cell-cycle progression or that protects the genome from alterations. Loss-of- function mutations in tumour-suppressor genes promote cancer.

loss-of-heterozygosity (LOH) – If a cell is heterozygous for a loss-of-function mutation in a tumour-suppressor gene, then one allele of the gene provides wild-type function while the other allele is nonfunctional. Any event that removes or inactivates the remaining wild-type allele results in a *loss-of-heterozygosity*; the cell is left with no functional copies of the tumour-suppressor gene, and this can contribute to cancer.

chemotherapy – treating cancer patients with drugs that kill cancer cells.

personalized cancer treatment – tailoring cancer treatments to the individual based upon the suite of mutations in oncogenes and tumour-suppressor genes found by comparing the genomic sequences of tumour tissues and normal tissues in that patient.

driver mutations – the mutations found in the genomes of the cancerous cells in the patient that are most likely to contribute to tumour formation. Other mutations in the genomes of cancer cells that are unlikely to contribute to tumour formation are often called *passenger mutations*. Because of *genome instability*, cancer cell genomes are likely to accumulate several driver mutations and many passenger mutations.

druggable targets – the protein products of genes that have been mutated in cancer cells; most druggable targets are the proteins encoded by oncogenes.

cancer landscapes – tabulations of the mutations in the cancer cells from many patients that help scientists determine both what phenotypes are likely to occur when particular suites of oncogenes and tumour-suppressor genes are mutant, and what kinds of drugs are most likely to be successful in treating specific subclasses of tumours.

Problem Solving:

The most critical figures in this chapter are:

- Figure 16.6, which illustrates the hypothesis that cancers result from the accumulation, within a line of somatic cells, of mutations within certain key genes (proto-oncogenes and tumour-suppressor genes).
- Figure 16.19, which shows the key differences between oncogenes and tumour-suppressor genes.
- Figure 16.24, which depicts the various types of events than can cause a *loss-of-heterozygosity* by removing or inactivating the remaining functional copy of a tumour-suppressor gene from a cell in which the other copy of the gene was non-functional.

Oncogenes versus tumour-suppressor genes:

This distinction is central to solving many problems in this chapter.

Oncogenes are gain-of-function mutations in normal genes called **proto-oncogenes**. The proto-oncogenes often encode proteins that are involved in *signal transduction pathways* through which cells respond to mitogenic signals. The gain-of-function mutations may increase the amount of the normal gene product (for example, duplications, HSRs, and double minutes can increase the dosage of proto-oncogenes and therefore the amount of gene product), or they can be mutations that increase the efficiency of the gene product or that remove a domain of the protein that could inhibit its function. As is the case for most gain-of-function mutations, oncogenic alleles are dominant to wild-type alleles of the proto-oncogenes, so one copy of an oncogene (that is, one mutant allele) is sufficient to contribute to tumour progression.

Tumour-suppressor genes are normal genes whose products either impede or delay the cell cycle (for example, they may participate in cell cycle checkpoints) or protect the genome from mutation and other instabilities. The mutations of tumour-suppressor genes that matter are loss-of-function mutations.

A point critical for understanding cancer is that *mutations of tumour-suppressor genes have effects that are recessive at the level of the cell but dominant at the level of the organism.* This statement means first that two "hits" (mutations) are necessary to knock out the function of the tumour-suppressor gene so that its product can no longer protect a cell from acquiring cancerous properties. However, if an individual inherits one wild-type allele of a tumour-suppressor gene from one parent and one loss-of-function allele from the other parent, this inheritance constitutes a head-start for cancer formation as one of the "hits" is always present. The reason predilection for cancer is dominant at the level of the organism (as would be seen in pedigree analysis) is that it is highly likely that in a single cell, the one remaining wild-type copy of the tumour-suppressor gene will be inactivated or lost. Many opportunities exist for the second "hit" to occur, and as Figure 16.24 shows, in any of the appropriate cells, many types of potential events could happen that would provide the second "hit."

Solutions to Problems:

Vocabulary
16-1. i. **7**; ii. **6**; iii. **8**; iv. **2**; v. **1**; vi. **9**; vii. **3**; viii. **5**; ix. **4**.

Section 16.1 – Characteristics of Cancer Cells
16-2.

a. **Contact inhibition:** Normal cells stop growing when they come into contact with each other. This property is observed mostly in culture, where normal cells form a *monolayer* one cell thick; they stop growing when they take up the entire surface of the Petri plate. Cancer cells do not have this property, so they continue to grow after contacting each other, leading to the formation of piles of cells called *transformed foci*. The loss of contact inhibition contributes to cancer because cells no longer have one of the controls on their growth. In addition, recall that the more cells divide, the more mutations they can accumulate that can contribute further to the aggressiveness of the tumour. [This latter point is also part of the answers to parts *b-e* of this question, but it will not be repeated in the answers below.]

b. **Autocrine stimulation:** Normal cells will divide and grow only when they are stimulated to do so by the binding of a growth factor such as a hormone to a receptor protein on the cell surface. Most cancer cells exhibit *autocrine stimulation*, meaning that they can divide rapidly in the absence of a growth factor. Autocrine stimulation contributes to cancer because the organism cannot limit the growth of cells that have this property.

c. **Apoptosis:** When the DNA of normal cells is damaged beyond the capacity of repair systems to deal with the damage, the cells undergo *apoptosis* (programmed cell death). As a result, cells with damaged DNA cannot grow and replicate. Many cancer cells do not undergo apoptosis in response to cell damage. As a result, cells that have accumulated (through DNA damage) mutations that can increase the aggressiveness of cancer are allowed to multiply.

d. **Telomerase expression**: Normal somatic cells do not express the enzyme *telomerase*. Thus, the chromosomes of these cells become shorter each time the cells replicate, providing somatic cells with an upper limit to the number of times they can divide before essential DNA is lost. Many lines of cancer cells express telomerase, which counteracts this shortening. As a result, such cancer cells become effectively immortalized; they can continue to divide indefinitely. Again, these cancer cells have lost one of the normal controls on their division and growth.

e. **Senescence due to telomere shortening:** This is the flip side to part *d*. *Senescence* is the property of normal somatic cells that results in their failure to divide further once telomeres have shortened so far that essential DNA is lost. Many cancer cells are instead immortalized because they express telomerase; they do not undergo senescence.

f. **Genomic stability:** Normal mitotic cell division ensures that (with the exception of rare mistakes) progeny cells have the same genome as the parental cell. The number of chromosomes remains the same, and chromosomal rearrangements do not occur. Cancer cells have unstable genomes that accumulate many alterations, including point mutations, chromosomal rearrangements, and changes in chromosome number. These alterations can mutate or alter the expression of oncogenes and tumour-suppressor genes, contributing to cancer.

g. **Angiogenesis:** Solid tumours require nourishment from blood; large tumours thus generate molecular signals that stimulate the growth of blood vessels into the tumour.

h. **Metastasis:** Normal cells grow within particular regions of the organisms that are usually defined by membranous structures. If cancer cells *metastasize*, they break these boundaries and can start to colonize other parts of the body, forming new tumours at new sites.

i. **Susceptibility to immune surveillance:** Our bodies normally can identify cancerous cells and destroy them by a variety of immune system measures. For a tumour to become established in the body, the tumour cells must accumulate mutations that allow them to evade this immune surveillance.

Section 16.2 – The Genetic Basis of Cancers

16-3. You need to conduct epidemiological studies of the colorectal cancer profile looking for possible correlations between either diet or genetic differences and the incidence of cancer. **To assess the role of diet, you need to control (as best possible) the genetic make-up of the population examined and vary the diet. You could set up studies contrasting the cancer rates between a population of recent immigrants from India now residing in Canada and a population of people of the same ethnic background who have remained in India.** If possible, you might also be able to distinguish within each group subpopulations who favor either a Westernized diet or the historical diet of the ethnic group in India.

To assess the role of genetic differences in influencing cancer rates, it is necessary to keep other factors, most importantly the diet, as constant as possible. You would thus compare the incidence of cancer between genetically dissimilar groups who have similar diets. Researchers often accomplish this task by studying cancer rates among different ethnic groups living in the same area. For example, people of Indian heritage who have lived in Toronto for a long period of time could be compared with Torontonians from other ethnic groups, as long as all of the individuals surveyed had similar diets.

16-4. These 'conflicting views' are easily reconciled. We know that **some of the environmental agents that are implicated in increased cancer risk cause increased levels of mutations**, so this fact is consistent with the idea that mutations in genes are necessary to cause cancer. **The inherited mutations that predispose an individual to cancer inactivate one allele of a gene (often a tumour-suppressor gene) that inhibits cell growth.** This inherited mutation is just one of several mutations that must occur within a cell to lead to cancer. The environmental and hereditary factors are therefore both affecting genes that are important for regulating the cell cycle.

16-5.

a. The facts that that many affected individuals are observed over three generations and that all the patients develop the disease at an early age are both clues that an inherited mutation is an important factor in the development of colorectal cancer in this family. Examination of the pedigree suggests that **predisposition to colorectal cancer in this family could be an autosomal dominant trait. If this is true, then individual II-2 must have the mutation but not express it.** Two possibilities exist with regard to individuals I-1 and I-2: Either one of them has the mutation but does not express it, or the mutation arose anew in one of their germ lines.

Although the evidence is strong that genetics plays a major role in the development of colorectal cancer in this pedigree, the data do not prove that the prevalence of colorectal cancer in this family is entirely due to inheritance. As discussed in part *b*, it is also conceivable that some family members have been exposed to an environmental factor that contributes to development of the disease.

b. **Individuals I-1 and II-2 are not among the high coffee consumers. Perhaps the predisposition to colorectal cancer is a combination of a particular genotype and the environmental factor of consumption of the special coffee.** Thus, the interaction of a certain genotype and an environmental factor results in the phenotype of colorectal cancer. In this scenario, the genotype alone is not enough to predispose one to cancer: Individuals I-1 and II-2 might have the cancer-promoting mutation, but they do not develop the disease because they are not coffee drinkers. Note also that none of the people who refrain from drinking this special coffee have the disease, including five additional genetic relatives of I-1 and I-2 (II-4, II-9, II-13, IV-1, IV-3). On the other hand, note that a substantial number of individuals who do drink this special coffee are not affected (for example, III-8, III-9, III-10, III-11, and III-12), so coffee alone does not appear to have a major effect on the early onset of colorectal cancer.

16-6. If there is a dominant predisposing allele segregating, **individual II-2 carries the mutant allele** since individual III-2 has colorectal cancer and thus has the mutant, predisposing allele. Two individuals in the second generation carry the mutation, so one of the generation I parents must have had the mutant allele and passed it on to individuals II-2 and II-3. Thus, **either I-1 or I-2 also carries the mutation.** Note that it also possible that the mutation arose in the germline of either individual I-1 or I-2. In this case, the somatic tissues of that parent would <u>not</u> contain the mutation.

16-7. The development of tumours depends upon random mutational events that must "hit" several oncogenes and tumour-suppressor genes within a cell lineage. A single mutation, even if it hits one such gene, is rarely enough by itself to cause a cell to become cancerous; instead, among the descendants of that cell, additional mutations in other key genes must occur, and it takes time for these mutations to accumulate through random, rare events. In some cases, tumours will not develop either because the carcinogen (presumably, a mutagen) has not caused a mutation in any key gene, or because not enough such mutations occur among the descendants of a cell that has sustained a mutation in a single cancer gene. Tumours do sometimes develop at the site of carcinogen application because the chemical induces a mutation in a key gene, and this gives the cell a "head-start" on becoming cancerous.

16-8.

a. **The reason that the blood of patients with B cell lymphomas has mostly one type of antibody molecule reflects the fact that a single B cell (or B-cell precursor), whose antibody genes have already undergone rearrangements to produce a particular antibody protein, now becomes cancerous and starts to divide out of control.** A large percentage of the B cells in the patient will be making this one single type of antibody protein. In contrast, in normal individuals, B cells can only divide a discrete number of times, and the blood will contain millions of different kinds of antibody proteins made from millions of different B cells; no single B cell will have enough descendants for its particular antibody to predominate.

Of interest, the existence of B cell lymphomas allowed researchers (who subsequently won a Nobel Prize) to study the structure of antibody molecules. By obtaining the antibody proteins from the blood of such patients, the researchers started with substantially pure preparations of a single type of antibody. Their studies would have been impossible if they had started with samples from normal blood composed of millions of different kinds of molecules.

b. **B cell lymphomas provide support for the clonal theory of cancer because it is clearly the case that the cancerous cells in the blood all derive from a single B cell** (whose antibody genes had previously undergone rearrangement, so that the cell produces only one kind of antibody). This cell lineage divides uncontrollably, producing a huge clone of B cells all making the same antibody molecule.

Section 16.3 – How Cell Division is Normally Controlled
16-9. c, e, a, b, d. (see Figure 16.3 and Figure 16.12).

16-10.

a. Molecules outside the cell that regulate the cell cycle include **hormones and growth factors** (see Figure 16.10 and Figure 16.11). The external parts of growth factor receptors would also qualify, although other parts of these receptors are found embedded in the cell membrane or are located in the cytoplasm.

b. Most of Section 16.2 is a discussion of the molecules inside the cell that regulate the cell cycle. These include **cyclins, cyclin-dependent protein kinases, molecules in signal transduction pathways (the internal domains of growth factor receptors, intermediaries such as Ras and MAP kinases, and the transcription factors targeted by the pathway), and the proteins that participate in various cell-cycle checkpoints.**

16-11.

a. Ras is inactive when it is bound to GDP (Ras-GDP) (Figure 16.12d). When Ras is bound to GTP, it is activated and in turn activates three protein kinases (the MAP kinase cascade). This cascade activates a transcription factor which causes cells to divide. Therefore, **a Ras mutant protein that stays in the GTP-bound state is permanently activated and will cause the cell to continue dividing.**

b. This second Ras mutant protein is blocked in the Ras-GDP form at the restrictive (non-permissive) temperature. Therefore, **under the restrictive conditions the cells will not divide.**

16-12.

a. You would treat a culture of haploid yeast cells with a mutagen, and then plate out the yeast so that individual cells will form colonies. **You would grow the master Petri plate at the low (permissive) temperature so that colonies would grow whether or not they had a *ts* mutation in a gene needed for survival. You would then make a replica of this plate and grow the cells at the higher (restrictive) temperature.** If the cells in the colony had a *ts* mutation in an essential gene, then a colony would not appear on this replica plate. You would then retrieve the colony with the *ts* mutation from the original master plate.

b. **You would grow cells from the colony first at the low (permissive) temperature, and then shift the culture to the higher (restrictive) temperature. You would then look at the cells to see if they arrested their growth at a particular point in the cell cycle.** Do the cells all stop growing when they have a single large bud, as was seen in Figure B in the Tools of Genetics box

"Analysis of Cell-Cycle Mutants in Yeast"? Do they have no bud at all? Do they have buds of a particular size? Cell-cycle mutants will arrest at a particular time in the cell cycle, while mutants in other essential genes will die or stop growing at random phases of the cell cycle.

You could then go further and look at structures like the spindle and chromosomes to see if all the cells arrest with M phase-like spindles or with contracted chromosomes. In fact, using new technology based on the Green Fluorescent Protein, you could even make movies of these structures to see when arrest occurs.

c. **Once you have obtained a collection of *ts* mutants in cell-cycle genes, you would determine which mutants are allelic by complementation analysis.** Assuming that the mutations are recessive and represent loss of function, you would make diploid yeast cells that combine two different *ts* mutations. If the diploid cells still exhibit temperature-sensitive growth, you would conclude the mutations do not complement each other and therefore are in the same gene. If the diploid cells can grow normally at the restrictive (high) temperature, you would conclude that the mutations complement each other because they are in different genes.

Note that to make diploid yeast cells, you need to mate haploid cells of opposite mating types. This can be done if you found mutations in haploid cells that were mating type a and others in haploid cells that were mating type α. Other methods exist for converting cells of one mating type into another, but these were not explained in the text.

d. Note that cells with large buds just before the temperature shift arrest as two cells with large buds after the temperature shift. This finding indicates that the protein encoded by this *ts* gene is not required for any process that occurs after some stage of large bud formation, or for the initiation of the cell cycle (because new buds can still form at the restrictive temperature). Thus, **the protein product of the gene is essential for some process that occurs after the cell cycle begins (after new buds form) but prior to cytokinesis (because cells with large buds that were already past the arrest point at the time of the temperature shift can produce two daughter cells).** It turns out that cells with disrupted DNA synthesis during S phase can arrest with large buds, but the same is true for cells that have defects in M phase.

To distinguish among these possibilities, you would need to look more carefully at the arrested cells. For example, if the cells had only one copy of all their chromosomes, the gene product would be needed for S phase. If the cells had two copies of all their chromosomes but had not formed spindles, the gene product would be needed for an early step in M phase.

e. **You would take yeast cells that have a *ts* mutation in the gene encoding the yeast CDK1, and then add to these cells a gene that has the corresponding human gene.** One way to do this is to take advantage of the fact that yeast plasmids are known to exist. You would make a recombinant DNA molecule in a yeast plasmid vector that contains a cDNA for the wild-type human CDK1 kinase. Ideally, you would place this cDNA sequence downstream of the promoter sequence for the yeast *CDK1* gene (so that the cells would make approximately the same amount of the human protein as would be found in a normal yeast cell, and according to the same cell cycle schedule. You would then transform this plasmid into yeast cells. If the growth of the cells was normal even at restrictive (high) temperature, then the human gene could replace the function of the homologous gene in yeast. Historically, this experiment demonstrated that all eukaryotic cells share important cell cycle regulators.

16-13.

a. Figure 16.14 is reproduced below, with two additional *red arrows* indicating when the SCF and the APC become activated. **The SCF complex couples ubiquitin to cyclinE (and perhaps cyclinD), because those are the cyclins that are present during S phase. The APC couples ubiquitin to cyclinB (and perhaps cyclinA), because those are the cyclins that are present during M phase.** By coupling ubiquitin to cyclins that will then be degraded, the SCF and APC ensure the end of S phase and M phase, respectively.

b. The simplest hypothesis for the activation of the SCF and the APC at the proper times is that **this activation depends on the cyclin-dependent kinases (CDKs) present during a particular cell cycle phase. Thus, CDKs containing cyclins D and E would activate SCF** (possibly by adding phosphate groups to protein components of SCF), **and SCF in turn would cause the degradation of those cyclins, the loss of the activity of these CDKs, and the exit from S phase. CDKs containing cyclins A and B would activate the APC** (again through phosphorylation of APC subunits), **and the APC would in turn cause degradation of those cyclins, loss of the activity of these CDKs, and the exit from M phase** (that is, the beginning of anaphase).

This mechanism for the progression of the cell cycle is fundamentally elegant. The transcription and translation of particular cyclins initiate the process. These cyclins, in the context of CDKs, promote the events that must occur in each cell cycle stage. But in addition, the cyclins ensure that the stage will eventually end because they activate the enzyme complexes (SCF and APC) that lead to cyclin degradation.

16-14. As explained in Chapter 6, kinetochores that are not properly attached to spindle fibres generate molecular checkpoint signals that prevent anaphase onset. The M-phase checkpoint ensures that cohesin remains intact until all the chromosomes are connected to the spindle. **In the M-phase checkpoint, molecules made by unattached kinetochores prevent activation of the anaphase-promoting complex (APC).** If the APC is not active, then M-phase cyclins remain at high levels and cohesin remains intact. In other words, the cells stay in prometaphase or metaphase while unattached kinetochores are present and the checkpoint is signalling.

As seen in <u>Problem 16-13,</u> **the APC must become activated at the beginning of anaphase to destroy M-phase cyclin, allowing cells to leave M phase. The activated APC adds ubiquitin to protein substrates. When this happens, the ubiquitylated proteins are rapidly destroyed by the proteasome. One simple hypothesis is that cohesin is also targeted by the APC since it must be destroyed at the beginning of anaphase,** thus ensuring that sister chromatids separate at the beginning of anaphase.

Activated APC does in fact lead to cohesin degradation and thus sister chromatid separation, but the actual situation is slightly more complicated than you could have predicted from the given information. The APC-directed degradation of cohesin turns out to be indirect. Active APC adds ubiquitin to another protein called Securin which is found in a complex with a proteolytic enzyme named Separase during M phase. When Securin and Separase are together in the complex, the Separase is non-functional. When Securin is destroyed, then Separase cleaves cohesin and separates the sister chromatids.

<u>Section 16.4 – How Mutations Cause Cancer Phenotypes</u>

16-15. Genome and karyotype instabilities are both causes and consequences of cancer because of the intimate relationship between mutation and cell division. Consider, for example, the case of mutations in a tumour-suppressor gene encoding an enzyme that helps repair DNA damage. The lack of the DNA repair enzyme causes genome instability (because it will cause new mutations to accumulate in other genes), and some of these new mutations will promote cancerous cell growth. On the other hand, unrestricted cancerous cell growth creates new opportunities for mutation; that is, more genome instability.

16-16. Proto-oncogenes are genes that code for proteins that stimulate cell division. Therefore, oncogenic mutations in such genes usually increase the level of expression of the gene product. Increasing the level of expression of the proto-oncogene results in cells that divide too frequently or at the wrong time, increasing the probability of cancer. A deletion of a proto-oncogene will decrease the level of expression, not increase it. Therefore, **choice c. will not be associated with cancer.** All of the other changes will increase the probability that the affected cell, or its mitotic descendants, will become cancerous.

16-17.

a. A **tumour-suppressor gene** - most inherited tumours are due to the inheritance of an inactive allele of a tumour-suppressor gene. The inheritance is dominant because it is highly likely that the wild-type allele of the tumour-suppressor gene obtained from the unaffected parent will be inactivated or lost in some of the progeny's cells.

b. As implied in part *a*, the allele inherited from the affected parent is a **loss-of-function** mutation that inactivates the *NF1* gene.

c. **Ras-GDP**. If neurofibromin is a tumour-suppressor protein, its presence would slow down or restrict the cell cycle. This could be accomplished if neurofibromin favours the formation of the inactive form of Ras, Ras-GDP.

d. **ii, iv, v,** and **vi** could all be "second hits" that would inactivate or cause the loss of the functional allele of *NF1* inherited from the normal parent. The allele from the afflicted parent is already inactivated or deleted, so additional mutations in that allele would have no effect. Mitotic chromosome nondisjunction or chromosome loss (v) might produce an aneuploid cell without a functional copy of the *NF1* gene. Mitotic recombination in a heterozygote could produce a cell homozygous for the inherited *NF1* mutation, but the recombination event would have to occur between the *NF1* gene and the centromere of the chromosome carrying it.

e. The neurofibromas in these patients are **sporadic**. In other words, these patients inherit wild-type alleles of *NF1* from both parents. Then **there must be a clone of cells in which one of the copies**

of *NF1* is inactivated by some rare event, while the other allele of *NF1* is inactivated or lost. These tumours are extremely rare because two rare events must happen in the same line of cells. In contrast, the inherited disease requires just one rare event as the patient starts out with a defective allele. Sporadic tumours are restricted to one part of the body because these clones of cells with no *NF1* function are so rare; in addition, the second inactivating event is likely to occur late in the patient's life and only in one tissue. Patients with the inherited form of neurofibromatosis instead have many pre-cancerous growths

16-18. Note: In Problems 18 and 19, we make the reasonable assumption that the normal (non-translocated) homologues of the chromosomes involved in the translocation do not have any mutations in any cancer-related genes near the translocation breakpoints.

a. **False.** Notice that the leukaemic cells of the patient are heterozygous for the translocation. This fact means that the cancer-promoting properties of the translocation must be dominant at the level of the cell. This fact is thus not consistent with the characteristics of a tumour-suppressor gene, but makes more sense if some kind of dominant gain-of-function mutation has occurred that involves a proto-oncogene near the translocation breakpoint that is converted into an oncogene because of the translocation.

   The actual situation for chronic myelogenous leukaemia (CML) was presented in the text in Figure 9.20. The dominant gain-of-function mutation associated with the translocation converts the *c-abl* proto-oncogene into a fused *bcr/c-abl* oncogene. The protein encoded by the *c-abl* proto-oncogene is a kinase that participates in a signal transduction pathway; the kinase is regulated so that it is active only when it is needed. The protein encoded by the fused *bcr/c-abl* oncogene still functions as a kinase, but its activity can no longer be turned off. As a result, the signal transduction pathway leading to cell proliferation is constitutive: It is "on" all of the time, even when it should be "off".

b. **False.** As just stated in part *a*, the mutation must involve a gain-of-function, not a loss-of-function, of a proto-oncogene, so that it is converted into an oncogene.

c. **False.** The germline cells of the patient are still normal and do not have the translocation. The event producing the translocation must have occurred in some somatic cell in the lineage of white blood cells.

d. **True.** Most of the cells in this individual have a normal karyotype and are not cancerous, while the leukaemic cells are heterozygous for the translocation.

e. **True.** Fragments of DNA from the leukaemic cells will include the region around the breakpoint that has the mutant oncogene. When normal mouse tissue culture cells are transformed with this DNA, they will form transformed foci because the effect of the mutant oncogene is dominant. (That is, the mouse cells will have two copies of the normal proto-oncogene, but if one copy of the human mutant oncogene is added, this can cause the cells to acquire cancerous properties.) If cells from the transformed foci are injected into mice, the mice can in turn develop tumours. This type of experiment was shown in Figure 16.21.

f. **False.** As stated in part *a*, the gene near the translocation breakpoint must have been a proto-oncogene. Proto-oncogenes encode gene products that drive the cell cycle forward rather than gene products that restrain the cell cycle (as do tumour-suppressor genes).

g. **False.** One (gain-of-function) mutational event that converts a proto-oncogene into an oncogene is sufficient to promote cancer. Two loss-of-function mutational "hits" in a tumour-suppressor gene are needed to promote cancer, but the gene at the breakpoint is clearly a proto-oncogene rather than a tumour-suppressor gene.

h. **False.** A cancer treatment would need to turn off the activity of the proto-oncogene at the translocation breakpoint. A drug that turns on the proto-oncogene's activity even more would have exactly the wrong effect; it would promote cancer rather than alleviating the condition.

16-19. The genesis of the chronic myelogenous leukaemia (CML) in Problem 16-18 is a reciprocal translocation between non-homologous chromosomes that is found in the cancerous cells of this patient, while normal cells do not contain this rearrangement. **You would diagnose whether the patient's blood is free of leukaemic cells by performing routine PCRs that would amplify only DNA from the translocation. If one PCR primer binds to one of the chromosomes at one side of the translocation, while the other primer binds to the other chromosome on the other side of the breakpoint, then the PCR primers will span the translocation.** One advantage of this method is its sensitivity, because PCR could detect only one or a few leukaemic cells that remain after treatment among a large population of normal cells.

16-20.

a. **All of these genes (i-v) are potential oncogenes** since their normal function is to promote cell division and growth. None of them could be tumour-suppressor genes.

b. **If adding a phosphate group inhibited the phosphatase, then all of the actions of kinase A would ensure that the transcription factor was activated.** That is, kinase A would make the transcription factor active both by phosphorylating the transcription factor and by preventing the phosphatase from removing the activating phosphorylation. By contrast, if adding a phosphate group activated the phosphatase, then kinase A would simultaneously add and remove phosphates from the transcription factor; in such a circumstance, kinase A functions would cancel each other out.

c. **The phosphatase gene is likely to be a tumour-suppressor** since its protein product inhibits the production of growth factors. The phosphatase would keep the transcription factor inactive. In the absence of active transcription factor, the mitosis-promoting factors would not be synthesized.

d. In the table below, homozygous means homozygous for the particular mutation for the row, heterozygous means one mutant allele and one wild-type allele, E = excessive cell growth, D = decreased cell growth, N = normal cell growth.

Mutation	Homozygous	Heterozygous
i.	E	N
ii.	D	N
iii.	D	N
iv.	D	N
v.	E	E
vi.	E	E
vii.	E	E
viii.	D	D
ix.	E	N

Section 16.5 – Personalized Cancer Treatment

16-21.

a. Assuming that the presence of EGFRvIII (the mutational variant of the epidermal growth factor receptor) protein contributes to the cancerous phenotype, then **you would classify the gene encoding EGFR as a proto-oncogene.** The reason is that the cancerous cells express both EGFRvIII and wild-type EGFR. This fact means that the EGFRvIII mutation has dominant effects. Dominant, gain-of-function mutations that convert proto-oncogenes into oncogenes contribute to cancer. In contrast, loss-of-function alleles of tumour-suppressor genes are recessive in terms of their contribution to cancer.

b. **You would need to treat patients expressing EGFRvIII with a higher-than-normal dose of X-rays.** Remember that apoptosis is a cell program that allows cells with DNA damage to self-destruct. Apoptosis is necessary for the body to rid itself of cells that would be dangerous because they have accumulated a great deal of DNA damage. If the cancerous cells do not undergo apoptosis easily, then they will be relatively resistant to X-rays and will not die. You would need to "zap" the cells with very high levels of X-rays to kill the cells directly. In fact, treating such patients with the usual dose of X-rays would be very dangerous, because the X-rays would cause these cells to accumulate mutations, including some in oncogenes and tumour-suppressor genes.

c. The wild-type allele of the *EGFR* gene is a proto-oncogene whose product promotes cell division by serving as a receptor for epidermal growth factor (EGF). The N-terminal domain is extracellular and binds the growth factor, while the C-terminal part of the protein is a kinase. Function of the kinase (to add phosphate groups to other proteins) is needed to promote cell division in the presence of the growth factor. EGFRvIII protein has the kinase domain but does not have amino acids 6 through 273 of the N-terminal domain. Thus**, the most likely explanation is that deletion of the N-terminal domain makes a form of the EGFR receptor that can signal constitutively, even in the absence of the EGF growth factor.**

d. **Iressa™ would be an excellent candidate drug for the treatment of glioblastomas expressing EGFRvIII.** The drug should block the kinase activity of EGFR, for example by occupying the site at which ATP binds the enzyme so that one phosphate from ATP can be transferred to target proteins. This drug should stop the constitutive signalling from the EGFRvIII protein because it would interfere with its kinase function; in this way the drug would prevent unwanted cell proliferation. One issue with this drug is of course that it would also prevent the function of the normal EGFR receptor in all cells, which would produce unwanted side effects.

  Although Iressa™ theoretically makes a great deal of sense for treating glioblastomas, it has unfortunately not proven to be very effective in actual clinical studies. The reasons are unclear; perhaps not enough drug crosses the blood-brain barrier to reach the tumours in the brain. Another possibility is that many glioblastomas may have additional mutations that cause constitutive signalling from other growth factor receptors that are not inhibited by Iressa.

e. **You would need to treat patients with glioblastomas that have higher levels than normal of *ERCC1* transcription and gene product with higher-than-normal doses of cisplatin.** The reason is that these cells can easily remove cisplatin-produced DNA damage because the ERCC1 protein helps repair DNA damage. Thus, you would need to use more cisplatin to achieve the amount of DNA damage that would be needed for the cells to undergo apoptosis.

  You should note that cisplatin treatment may be a bad idea for patients with defects in the *p53* tumour-suppressor gene or in the genes that participate in the apoptosis pathway. In such cases, the cells could accumulate much DNA damage but they would not be removed by apoptosis; such cells might contribute to cancer progression.

16-22. *Note:* Throughout this problem, the identities of the three point mutations vi, vii, and viii, cannot be distinguished.

a. **iii (trisomy), iv (duplication of a chromosomal region), and [vi, vii, or viii] (a rare hypermorphic or neomorphic point mutation).** Genetic alterations that could convert proto-oncogenes into tumour-promoting oncogenes would be gain-of-function mutations (vi, vii, or viii) or increases in gene dosage (iii and iv).

b. **i (mitotic recombination), ii (deletion of a chromosomal region), v (uniparental disomy), and [vi, vii, or viii] (a null or hypomorphic point mutation).** [If one point mutation was assigned previously in part *a* as a gain-of-function mutation, it cannot also be a gain-of-function mutation in part *b*.] Genetic alterations of tumour-suppressor genes that promote cancer would be loss- of-function mutations (vi, vii, or viii) or decreases in gene dosage (ii). In heterozygotes for a loss-of-function mutation of a tumour-suppressor gene, mitotic recombination (i) or uniparental disomy (v) could result in loss of the remaining wild-type copy of the gene.

c. **i (mitotic recombination) and v (uniparental disomy).** The idea here is that prior to the event listed, a cell has two copies of a tumour-suppressor gene but one copy is inactive (that is, the cell is heterozygous for a loss-of-function mutation – but not a deletion – in a tumour-suppressor gene). Mitotic recombination (i) or uniparental disomy (v) would make the cell homozygous for the mutant allele, so there would still be two copies of the gene although both would be mutant.

A new null point mutation (vi, vii, or viii) in the previously wild-type copy of the tumour-suppressor gene would likewise result in a cell with two copies of the gene, both of which are inactive. This situation is technically not a loss-of-heterozygosity (because the cell would be heterozygous for two different loss-of-function mutations), but you are still essentially on the right track if you also answered vii.

For parts *d – h*, you first need to understand the difference between the representation of a locus and a specific allele. Each column is a specific locus (nucleotide pair) along the chromosome; each row represents the possible alleles of that locus (that is, A, G, C, and T). It is next crucial to pay attention to the number of copies of each SNP analyzed in the microarray. *White* means no copies of the indicated allele, *orange* means one copy, and *red* means two copies. You then add up the number of copies of all the alleles of a locus in the sample; for example, the tumour has 3 total copies of locus *a* on Chromosome 15 (1 A and 2 Gs).

d.

i (mitotic recombination)	ii (deletion)	iii (trisomy)	iv (duplication)	v (uniparental disomy)
16 *a-g*	16 *s-x*	15 *a-z*	14 *n-t*	17 *a-z*

You were not asked to locate any point mutations (vi-viii) because this is impossible (with one special exception noted in part *f* below). The possibility that any of the SNP polymorphisms examined on the microarray contributes to cancer is extremely remote given that these constitute only a very small sample of all possible polymorphisms on these chromosomes. The SNPs examined are instead anonymous in the sense that they would have no effect on phenotypes, including cancer.

e. **The mitotic recombination event must take place in the interval between SNPs *g* and *h* on Chromosome 16.** Note that in the tumour tissue, the sequences distal to the mitotic recombination site (that is, further from the centromere) become homozygous, while those proximal to the mitotic recombination site remain heterozygous as in the normal tissue.

f. Although none of the SNP polymorphisms examined on the microarray is likely to promote cancer, the data do suggest that there are three places in the genome in which the patient might have inherited a point mutation in a tumour-suppressor gene or developed a somatic point mutation in a liver cell. **One location is region *a - h* of Chromosome 16.** (The tumour-suppressor gene could be in the *g-h* region because we do not know where the breakpoint lies in this interval.) If a point mutation existed in a tumour-suppressor gene in this region, then mitotic recombination in region *g-h* of this chromosome could generate a cell homozygous for this point mutation. **A second possibility is anywhere on Chromosome 17 (regions *a-z*)**, where uniparental disomy could generate a cell homozygous for a point mutation in a tumour-suppressor gene. **The third region is Chromosome 16 region *r - y*,** where the patient inherited a deletion, and a point mutation in a tumour-suppressor gene may have developed subsequently in a liver cell. (The gene of interest could be in the interval between the shift from two copies to one copy or in the interval between the shift from one copy to two copies of the chromosome.)

g. **Alteration ii.** The most clear-cut evidence that the patient inherited a mutation that could promote cancer is that the interval containing SNPs *s-w* on Chromosome 16 is deleted (the normal tissue has only one copy of these loci). On a normal chromosome, this region presumably contains a tumour-suppressor gene, so the patient starts out (as a zygote) with only one copy of this gene.

As just discussed in part *f*, the possibility exists that the patient may have inherited a point mutation in region *g-h* of Chromosome 16 and/or somewhere on Chromosome 17 (*a-z*), but the evidence for the existence of such point mutations is only indirect.

h. Consistent with the answers to parts *f* and *g*, the three scenarios are as follows.

The three point mutations (vi-viii) are interchangeable.

<u>**Scenario 1**</u>: **The first hit (ii) is that the patient inherited from a parent a deletion of a tumour-suppressor gene in region *s - w* of Chromosome 16. The second hit (vi) would be a point mutation in the remaining wild-type copy of the tumour-suppressor gene.**

<u>**Scenario 2**</u>: **The first hit is that the patient inherited from a parent a loss-of- function point mutation in a tumour-suppressor gene lying in region *a - g* of Chromosome 16 (vii).** (This mutation could also have occurred somatically in a liver cell; the data do not address this point.) **The second hit would be the mitotic recombination event (i) that occurred in region *g - h* in a liver cell originally heterozygous for the point mutation.** The mitotic recombination would make a daughter cell homozygous for the point mutation.

<u>**Scenario 3**</u>: **The first hit is that the patient inherited from a parent a loss-of- function point mutation in a tumour-suppressor gene lying somewhere on Chromosome 17 (viii).** (This mutation could also have occurred somatically in a liver cell; the data do not address this point.) **The second hit would be the uniparental disomy event (v) in a liver cell originally heterozygous for the point mutation.** The result would be a liver cell that is now homozygous for the point mutation.

16-23. Alterations i-v would be relatively easy to find from whole-genome sequencing. **For alterations that change the copy number of a region [the deletion (ii), trisomy (iii), and duplication of a region (iv)], you would look for either fewer (ii) or more (iii and iv) "reads" of the corresponding region as compared with the reads of other regions of the genome in which the normal and tumour tissue had only two copies. For the alterations that produce loss-of-heterozygosity that is copy-neutral [mitotic recombination (i) and uniparental disomy (v)], you would compare the reads from the normal tissue and from the tumour tissue. In the regions of interest, the normal tissue should show two alleles of many of the polymorphic SNP loci, but the tumour tissue would show only one kind of allele even though the number of reads would indicate that two copies of this allele are present.**

Point mutations that contribute to cancer would be much harder to find and may still go undetected even if you have sequenced the whole genome. You could look specifically at the regions discussed in the three scenarios in the answer to Problem 22 part *h* for alterations in known tumour-suppressor genes. You could also look for point mutations that would affect known proto-oncogenes to produce some kind of gain-of- function mutation. But it is also possible that the tumour contains point mutations that affect cancer-related genes that are unknown or poorly characterized. Here, you would look for mutations that disrupted open reading frames of genes (like nonsense or frameshift mutations), or missense mutations that affect highly-conserved amino acids within proteins. Mutations outside of the coding sequences that affected the regulation of proto-oncogenes or tumour-suppressor genes would be even harder to identify.

16-24. "Deep sequencing" (RNA-Seq) might reveal the identity of mRNAs or other transcripts whose levels are higher (for oncogenes) or lower (for tumour-suppressor genes) in tumourous tissue than in normal cells of the same tissue type. That is, the proportion of total mRNA "reads" for these genes in the cancerous cells would be much different from that in normal cells. As just discussed in Problem 23, if a cancer-related gene had some type of mutation in a regulatory region that affects the amount of transcript, such a change would be hard to find just by looking at the genomic DNA sequence. RNA-Seq thus has the potential to provide medical scientists with new information relevant to a patient's cancer.

Of course, just finding an alteration in the levels of a transcript does not mean that a mutation must be in or near the corresponding gene; the problem could be in the gene encoding a *trans*-acting factor. Also, changes in mRNA levels might not be driving tumour progression, but instead might be a response to other genomic alterations that are driving the cancer. So this type of analysis can certainly provide important clues as to the genetic basis for a particular cancer, but much additional work would need to be done to understand the meaning of any change in transcript level that is observed.

Chapter 17   The Genetic Analysis of Development

Synopsis:

A resounding success of modern-day genetics is its use as a tool for understanding the development of multicellular organisms from their beginnings as fertilized eggs. Much of what has been learned about the mechanisms of development emerged from genetic screens conducted in *Drosophila* to find strains harbouring mutations that disrupted specific developmental processes. Using techniques of molecular genetics such as positional cloning, scientists could identify the genes affected by the mutations and determine the nature of the protein products of these genes. Further genetic and molecular experiments allowed the researchers to understand how these genes and their products interact in pathways that guide the specific aspect of development being investigated. Many of the lessons derived from these studies of fruit flies are transferrable to other organisms including humans because evolution tends to repurpose and embellish developmental pathways, rather than invent new ones from scratch.

Key Terms:

developmental genetics – the use of genetic analysis as a tool to study the molecular mechanisms of *development* – that is, how a zygote becomes a multicellular organism.

mutant screen – a process where researchers examine a large number of mutagenized organisms and identify rare individuals with a mutant phenotype of interest.

signal transduction cascade (or **pathway**) – a form of molecular communication in which the binding of a *ligand* to its *receptor* on cell surfaces constitutes a signal that is converted through a series of intermediate steps to a final intracellular regulatory response, usually the activation or repression of transcription of target genes.

developmental pathway – the interactions between genes and gene products that produce a particular outcome in development.

sensitized phenotype – a mutant phenotype that is particularly sensitive to subsequent alteration by changes in the activities of other genes.

enhancers and **suppressors** – mutations that (in double mutants) make the sensitized phenotype caused by mutation in a different gene appear more mutant (*enhancers*) or less mutant (*suppressors*); these effects may be either dominant or recessive. Often, the phenotypic effect of enhancers and suppressors is seen only in a sensitized genetic background; that is, the mutation does not alter phenotype in an otherwise wild-type organism.

RNA *in situ* hybridization – an experimental approach to determine the expression pattern of a particular mRNA in the context of an entire organism or tissue. Labelled cDNA sequences corresponding to the gene's mRNA are used as a probe on preparations of thinly-sectioned tissues, or sometimes whole organisms or tissues. Signals where the probe is retained through complementary base pairing (*hybridization*) indicate cells containing the gene's mRNA.

RNA-Seq – method for analysis of the transcriptome of an organism in which millions of cDNAs are sequenced by high-throughput techniques. The frequency at which *reads* of cDNAs corresponding to a particular mRNA are observed indicates the level of expression of the mRNA in the tissue being analyzed.

antibody staining – method for monitoring the presence of a particular protein in a cell or tissue. When the purified protein is injected into an animal, the protein acts as an **immunogen** against which the animal generates antibodies. These antibodies are then purified and tagged with a fluor. When applied to the tissue, the antibody binds the immunogen protein and labels it fluorescently.

fusion gene – gene made up of parts of two or more genes.

fusion protein – protein encoded by open reading frames from more than one gene.

genetic mosaic – an organism made of cells with different genotypes.

mosaic analysis – observation of tissues from a mosaic organism in order to determine the cells in which a particular gene must be active to allow the animal to develop or function normally— the **focus of action** of a gene. Typically, most cells of the organism are heterozygous for wild-type and loss-of-function alleles of the gene (*gene⁺/gene⁻*) while some cells have lost the wild-type allele (and are thus *gene⁻* hemizgotes or homozygotes).

FLP/FRT recombination system – the use in transgenic organisms of FLP recombinase enzyme from yeast and the DNA site that it binds (FRT) to perform site-specific recombination; one purpose is to cause mitotic recombination for mosaic analysis.

temperature-sensitive (ts) mutations – mutant alleles that function like wild type at low temperatures (**permissive temperature**) but are loss-of-function alleles at high temperatures (**restrictive temperature**).

epistasis – a gene interaction in which the effects of alleles at one gene hide the effects of alleles at another gene. Epistatic interactions are sometimes observed in **double mutants** – organisms with mutant alleles of two different genes – when the two genes work in the same pathway.

switch/regulation pathway – a linear developmental pathway in which a signal controls a switch that can be either "on" or "off" in any particular cell. An "on" switch initiates a cascade of gene regulation events that lead to a change in the cell's fate. The outcome of the pathway is thus one of two developmental states, depending on whether the switch is "on" or "off".

maternal-effect genes – genes encoding maternal components (mRNAs or proteins) synthesized by the mother and deposited in the eggs that enable the development of her progeny.

zygotic segmentation genes – in *Drosophila*, three groups of genes transcribed from the genome of the zygote that function in a hierarchy to divide the organism into an array of identical segments. At the top of the hierarchy are the **gap genes**; their products are transcription factors expressed in broad regions along the anterior-posterior (AP) axis. Next are the **pair-rule genes**, which also encode transcription factors, and are expressed in a periodic pattern of seven stripes in the early embryo. Finally, the **segment polarity genes** are expressed in fourteen stripes, one in each segment. The segment polarity genes encode cell communication proteins that enable cells within a segment to detect their position in that segment.

homeotic gene – a gene that gives originally identical segments individual identities during development.

morphogen – a substance that defines different cell fates in a concentration-dependent manner.

homeobox – a region of DNA (~180 bp) that encodes the DNA-binding domain (called the **homeodomain**) in transcription factors encoded by homeotic genes.

bithorax complex (BX-C) – in *Drosophila*, a cluster of homeotic genes encoding several homeodomain-containing transcription factors that control the identity of segments in the abdomen and posterior thorax.

Antennapedia complex (ANT-C) – in *Drosophila*, a cluster of homeotic genes encoding several homeodomain-containing transcription factors that control the identity of segments in the head and anterior thorax.

Hox genes –a gene superfamily encoding homeodomain-containing transcription factors. The *Hox* genes pattern animals along the AP body axis during development.

ectopic expression – gene expression that occurs outside the cell or tissue where the gene is normally expressed.

Mutant Screens:

Although the details of how researchers perform mutant screens depend on the reproductive biology of the particular organism, the general principles of mutant screens are illustrated well in the *Drosophila* screens presented in this chapter:

- Mutant screens are called F_1, F_2, F_3, or F_4 screens, depending on the generation (post-mutagenesis) which is examined for the mutant phenotype.

- In most *Drosophila* screens, a mutagen is fed to males of the Parental (P) generation in order to mutagenize the sperm. The F_1 flies will each contain a single mutagenized homologue (from the male parent) and a normal homologue (from the female parent) of each chromosome.

- It is important to realize that in the F_1, any mutation of interest exists initially only on a single chromosome in one individual. Further crosses are performed to generate additional copies of the chromosome bearing a potentially interesting mutation. Amplification of this chromosome is essential either to generate a stock of that mutation for further study, or to make animals homozygous for the mutation.

- The modifier screens described in Figure 17.5 and Figure 17.7 were F_1 screens. Researchers prefer to perform F_1 screens when possible: Only one cross (the Parental cross) needs to be set up, and so thousands or potentially even millions of F_1 progeny may be screened for a phenotype. However, F_1 screens are possible only when the mutant phenotype is dominant so that it can be observed in organisms with only one copy of the mutation ($m-/m+$).

- The mutant screen shown in Figure 17.19 (*lefthand side*) is an F_3 screen for zygotic segmentation genes. To screen for zygotic lethals affecting segmentation, it was necessary to screen the F_3 generation because the mutant phenotypes were observed only in homozygotes, and also because animals with the mutant phenotype could not survive. The F_1 and F_2 crosses were needed to make homozygous individual mutagenized chromosomes and to make balanced stocks of the different mutagenized chromosomes, so that mutations of interest could be maintained in heterozygotes.

- The mutant screen shown in Figure 17.19 (*righthand side*) is an F_4 screen for maternal-effect genes affecting segmentation. In this case, the F_4 embryos had to be screened because their mothers had to be homozygous for a particular mutagenized chromosome.

Epistasis Analysis:

Epistatic interactions observed in double mutants are extremely useful for ordering genes in a developmental pathway, but this type of analysis can be exceedingly complex because scientists must make many assumptions in order to draw valid conclusions from the results. A few important points to keep in mind:

- The two single mutants must cause different phenotypes: In epistasis analysis, a scientist asks: Do the double mutants ($a-$ $b-$) have the $a-$ phenotype, or the $b-$ phenotype? Obviously, $a-$ and $b-$ have to cause different mutant phenotypes in order for that question to be answerable.

- Not all double mutants will show epistasis: Even if two mutants cause different phenotypes, they may not display epistatic interactions; the double mutant phenotype may not be identical to the phenotype of either single mutant. Other kinds of results include additive interactions, enhancement, and suppression.

- Mutant alleles must be nulls or constitutively active: The reason why only "full off" (null) or "full on" (constitutively active) alleles must be used for epistasis analysis is that if hypomorphic or hypermorphic (but not fully on) alleles are used, the interaction you are observing may not be epistasis, but simply additive effects.

Problem Solving:

Maternal-effect genes versus organelle-based maternal inheritance:

- The idea that the genotype of an organism's mother, rather than the genotype of the organism itself, may control a phenotype is not new. In particular, you will see in Chapter 18 that in humans and many other organisms, mitochondria come from the maternal gamete exclusively. However, a major difference exists between organelle-based maternal inheritance and maternal-effect inheritance: In mitochondrial inheritance, it is the mitochondrial DNA (mtDNA) itself that is being passed from the egg to the progeny, while in maternal-effect inheritance, it is gene products (RNAs and proteins) made from the maternal nuclear genome that are deposited into the egg and influence the phenotype, rather than maternal DNA itself.

Solutions to Problems:

Vocabulary

17-1. i. **11**; ii. **4**; iii. **8**; iv. **7**; v. **12**; vi. **9**; vii. **13**; viii. **3**; ix. **1**, x. **5**; xi. **6**; xii. **10**; xiii. **2**.

Section 17.1 – Model Organisms: Prototypes for Developmental Genetics

17-2.

a. To analyze the role of a particular gene in heart development, you would want to make loss-of-function mutations, and also (if possible) gain-of-function mutations, in the gene; analyze the mutant phenotypes to examine in detail how they disrupt heart anatomy and physiology; and monitor the mRNA and protein products of the gene to determine the particular tissues in which these are expressed. **Most of these experiments could not be performed with humans for both practical and ethical reasons.** (However, if you found by rare chance a patient with a mutation in the gene you could certainly examine the heart by non-invasive means.) **The best model organism to use would probably be a mouse.** The reason is that mice have hearts that are similar to those of humans and the manipulations outlined above can all be done with mice. A primate would have a heart closest to that of a human, but primarily for ethical reasons, most scientists would avoid the study of primate models.

b. To find genes required for heart development, you would want to perform some kind of genetic screen (looking for mutations that disrupt heart development) or molecular screen (looking for proteins or other molecules expressed in developing heart tissues). In choosing a model organism, the considerations include: How similar is the organism's heart to the human heart? (The greater the similarity, the more likely it is that the genes you find will have similar functions in humans.) How easy is it to perform the desired screen? (For example, will complex dissections be required in order to look at the developing heart?) How many animals with mutagenized chromosomes can I screen? (This number depends on the generation time of the organism, how many progeny a mating pair produce, and how expensive it would be to maintain large numbers of animals.) **Mice, zebrafish, and *Drosophila* would all be good choices for different reasons.**

Mice would probably be the best choice for a molecular screen, such as RNA-Seq analysis of heart tissue to find genes that are transcribed at specific times during heart development. Mouse and human hearts are the most similar because both organisms are mammals, and the dissections required to isolate heart tissue are probably easiest in mice because they are the largest of the animals. Although the costs of animal husbandry are highest for mice, you would not need to maintain many individuals to perform this type of experiment.

Each of the three models would have advantages and disadvantages for a genetic screen. The main advantage of mice is their similarity to humans. Genetic screens are possible with mice, but they are expensive and time-consuming. In addition, loss-of-function mutations affecting heart development are likely to be homozygous lethal, and balancer chromosomes that help to maintain lines of lethal mutations exist only for a few mouse chromosomes. Zebrafish genetic screens are also labour-intensive and time-consuming. However, a major advantage of zebrafish is that the embryos are transparent, so the heart is visible in live fish. Even though *Drosophila* hearts are quite different from human hearts, genetic screens using fruit flies are much easier to perform. The generation time of *Drosophila* is less than two weeks, each female produces hundreds of progeny, balancer chromosomes enable stocks of homozygous lethal mutations to be maintained easily, and flies are cheap and easy to culture. Thus, many more potential mutants could be screened in *Drosophila* than in the other two models, and more genes could be identified. At least some of these genes should be relevant to human heart development.

17-3.

a. **In *C. elegans*, laser ablation at this early stage of development would almost certainly be lethal**, since you would destroy a large proportion of the cell types that would eventually develop from the descendants of the ablated cell, and there are no other cells that could replace these. **In mice, the loss of one out of four early embryonic cells would likely have no effect**, since the descendants of the cells that were not destroyed could take the place of the descendants of the cell that was destroyed.

b. Separating the four cells would be **lethal to *C. elegans*** since none of these cells would be able to develop into a complete organism. **In mice, it is possible that each of the separated cells could develop into a mouse**.

c. Fusing two four-celled embryos **in *C. elegans* would likely be lethal**, since proper development depends upon signals between the various cells and such signals would almost certainly be disrupted by the fusion event. **In mice, such a fusion would likely be tolerated giving rise to a chimeric animal**. Recall from Figure 17.9 that similar fusions (the injection of embryonic stem cells from one strain into blastocysts of a second strain) in fact constitute an important step in the procedure for making knockout mice.

Section 17.2 – Mutagenesis Screens

17-4.

a. **Screen homozygous mutants for failure to move toward UV light.** For example, you could place stocks homozygous for mutagenized chromosomes at one end of a long tube and a UV source at the other end of the tube. After a certain period has elapsed, you would count the flies that did not move towards the UV source. A screen of this nature was, in fact, how the first *sevenless* mutants were identified.

b. **Mutations in every gene required for R7 development would <u>not</u> be recovered in the screen described.** Such a screen requires that the homozygous loss-of-function mutants are viable, which precludes the recovery of mutations in **pleiotropic genes** required not only for R7 development, but also for essential developmental pathways. (Hypomorphic alleles of pleiotropic genes that are homozygous viable potentially could be identified.) In addition, mutations in **genes**

with redundant functions in the R7 developmental pathway would not be identified: If one gene was knocked out, the redundant gene would still be present to supply the same function, so no mutant phenotype would be apparent.

c. **You could perform complementation tests** to determine if newly identified mutants (*m−*) are alleles of *sev* or *boss*. Simply cross flies carrying the mutations with *sev* or *boss* homozygotes and determine whether *m−/sev* or *m−/boss* flies lack R7s (no complementation – the mutations are in the same gene) or whether the flies are wild-type (complementation – the mutations are in different genes).

d. **You could identify additional mutant alleles of a gene (*m*) required specifically for eye development by performing a screen for noncomplementing mutations.** For example, you could mutagenize male flies, cross them to *m−/m−* females, and screen the F_1 progeny (mutagenized chromosome/*m−*) for a mutant eye phenotype. A mutant F_1 animal will likely have a new mutant allele of gene *m* on the mutagenized chromosome.

A researcher might want to generate many different *m−* alleles for several reasons. First, it is possible that the original allele was hypomorphic rather than null; the phenotypes associated with homozygosity for a null allele would help the scientist understand the range of roles played by the gene product. Second, the availability of multiple alleles may help researchers identify the gene at the molecular level: Gene identification often involves comparing the base-pair sequences of wild-type and mutant alleles, and this is much easier to do when many different mutant alleles are available. Finally, the base-pair sequences of many different mutant alleles can also help scientists analyze the relationship of a gene's structure to its function; the mutant base pairs could reveal specific regulatory elements or amino acids that are important to the function of the gene or its protein product.

17-5.

a. **The *rg^{γ3}* allele** causes the more severe phenotype (very rough eyes) and is therefore the stronger allele.

b. Since the *rg^{41}* phenotype is more similar to wild type (less severe), this allele directs either the production of more Rugose protein, or the production of the same amount of a more active Rugose protein than the *rg^{γ3}* allele. (Onthe other hand, the *rg^{41}* allele produces either less Rugose protein or the same amount of a less active Rugose protein than does the wild-type allele.)

c. **Muller's test compares the phenotype associated with homozygosity for a recessive mutation with that associated with heterozygosity for the mutation and a deletion of the gene. If the phenotypes are identical in these two genotypes, then the mutation is a null mutation. If the mutation/deletion has a more severe phenotype, then the mutation is not null but is instead hypomorphic.** The answers to parts *a* and *b* above establish that rg^{41} **is a weak hypomorphic allele that makes at least some Rugose protein**, so it cannot be a null (no activity) allele. This leaves $rg^{\gamma 3}$ as the only candidate for a null allele. Muller's test suggests that $rg^{\gamma 3}$ **is likely a null allele** because the phenotype of a $rg^{\gamma 3}$ homozygote is the same as that of $rg^{\gamma 3}$ / *Df(1)JC70.* We know that the deletion must be null for the *rg* gene because the gene is missing entirely. If $rg^{\gamma 3}$ encoded some Rugose protein, then you would expect that $rg^{\gamma 3}$ / *Df(1)JC70* would make half the amount of gene product of $rg^{\gamma 3}$ homozygotes, resulting in a more severe phenotype, but this is not what was observed.

d. **A researcher who wants to understand all the functions of a gene would want to know the consequence to the organism of a complete loss of that gene's function – the null phenotype.**

e. Muller's test could be used to determine if the dominant allele is hypermorphic. The mutant phenotype of rg^{hyper}/rg^{+} flies is due to levels of Rugose activity in excess of wild-type levels. **Heterozygous rg^{hyper}/rg^{+} flies should have more rg^{+} activity and thus a <u>more severe</u> mutant phenotype than rg^{hyper} / *Df(1)JC70* flies** if this allele is indeed hypermorphic.

f. The mutant phenotype of rg^{anti}/rg^{+} flies is due to levels of Rugose activity that are lower than wild-type levels [recall that in a heterozygote, an antimorphic (dominant-negative) allele somehow interferes with the activity of the wild-type allele or its product]. **Heterozygous rg^{anti} / $Dp(rg^{+})$ flies should have more Rugose activity and thus a <u>less severe</u> mutant phenotype than rg^{anti}/rg^{+} flies.**

17-6.

a. **You could use the *myo-2::GFP* transgenics as the genetic background in which to perform a mutagenesis screen for worms with a morphologically abnormal pharynx. Expression of GFP in the pharynx will make the structure easily visible in living worms.**

b. **First, generate a gene construct where *pha-4* wild-type coding sequences are fused to the regulatory region of a gene expressed in an organ other than the pharynx** (for example, the vulva, which is part of the external genitalia of the female). **If *pha-4* is a master regulator of pharynx formation, then worms transformed with the *pha-4* fusion gene should transform** vulval cells into pharyngeal cells. If the worms also contain the *myo-2::GFP* transgene, the transformation would be obvious in living worms because GFP would be expressed not only in the pharynx, but also in cells located where the vulva would normally be.

17-7. You want to determine if gene *X* is important for specification of the pharynx, so you want to disrupt expression there; however, you also want to maintain normal expression of gene *X* in all other tissues. Therefore, you would **express a double-stranded RNA (RNAi) corresponding to gene *X* specifically in the pharynx**. One way to accomplish this goal is to place gene *X* between two regulatory regions (promoters) for *myo-2* so that gene *X* will be transcribed in opposite directions (the figure on the left below). Alternatively, you can place two copies of gene *X* oriented in opposite directions downstream of a single regulatory region (promoter) for *myo-2* (as seen in the figure on the right below); when these genes are transcribed, the result will be a double-stranded hairpin RNA. When you **transform these constructs into worms containing *myo-2::GFP*, dsRNA will be made only in the pharynx because the *myo-2* regulatory region is active only in that tissue. You will then examine the pattern of green fluorescence to see whether RNAi for gene *X* affects pharyngeal development**.

17-8.

a. The screen for modifiers of the hypomorphic *sev−* phenotype (Figure 17.5) relied on the viability and fertility both of the starting strain flies (homozygotes for *sev^{hypo}*) and the F$_1$ flies with a modified (enhanced or suppressed) *sev−* phenotype. **Because EGFR is expressed in many tissues, you would expect that almost all hypomorphic *Egfr* alleles are recessive lethals.** It might be possible to find a rare, weakly hypomorphic *Egfr* allele that would be viable and fertile and would also have a morphological mutant phenotype useful for a modifier screen. Interestingly, even if this were the case, you would likely only be able to find suppressor mutations: Enhanced F$_1$ flies would likely be dead, making it impossible to recover enhancers in the same sort of modifier screen.

b. Using transgenic flies in which expression of an *Egfr* mutant allele is confined to an organ that is non-essential in the laboratory (such as the eye) is one way to get around the lethality problem noted in part *a*. For example, you could **construct a fusion gene where eye-specific**

transcriptional regulatory sequences drive expression of an *Egfr* cDNA encoding a hypermorphic receptor protein. (This is similar to the transgene described in Figure 17.7) Because EGFR signalling is used in a variety of developmental decisions in the eye, the Ras/MAPK pathway proteins are present in essentially all eye cells. Therefore, hypermorphic EGFR would alter many developmental pathways and cause eye malformations that could be used as the background for a modifier screen. **With this transgene, enhancers would identify genes that antagonize EGFR signalling, because a loss-of-function mutation in such a gene would increase EGFR signalling in the eye**, which is already too high because of the hypermorphic mutation. **Any suppressors found in the screen would be loss-of-function mutations in genes that help relay the EGFR signal.**

Alternatively, an RNAi transgene could be constructed in which eye-specific regulatory sequences drive expression of an *Egfr* exon in both directions. A transgenic line could be identified in which EGFR protein expression is knocked down, but not completely gone; these flies would essentially have an eye-specific hypomorphic *Egfr* allele. **If such an RNAi transgene were used as a screen background, enhancer mutations would identify genes that help relay EGFR signals, and suppressors would be loss-of-function mutations in genes that antagonize EGFR signalling.**

17-9.

a. **A dominant-negative Ras protein expressed in R7 precursors would prevent Sevenless receptor signalling; some ommatidia in the fly eyes would lack R7s.**

b. Using a *sev-Ras^{S17N}* (Ras dominant-negative) transgenic line as a screen background, the mutant phenotype is due to loss of Ras function. This means that loss-of-function mutations in genes that relay (promote) the Sevenless signal would be recovered as enhancers, while loss-of-function mutations in genes that antagonize Sevenless signalling would be suppressors. Therefore, **the genes encoding Ras, Drk, Sos, Raf, Mek, MAPK, and Pnt could be identified as enhancers, and the genes for Gap and Yan as suppressors.**

c. If the screen background were *sev-Ras^{G12V}* (hypermorphic Ras), the mutant phenotype is due to too much Ras function. This means that loss-of-function mutations in genes that relay the Sevenless signal would be recovered as suppressors, while loss-of-function mutations in genes that antagonize Sevenless signalling would be enhancers. Therefore, **the genes encoding Ras, Drk, Sos, Raf, Mek, MAPK, and Pnt could be identified as suppressors, and the genes for Gap and Yan as enhancers.**

17-10.

a. Diagram the testcross:

w/w ; ro^-/ro^+ $P[w^+]$ ♀ × w/w ; ro^-/ro^- ♂ → the four classes of progeny listed in the table. The ro^- allele from the male parent reveals the rough eye phenotype if the chromosome from the female parent is ro^-. The $P[w^+]$ transgene is a dominant allele; in the w/w background, flies with one copy of $P[w^+]$ have red eyes, and flies with no $P[w^+]$ have white eyes. Therefore, the parental phenotypes are 145 red, smooth eyes (ro^+ $P[w^+]$) and 152 white, rough eyes (ro^-), and the recombinant phenotypes are 2 white, smooth eyes (ro^+) and 1 red, rough eyes (ro^- $P[w^+]$). RF = $(1+2)/(145+152+1+2) = 3/300 = 1\%$. **The ro gene and the $P[w^+]$ insertion are linked, and the $ro \leftrightarrow P[w^+]$ distance is 1 m.u.**

b. **The data in part *a* do not indicate whether ro is centromeric (proximal) or telomeric (distal) to the $P[w^+]$ element. To determine the relative positions of the centromere, ro, and $P[w^+]$, the $P[w^+]$ chromosome in the original testcross should also contain another mutation (m^-) that causes a scorable mutant phenotype and that is very close to the centromere. (The mutation can be either dominant or recessive; in the following example, m^- is recessive to wild type):**

$$w/w \; ; \; ro^-, m^+/ro^+, m^- \; P[w^+] \; ♀ \times w/w \; ; \; ro^-, m^-/ro^-, m^- \; ♂ \to ??$$

If ro is centromeric to $P[w^+]$ (as shown on the left side of the following diagram), then single crossovers between ro and $P[w^+]$ yield m^+ ro^- $P[w^+]$ chromosomes. In contrast, if ro is telomeric to $P[w^+]$ (as shown on the right side of the following diagram), then single crossovers between ro and $P[w^+]$ would yield m^- ro^- $P[w^+]$ chromosomes.

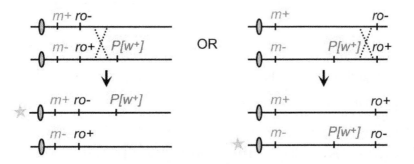

Therefore, **look at the testcross progeny with rough, red eyes: If most of them have the m^+ phenotype, then ro is centromeric to $P[w^+]$; if most of them have the m^- phenotype, then ro is telomeric to $P[w^+]$.**

c. The problem states that the insertion sites of the two different $P[w^+]$ elements are 5000 bp (5 kb) apart. *Drosophila* geneticists are able to determine this distance accurately because they can use inverse PCR to find the insertion sites of the transposable elements and then compare these positions with respect to the genomic reference sequence of *Drosophila*, which is available online. **In a region of 5000 bp, likely only one gene is present, although the region could contain a few small genes.** (The fly genome is about 130 Mb in total length and contains about 13 000 protein-coding genes, so on average there is only one gene per 10 kb of DNA.)

To discriminate among the candidate genes, you would use the genomic DNA sequence of this gene to design PCR primer pairs that allow you to amplify exons of the candidate genes from several *ro⁻* mutant strains. You would then sequence the PCR products to find mutations likely to alter gene function. As stated previously in the answer to Problem 4d, the more alleles that could be analyzed in this way, the firmer would be your identification of the proper candidate gene.

Finally, you would verify the association of the candidate gene with the mutant phenotype by introducing a transgene containing the suspect gene's wild-type genomic DNA into *ro⁻* flies. If the transgene rescues the *ro⁻* mutant phenotype to wild type, then the transgene must contain the gene corresponding to the *ro⁻* mutation.

d. **The *Drosophila* genome project database will contain a virtual translation of the *rough* gene ORF. You can then use a computer program such as BLAST to compare the amino acid sequence of the *rough* gene product with the amino acid sequences of other proteins in other organisms. The output of the BLAST program will show common sequence motifs that signify particular functions, such as DNA-binding, insertion in the cell membrane, etc.** In fact, *rough* encodes a transcription factor with a DNA-binding domain called a *homeodomain.*

17-11.

a. The diagrams that follow show three different ways to generate double-stranded RNA corresponding to a gene that should knock out or knock down the gene's expression by RNAi. In the diagrams, the *purple* rectangle corresponds to a regulatory region (enhancer and promoter) and the *blue* rectangles are all or part of a gene's cDNA. The arrows represent the direction RNA polymerase would travel when transcribing the *gene X* sequences starting at each promoter.

What regulatory region(s) should be added to these constructs? The answer is not simple and depends on the purpose of the experiment. If you wanted to knock down expression of *gene X* in all tissues where it is expressed, then ideally the regulatory region would be that of *gene X*. However, it is not always clear what DNA sequences in the vicinity of the gene would need to be included to ensure that all the regulatory elements would be included. An alternative is to express the RNAi construct in all tissues; for example, the regulatory region could be that for a heat-shock gene, and the animals could be raised at high temperature. Yet another alternative is to express the *gene X* sequences specifically in one tissue of interest; part *b* of this problem describes an efficient method to achieve this goal.

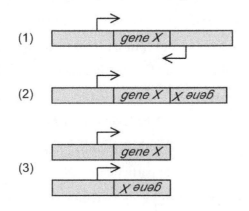

b. **The best way to perform an RNAi screen for wing development genes is to employ the Gal4/UAS$_G$ binary expression system** (see Solved Problem II). One strength of this method is that you could take advantage of transgenic fly lines that already exist, each of which has an RNAi transgene that targets a different gene, and whose expression is driven by *UAS$_G$*. As shown in the following figure, you would then cross each RNAi line with a wing-specific Gal4 driver line to obtain flies that contain both transgenes. The Gal4 transcription factor will be expressed specifically in the wings, and it will activate in wing tissue transcription of a dsRNA for *gene X* that will knock down expression of the endogenous *gene X*.

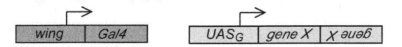

Finally, you would screen the fly strains for abnormal wings caused by the knockdown of *gene X* expression in the wings.

Some *gene X's* with roles in wing development could be pleiotropic, so traditional mutants in such genes knocking out their expression everywhere would lead to lethality; thus, these genes would not be found in traditional mutant screens. **The Gal4/UASG binary expression system circumvents this problem because the interfering RNA will be expressed only in the wing; thus researchers would be able to identify pleiotropic genes that function in wing development.**

Section 17.3 – Determining Where and When Genes Act

17-12.

a. **The pattern of *rugose* mRNA expression** in whole fly embryos or dissected tissues from different developmental stages **can be monitored through RNA *in situ* hybridization experiments** such as that shown in <u>Figure 17.21a</u>. **Alternatively, you could isolate samples of many kinds of tissues and determine relative levels of mRNA expression through *deep sequencing* (*RNA-Seq*) of millions of cDNAs prepared from the total mRNA in each tissue.** The frequency of obtaining "reads" of any type of cDNA indicates the relative abundance of the corresponding mRNA. **Protein expression can be detected by staining whole embryos or tissues with antibodies.** Although in most cases the levels of mRNA expression and protein expression in a tissue will be directly correlated, this is not always the case because translational regulation may boost or inhibit the translation of particular mRNAs.

   Gene expression in a particular cell type <u>does not</u> mean that the gene product is necessarily required there; genes can have redundant roles.

b. If the experiments you performed in part *a* show no mRNA and no protein (or mRNA but no protein, as might be expected for a nonsense mutation soon after the initiation codon), then the allele is potentially null. However, such a result by itself would not be absolutely definitive, because the allele could still be a hypomorph and the mRNA or protein product could be present at levels so low that they are beyond the level of detection. On the other hand, even if you detect mRNA and protein (whether in normal or lower than normal amounts), you cannot conclude that the allele is not a null mutation because the protein product you observe might be completely nonfunctional. **Therefore, observing levels of mRNA and protein is useful but not conclusive for distinguishing between hypomorphic and null alleles.** Additional information that could strengthen a provisional conclusion include the molecular nature of the mutant allele (is it a nonsense or frameshift mutation?), assays for the function of the protein, and crossing the mutant strain with a strain bearing a deletion for the region to conduct Muller's test as described in Problem 5 in this chapter.

   RNA *in situ* hybridization (or RNA-seq) and antibody staining could sometimes be useful to discriminate among the different types of dominant alleles. Antimorphic alleles often but not always have elevated levels of mRNA and protein relative to wild type; the reason is that overexpression of the mutant gene product may be necessary to antagonize the function of the wild-type gene product. Hypermorphic alleles can make either excessive amounts of the normal gene product, or altered gene products that function more efficiently than wild type. Thus, a hypermorphic allele may or may not produce elevated levels of mRNA or protein. Neomorphic alleles may make mutant gene products that function differently from wild type, or they may make wild-type gene products in abnormal expression patterns (ectopic expression). In summary, **if the RNA and protein expression patterns appear wild type, the allele could be antimorphic, hypermorphic, or neomorphic; if ectopic expression is observed, the allele is likely neomorphic; if more mRNA or protein than wild-type amounts are observed, then the allele is likely antimorphic or hypermorphic.**

17-13.

a. Boss is the ligand, expressed in R8, for the Sevenless receptor, expressed in five R7 precursor cells. **Mosaic ommatidia with a wild-type phenotype (R7 present) must have red R8s that are w^+ $boss^+$; mosaic ommatidia with a mutant phenotype (R7 absent) must have white R8s that are w^- $boss^-$.** The genotypes for the w and $boss$ genes of the other cells in any ommatidium do not affect whether the ommatidium will or will not have an R7 cell. Thus, **the focus of action of the $boss^+$ gene is the R8 cell.**

b. The diagram that follows shows the two chromosome 3 homologues in the flies used for the mosaic experiment described in part a. The genome of these flies must also contain a gene encoding FLP recombinase whose expression can be induced during the process of eye development in *Drosophila* larvae (*not shown*). One way to accomplish this goal is to employ a transgene in which coding sequences for FLP are placed under the control of a heat-shock enhancer/promoter, and then growing the larvae at high temperatures during the key time period.

You should note that in the diagram that follows, it is critical that FRT be placed proximal to both $P[w^+]$ and $boss$ (that is, FRT should be closest to the centromere), so that when FLP catalyzes site-specific mitotic recombination between the FRT sites, the resultant progeny can become homozygous for both loci and you will know that all cells that are white in colour (that is, cells lacking $P[w^+]$) must be homozygous for $boss^-$.

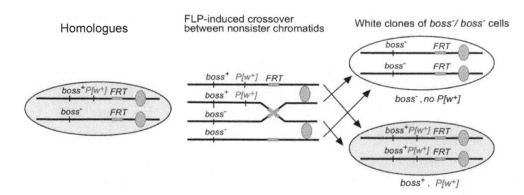

17-14.

a. The figure that follows shows the genotype of flies in which the MARCM technique could be used to generate GFP-expressing clones of cells that are homozygous for a mutant allele of a gene of interest (m^-/m^-). All cells that contain coding sequences for the yeast *Gal80* gene will express the GAL80 protein because it is placed downstream of an enhancer/promoter that functions in all cells. These flies also contain three other transgenes that are located elsewhere in the genome and are *not shown*: (1) a UAS_G-*GFP* transgene; (2) a transgene that can express the FLP recombinase; and (3) a transgene that can express GAL4 protein ubiquitously. None of the cells in this animal will make GFP, with the exception of the cells derived from FLP/FRT mitotic recombination that are m^-/m^- and that also lack the GAL80 protein that negatively regulates the GAL4 protein driving the expression of GFP. Thus, all of the green-glowing cells must be m^-/m^-, allowing investigators to examine the phenotype of cells they know must be homozygous mutant.

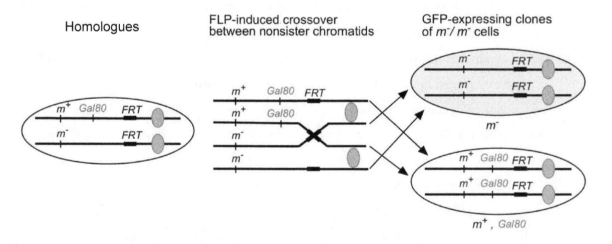

b. Clones homozygous for m^-/m^- could be restricted to the adult nervous system by having **FLP expression driven by an adult nervous system-specific enhancer.**

17-15. The best method would take advantage of the FLP/FRT system described in Figure 17.12 and Problems 13 and 14. In addition, it would be good to include a transgene expressing GFP ubiquitously (as in Problem 14) so that researchers can identify the desired $M^+ l^- / M^+ l^-$ doubly homozygous clones because they will be the only cells that do not fluoresce in green. The FRT site must be proximal (closer to the centromere) than the *M* gene, the *l* gene, and the *GFP* transgene. The order of the other elements is less important because almost all of the mitotic recombination events that occur will take place between the FRT sites.

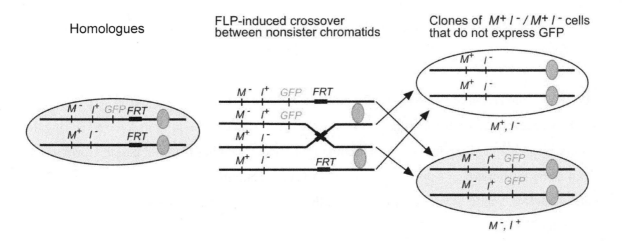

17-16. Mutant alleles whose finished protein products misfold when the temperature is raised (activity ts alleles) are more useful for temperature-shift experiments than are mutant alleles whose protein products misfold only if the temperature is raised while the product is being translated (translation ts alleles). The reason is that the protein encoded by the activity ts allele will become inactive immediately when the temperature is raised. In contrast, for translation ts alleles, only protein synthesized after the temperature shift will be affected; previously synthesized protein could be stable for a very long time after the temperature shift and its presence could complicate the determination of when the protein is required.

17-17.

a. The data indicate that *zyg-9* is required starting **at about 52 minutes up until 70 minutes after fertilization.** (We are assuming that the *zyg-9* ts allele used is ts for activity as defined in the answer to Problem 16). If the embryos are pulsed with high temperature before or after this window of time, the animals develop normally even though the Zyg-9 protein was inactivated during the pulse.

b. A wild-type (*zyg-9*⁺) allele provided to the early embryo by the sperm has no effect on the polarity of the embryo; it cannot rescue the *zyg-9* mutant phenotype to wild type. **One possibility is that some sort of imprinting is occurring so that the allele from the male is not expressed** (review Section 11.3). **In this scenario, the ts Zyg-9 protein in the egg comes from the embryo's maternal allele. Another possibility is that *zyg-9* is a maternal-effect gene;** in this case, neither the maternal nor the paternal allele in the embryo genome is expressed at this early stage of embryogenesis. **The ts Zyg-9 protein would have been transcribed from the mother's genome and deposited in the egg.** It turns out that the second possibility is the correct one: Zyg-

9 protein is maternally deposited in the egg. In fact, the temperature-sensitive period occurs so soon after fertilization that the *zyg-9* genes in embryonic cells have not yet been transcribed.

17-18. A comparison of the two leftmost columns in the diagram shows that after 4 hours at the restrictive temperature, the morphogenetic furrow has advanced anteriorly by 2 rows. During these 4 hours, each ommatidium in the very left column of the diagram has matured into the form to the right of it along the horizontal (row). Five examples of such maturation are shown in the diagram, including two examples where unpatterned cells anterior to the morphogenetic furrow have begun to assemble into ommatidia.

To determine the different requirements for Notch protein, compare the development of wild-type ommatidia (middle column in the diagram) with N^{ts} mutants (rightmost column in the diagram) after 4 hours at the restrictive temperature. Starting with the most anterior ommatidium, and thus the earliest developmental event (row 1), and moving posteriorly to row 5, we can determine that **Notch is required for:**

(Row 1) R8 determination (if Notch protein is inactive before R8 cells have formed in a row, then no R8 cells form in that row);

(Row 2) spacing of separate ommatidia within rows (if the Notch protein is inactivated after R8 cells have formed in a row, then these R8 cells become more closely juxtaposed than they are if Notch is continuously active);

(Row 3) preventing extra photoreceptors from joining the ommatidium between R3 and R4 (if Notch is inactivated after R8 cells have been determined and the proper spacing of ommatidia has already been established, the ommatidia in the row have an extra photoreceptor between R3 and R4);

(Row 5) R7 determination (if Notch is inactivated prior to R7 cell determination, then the R7 cells do not form).

Section 17.4 – Ordering Genes in a Pathway

17-19.

a. The *sev⁻* mutant phenotype has no R7; the *yan⁻* mutant phenotype has up to five R7s. As the *sev⁻ yan⁻* double mutants have the *yan⁻* phenotype, **yan⁻ is epistatic to *sev⁻*.**

b. Yan represses transcription of target genes that promote R7 development, and modulation of Yan function happens downstream of Sevenless. **Activation of Sevenless results in Yan inactivation, and thus derepression of genes that promote R7 cell determination. If Yan is**

absent, Sevenless activation is no longer required to derepress the target genes. Therefore, it is expected that *yan⁻* **would be epistatic to** *sev⁻*.

c. **Two null mutations, like** *sev⁻* **and** *yan⁻*, **can elicit different mutant phenotypes if they function antagonistically in the same pathway.**

d. <u>Figure 17.7</u> shows that constitutively active *sev-Ras^{G12V}* causes 5 cells in each ommatidium to become R7s (just as was the case for *yan⁻* null mutations); <u>Figure 17.15</u> shows that this 5 R7 cell phenotype is in both cases epistatic to the *sev⁻* phenotype. **Ras and Yan both function downstream of Sevenless, but Ras works in the same direction in the pathway as Sevenless, while Yan and Sevenless functions are antagonistic.** It therefore makes sense that a constitutively active *Ras* mutant allele and a null allele of *yan* could cause the same mutant phenotype and that both of these mutations could be epistatic to a *sev* null allele.

e. **A constitutively active Yan protein made by** *yan^{D}* **would always repress the genes that promote R7 development, whether Sevenless was activated or not. Therefore, no R7s would be present in** *yan^{D}* / *yan⁺* **eyes and** *yan^{D}* **would be epistatic to both** *sev⁻* **and** *Ras^{G12V}*. **Because** *yan^{D}* **functions downstream of both** *sev* **and** *Ras*, **neither the absence of Sevenless nor the presence of constitutively active Ras^{G12V} prevents Yan^{D} protein from repressing its target genes and inhibiting R7 development.**

17-20.

a. The *Drosophila* sex determination cascade is a switch/regulation pathway. **The switch is the activation of** *Sxl* **transcription; the signal that controls the switch is the number of X chromosomes. In cells with two X chromosomes (XX), the switch is flipped ON; in cells with one X chromosome (XY), the switch is flipped OFF.**

b. **In terms of morphology, XY animals that are either** *tra⁻* **or** *ix⁻* **are normal males.** The reasons are that XY flies normally make neither Tra protein nor Dsx-F, and Ix is required only for Dsx-F function. (As a point of nomenclature, recall that in this book the names of proteins are <u>not</u> italicized.) **XX animals that are** *tra⁻* **are morphological males;** without Tra, the *dsx* primary transcript is spliced to produce Dsx-M, which causes male morphology. **XX animals that are** *ix⁻* **will be morphologically intersex;** Dsx-F is made and it can activate female morphology genes, but without Ix, Dsx-F cannot repress male morphology genes. Thus, both male and female morphology genes are active in these animals.

c. **In XY animals,** *tra⁻ ix⁻* **double mutants should have no mutant phenotype** (that is, they would be normal males as explained in the answer to part *b*). **In XX animals,** *tra⁻ ix⁻* **double**

mutants would be expected to have the *tra⁻* mutant phenotype (that is, these animals would be morphological males). Regardless of the sex chromosomes, Dsx-M is produced instead of Dsx-F in the absence of Tra. As Ix is required only for Dsx-F function, its absence has no effect in a *tra⁻* background; therefore, **_tra⁻_ is epistatic to _ix⁻_.**

d. In the previous examples of *sev⁻ Ras^{G12V}*, and *sev⁻ yan⁻* (discussed in Problem 19), the epistatic gene was the downstream gene. But as you can see from part *c* above, in some pathways the epistatic gene can be the upstream gene. What explains this difference? The answer has to do with the state of the signal in the cells affected by the mutation – whether the cells that are expressing the mutant phenotype are cells in which the signal normally flips the switch ON, or cells in which the signal normally flips the switch OFF.

The *sev⁻ Ras^{G12V}* and *sev⁻ yan⁻* examples have a feature in common; in both cases, one of the mutations (*sev⁻*) causes cells in which the signal would normally flip the switch ON to have a mutant phenotype, and the other mutation (*Ras^{G12V}* or *yan⁻*) causes cells in which the signal would normally flip the switch OFF to have a mutant phenotype (review Figure 17.15). In *sev⁻* eyes, the R7 precursor cell that touches R8 would be switched ON by the signal (it touches R8 with Boss on its surface), but without a functional Sevenless receptor, it cannot respond to the signal. On the other hand, in *Ras^{G12V}* or *yan⁻* mutants, the mutant phenotype occurs in cells in which the switch would normally be OFF – cells that do not touch R8 and whose Sevenless receptors are not activated by Boss ligand become R7s inappropriately. In cases like this, **when in double mutants the two mutations cause a mutant phenotype in cells with opposite signal states, the epistatic gene is the one downstream in the pathway.**

In the case of *tra⁻* and *ix⁻* mutants, the cells in which each mutant phenotype occurs are XX cells. In parts *a* and *b* above, we determined that the signal for sex determination in *Drosophila* is the number of X chromosomes, and that in XX cells, the switch is flipped ON, meaning that transcription of the *Sxl* gene is activated. We also determined that both *tra⁻* and *ix⁻* cause mutant phenotypes only in XX animals, in whose cells the switch is flipped ON. In cases like this, **when both mutations in double mutants cause phenotypes in cells in which the switch is normally flipped ON, the epistatic mutation affects the upstream step in the pathway.** (The same would be true if both mutations have phenotypes in cells where the switch is normally flipped OFF.)

The purpose of this question is to show you that the interpretation of the results of epistasis analysis can be complex. Clearly, scientists must verify any provisional order of events that were inferred from epistatic interactions with other experiments that reveal the underlying biochemistry.

Section 17.5 – A Comprehensive Example: Body-Plan Development in *Drosophila*

17-21. Injection of *bicoid* mRNA synthesized *in vitro* into the posterior pole of wild-type eggs results in embryos with two, mirror-image anterior poles; heads develop at both end of the embryo. Alternatively, **injection of *bicoid* mRNA into the anterior pole of *bicoid* mutant eggs would indicate that *bicoid* alone is sufficient to rescue the mutant phenotype.**

17.22

a. In a pure-breeding line of sinistral snails, all of the snails are s^-/s^-; in a pure-breeding line of dextral snails, the genotype is s^+/s^+. In a cross of s^-/s^- hermaphrodites to s^+/s^+ males, the hermaphrodites provide the eggs. Because s is a maternal-effect gene, **all of the progeny have the s^- (sinistral) phenotype.**

b. In a cross of s^+/s^+ hermaphrodites and s^-/s^- males, the s^+/s^+ hermaphrodites provide the eggs. Because s is a maternal-effect gene, **all of the progeny will have the s^+ (dextral) phenotype.**

c. **The F_1 from part *a* and part *b* are both s^+/s^- regardless of the maternal phenotype they display. If the F_1 hermaphrodites self-fertilize, all of the F_2 progeny will be dextral** regardless of their own genotypes. The reason is that the gene product encoded by the dominant maternal s^+ allele in the F_1's genome will be present in all of the eggs that give rise to the F_2 generation.

d. The F_2s from both part *a* and part *b* are $1/4\ s^+/s^+ : 1/2\ s^+/s^- : 1/4\ s^-/s^-$. **The selfed s^+/s^+ and s^+/s^- F_2s will produce all dextral progeny** (the maternal s^+ allele will provide wild-type gene product to the eggs), **while the selfed s^-/s^- F_2s will produce all sinistral progeny** (no s^+ allele is present in the maternal genome, so no wild-type gene product is deposited into the eggs).

17.23

a. **The F_3 females were homozygous for random loss-of-function mutations, while the screen required researchers to examine the F_4 progeny for segmentation defects. If the product of a particular mutant gene played an essential role outside of the germ line, the homozygous F_3 females would be dead rather than sterile so no F_4 progeny would be produced.**

b. **Examine the F_3 males homozygous for the mutation in question and determine if they have a mutant phenotype;** if they do, the maternal-effect mutation also plays a role in males. In addition to visual inspection of these F_3 males, other phenotypes you would want to analyze include their longevity and their fertility.

c. **The balancer chromosome enabled both the maintenance and identification of homozygous mutants.** The balancer prevented recovery of recombined second chromosomes in the F_3, thereby keeping the *Cy* marker and the m^- mutation on separate chromosomes. This fact means that $m^-/$ m^- homozygotes could be identified as non-curly-winged F_3 flies, and the m^- chromosome could be propagated in $m^-/$ *Balancer* flies. (The mutant could not be maintained as a homozygous stock because females homozygous for a maternal-effect mutation are sterile.)

17-24.

a. The observations taken together indicate that if an embryo is not maternally supplied with *hunchback* (*hb*) mRNA, Nanos protein (which is also maternally supplied) is not needed. The implication is that **the only function of Nanos is to inhibit the function of maternally-supplied *hunchback* mRNA.** As described in the answer to Problem 27c, Nanos protein prevents the translation of maternal *hb* mRNA. Note that the maternal *hb* mRNA is not required for proper development, but if this mRNA is present, it is critical that Nanos protein suppresses its function. (Maternal Nanos is gone before it could repress zygotic *hb* translation.)

b. It may seem puzzling to you that the fly has a gene, *nanos*, whose sole function is to inhibit the maternal function of another gene, *hunchback*. Why doesn't the fly just not make maternal *hunchback* in the first place, and then it wouldn't need the *nanos* gene at all? **Developmental biologists have discovered many double-negative mechanisms like this one because the process of evolution is messy and results in inefficiencies.**

How could this particular situation with *hunchback* and *nanos* have come about? We do not know the answer, but one possibility is that in ancient ancestors of *Drosophila*, maternal stores of *hunchback* may have been required for proper development. Alternatively, perhaps Nanos was present in the egg because it had a different target gene, and its presence allowed the regulatory region of *hunchback* to express the gene maternally (with no harm done) as well as zygotically. Hypotheses like these can be investigated by analyzing the expression of *hunchback* and *nanos* in fly species that are related to *Drosophila*.

17-25. Human females homozygous for mutations in maternal-effect genes would be sterile – their eggs would lack an RNA or protein required for early development. Of course, females can be sterile for reasons other than mutations in maternal-effect genes; for example, hormonal issues might prevent the woman from producing mature eggs. Likely, many additional investigations would be required to determine the cause of the sterility.

17-26.

a. **If gene X is located on the X chromosome, females *trans*-heterozygous for a gene X^- mutation and an ovo^D mutation, both on chromosomes with FRTs near the centromere, could be used to generate FLP-induced gene X^- homozygous clones in the germ line, as shown in the following figure.** [The flies must also carry a transgene that can express FLP in the female germ line (*not shown*).] **Because ovo^D/ovo^+ germline cells do not make eggs, any eggs these females produce must result from mitotic recombination and therefore must have come from gene X^- ovo^+ / gene X^- ovo^+ germline cells** (shaded in *blue* in the following figure). Note that **it is critical for both gene X and the ovo gene to be distal to the FRT site**, and it is desirable that ovo be proximal to gene X.

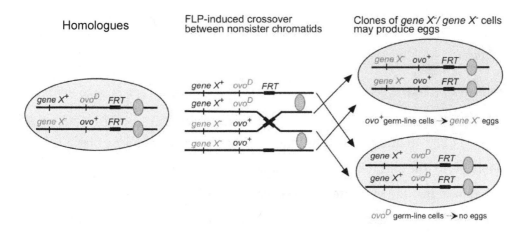

(i) To determine if gene X RNA and/or protein are normally supplied to eggs, **eggs from homozygous gene X^- germline cells may be useful as negative controls in experiments to monitor RNA (by RNA *in situ* hybridization or RNA-seq) or protein (antibody staining).** The gene X^- allele would be most useful for this purpose if it were a true null that produced no RNA and no protein.

(ii) If maternally supplied gene X products are not required for proper embryogenesis, then the fertilized eggs from homozygous gene X^- germline cells, if fertilized with wild-type (gene

X^+) sperm, should develop normally. **If maternal supplies of gene X products are required for embryogenesis (that is, if gene X is a maternal-effect gene), the gene X^- fertilized eggs will not develop properly, even if fertilized by gene X^+ sperm.**

b. The ovo^D mutant gene has been cloned, and this allele is dominant to the wild-type allele. Thus, **using P element-mediated transformation, you could generate flies containing an ovo^D transgene inserted into random locations in the genome. If the genome already contained an FRT site very close to the centromere of an autosome, some of these transformant flies would have the ovo^D transgene on the same chromosome as an FRT site. You could then mate the transformants with a stock containing a putative maternal-effect gene and another copy of FRT on a homologous autosome.** You would thus be able to conduct the same experiment shown in the answer to part a for genes of interest on any chromosome.

c. As described in part a, if gene X is a maternal-effect gene, gene X^- eggs will be produced by homozygous gene X^- / gene X^- germline cells; but even if they are fertilized by gene X^+ sperm, they will not undergo embryogenesis normally. **If gene X is needed for oogenesis, even the gene X^- / gene X^- germline cell clones that have lost the ovo^D mutation (see diagram in part a) will not produce eggs.** If a gene is required for oogenesis and is also a maternal-effect gene, the maternal-effect function would be obscured.

17-27.

a. The *hunchback* gene is transcribed in the female germ line (as can be seen in <u>Figure 17.22</u>), but it is also transcribed in the early embryo and in fact was first identified as a zygotic gap gene (<u>Figure 17.23</u>). **In addition to a promoter, either a single enhancer that is active in both the female germ line and the early embryo must be present, or alternatively, the *hunchback* gene should include separate female germ line and early embryo enhancers.**

b. Recall that *hunchback* is both a maternal-effect gene and a gap gene. The *hunchback* open reading frame encodes a transcription factor that is recognizable by its **Zinc finger DNA-binding domain.**

c. **The 3' UTR of *hunchback* mRNA has binding sites for Nanos protein;** Nanos prevents translation of maternally-supplied *hunchback* mRNA in the posterior half of the embryo. This mechanism helps establish the anterior (high)-to-posterior (low) gradient of Hunchback protein seen in early embryos, even though the *hunchback* mRNA is distributed uniformly in the egg (<u>Figure 17.22</u>).

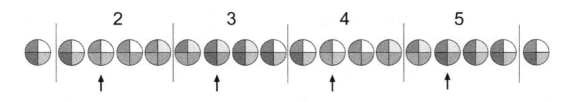

In the preceding diagram, each pair-rule protein is expressed in a stripe that is four-cells wide, and each pair-rule protein stripe is one cell out-of-register with the next pair-rule protein stripe. The result is a combinatorial code; each cell in a 2-division wide (8-cell wide) stripe expresses a unique combination of pair-rule proteins. If a single *engrailed* enhancer, for example, is activated by either of the two combinations of proteins indicated by the arrows in the diagram above, then *engrailed* would be transcribed in fourteen stripes – a pattern with a periodicity of every segment. Alternatively, the fourteen-stripe *engrailed* expression pattern could be achieved by two different enhancers; one enhancer with binding sites for a particular combination of pair-rule proteins in the even-numbered segments (*blue, orange, grey,* and *white* in the preceding diagram) and the other enhancer binding a specific combination of pair-rule proteins present in some cells within the odd-numbered segments (*pink, orange, green,* and *yellow* in the preceding diagram).

17-29.

a The absence of *knirps* function has no effect on Hunchback protein distribution, but it does affect Krüppel protein localization. More specifically, these results show that **Knirps is needed to restrict the posterior limit of the zone of Krüppel expression.** Since these gap gene proteins are all transcription factors, the implication is that Knirps represses Krüppel transcription, at least in this part of the embryo.

b. **In the absence of Nanos, Hunchback protein would be seen throughout the early embryo** because there is no Nanos protein to inhibit the translation of maternally-supplied *hunchback* mRNA. Later in embryogenesis, starting just before cellularization, this pattern would begin to change because the *hunchback* gene would begin to be transcribed from zygotic nuclei. Zygotic transcription of *hunchback* occurs only in the anterior region of the embryo where the Bicoid morphogen concentration is highest. Thus, an anterior (high)-to-posterior (low) gradient of Hunchback protein would slowly begin to form as zygotically-supplied protein replaces the protein translated from maternal *hunchback* mRNA in the absence of Nanos.

17-30. The easiest way to think about how the BX-C controls the identities of segments T3-A8 is that the cells in each segment have a "codeword" – a particular combination of BX-C gene expression. The diagram that follows illustrates this concept:

Wild type

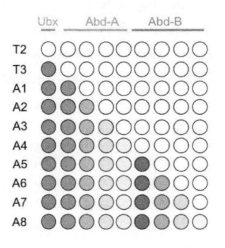

In the preceding diagram, the codeword for T3 is *Ubx* expression but a lack of expression of *abd-A* or *Abd-B*; the codeword for A1 is the T3 codeword plus a particular level of *abd-A* expression; the codeword for A2 is the A1 codeword plus additional *abd-A* expression; etc. The most important element of each codeword is the final element, which makes each segment different from the one anterior to it.

Using this model, it's easy to see (as shown in the following diagram) that in the complete absence of *Ubx*, T3 is transformed into T2; the cells that would normally form T3 now have the T2 codeword – no expression of any of the BX-C proteins:

Ubx⁻

You should note that *bx* mutations disrupt an enhancer that directs the transcription of *Ubx* in the anterior part of T3, while *pbx* mutations disrupt an enhancer needed for *Ubx* transcription in the posterior part of T3. These facts explain the transformations associated with *bx* and *pbx* mutations shown in Figure 17.27. This idea also clarifies why a double *bx pbx* mutant fly has 4 wings. Because *Ubx* is not expressed in the segment that should normally become T3, this segment develops as T2 and makes wings, not halteres.

a. In embryos lacking all *Abd-B* gene function, there would be an anterior-directed transformation of the segments in which *Abd-B* is expressed. The result would be that **the segments A5-A8 would all be transformed to look like A4**, which is the next most anterior segment in which *Abd-B* is <u>not</u> expressed. According to the model, in the absence of Abd-B, A5-A8 would all have the A4 codeword:

$$Abd\text{-}B^{\,-}$$

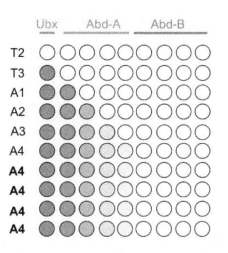

b. Segments A5-A8 are morphologically distinguishable from each other, even through they each express all three BX-C genes. Each has a different codeword because in a wild-type animal, **the level of *Abd-B* expression is different in each segment A5-A8.**

c. Without any expression of any of the three genes in the BX-C, every segment from T2-A8 would have the codeword for T2; **all of the segments that normally express BX-C genes would be transformed to T2:**

BX-C⁻

d. In wild-type flies, the wing is in segment T2 while the haltere is in segment T3 (Figure 17.28), so *Contrabithorax* mutations result in a transformation from an anterior structure to a more posterior structure. Since posterior-to-anterior transformations (T3 to T2) are associated with loss-of-function mutations of the *Ubx* gene, **it is likely that *Contrabithorax* mutations are gain-of-function mutations in which the *Ubx* gene is expressed ectopically in T2.** (Remember that *Ubx* is ordinarily expressed in T3 but not in T2.) **Most gain-of-function mutations are dominant.** The majority of *Contrabithorax* mutations are chromosomal rearrangements that place the *Ubx* gene near an enhancer element that turns on gene expression in T2. This situation is similar to that of gain-of-function mutations in *Antennapedia* that place a leg on the head of the fly.

17-31.

a   In the A8 segment, all three of the BX-C genes are expressed to the maximum extent. Because the phenotype of loss-of-function mutations of the PcG genes is a transformation of T2-A7 into A8, PcG gene function likely normally blocks expression of *Hox* genes (such as those in the BX-C) in segments T2-A7. **The PcG genes encode repressors and corepressors.** The repressors bind specific DNA sequences within the silencers and recruit complexes of corepressors such as histone methyltransferases and histone deacetylases that close chromatin.

b. **When any one of PcG proteins is absent, the silencers cannot function and the BX-C genes are derepressed. Thus, in animals with loss-of-function mutations in PcG genes, segments T2-A8 all have the particular combination of BX-C gene expression normally present in the A8 segment:**

PcG[−]

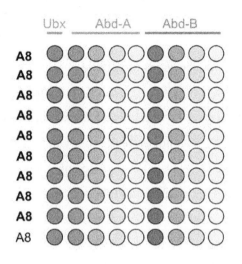

Chapter 18   Prokaryotic and Organelle Genetics

Synopsis:

This chapter describes characteristics of genetic analysis in bacteria, with a focus on gene transfer in *E. coli*. Two key features have made *E. coli* a powerful model organism for understanding basic cell processes. First, the ability to grow massive numbers of bacteria on defined media allows easy and quick isolation of mutants. Second, there are many naturally occurring ways to transfer DNA from one cell to another. The DNA transfer mechanisms - transformation, conjugation, and transduction (generalized and specialized) and the ways in which geneticists use these are described. In addition to their value for research, DNA transfer mechanisms are important for survival and evolution of bacterial species.

This chapter goes on to discuss mitochondria and chloroplasts. Mitochondria and chloroplasts are eukaryotic organelles that contain their own genomes. The genomes of both share similarities with prokaryotic genomes in the types of genes, the organization of the genes as well as chromosome structure. The presence of several organelles per cell in most organisms leads to many different combinations of organelle types in the same cell. Heteroplasmy refers to the presence of more than one type of genome per cell; homoplasmy is the state in which there is uniformity of the genome copies. Mitotic segregation produces an uneven distribution of organelle genes in heteroplasmic cells. Inheritance of organelle genomes is not dependent on the same cell machinery as nuclear chromosomes use for mitosis and meiosis, so the inheritance of these organelles is non-Mendelian. In most organisms, organelles are inherited from one generation to the next from the mother. This leads to distinct patterns of inheritance as seen in pedigrees.

Mitochondria and chloroplast functions require cooperation between the organelle and nuclear genomes.

Key Words:

insertion sequences (ISs) small *transposable elements* that dot the chromosomes of many types of bacteria; they are *transposons* that do not contain selectable markers.

plasmids minute circles of double-stranded DNA that can gain admission to and replicate in the cytoplasm of many kinds of bacterial cells, independently of the *bacterial chromosome*.

genetic screen an examination of each colony in a *population* for its *phenotype*.

horizontal gene transfer the introduction and incorporation of DNA from an unrelated individual or from a different species.

transformation one of the mechanisms by which bacteria transfer genes from one strain to another; occurs when DNA from a *donor* is added to the bacterial growth medium and is then taken up from the medium by the recipient. The recipient cell is known as a *transformant*. Contrast with *conjugation*.

conjugation one of the mechanisms by which bacteria transfer genes from one strain to another; in this case, the *donor* carries a special type of *plasmid* that allows it to transfer DNA directly when it comes in contact with the recipient. The recipient is known as an exconjugant. Contrast with *transformation.*

transduction one of the mechanisms by which bacteria transfer genes from one strain to another; *donor* DNA is packaged within the protein coat of a *bacteriophage* and transferred to the recipient when the phage particle infects it. Recipient cells are known as *transductants.*

conjugation one of the mechanisms by which bacteria transfer genes from one strain to another; in this case, the *donor* carries a special type of *plasmid* that allows it to transfer DNA directly when it comes in contact with the recipient. The recipient is known as an exconjugant. Contrast with *transformation.*

F plasmid a *conjugative plasmid* that carries many genes required for the transfer of DNA. Cells carrying the F plasmid are called F^+ cells. Cells without the plasmid are called F^- cells.

episomes *plasmids*, like the *F plasmid*, that can integrate into the host genome.

genomic islands large segments of *DNA* (10–200 kb in size), showing properties that suggest that they originated from the transfer of foreign DNA into a bacterial cell.

gene targeting method for inserting DNA into a genome that relies on homologous recombination; the DNA is "targeted" for insertion into a specific place in the genome by sequence similarity.

mitochondria organelles that convert energy derived from nutrient molecules into ATP; mitochondria have their own genomes.

RNA editing specific alteration of the genetic sequence carried within an *RNA* molecule after *transcription* is completed.

chloroplasts plant organelles that capture solar energy and store it in the chemical bonds of carbohydrates through the process of photosynthesis.

endosymbiont theory proposes that chloroplasts and mitochondria originated when free-living bacteria were engulfed by primitive nucleated cells. Host and guest formed cellular communities in which each member adapted to the group arrangement and derived benefit from it.

heteroplasmic genomic makeup of a cell's organelles characterized by a mixture of organellar genomes. Contrast with homoplasmic.

homoplasmic genomic makeup of a cell's organelles characterized by a single type of organellar DNA. Contrast with heteroplasmic.

threshold effect a phenomenon in which a certain fraction of wild-type organellar DNAs is sufficient for the normal phenotype.

mitochondrial gene therapy nuclear transfer from an oocyte with mutant mitochondria to an enucleated oocyte with normal mitochondria.

Significant Elements - Gene Transfer in Bacteria:

After reading the first part of the chapter and thinking about the concepts, you should be able to:

- Distinguish between selection (only one specific genotype can grow) and screening (more than one genotype can grow, but additional analysis is needed to establish the genotype of each cell).

- Describe how Hfr cells are formed and how they are used for mapping genes and complementation analysis.

- Understand the differences in DNA transfer between matings with F^+ cells and Hfr cells.

- Set up Hfr crosses to map genes (describe the genotypes of donor and recipient and the selective media used.

- Analyze time of entry data to map genes and origins of transfer for different Hfr strains.

- Map genes using cotransduction or cotransformation frequencies.

- Describe the differences between transformation, transduction, and conjugation.

- Describe the similarities between transformation and generalized transduction.

- Map genes using specialized transduction.

Significant Elements - Genetics of Chloroplasts and Mitochondria:

After reading the chapter and thinking about the concepts, you should be able to:

- Differentiate between heteroplasmy and homoplasmy experimentally.

- Recognize organelle inheritance in human pedigrees.

- Suggest explanations for unusual phenomenon involving organelle genomes that may arise from heteroplasmy and different proportions of affected cells.

- Describe the endosymbiont theory and discuss the supporting evidence.

- Recognize a 4:0 segregation of a phenotype in the gametes as showing that the trait is controlled by a mitochondrial or chloroplast gene. Remember that nuclear genes always segregate 2:2.

Problem Solving Tips - Gene Transfer in Bacteria:

- The F plasmid can integrate at different locations around the *E. coli* chromosome to generate Hfr strains that have different origins of transfer. These locations for integration are determined by the presence of IS elements scattered around the genome. The same IS elements are found on the F plasmid.

- Genes closest to the origin of transfer are more likely to be transferred into a recipient than those further from the origin.

- The time at which genes are transferred into a recipient in an Hfr cross is a reflection of the distance from the origin of transfer.

- Hfr crosses are usually used to get a low resolution map; P1 transductions (generalized transduction) are useful for finer genetic mapping.

- Bacteriophage lambda (λ) can integrate into the chromosome (lysogeny) to generate a lysogen.

- Bacteriophage lambda can excise imprecisely from the bacterial chromosome, picking up adjacent bacterial genes.

Problem solving tips - Genetics of Chloroplasts and Mitochondria:

♦ Remember that mitochondria are are passed on maternally and thus show non-Mendelian inheritance Remember that there can be several organelles in a cell and several copies of the genome in each organelle.

Solutions to Problems:

Vocabulary

18-1.

a. 8; b. 5; c. 9; d.7; e. 6; f. 3; g. 1; h. 4; i. 2

a. transformation	8. transfer of naked DNA
b. conjugation	5. transfer of DNA requiring direct physical contact
c. transduction	9. transfer of DNA between bacteria via virus particles
d. lytic cycle	7. infection by phages in which lysis of cells releases new virus particles
e. lysogeny	6. integration of phage DNA into the chromosome
f. episome	3. small circular DNA molecule that can integrate into the chromosome
g. auxotroph	1. requires supplements in medium for growth
h. pangenome	4. the core genes that define a bacterial species plus all of the genes unique to individual strains
i. gene targeting	2. a method for mutagenizing genes in bacterial genomes

Section 18.1

18-2.

It is not easy to discriminate unicellular organisms as eukaryotes, bacteria, or archaea. As the problem states, neither cell shape nor cell size is diagnostic. Eukaryotes have nuclei and mitochondria enclosed in their own membranes, while bacteria and archaea (being prokaryotes) do not. However, because many unicellular organisms have cell walls it is not always possible to look through the cell walls to visualize the presence or absence of nuclei, and mitochondria are often hard to see. Views of these structures in the electron microscope could discriminate eukaryotes from the other two groups, but not bacteria from archaea. The nature of the genome is not completely predictive. Most bacteria have a single circular chromosome while eukaryotes have multiple linear chromosomes, but some bacteria have linear chromosomes or multiple circular chromosomes. All known archaea have circular chromosomes, but there is no particular reason a currently uncharacterized species of archaea might have a linear chromosome. There are many other interesting comparisons that could be made between these three groups: for example, eukaryotes and archaea have translational systems with methionine as the initiating amino acid, not formylmethionine as in bacteria; eukaryotes and bacteria have lipids of a particular type while those in archaea are of another type; all three groups have genes interrupted by introns although these are far more common in eukaryotes than the other two groups. The most reliable measure for characterizing unicellular organisms is actually DNA sequence comparisons with known members of each group. Historically bacteria and archaea were in fact grouped together until DNA sequence comparisons made it clear that they comprised two groupings that were separated a very long time ago in evolution.

Section 18.2

18-3.

a. In order to determine the number of nucleotides necessary to identify a gene, you must calculate how many bases represent a unique sequence in a DNA molecule of the size of the *E. coli* genome (4.6 Mb or 4,600,000 bases), assuming that the sequence is random. There are 4 bases possible at each position in a sequence, so $4n$ represents the number of combinations found in a sequence n bases long. For example, $4^2 = 16$ is the number of unique sequence combinations that could be made with 2 positions. Therefore, if you were looking for a unique 2-nucleotide sequence, you might expect to find it, on average, every 16 nucleotides. A sequence of 11 nucleotides would appear 1 in 4^{11} or once in every 4 Mb; a sequence of 12 nucleotides would appear uniquely 1 in 4^{12} or one in 16.8 Mb. Therefore you need a sequence of about 12 nucleotides in order to define a unique position in the *E. coli* genome. This problem can also be solved using the equation $4n = 5 \times 10^6$ (= 5 Mb). To solve for n, rearrange the equation: $n\log4 = \log5 \times 10^6$; $n = 11.1$. Thus you need at least 12 nucleotides to find a unique nucleotide sequence in a random sequence of 5 Mb.

b. This part of the problem assumes that you have determined a sequence of contiguous amino acids within a protein. The 12 nucleotides shown in part (a) define a unique position in the genome that would encode 4 amino acids. However, because of the genetic code's degeneracy, you actually know the identity of only about 8 of these nucleotides. (For amino acids specified by 6 codons, you would potentially know one less nucleotide per codon; for tryptophan and methionine, which are specified by only a single codon, you would know all three nucleotides in the codon.) If you had a sequence of 6 amino acids, you would probably know at least 12 unique nucleotides. Because many genes evolved through a pattern of duplication followed by divergence, some protein domains of 6 amino acids might appear in more than one protein. As a result, knowing a few more than 6 amino acids would make the case that you have identified the correct gene even stronger.

c. The gene you found might be strain-specific; that is, the gene is a part of the *E. coli* pangenome, but it is not part of the core genome.

18-4.

a. Because replication from a single origin is bidirectional (there are two replication forks), the rate of synthesis is 2000 nt/sec. As the *E.coli* genome size is about 4.6 Mb, the minimum time to replicate the *E. coli* chromosome is 4,600,000 nt / 2000 nt/sec = 2300 sec; 2300 sec / 60 sec/min = 38.33 minutes.

b. Under optimal conditions, the origin of replication can "fire" before the previous round of replication and cell division are complete. This fact means that *E. coli* cells growing under these conditions can have multiple copies of regions around the origin of replication, as shown in the following figure. You can think of this phenomenon as the existence of replication bubbles within replication bubbles. Immediately after cell division, the daughter cells that are "born" have genomes that are already partially replicated, so they can finish replicating such genomes in less than ~38 minutes required to copy the whole chromosome. The figure that follows compares the replication of the *E. coli* chromosome under slow growth (left) and rapid growth (right) conditions. *oriC* denotes the origin of replication of the chromosome, from which the replication bubble extends in both directions by extension of the two replication forks. *terC* signifies the position of replication termination (that is, where the replication forks going in opposite directions from *oriC* would eventually meet with each other). *Gene A* is located close to *oriC*, while *gene B* is located near *terC*. You can see that the origin of the parental chromosome fired once and part of this molecule has been replicated; then, before the forks met each other at *terC*, the origins of the two partial daughter molecules then fired again. One interesting result of the rapid firing of origins in high growth conditions is that the dosage, and thus the expression level, of genes near *oriC* (like *gene A*) is higher than those of genes (like *gene B*) near *terC*.

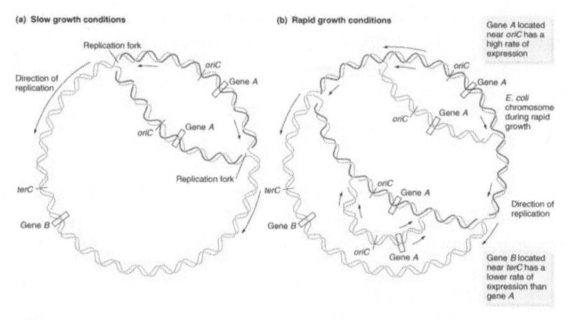

(a) Slow growth conditions

(b) Rapid growth conditions

Gene A located near oriC has a high rate of expression

Replication fork

oriC

Gene A

Direction of replication

oriC

Gene A

E. coli chromosome during rapid growth

oriC

Gene A

Replication fork

oriC

Gene A

terC

terC

Direction of replication

Gene B

Gene B

oriC

Gene A

Gene B located near terC has a lower rate of expression than gene A

18-5.

Genome features unique to eukaryotes include: multiple chromosomes, linear chromosomes, centromeres and telomeres, introns and exons, large intergenic regions, enhancers, methylation of Cs; chromatin (packaging into nucleosomes).

18-6.

Genes can move between plasmids and the bacterial chromosome and *vice versa* by transposition; a gene flanked by IS elements can become a composite transposon.

18-7.

Bacteria that grow in high saline environments likely make proteins that don't aggregate under high salt conditions. A metagenomics analysis of bacteria in salt lakes could identify genes that potentially encode such proteins. To test the function of the candidate proteins you find, you could proceed in any of three ways: (i) You would knockout individual genes encoding the candidate proteins using the *gene targeting* methods described in Fig. 18.31. If the gene product was involved in helping proteins retain their solubility in high salt, then the mutant bacteria would no longer be able to grow in a high salt environment. (ii) You could construct recombinant DNA plasmids that place genes encoding candidate proteins into a plasmid vector, and use these to transform bacteria that could not normally grow in high salt. You would then select for transformants that could grow in high salt. This approach would not work if more than one such protein were needed to allow this growth. (iii) You could construct recombinant DNA plasmids that encode fusion proteins in which a protein tag is added to the sequences coding for a candidate protein. You could then purify the fusion proteins from *E. coli*, and add them to solutions containing protein aggregates formed in high salt. It is possible that the fusion protein might reverse the aggregation.

Section 18.3

18-8.

a. To find the original linezolid-resistant strains, you would take a wild-type (linezolid-sensitive) isolate of pneumococcus and place it on petri plates containing linezolid. This is a direct selection for the desired linezolid-resistant bacteria. You will find very rare resistant colonies amidst a very large number of originally sensitive bacteria without using replica plating or treatment with mutagens. Finding linezolid-sensitive derivatives of the linezolid-resistant mutants is much harder. You must somehow screen to find the rare desired bacteria, because they will not grow in the presence of the antibiotic as the resistant bacteria do. You would likely use replica plating to identify the desired bacterial colonies that grow in the absence of the drug and not in its presence. You would probably use mutagenesis with chemical mutagens to increase the frequency of desired mutations.

b. In general, mechanisms that affect the bacterial toxicity of an antibiotic include the import of the antibiotic into the cell or its removal from the cell; chemical modifications of the antibiotic and thus its activation or detoxification; and the interactions of the antibiotic with its cellular targets. In terms of linezolid-resistant mutants, you could imagine either loss-of function or gain-of-function mutations that would affect antibiotic import. For example, a loss-of-function mutation in a gene encoding a receptor or pump that imports the antibiotic into the cell would prevent the antibiotic from entering the cell. Less likely, a gain-of-function mutation that would increase the efficiency of a system that exports the antibiotic out of the cell would lower the intracellular concentration of linezolid, making mutant cells more resistant to the drug. Similarly, gain-of-function mutations in genes encoding proteins that participate in a system that normally detoxifies the antibiotic would increase the cell's resistance. Loss-of-function mutations in genes whose protein products could modify linezolid in ways that increase its toxicity are also possible ways to increase linezolid resistance. Finally, it is possible that a mutation might disrupt an RNA or protein component of the 50S ribosomal subunit so that it could no longer be bound by linezolid. Such mutations could not be loss-of-function mutations in terms of the function of the component in translation, because the cell would die if it could not synthesize proteins. These are only some of the possibilities. The linezolid-sensitive derivatives could be due to a reversion of the original mutation. Alternatively, they could be caused by the opposite of any of the types of mutations described above. For example, a gain-of-function mutation in a gene encoding a protein that helps import the antibiotic into the cell would raise the intracellular concentration of linezolid and make the cells more sensitive to the drug's action at lower extracellular concentrations of linezolid.

18-9.

The initial tube of bacteria has 2×10^8 cells/ml. The first step of the dilution series is a 10^{-2} dilution (0.1 ml of the initial tube into 9.9 ml of diluent = 0.1 ml/10.0 ml = 1/100). The second step of the dilution is again 10^{-2}, so at this point the total dilution is 10^{-4}. The third step is a 10^{-1} dilution (1 ml/10.0 ml = 1/10) for a total dilution of 10^{-5}. You then put 0.1 ml (10^{-1} ml) of this dilution on the petri plate. Therefore, you are putting $10^{-5} \times 10^{-1}$ ml $\times$ (2×10^8 cells/ml) = 2×10^2 cells on the first petri plate, which should grow into 200 colonies. The fourth step of the series is another 10^{-1} dilution, for a total dilution of 10^{-6}. You again plate 0.1 ml of this dilution, so you expect $10^{-6} \times 10^{-1}$ ml $\times$ (2×10^8 cells/ml) = 2×10^1 cells = 20 colonies on this second plate.

18-10.

In this problem, "minimal media" contain no carbon sources, so growth of bacteria on minimal medium requires supplementation with the indicated sugars. In rich medium (e.g. rich medium + X-gal), it is easiest to assume that the sugar is glucose. Note that Xgal is a substrate for the ß-galactosidase enzyme, but it cannot serve as a carbon source.
a. (iv) Lac+ cells are able to use lactose as the sole carbon source for growth, while Lac- cells would not be able to grow if the only sugar in the media were lactose. Medium iv is thus selective, because Lac+ cells can grow on it but Lac- cells cannot. Note that this selective medium requires supplementation with the amino acid methionine because the original bacterial strain is Lac- Met-.
b. (iii) A screen is different from a selection. For a genetic screen, you need to be able to examine the phenotype of each individual cell or colony. To screen for Lac+ cells, you therefore need a medium on which both Lac+ and Lac- cells can grow but on which they have different visible phenotypes. In a selection, only certain genotype(s) of cells can grow (min + lac selects for Lac+ cells and against Lac cells). The rich medium (iii) has glucose, so it allows both Lac+ and Lac- cells to grow; medium iii is therefore not selective. However, the X-gal in these plates distinguishes between the two phenotypes (Lac+ cells are blue; Lac- cells are white).

c. (ii) To select for Met+ cells, the medium should lack methionine, demanding that the bacteria must be able to synthesize methionine in order to grow. Medium ii is the only choice that lacks methionine. This medium also contains glucose so Met+ cells would grow whether they are Lac+ or Lac-.

Section 18.4

18-11.

a. As expected, no strain A or strain B revertants were recovered in 10^8 cells. If the reversion rate is 1 in 10^7 cells, the chance that two independent reversions would occur in the same bacterial chromosome in strain A is $(1 \times 10^{-7})^2 = 1 \times 10^{-14}$. In strain B, the chance of three independent reversions is $(1 \times 10^{-7})^3 = 1 \times 10^{-21}$. In the experiment, the cultures were grown only long enough to generate 10^8 cells – not long enough statistically for reversion. (That is, to have a reasonable chance of obtaining just one revertant of either strain, you would have to grow a minimum of 10^{14} cells. Because wild-type colonies were recovered when strains A and B were grown together, and not when they were grown separately, the wild types must have come about through some mechanism other than reversion that involved gene transfer.

b. In 1953, about a year after Lederberg and Tatum demonstrated the existence of gene transfer between bacterial strains A and B, William Hayes demonstrated that this transfer was *asymmetrical*, meaning that one strain was the donor and the other was the recipient. He established which strain was which by including antibiotic sensitivity/resistance markers in strain A and strain B. For example, suppose strain A is resistant to the drug streptomycin, while strain B is sensitive to the same drug. Hayes then checked the Met+ Bio+ Thr+ Leu+ Thi+ exconjugants that he obtained to see if they were resistant to streptomycin. Almost none were. But if he now made strain A sensitive to streptomycin and strain B resistant, almost all of the exconjugants were streptomycin resistant. Taken together, these two results implied that strain A was the donor and strain B was the recipient. (Presumably, the gene for streptomycin resistance/sensitivity either was located very far from origin of transfer in the Hfr strain Hayes used, or it was present on a plasmid that was not transferred into the donor. Thus, for the trait of streptomycin resistance/sensitivity, the phenotype of the exconjugant reflected the genotype of the recipient.)

18-12.

a. In order to be sure that gene transfer is taking place, you would require other markers in addition to ampicillin resistance; only in this way could you discriminate among donor cells, recipient cells, and the cells that result from gene transfer. For example, suppose the donor cells were sensitive to the drug streptomycin as well as being resistant to ampicillin, and that the recipient cells were resistant to streptomycin as well as being sensitive to ampicillin. Cells that grew on plates containing both antibiotics must be the result of gene transfer, as long as the frequency of gene transfer is higher than the frequency of reversion.

b. Transduction is the transfer of bacterial genes mediated by phage. The DNA is protected from exposure to enzymes when it resides inside the protein head of the phage. Transformation is gene transfer using naked DNA, which is not enclosed in any protective structure. The DNA being transferred by transformation will therefore be susceptible to degradation by DNase. If the transfer of the *amp*[r] allele occurs after DNase treatment, transduction must be occurring.

c. This famous so-called "U-tube experiment," is diagrammed in part (b) of the figure that follows. [Part (a) essentially iterates Fig. 18.14] The membrane separates solutions containing strain A and strain B; the membrane allows small molecules like sugars to flow between the two halves of the "U", but cells or molecules larger than the size of the pores could not. The membrane would prevent conjugation, because the cells could not touch each other but the membrane would allow transformation and transduction to proceed. Thus, if no recombinant colonies were formed, conjugation would be ruled out, but transformation and transduction would be possible. To distinguish between these two latter possibilities, you could use a membrane in which the pores are smaller than the size of a bacteriophage but larger than a fragment of DNA.

(a) Demonstration of gene transfer

Strain A
met⁻ bio⁻ thr⁺
leu⁺ thi⁺

Mixture of A and B

Strain B
met⁺ bio⁺ thr⁻
leu⁻ thi⁻

For each sample, wash and plate ~10^8 cells onto minimal medium.

No growth

met⁺ bio⁺ thr⁺
leu⁺ thi⁺ cells
grow into colonies

No growth

(b) Conjugation requires cell-to-cell contact

Cotton plug — Medium moved through filter using pressure or suction.

Strain A   Strain B

Filter

After incubation, cells plated onto minimal medium.

No growth   No growth

18-13.

Do a mating between the mutant cell with 3-4 copies of F and a wild-type F recipient. If the mutation responsible for the increased copy number is in the F plasmid, you expect the exconjugant (the recipient strain into which the plasmid is transferred so that it now becomes F+) to have the higher copy number. If the mutation is in a chromosomal gene, the higher copy number phenotype would not be transferred into the recipient. There is however a potential complication with this experiment. When you do an F+ × F- mating, some of the F+ donor cells will have converted to Hfr cells that can transfer bacterial DNA (possibly including a gene that influences the copy number of the F plasmid). An alternative experiment using transformation could avoid this complication. You could isolate the F plasmid DNA from the mutant cell, and then transform this plasmid into new recipient cells. By examining the number of copies of the F factor in the transformed cells, you could tell whether the trait was carried by the plasmid.

18-14.

The donor DNA is fragmented into small pieces of about 20 kb during transformation. Furthermore, in the transformant, the donor DNA replaces only a small percentage of the recipient's chromosome. Thus only genes that are close together on the chromosome can be cotransformed. The entire *E. coli* chromosome is about 4.6 Mb long. If *purC* and *pyrB* are located half way around the chromosome from each other, they are roughly 2.3 Mb apart, making it impossible for them to be cotransformed.

18-15.

The *purE* and *pepN* genes will be cotransformed at a higher frequency if the *H. influenzae Rd* non-pathogenic strain was used as a host donor strain rather than the pathogenic *b* strain. There is a lower likelihood that the two genes will be on the same piece of DNA in the pathogenic strain because they are separated by 8 more genes-worth of DNA (~ 8 kb of DNA – if we assume 1Kb per gene) that is not present on the chromosome in the *H. influenzae Rd* non-pathogenic strain.

18-16.

Transfer the plasmid (by transformation) into a non-toxin producing recipient strain. If the gene is encoded on the plasmid, the transformed cells will produce the toxin. This approach requires that the plasmid carry all of the genes needed to produce the toxin that are not found in the recipient strain.

18-17.

a. The partner strain should be F-, Str^r, and mutant for all the markers to be transferred from the Hfr strain (Pyr-, Met-, Xyl-, Tyr-, Arg-, His-, Mal-). Note that to perform this conjugation experiment, you require one marker (Str^r in this case) that allows you to kill off the donor cells and only to examine exconjugants in which other genes are transferred into the recipient. It is always a good idea to know beforehand that the gene conferring streptomycin (Str) resistance/sensitivity is located further from the origin of transfer than any of the genes whose transfer you will be measuring. The reason is that you want to make sure you are looking only at exconjugants in which genes from the donor are transferred into the Str^r recipient.

b. Selecting for Pyr+ exconjugants selects for an early marker transferred from the donor into the recipient. The frequency with which genes beyond *pyrE* are transferred decreases with distance from this early marker; this phenomenon is called the *gradient of transfer*. The gradient of transfer is due to the fragility of conjugation bridge between the cells, and the fragility of the DNA being transferred as well. The further a gene is from *pyrE,* the more likely it is that the connection between the donor and recipient or the DNA will be broken before that gene can be transferred. The order of genes is: *pyrE xyl mal arg met tyr his*.

18-18.

As shown in the diagram that follows, transfer of Pyr+ and Arg+ requires at least 2 crossovers – one to the left of *pyrE* (closer to the F factor origin of transfer) and one to the right of *arg* (further from the F factor origin). [Note that in all of the following diagrams, the donor DNA (*orange*) is linear, and the recipient chromosome (*blue)* is a circle. The exconjugant chromosome with *blue* and *orange* regions is also a circle.]

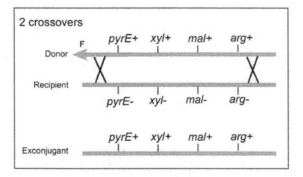

Additional crossovers within those two points, as long as they occur in even numbers, will also result in Pyr+ Arg+ exconjugants. For example, as shown in the following diagram, Pyr+ Arg+ Xyl- Mal- exconjugants can be generated by 4 crossovers.

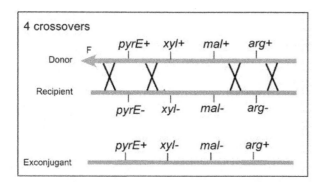

Two other kinds of exconjugants – Pyr+ Arg+ Xyl- Mal+ and Pyr+ Arg+ Xyl+ Mal-

can also be generated by 4 crossovers:

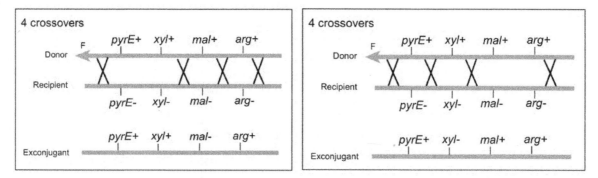

As 4 crossovers are much less likely to occur than 2 crossovers, by far most of the Pyr+ Arg+ exconjugants will also be Xyl+ Mal+.

18-19.

a. The exconjugants were all selected to be Arg+, so 1 crossover occurred to the right of *arg* (that is, further from the F factor origin of transfer). In the four most frequent exconjugant types (with 80, 40, 20 and 20 colonies), a second crossover occurred in different locations closer to the F factor, while the two infrequent exconjugant types (one colony each) required 3 additional crossovers closer to the F factor – for a total of 4 crossovers. These various crossover events are depicted in the diagrams that follow. [Note that in all of the following diagrams, the donor DNA (*orange*) is linear, and the recipient chromosome (*blue*) is a circle, as is the exconjugant chromosome.]

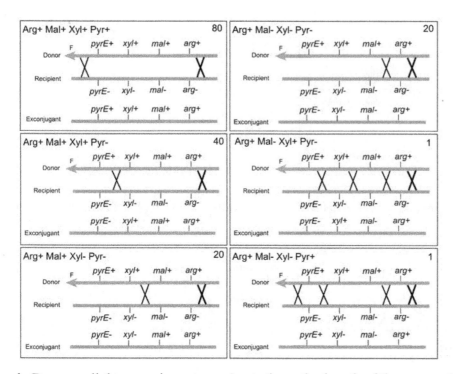

b. Because all the exconjugants are Arg+, the entire length of the orange donor DNA shown in the figures in part (a) – at least through the *arg* gene – had to be transferred into the recipient. The other crossover necessary for transfer of the *arg*+ allele is between the *arg* gene and the F factor origin (F in the diagrams above). This second crossover can occur at any random position along the length of the *orange* DNA to the right of the origin and to the left of the *arg* gene. The frequency with which the second (or third or fourth) crossover occurs between any of the two genes is proportional to the distance – the number of base pairs – between those two genes. Thus, the relative numbers of the crossovers that occur between any two genes indicate the relative distances between the genes. The number of exconjugants where a crossover occurred between *arg* and *mal* is (20 + 1 + 1) = 22; between *mal* and *xyl* is (20 + 1) = 21; between *xyl* and *pyrE* is (40 + 1 + 1) = 42. Therefore, expressed as a fraction of the largest of three distances, the relative distances between the genes are: 22/42 = 0.52 (*arg* ↔ *mal*); 21/42 = 0.50 (*mal* ↔ *xyl*); 42/42 = 1.0 (*xyl* ↔ *pyrE*). In other words, the *arg* ↔ *mal* and *mal* ↔ *xyl* distances are nearly the same, and each is about half the *xyl* ↔ *pyre* distance.

c. The relative distance between *pyrE* and the F factor origin can also be determined in the same manner. You can see from the diagram in part (a) that the number of exconjugants where a crossover occurred between *pyrE* and the F factor origin is (80 + 1) = 81. Normalized to the *xyl* ↔ *pyrE* distance, 81/42 = 1.9. Thus, the *pyrE* ↔ F distance is 1.9× the *xyl* ↔ *pyrE* distance.

Relative distances

18-20.

a. Arbitrarily place and orient the first Hfr insertion site (HfrA) on the bacterial chromosome and then order the genes that are transferred by that Hfr. When you place HfrB on the same map, notice that the first gene transferred by this Hfr is *lys*. HfrB could be placed on either side of this gene. However, the second gene transferred determines on which side of the first gene the F factor is inserted and the directionality of transfer. The time of transfer for four of the markers [*gly, phe, tyr, ura*] is indistinguishable, so we cannot put them in an order on the map, but this cluster of four genes can be placed relative to *lys* and *nic*. To introduce a convention used in several other problems in this chapter, the tip of the arrowhead in the following indicates the first DNA sequence transferred from the Hfr donor to the F- recipient. So for Hfr B, *lys* is the first marker transferred, followed by [*gly, phe, tyr, ura*], and then *nic* For the conjugation with HfrA, 60 minutes is insufficient time to transfer the *lys* gene from the donor to the recipient.

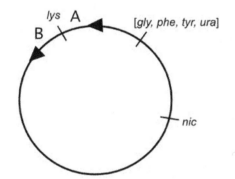

b. Note that *phe* was cotransduced with *ura* more frequently than with *tyr*, and that all of the Tyr+ transductants are also Ura+. These two facts both indicate that the order is *phe-ura-tyr*. None of the cotransduction classes is very rare, so none of these result from quadruple crossovers. The relationship of these three genes to other markers and the order of *gly* gene is still unknown, and this uncertainty is represented in the figure that follows by placing *gly* in parenthesis and the flanking marker *lys* and *nic* in brackets.

c. To map the *gly* gene with respect to other markers, select for Gly+ transductants on min + lys + phe + tyr + ura+ nic. Then score the other markers to determine which genes are cotransduced with *gly*+ at the highest frequency. The Gly+ transductants would be selected on min + lys + phe + tyr + ura, and then individual transductants would be tested for growth on media lacking one or more of the unselected amino acids.

18-21.

a. The order of the genes is *pab ilv met arg nic (trp pyr cys) his lys*. (See the following diagram.) This order is established only by looking at the time of entry after the start of mating; this parameter is directly related to the distance of a gene from the origin of transfer in the given Hfr strain. Note the *arrowheads* that indicate the location and orientation of the origin of transfer in the Hfr strains A-E. (See the answer to Problem 20 for an explanation of the directionality of the arrowheads.)

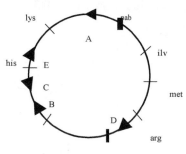

Where is nic, *(trp, pyr and cys)* The " |" near D and A is in bold. There is no legend for the symbol |. *Pab* is not clear. Can it moved a few spaces away from the circle?

b. After mating with HfrB long enough for transfer of *nic,* and then selecting for Trp+, most of the exconjugants (790/1,000) also recombined in the *pyr*+ *cys*+ alleles from the donor. This result reinforces the conclusion from the interrupted mating experiment in part (a) that the three genes (*trp, pyr,* and *cys*) are closely linked. The reason is that all Trp+ exconjugants must have had a crossover on either side of the *trp* gene, and the frequent transfer of *pyr*+ and *cys*+ along with *trp*+ indicates that most of these crossovers must have occurred outside the *pyr-trp-cys* region. The low crossover frequency within the *pyr-trp-cys* region means that most of the base pairs of DNA transferred into the recipient from the donor are to the left and right of this three-gene region. This situation is diagrammed in the figure that follows. Note that although we know sufficient time elapsed to allow transfer of the *nic*+ gene from the donor to the recipient, we did not score the phenotype associated with this gene. Thus, the crossover to the right in the figure could have been to the left or the right of the *nic* gene; it is shown arbitrarily to the left of *nic*.

Pyr+ Trp+ Cys+ exconjugants are the most frequent

In most conjugation experiments, the smallest class of recombinants reveals the gene in the middle. Usually, the smallest class of recombinants represents those produced by four crossovers instead of two. In these kinds of exconjugants, after the four crossovers have occurred, the two outside genes will have the genotype of the Hfr parent and the gene in the middle will have the genotype of the F- parent. However, this problem has an interesting twist because the smallest exconjugant class cannot be produced by four crossovers. In the data in the table, neither of the two exconjugant classes that have two genes from the Hfr recombined into the F-chromosome [(Trp+ Pyr+ Cys-) or (Trp+ Pyr-Cys+)] is the smallest class of exconjugants. Instead, the smallest class is represented by Trp+ Pyr-Cys-, in which only the *trp+* gene from the Hfr was transferred into the F- chromosome by recombination. This result indicates that the *trp* gene is the one in the middle. The exconjugant class produced by four crossovers was not recovered because it was Trp- and exconjugants were selected on the basis of them being Trp+. The following figure illustrates this point. The quadruple crossover class from this cross is Pyr+ Trp- Cys+, but such exconjugants could never be seen because the original selection was for Trp+. (In the following figure and all subsequent diagrams, the placement of *pyr* and *cys* with respect to *nic* was chosen randomly.)

Pyr+ Trp- Cys+ not recovered

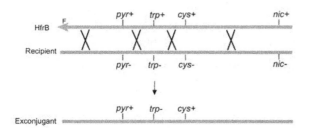

Instead, the smallest exconjugant class (Pyr- Trp+ Cys-) is the one where the two crossovers required to produce it are the least likely (lowest frequency) crossovers. Because *pyr, trp,* and *cys* are all closely linked, the lowest frequency crossovers will be those that occur between the two outside genes and the middle gene of the three [that is, between (*pyr* and *trp*) and (*trp* and *cys*)], resulting in transfer of the Hfr allele of the middle gene (*trp+*) into the F- strain:

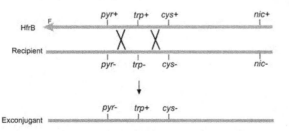

Crossovers between these closely linked gene pairs are less frequent than crossovers to the left of all three genes (between the F factor origin of transfer and the leftmost of the three genes) or crossovers to the right of all three genes (a position somewhere to the right of *cys.*) This must be the case because, as explained above, the data tell us that less DNA (a smaller number of base pairs) exists between the three tightly linked genes than exists in the regions to the left or the right. Exconjugants in which one rare crossover occurred within the *pyr-trp-cys* region, and one more frequent crossover outside that region occurred, represent the two more frequent classes:

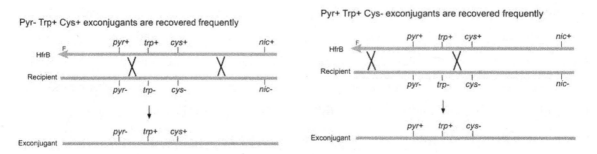

Therefore, the data indicate that the order is *pyr trp cys* (that is, *trp* is the gene in the middle). We do not know whether *pyr* or *cys* is closer to *nic*. Surprisingly, we cannot determine any relative gene distances from these data. The reason is that the three double crossover classes whose origins were just diagrammed all vary in the positions of both crossovers. Thus, the frequencies of each of the classes reflect crossovers in two intervals, and we cannot compare them. We can only determine relative distances when one of the intervals in two different classes is the same; see Problem 19.

18-22.

To obtain a stable exconjugant cell from an Hfr mating requires *recA*-mediated recombination of some of the donor genes into the chromosome in the F- recipient cell. Therefore, this assay would detect *recA*- mutants in the F- cell based on the inability to form stable exconjugants on the selective medium. Note that selective medium means here that only exconjugants that have obtained markers from the donor strain would grow, but neither donor cells nor the original recipient cells would be able to multiply under these conditions.

18-23.

Transfer into bacteria of virulence genes next to phage genes suggests that the transfer occurred through specialized transduction. This mechanism of horizontal gene transfer would begin with the infection of a pathogenic bacterial host cell with a *temperate bacteriophage*. The bacteriophage DNA becomes incorporated as a *prophage* into the bacterial chromosome, making the bacterial cell into a *lysogen*. Suppose that the site of prophage integration is next to a *pathogenic island* of virulence genes in the chromosome of the pathogenic host. When the prophage DNA is excised from the lysogen's chromosome, a mistake happens, creating a DNA molecule that has some genes from the bacteriophage as well as some genes from the host bacterium's pathogenic island. This DNA molecule can be incorporated into a new bacteriophage particle. When this bacteriophage infects a new non-pathogenic host, recombination between this DNA molecule and the genome of the new host would transfer both phage genes and pathogenic genes into the host. The host cell would then acquire pathogenic properties, and the phage genes and pathogenic genes would be adjacent to each other.

18.24.

Generalized transduction occurs during the lytic cycle, when a phage packages into its head a segment of the fragmented bacterial chromosome from lysed cells instead of its own (phage) genome, and then transfers that DNA fragment into another bacterium that it infects. Specialized transduction occurs when, upon induction, a lysogen excises from the bacterial chromosome aberrantly, such that a segment of adjacent bacterial DNA is attached to a partial phage genome, and is packaged into the phage particle. In generalized transduction, any fragment of the bacterial chromosome can be packaged in the phage head as long as it is the correct size. In specialized transduction, only DNA adjacent to the lysogen insertion site can be packaged into the phage particle.

Section 18.5

18-25.

In both parts of this question, you will be transforming bacterial cells with a plasmid library. Each clone that results will be a *merodiploid*, that is, a partial diploid cell that contains a full bacterial chromosome and a plasmid that has only one or a few genes.

a. A nonsense mutation is likely to cause a loss of gene function. Transform the mutant strain with a plasmid library made from a wild-type strain; colonies in which the mutant phenotype is rescued to wild-type should contain a plasmid with a wild-type copy of the gene in which the nonsense mutation had been found. Note that this strategy is based on the idea that in almost all cases, loss-of-function mutations on the chromosome will be recessive to the wildtype allele on the plasmid.

b. Generate a plasmid library of genomic DNA from the mutant strain, and use it to transform wild-type bacteria. Transformants with the mutant phenotype should contain a plasmid with the mutant gene. Here, the underlying assumption is that a gain-of-function allele on the plasmid is dominant to the wildtype allele on the bacterial chromosome.

18-26.

In this question, four methods are being explored to determine if the mutation lies in gene X or gene Y.

(1) The Trp- phenotype in the original mutant strain could be mapped to a position on the bacterial chromosome relative to other genes using any one of the various methods described, particularly conjugation or cotransformation/cotransduction with other markers at known locations. The mutation should map to either *gene X* or *gene Y*.

(2) The two plasmids could each be used to generate a loss-of-function mutations in *gene X* or *gene Y* by gene targeting. Whichever new loss-of-function mutant has a Trp- mutant phenotype is the gene corresponding to the original mutant.

(3) Complementation tests in merodiploids with single copy plasmids (for example, the F factor) containing either *gene X* or *gene Y* could determine which gene corresponds to the Trp- mutant phenotype. (The idea here is that the reason the "wrong" plasmid corrected the Trp- phenotype is that the plasmid was present in many copies in each bacterium; you assume that this effect would not be seen if the "wrong" gene was present on a plasmid found in only a single copy per bacterial cell.)

(4) Both *gene X* and *gene Y* could be amplified by PCR from the Trp- mutant, and the sequences of the genes determined. By comparison to the gene sequences in a wild-type *E. coli* strain, mutations in one or the other gene that would be likely to inactivate gene function could be detected.

18-27.

a. The easiest way to get the plasmid into *S. parasanguis* cells is by transformation. *Streptococci* take up DNA naturally, as seen in the early experiments of Griffith's with *Streptococcus pneumoniae*, but artificial transformation could be used to increase the efficiency of cells that uptake the plasmid. It is critical that the transformation be done at low temperature, so that the plasmid with the temperature-sensitive origin ($repA^{ts}$) can replicate in transformed cells. Select for transformed cells containing the plasmid by plating on media containing kanamycin and erythromycin. Next, raise the temperature to the restrictive conditions and allow the cells to grow. The plasmid is unable to replicate at the high temperature, but the transposon will insert into random positions in the bacterial genome. These insertions will contain the erm^r gene. To identify the bacteria with insertions plate them at high temperature on medium containing erythromycin but not kanamycin. Use replica plating to make sure that individual colonies are susceptible to kanamycin. Each individual Erm^r Kan^s colony should have an *IS256* insertion in a different genomic location.

b. Using this plasmid as the basis for transposon-based mutagenesis has several advantages.

 (1) The frequency of strains with transposon insertions will be high among the cells that you screen because (i) the plasmid cannot be maintained at high temperature due to the temperature-sensitive origin, and (ii) cells that are Erm^r Kan^s are most likely to have formed by transposition of *IS256* into the bacterial chromosome.

(2) The presence of the transposon allows the researchers to identify rapidly new mutations that might disrupt the ability of the bacteria to cause dental plaque because the transposon "tags" the mutant gene (see part [c] below).

c. Inverse PCR could be used to purify DNA adjacent to the *IS256* in the key mutant strains, and the amplification product could be sequenced to determine the particular gene disrupted by the insertion.

18-28.

a. The *Mbo*I site would be cleaved by the restriction enzyme as indicated by the *red lines* in the diagram that follows. You would then use DNA ligase to a dilute solution of the resultant DNA fragments. Among the products of the ligation is a small circle of DNA in which the *Mbo*I sticky ends shown in the diagram a joined together. (The low concentration of DNA fragments in the ligation mix reduces the probability that separate restriction fragments will be connected.) You now use PCR to amplify the region shown in the figure. The PCR primers within the Mariner element that would amplify a product including adjacent genomic DNA are: 5' CTCCCTTCCGCCTTTTT 3' and 5' GATATTTGCCAAACTAA 3' (see the following diagram).

b. The DNA fragment that the primers would amplify is shown as a thick black line on the diagram above. The sequence of *blue* genomic DNA region would identify the insertion site of the transposon.

18-29.

a. The DNA construct that would be used to exchange the *yodA* coding sequences for those of *GFP* is shown in the following figure. The coding region for GFP in *green* in the figure would start with the initiation codon for this protein and end with the stop codon. The *GFP* sequences would be cDNA because *E. coli* genes don't have introns and so *E. coli* does not have splicing machinery. A few thousand base pairs 5' and 3' to the coding would be required for efficient gene targeting. Note that the regions needed for gene expression, particularly the *yodA* gene promoter and the Shine-Dalgarno sequences involved in the initiation of translation, will need to remain in place in the bacterial chromosome after the gene exchange. Ultimately, the cells containing the altered *yodA* gene will glow green when cadmium is present because transcription from the *yodA* promoter takes place only when the environment contains this heavy metal.

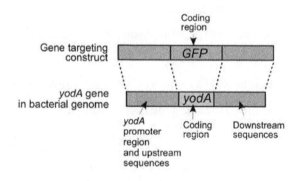

b. The *yodA* gene is nonfunctional after gene targeting because the ORF of the gene is completely replaced by that of GFP; no YodA protein is made.

c. If the gene targeting construct was altered so that *GFP* coding sequences were fused in-frame with *yodA* coding sequences – either at the 5' end or the 3' end - the fusion protein could potentially function like YodA and also like GFP (fluoresce). An example of *yodA-GFP* fusion gene construct for gene targeting (*GFP* fusion at the 3' end of *yodA*) is shown in the following diagram:

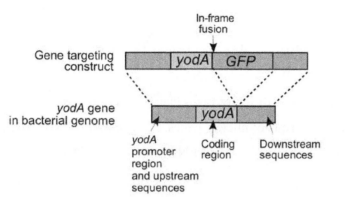

Section 18.6

18-30.

a. 4; b. 6; c. 2; d. 1; e. 7; f. 3; g. 5

a. cytoplasmic segregation	4. a cell with a mixture of different mtDNAs generates a daughter cell with only one kind
b. heteroplasmic	6. cell with mtDNAs or cpDNAs with different genotypes
c. homoplasmic	2. cell that has mtDNAs or cpDNAs that are all of one genotype
d. maternal inheritance	1. transmission of gene through maternal gamete only
e. uniparental inheritance	7. transmission of genes through either a maternal or a paternal gamete – not both
f. isogamous	3. having gametes of a similar size
g. threshold effect	5. a specific fraction of wild-type organellar DNAs is required for a wild-type phenotype

18-31.

Human mitochondrial DNA is 16,500 bp; each cell has on average 1000 mitochondria; each mitochondrion has on average 6 copies of its genome. Therefore, a human cell has on average 16,500 bp/mtDNA × 1000 mitochondria × 6 mtDNAs/mitochondrion = 990,000,000 bp of mtDNA in total. The diploid nuclear genome has 6,000,000,000 bp (6 billion bp). Thus, 990,000,000 bp/ 6,990,000,000 bp = 0.142 = 14.2% mtDNA.

18-32.

a. Based on the universal genetic code, the human DNA sequence that could encode Trp His Ile Met is (RNA-like strand): 5' TGG CA(T/C) AT(T/C/A) ATG 3'.

b. Based on the human mitochondrial genetic code, the human mtDNA sequence that could encode Trp His Ile Met is (RNA-like strand): 5' TG(G/A) CA(T/C) AT(T/C) AT(G/A) 3'.

18-33.

Fewer tRNAs are needed to translate mitochondrial mRNAs than to translate mRNAs transcribed from nuclear genes because the wobble rules are different in each case. The wobble bases of mitochondrial tRNAs can generally recognize more different bases than the wobble bases of the cytoplasmic tRNAs that help translate the transcripts of nuclear genes. For example, unmodified U present in the wobble positions of eight different mitochondrial tRNA anticodons [(1) 5' UAG; (2) 5' UAC; (3) 5' UGA; (4) 5' UGG; (5) 5' UGU; (6) 5' UGC; (7) 5' UCG; and (8) 5' UCC] enables each of these tRNAs to recognize four different codons [(N = A, G, C, or U): (1) 5' CUN (Leu); (2) 5'GUN (Val); (3) 5' UCN (Ser); (4) 5' CCN (Pro); (5) 5' ACN (Thr); (6) 5' GCN (Ala); (7) 5' CGN (Arg); and (8) 5' GGN (Gly)]. At least two different cytoplasmic tRNA species are usually required to cover the four codons corresponding to each of these amino acids using the genetic code wobble rules for translation of nuclear gene mRNAs. (Note that in the wobble rules used for translation on cytoplasmic ribosomes, xo^5U-modified tRNAs usually cannot cover codons with C in the wobble position.)

18-34.

The tRNA synthetases for making charged mitochondrial tRNAs are encoded by genes in the human nuclear genome. These genes are transcribed in the nucleus, and the resultant mRNAs are translated on ribosomes in the cell cytoplasm. The tRNA synthetase proteins are then imported into the mitochondria, where they can function to add the correct amino acid to the mitochondrial tRNA. It turns out that in humans, separate nuclear genes exist for each type of cytoplasmic and mitochondrial tRNA synthetase, with two exceptions: A single glycine– tRNA synthetase and a single lysine-tRNA synthetase aminoacylate both cytoplasmic and mitochondrial $tRNA^{Gly}$ and $tRNA^{Lys}$, respectively. Also, mitochondria need only 19 tRNA synthetase enzymes because $tRNA^{Gln}$ is aminoacylated by glutamic acid (Glu) tRNA synthetase; the glutamic acid on the charged $tRNA^{Gln}$ is subsequently transamidated (enzymatically modified) to glutamine (Gln).

18-35.

a. Both cpDNA and mtDNA encode tRNAs.

b. Both cpDNA and mtDNA encode electron transport proteins.

c. In neither cpDNA nor mtDNA are all genes necessary for organellar function present; both organelles import important proteins encoded in the nuclear genome.

d. Only mtDNA varies greatly in size depending on the species; cpDNA is fairly uniform in size across species.

18-36.

a. Each cell has 2 copies of the nuclear genome. Each cell also has 1000 mitochondria × 10 mtDNAs/mitochondrion = 10,000 copies of mtDNA; each cell has 50 chloroplasts × 20 cpDNAs/chloroplast = 1000 copies of cpDNA. For every copy of the nuclear genome, there are 5000 copies of mtDNA and 500 copies of cpDNA. Therefore, if you obtained 100 reads of a single-copy nuclear DNA sequence, you would get 5000 × 100 = 500,000 reads of a mtDNA sequence and 500 × 100 = 50,000 reads of a cpDNA sequence.

b. The answer to part (a) demonstrates that one simple criterion for determining whether a sequence is part of the nuclear genome or of an organellar genome is the number of reads; each part of an organellar genome will be represented in many more reads that each part of the nuclear genome. However, other independent criteria can help distinguish these sequences:

(i) The organellar DNAs of a previously uncharacterized plant species should display similarity with the organellar DNAs of other plant species. This criterion, though simple and usually effective, is not absolute because during evolution, some organellar genes have been relocated to the nucleus. Thus, a gene found in mtDNA or cpDNA in one species is not always guaranteed to be found in the organellar genomes of a different species.

(ii) The organization of organellar and nuclear genes differ. Mitochondrial and chloroplast genes are much more densely packed than nuclear genome genes; mitochondrial genes in most species have no introns, and mitochondrial genes in many species differ from nuclear genes in terms of the start and stop codons employed in their genetic codes.

(iii) If enough reads are made, computer analysis will assemble nuclear DNA sequences into long, linear contigs. The situation is clearly different in the case of cpDNA, because the reads of cpDNA will assemble into circles that will probably be no longer than ~200 kb in length. Some plant mtDNAs are also circular (as is also the case in all animals), but other plant mtDNAs are actually linear. The lengths of mtDNAs may also be quite variable, from less than 10 kb to more than 2400 kb. If the reads of mtDNA do not assemble into a circle and instead are seen only as linear contigs, it may be difficult to differentiate them from nuclear DNA.

18-37.

a. spectinomycin resistance gene   2. gene used to select choloroplast transformants
b. chloroplast DNA   1. homologous DNA that mediates integration
c. unique restriction site   4. site at which DNA can be inserted
d. *ori*   3. sequence for replication in *E. coli*

Section 18.7

18-38.

(a) and (d) are characteristics of chloroplasts and mitochondria that are similar to the characteristics of bacteria but dissimilar to those of eukaryotic cells. While alternate codons [choice (b)] are used in the mitochondria of many species, such variations from the 'universal' code are also found in the nuclear genes of unicellular eukaryotes like ciliates and certain yeasts. Most bacteria use the universal genetic code, with the exception of some species that use UAG stop codons to specify pyrrolysine. Introns [choice (c)] are found in genes in chloroplast genomes and are also found in the mitochondrial genomes of some species like yeast but not in the mtDNA of animals; in contrast, introns occur only very rarely in bacterial genomes.

18-39.

a. Several changes must be made to a nuclear gene like *ARG8* in order for it to be transcribed and its mRNA translated in mitochondria. First, any introns would have to be removed. (Some genes in yeast mtDNA do have introns, but the mechanisms of splicing in mitochondria and in the nucleus are not the same and depend on different kinds of sequences in the primary transcripts.) Removal of introns can be accomplished by starting with cDNA, rather than genomic sequences. Next, some of the codons in the nuclear gene would have to be changed because the genetic code is somewhat different in the nucleus than in mitochondria. The Table in Chapter 18 shows the changes in the genetic code specific to human mitochondria, not yeast mitochondria. The actual changes in the yeast mitochondrial genetic code are: AUA encodes Met, not Ile; UGA encodes Trp, rather than signaling "stop"; and any codon whose first two letters are CU encodes Thr, not Leu. Thus, an AUA codon in the nuclear gene would have to be changed to a different Ile codon; UGA could not be used as a stop codon, but rather would cause Trp to be inserted into the protein. Using UGA for Trp codons in the *ARG8* gene has an additional experimental advantage: this would prevent expression of the novel gene in the event it somehow escaped from the mitochondria back into the nucleus. Any codon starting with CU would have to be changed to an alternative Leu codon. Third, the open reading frame of the altered nuclear gene would have to be placed under the control of a promoter, a translational start site, and a transcriptional termination site that work in mitochondria. The nature of these regulatory sites differ for mitochondrial and nuclear genes. The researchers who actually conducted these experiments used a DNA synthesizer to make an *ARG8* open reading frame without introns and with the proper genetic code alterations. This achievement was possible because the *ARG8* gene is quite small, but it would also be possible to do this by altering an *ARG8* cDNA using *in vitro* mutagenesis. The investigators then replaced the open reading frame of an actual cloned mitochondrial gene with the open reading of the altered *ARG8* that they made. This step put the *ARG8* sequences in the proper position with respect to mitochondrial regulatory sequences. Next, the researchers introduced the cloned gene into yeast mitochondria using microprojectile bombardment (the biolistic gun).

b. A yeast strain with *ARG8*-expressing mitochondria has at least two advantages. First, transfer of *ARG8* into mtDNA provides a phenotype that depends on mitochondrial gene expression. Such a yeast strain allows one to select for function of the mitochondrial genetic system in mutants that are unable to respire (unable to grow on glycerol). If the nuclear *ARG8* gene was deleted or otherwise mutated, then the yeast cells could survive on medium lacking arginine only if they had mitochondria making this arginine biosynthetic enzyme. Second, because the expression of this *ARG8* gene was now controlled by authentic mitochondrial regulatory regions like promoters, scientists could use this strain to study mitochondrial regulatory sequences. For example, they could try to find arginine auxotrophs that could no longer make arginine because there was a DNA change that obliterated the function of the promoter. By sequencing such mutations in mtDNA, they could figure out a lot about the function of regulatory elements in the mitochondrial genome.

18-40.

a. Human cells contain only two copies of nuclear genomic DNA, but a typical cell contains hundreds of copies of mtDNA. Therefore, in situations where the DNA sample is substantially degraded or where there are very few cells available (both of which occur often in forensics), mtDNA is used to identify individuals because it is possible to recover enough of it.

b. The disadvantage of typing individuals with mtDNA versus nuclear DNA is that it is impossible to distinguish individuals with the same maternal lineage, such as siblings. A grandmother, mother, daughter, and son would all have the same mtDNA sequence (excepting rare mutations or unusual cases of heteroplasmy).

Section 18.8

18-41.

For a newly induced mitochondrial mutation to express itself phenotypically at the level of a single mitochondrion, it would have to be present in a sufficient number of mtDNAs; to cause a mutant phenotype at the level of a cell, a sufficient number of mitochondria expressing the phenotype would need to be present in the cell; to express itself phenotypically within a tissue or an organ, a sufficient number of cells expressing the mutant phenotype would need to be present to affect the function of that tissue or organ. The definition of a "sufficient number" would depend on the specific mutation in the particular gene and on the kind of cell being observed. Newly induced mitochondrial mutations have the best chance of affecting phenotype at the level of a tissue or organ when they either occur in or segregate into female germ-line cell precursors (oogonia). Each oocyte has about 100,000 mitochondria that all descend from only about 10-20 mitochondria present in each oogonium. During germ cell proliferation, a mutant mtDNA could easily proliferate and become a large fraction of the mtDNA population in an oocyte, and therefore in the resulting zygote after fertilization.

18-42.

Many mechanisms exclude the mitochondrial DNA from one parent in the zygotes. (i) Most often, the small size of the sperm excludes organelles. (ii) Cells can degrade organelles or organellar DNA from the male parent; for example, in some species the zygote destroys the paternal organelle after fertilization. (iii) Early zygotic mitoses can distribute the male organelles to cells that will not become part of the embryo. (iv) The fertilization process itself may prevent the paternal cell from contributing any organelles (only the sperm nucleus is allowed into the egg).

18-43.

Heteroplasmic cells have a mixture of the two genotypes in their organelles. Homoplasmic cells have only one type of genome. Thus, homoplasmic cells can either be totally normal or totally mutant. If the mutation is very debilitating to the cell, either because of the loss of energy metabolism in the case of mitochondria or of photosynthetic capability in the case of chloroplasts, a cell that is homoplasmic for the mutant genome will die. Therefore, you will find the mutant organellar genome only in heteroplasmic cells.

18-44.

a. Paternal inheritance of mtDNA is excluded because three of the four seedlings inherited mtDNA from the oocyte (plant 1). Maternal inheritance is possible because seedlings 1-3 have both maternal (plant 1) alleles, and although seedling 4 has only one of the maternal (plant 1) alleles, that outcome could be due to segregation into an oocyte of only mtDNA containing this allele. Biparental inheritance is possible because seedlings 1-4 all have the allele common to both parents, and so some of their mtDNAs could have come from the pollen.

b. To distinguish between maternal and biparental inheritance of mtDNA, make plant 2 the maternal parent and plant 1 the paternal parent. If inheritance is strictly maternal, all of the progeny plants should have only the variant of mtDNA seen in plant 2; if biparental, the progeny plants should have both alleles.

c. To determine if plant 2 is in fact homoplasmic, would need to isolate mtDNA from all the tissues of plant 2, and make sure that only the single variant is found in PCR analysis. This experiment would be more sensitive if you sequenced both variants of mtDNA and were able to design a primer pair that could amplify only the variant not seen in the leaf of plant 2. The reason this experiment is necessary is that the single leaf assayed originally could have come from a region of the plant that was homoplasmic for a single variant due to cytoplasmic segregation.

d. Differing proportions of the two mtDNA variants in the four seedlings is due to cytoplasmic segregation either in the germ line of plant 1, or during growth of the seedlings. Whether mtDNA inheritance is maternal or biparental, the differing proportions of the two variants in the seedlings could reflect the proportions present in individual oocytes of plant 1. [As explained in part (a), this proportion could be 100% one type in the oocyte that gave rise to seedling 4.] Alternatively, or in addition, cytoplasmic segregation during growth of the seedlings could explain the results. In the zygote, different cells with different proportions of the mtDNAs due to early cytoplasmic segregation events could proliferate at different rates. Because mitochondria divide when cells divide, the result could be a change in the proportion of mtDNA variants that were present originally in the fertilized egg.

18-45.

In all of the diagrams in this problem, *unfilled black outlined squares* = mtDNA; *black filled circles* = cpDNA; *red lines* = male sterile nuclear DNA; *blue lines* = male fertile nuclear DNA.

a. Remember that mitochondria and chloroplasts are inherited maternally in plants. Therefore, in the first cross diagrammed below, the female parent, which is the male sterile strain, provides progeny zygotes with both the organelle genomes and a haploid set of chromosomes, while the male parent, which is the male fertile strain, gives only a haploid set of chromosomes. In the diagram, only one homologous pair of nuclear chromosomes is shown, and it is meant to symbolize all nuclear chromosomes.

Female gametes   Male gametes   F₁ progeny

b. During meiosis in the germ line of the F1 in part (a), recombination occurs between the nuclear homologs from its two parents. In the female gametes, the organellar genomes come from the original male sterile strain. Two generations of F1 backcrosses are diagrammed below. First the F1, and then female backcross progeny (BC1) are backcrossed to the male fertile strain. Recombination also occurs between the nuclear homologs during meiosis in the BC1 germ line cells.

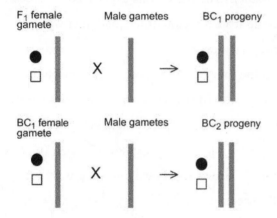

F₁ female gamete   Male gametes   BC₁ progeny

BC₁ female gamete   Male gametes   BC₂ progeny

Note that in each generation, only one of the many different possible recombinant chromosomes is pictured.

c. Each generation of backcrossing increases the fraction of the nuclear genome from the male fertile strain (*blue*). On the other hand, as the hybrid progeny were always the female parent in the backcrosses, the organellar genomes from the original male sterile strain have been inherited by the backcross progeny in an unbroken line. If male sterility continued to occur in all the progeny in each successive backcross generation, despite the dwindling proportion of the original male sterile strain genome present, the implication is that an organellar gene, as opposed to a nuclear gene, is responsible for the male sterile phenotype.

18-46.

a. Remember that this type of CMS is caused by mutant mitochondrial genomes that prevent pollen formation. You must also realize that the line used as the female parent produces both eggs and pollen (it can self-fertilize), but the line used as the male parent provides only pollen – the pollen is collected and applied to the female line. If the female parental inbred line is male sterile, then this line cannot self-fertilize and the seed companies would not have to do anything more to prevent self-fertilization. If the female parent instead had normal mtDNA (was male fertile), then much of the corn produced by the cross would not be hybrid corn, but would be instead simply more of the inbred line used as the female in the cross. Prior to the use of the CMS technique, seed companies would prevent self-fertilization by hiring high school and college students to go through the fields and manually remove the tassels from the plants used as the females in the cross before they produced pollen. This procedure is very labor-intensive and expensive.

b. Mitochondrial inheritance in corn is uniparental from the female parent. Thus, the F1 corn plants in part (a) inherit mutant CMS mitochondrial DNA. These F1 corn plants must nonetheless be fertile so that kernels form in the F1 ears of corn. (Each corn kernel is like one of Mendel's peas – each comes from a different fertilized egg that has developed into an embryonic plant.) If the *Rf* allele of the nuclear *Restorer* gene suppresses the mitochondrial sterility mutation, then the sterile inbred line in part (a) must also be homozygous for the recessive for the *rf* allele of *Restorer*. These plants are then male sterile and would thus be the female parent in the hybrid-generating cross, as discussed above. The other inbred line, the male parent supplying the pollen for the cross, would have to have at least one (and preferable two) dominant *Rf* alleles of *Restorer*. (Note that as long as the male parent was *Rf/–*, it could, like the female parent, have CMS mitochondria and yet be fertile because the nuclear *Rf* allele suppresses the sterile phenotype.) The F1 hybrid corn would thus have CMS mitochondria but also carry *Rf*, so the F1 corn plants would be fertile. In the following diagram, *filled black squares* represent mutant (CMS) mitochondrial DNA, and unfilled *black outlined squares* represent normal mitochondrial DNA.

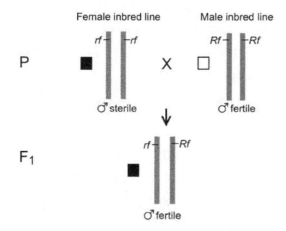

Note that if the inbred male line was *Rf/rf*, then half the F1 hybrid plants would be male sterile (*rf/rf*) and the other half fertile (*Rf/rf*). This would not be a practical difficulty because if many F1 seeds were planted in the same field, the male fertile plants would produce enough pollen to fertilize the ovules from the male sterile plants.

c. One method to produce CMS plants that are also *rf/rf* is to make a fertile "Maintainer" line that has mitochondria with a normal (non-CMS) genome but whose nuclear genomes are the same as the CMS plants and are also *rf/rf*. The *rf/rf* CMS plants are used as the female parent (they cannot produce pollen). When pollen from Maintainer plants fertilizes the CMS plants, the progeny will have CMS mitochondria and will also be *rf/rf*; in other words, these progeny will be identical to their maternal parents. In the following diagram, *filled black squares* represent mutant (CMS) mitochondrial DNA, and unfilled *black outlined squares* represent normal mitochondrial DNA.

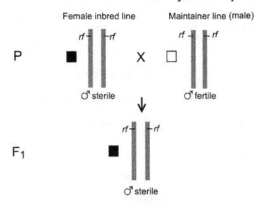

A second, more complicated method (not shown) uses CMS *Rf/rf* plants of the same inbred background. One fourth of the progeny would be CMS *rf/rf* plants that could be used to make hybrid seed, but you would need some way to identify these plants and isolate them from their male fertile CMS *Rf/rf* siblings.

d. There are two potential issues with using hybrid corn, both of which revolve around the idea of *monoculture.* As hybrid seed is made by seed companies, farmers now depend on the seed companies to provide their seed. In the past farmers saved part of their harvest and used this for corn seed the next season. However, the fact that most farmers now pay to buy hybrid seed shows the economic advantages of the increased yield due to hybrid corn. Second, farmers now grow only the few varieties of hybrid corn sold by the seed companies. The genetic variation of the corn crop overall is reduced. If the hybrid corn is susceptible to a newly emerging disease, this reduced genetic variation could have disastrous consequences. In 1970, a new mutant strain of a fungus causing leaf blight emerged that was particularly lethal to corn with a CMS called *Texas* (*T*). This fungus decimated the hybrid corn crop in the southern U.S. each year until new fungus-resistant forms of hybrid corn could be developed.

18-47.

a. Fermentation generates ATP independent of mitochondria. The *cox2-1* mutant yeast cannot grow on glycerol because glycerol is nonfermentable and the mutants lack mitochondrial function (electron transport), so they must rely on fermentation for energy.

b. To answer this question, remember that the inheritance of mtDNA in yeast is biparental, but that cytoplasmic segregation will occur rapidly after a few rounds of mitotic division of heteroplasmic yeast because the mitotic buds only inherit a few mtDNAs. As a result, yeast cells are usually homoplasmic. The data suggest that *cox2-1* is a mitochondrial gene. The diploids formed by a mating of *cox2-1* and wild-type strains have roughly half *cox2-1* and half normal mitochondria (they are thus originally heteroplasmic). After growing mitotically for some time, about half of the diploid cells have normal mitochondria, and half have mutant mitochondria; each type is now homoplasmic. The diploids that have *cox2-1* mutant mitochondria cannot grow on nonfermentable glycerol and cannot sporulate. The diploids with the normal mitochondria can grow on glycerol, and when they sporulate, all 4 spores have normal mitochondria, so they can all grow on glycerol. Because mating type is controlled by nuclear genes, the fact that half the spores are mating type *a* and half are mating type α underscores that the nuclear genes are segregating normally in the spores. The observations are inconsistent with *cox2-1* as a nuclear gene. If this were the case, you would expect that all of the heterozygous *cox2-1/+* diploids would remain heterozygous, and either all of the diploid cells would be able to grow on glycerol if *cox2-1* is recessive to +, or none of them would grow on glycerol if *cox2-1* is dominant to +. Additionally, under this scenario all of the *cox2-1/+* diploids should upon meiosis segregate 2 *cox2-1* (cannot grow on glycerol) : 2 + (can grow on glycerol) spores. Instead, all the haploid spores could grow on glycerol, which is consistent with the alternative hypothesis that *cox2-1* is a mitochondrial gene.

c. The *pet111-1* mutants behave exactly the way we would expect for a recessive mutation in a nuclear gene [see part (b)].

18-48.

a. The *petites* can grow on glucose plates because glucose is fermentable—it can be used to generate ATP without mitochondrial function (oxidative phosphorylation); they cannot grow on either glycerol or ethanol because using these molecules to generate ATP requires mitochondrial function, which they lack. The *grande* yeast (wild-types) can grow on glucose, glycerol, or ethanol because they have functional mitochondria. The reason that *petite* colonies are small is that fermentation is less efficient than oxidative phosphorylation (cells generate fewer ATP molecules from a given number of glucose molecules by fermentation as compared with oxidative phosphorylation in mitochondria).

b. The odd uniparental inheritance pattern of the *grande* phenotype in *grande* × *petite* crosses is due to the fact that the *petite* strains used by Ephrussi have no mtDNA at all. Thus, in the diploid cells resulting from the mating, all of the mtDNA comes from the *grande* parent that has wild type mtDNA. This situation differs from the cytoplasmic segregation that occurs in heteroplasmic diploids (as in Problem 18b) because in this case, one parent supplies all the mtDNA.

Section 18.9

18-49.

One characteristic of a mitochondrial mutation in many organisms is maternal inheritance. Most of the offspring (both male and female) of an affected female are affected. None of the offspring of affected males are affected. Another indication of mitochondrial inheritance is differing levels of expression of the mutant phenotype in different progeny due to differing amounts of heteroplasmy in either the egg or the cells of the embryo.

18-50.

a. The mother (I-1) may have been heteroplasmic with a very small proportion of mutant mtDNA. Alternatively, a spontaneous mutation could have occurred either in the mitochondrial genome of the mother's oogonia, her egg that gave rise to individual II-2, or in the early zygote of individual II-2. Due to cytoplasmic segregation, a mutation that occurred in one mtDNA genome could come to represent a large proportion of mtDNAs in the some mitotic descendants of the cell in which the mutation happened.

b. To distinguish between heteroplasmy and new mutation, you could analyze the mtDNA of somatic cells from various tissues in the mother (I-1). If the mother was heteroplasmic, most of her tissues should show at least a small fraction of mutant mtDNA. If the mutation occurred in her germ line and was inherited by II-2 (or if it occurred in the zygote) the mother's somatic cells would not show any defective mtDNA.

18-51.

The zygote that formed these twins was heteroplasmic, with both wild-type and mutant mitochondrial genomes. Early in embryonic development, two cell masses separated to become the two identical twins. The ratio of wild-type to mutant mtDNAs in the two cell masses may have differed.

Furthermore, during the individual development of the twins the ratios of wild-type to mutant mtDNAs may vary in different tissues. The more affected twin probably had a higher proportion of mutant mitochondria in tissues such as muscles and brain that particularly depend upon energy supplied by mitochondria.

18-52.

If the patient is male then you could reassure him that none of his children would be affected by the disease (assuming his mate is unaffected by MERRF). If the patient is female then she is most likely heteroplasmic. There is a strong chance that her child might be affected by MERRF, but there is no way to determine either the numerical probability that the child would be affected or the severity of the disease, because of the random events in mtDNA distribution through many rounds of cell division that will influence the ratio of wild-type and mutant mtDNAs in the egg and in various tissues in the fetus. It is relatively easy by amniocentesis and PCR (and sequencing)to check for the mutant mitochondrial DNA in the fetus. However, these results are not diagnostic because the distribution of wild-type and mutant mtDNA can vary considerably in various tissues. For example, the fetal cells shed into the amniotic fluid may be devoid of mutant mtDNA, but cells in other fetal tissues might still have some mutant mitochondrial genomes.

18.53

a. The three diseases can be caused by deletion of different mitochondrial genes that affect mitochondrial function to different degrees. It is even possible that all three syndromes could have the same genetic cause, but the differences could be due to heteroplasmy and cytoplasmic segregation.

b. The origin of replication must be outside of the DNA deleted in these syndromes. (That is, outside of the 7.6 kb removed in the largest of these deletions.) Deletion of the mtDNA replication origin would result in a mutant mtDNA that is unable to replicate; it would be lost and no cells would end up heteroplasmic.

c. One possibility to explain the lack of maternal inheritance of PEO is that germ-line cells carrying the mtDNA deletions are at a disadvantage either for multiplication or for oogenesis relative to homoplasmic segregants that do not have the deleted DNA. As a result, either the germ line would be populated mostly by cells without the deletions, or only the homoplasmic segregants would produce viable eggs. A woman who has the deleted mtDNAs in her somatic cells (and thus has PEO symptoms) might not have mutant mtDNA in her germ-line cells or in the eggs she makes.

18.54

a. The product of the nuclear gene is imported into the mitochondria and it works in the same pathway as the product of the mitochondrial gene. For example, some protein complexes that operate in oxidative phosphorylation include one subunit encoded by a nuclear gene and another subunit encoded by a mitochondrial gene. Loss of either gene function results in the failure of electron transport and thus in the symptoms of Leigh syndrome.

b. No, the pedigree shown does not enable you to distinguish between nuclear versus mitochondrial gene inheritance. One possibility consistent with the data is that Leigh syndrome is caused by a recessive mutation in an autosomal nuclear gene (*SURF1*); both parents would be heterozygous. The other possibility is a mtDNA mutation (*MT-ATP6*) and the mother is heteroplasmic; her overall or tissue-specific proportion of mutant mtDNA is below the threshold for disease symptoms. The tissue distribution and/or overall proportion of mutant mtDNA is high enough in 2 of her 3 children for them to display disease symptoms.

c. Knowing that the disease is mitochondrial would inform the affected male that he cannot pass it on to his children, and would inform both the affected female and her unaffected sister that potentially they both could do so. If the disease were caused by a rare recessive allele, the unaffected sibling could test her genomic DNA to determine whether or not she is a carrier. If so, all three siblings could test their partners for a mutation in the gene before they decide to have children.

18.55

Scientists could use a PCR assay that distinguishes SNPs in the mtDNAs from the nuclear donor and the cytoplasm donor oocyte to test cells from different tissues of Mito and Tracker. Likely these SNPs would lie in the hypervariable regions of mtDNA found in humans and other primates. These PCR assays would not however be absolutely conclusive. Without testing every single cell in Mito and Tracker, the researchers cannot be completely certain that a few mtDNA molecules from the nuclear donor oocyte are present.

Chapter 19 Manipulating the Genomes of Eukaryotes

Synopsis:

Scientists desire to manipulate genomes for several important reasons, ranging from the study of biological phenomena, to the improvement of agricultural crops and domesticated animals, to the production of protein drugs, to the treatment of genetic syndromes by gene therapy. Chapter 19 presents two general strategies for altering genomes. The first is the insertion of transgenes into random positions in plant and animal genomes. The second strategy is alternatively called gene targeting or targeted mutagenesis. Armed only with a gene's nucleotide sequence and cloned copies of a gene, researchers can now change at will any base pair of any gene in the genome of virtually any organism. It is thus possible, at least in theory, to knock out the function of any gene of interest, or to replace an allele of a gene with a different allele that could be created in vitro by recombinant DNA technology.

One goal of the chapter is to introduce you to the methodologies scientists use to create transgenic organisms and to perform targeted mutagenesis. As you will see, several of these strategies rely on biological events that are specific to the species whose genome is to be manipulated. Although it is useful for you to learn the details of some of these methods, it is more important for you to think hard about what kind of genome manipulation will allow researchers to achieve the ultimate goals of the work. What kinds of changes would you need to make in genomes in order to improve a crop or to make a mouse model of a human genetic disease? The techniques you would employ depend upon the end result you desire.

The chapter concludes with a discussion of experimental gene therapy in humans, in which potentially therapeutic genes are introduced into a patient's somatic cells in order to fight the effects of a disease. To date, the successes of gene therapy in humans have been limited, but in certain cases, such as with an inherited form of blindness, partial cures have been obtained. Gene therapy in humans has not yet lived up to its potential, but that potential for alleviating many diseases is vast.

Key Words:

gene therapy manipulation of the genome in order to cure a disease.

transgenic organisms individuals carrying a transgene.

transgene any piece of foreign DNA that researchers have inserted into the genome of an organism.

pronuclear injection method for generating transgenic mammals in which DNA is injected into a pronucleus after fertilization.

P element transformation a method for generating transgenic Drosophila in which a recombinant P element containing a transgene is injected into embryos; the recombinant transposon integrates into a chromosome of a germline cell.

T-DNA part of the Ti plasmid of Agrobacterium tumefaciens that integrates into the host plant genome. T-DNA is used as a vector for generating transgenic plants.

pharming the use of transgenic animals and plants to produce protein drugs.

reproductive cloning creation of a cloned embryo by insertion of the nucleus of a somatic cell from one individual into an egg cell whose nucleus has been removed. The hybrid egg is stimulated to begin embryonic cell divisions, and the resulting cloned embryo is transplanted into the uterus of a foster mother and allowed to develop to term.

somatic cell nuclear transfer the method for reproductive cloning; the nucleus of a somatic cell replaces the nucleus of an oocyte, which is subsequently fertilized in vitro, and the zygote is introduced into the womb of a surrogate mother.

targeted mutagenesis technology that enables scientists to alter the genome of any organism in virtually any way that they desire.

gene targeting method for inserting DNA into a genome that relies on homologous recombination; the DNA is "targeted" for insertion into a specific place in the genome by sequence similarity.

embryonic stem (ES) cells undifferentiated cells, originally derived from early embryos that can grow in cell culture and remain undifferentiated.

totipotent the description of cell state during early embryonic development in which the cells have not yet differentiated and retain the ability to produce every type of cell found in the developing embryo and adult animal.

chimeras genetic mosaics in which cells of different genotype originate from two different individuals.

knockout mice mice homozygous for an induced mutation in a targeted gene; the mutation destroys (knocks out) the function of the gene.

knockin mice mice in which a gene has been altered by targeted mutagenesis. The alteration might be a point mutation or a large insertion of DNA.

Significant Elements and Problem Solving Tips:

The problems in this chapter ask you to think creatively about how to use cloned DNA to

modify the genomes of organisms. A few key points to keep in mind:

Transgenes

- **Transgenes can be inserted into random locations** in an organism's genome using

the following methods:

- Pronuclear injection (random recombination)

- Transposon vectors

- Retroviral vectors

- T-DNA vectors (plants)

- **To be useful, the protein encoded by transgenes must have a dominant effect**

because the genome of the transgenic organism is otherwise usually intact. However,

it should be remembered that as a side product of the integration process, transgene insertions into random locations can disrupt the structure and/or expression of nearby genes.

Gene targeting

• **Linear double-stranded DNAs introduced into cells can be targeted to specific locations in the genome through homologous recombination.** The free ends of the DNA introduced determine the location where homologous recombination takes place. Gene targeting through homologous recombination is extremely inefficient. It is thus necessary to include a selectable marker like *neor* to identify cells in which a potential targeting event occurred. Furthermore, because the introduced DNA can also insert at random locations, it is necessary to screen the cells with the selectable marker for those in which the targeting construct indeed underwent homologous recombination with the intended target locus.

• **Knockouts are genes that have been targeted by homologous recombination so as to disrupt their function.** Typically, the selectable marker is inserted into a protein-coding exon. Knockouts for most genes are recessive alleles, so phenotypic effects are observed only in homozygotes for the knockout allele. However, if the targeted gene is haploinsufficient, the knockout will cause a dominant mutant phenotype.

• **Knockins are genes that have been targeted by homologous recombination so as to alter their structure in specific ways.** Often, knockin mice are designed to mimic point mutations in human disease genes in the hope that mouse models for the disease can be used to understand the biochemical and physiological basis for the disease and to screen for drugs that might ultimately treat the condition in humans.

• **TALENS are synthetic restriction enzymes used to cut genomes at specific locations to improve the efficiency of gene targeting.** Microhomology-mediated end-joining to repair the DNA ends produced by TALEN cleavage is imprecise and can thus lead to a knockout. Homologous recombination near these DNA ends with a linear fragment of DNA can lead to gene replacement (a knockin).

Conditional knockouts and knockins

• **Conditional knockouts/knockins allow researchers to study the effects of gene alteration in a specific tissue or under certain conditions; they are**

particularrly useful when whole organisms with the knockout/knockin cannot survive.

• Making mouse conditional knockouts and knockins involves the Cre/loxP recombination system. Cre is a site-specific recombinase that performs crossingover at two small (34 bp) loxP sites. The base pair sequence of a loxP site is asymmetrical – it has direction. When two loxP sites on the same DNA molecule are in the same orientation, Cre-mediated recombination between the two sites deletes the DNA between them. If the loxP are in opposite orientation, Cremediated recombination between two loxP sites inverts the orientation of the DNA between them. The diagram at the top of the next page illustrates these two possible outcomes of Cre-mediated recombination:

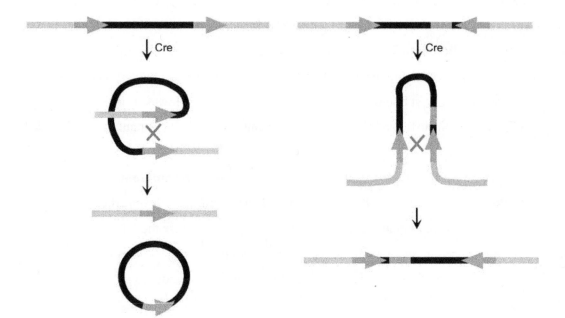

Solutions to Problems:

<u>Vocabulary</u>

19-1.

a. 7; b. 9; c. 3; d. 8; e. 1; f. 12; g. 10; h. 11; i. 2; j. 6; k. 4; l. 5.

a. transgene	7. gene transferred by a scientist into an organism's genome
b. pronuclear injection	9. method of DNA transfer used for many vertebrates
c. floxed gene	3. useful for making conditional knockouts

d. T-DNA	8. vector of bacterial origin used for constructing transgenic plants
e. AAV vector	1. genetically engineered viral genome that transfers a therapy gene
f. packaging cells	12. generate viral particles for gene therapy
g. TALEN	10. synthetic restriction enzyme
h. knockout mouse	11. loss-of-function mutant through gene targeting
i. knockin mouse	2. contains additional or altered DNA through gene targeting
j. Cre recombinase	6. causes crossovers at loxP sites
k. ES cells	4. can develop into any cell type
l. GM organism	5. plant or animal that carries a transgene

Sections 19.1 and 19.2

19-2.

a. The missense mutation is most likely a loss-of-function allele. Make transgene constructs that express wild-type cDNAs corresponding to each of the three different splice forms. These constructs would need to include sequences allowing them to be expressed properly in hair follicles [see part (b) below]. Using pronuclear injection, transform white mutant mice with each construct and test if any one of them rescues the white mutant phenotype to wild-type (gray). It could also be possible that a combination of two or all three splice forms is required for the wild-type phenotype (gray).

b. Because the constructs are based on cDNAs, they will require sequences not found in the cDNAs that allow the mRNAs to be expressed and processed correctly. Thus, as seen in the figure that follows, the constructs will include a hair follicle enhancer and a promoter that can interact with the enhancer; in addition, a poly-A addition site is needed to make sure that the mRNAs produced from these transgenes will have a poly-A tail to ensure their stability and translation.

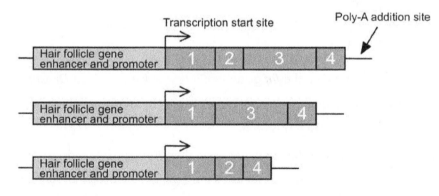

c. Pronuclear injection results in insertion of multiple copies of the transgene, and in random locations. Neither the copy number nor the insertion site can be controlled, and both potentially influence the amount of mRNA and thus the amount of protein made. Too little or too much protein could affect the ability of the construct to rescue.

Section 19.2

19-3.

a. Cross the transgenic strain to wild type, and cross F1 animals heterozygous for the transgene insertion to each other. If limb deformity is not caused by the transgene insertion, some F2 animals homozygous for the transgene insertion will not have the mutant phenotype. If the limb deformity is due to the transgene insertion, homozygosity for the transgene should correlate with limb deformity.

b. The transgene has inserted into the gene and caused a loss-of-function mutation. Inverse PCR should enable you to identify the gene into which the transgene inserted.

c. Conduct a complementation test. Cross the homozygous transgenic mutant mice with mice homozygous for the *ld* mutation. The progeny are *trans*-heterozygotes for the transgene insertion and *ld*. If the transgene insertion is a loss-of-function mutation in the same gene that is altered in *ld* (that is, if the mutations are allelic), the mutations will fail to complement each other and the progeny will show the limb deformity. The mutations will complement each other (no mutant phenotype will be seen in the progeny) if they are mutations in different genes.

19-4.

a. Make a fusion gene construct in which the *HoxA1* promoter and enhancer drive expression of a *HoxD4* cDNA.

b. If the absence of HoxD4 protein is what distinguishes the occipital bones (E) from the cervical vertebrae (C1 and C2), in animals transformed with the *HoxA1*driven *HoxD4* gene, the occipital bones should be transformed into cervical vertebrae.

19-5.

a. Transform *faf-* flies with a construct in which the *faf* gene regulatory sequences from *Drosophila* drive expression of a *Usp9* cDNA; if the rough eye phenotype is rescued to wild-type, the human USP9 protein can substitute functionally for fly Faf protein.

b. If mice with loss-of-function *Fam-* mutations have mutant eyes, then *Fam* must be required for mouse eye development. In Section 19.3, you will learn how to use cloned *Fam* DNA to generate mice with loss-of-function *Fam* mutants; these would be knockouts or conditional knockouts.

19-6.

a. Fly lines in which the enhancer trap construct integrated next to an enhancer will express GFP so you will see green fluorescent tissue(s). Depending on the nature of the enhancer in a particular GFP-expressing line, expression of GFP could be ubiquitous in every cell, or limited to specific cell types at particular stages of development.

b. Screen for lines that express GFP only in the wing. Use inverse PCR to amplify the genomic DNA adjacent to the enhancer trap transgene insertion site. Sequence the amplified genomic DNA and compare it to the *Drosophila* genome reference sequence to identify the gene at the insertion site. This gene should be expressed in the fly wing because it is located near a wing specific enhancer.

c. Enhancer trap insertions can sometimes insert within the gene normally regulated by the "trapped" enhancer, disrupt gene function, and cause a loss-of-function mutation. Homozygotes for the transgene insertion could, therefore, have a mutant phenotype. (Review Problem #3 above.)

19-7.

a. First, identify the gene that encodes the fish antifreeze protein. One way you could accomplish this goal is to purify the antifreeze protein, determine the amino acid sequence of this protein by chemical means, and then examine the fish genome for a gene that could encode it. Next, you would obtain a cDNA for the gene. Several techniques would allow you to do this; one method is to use primers specific for the gene and reverse transcriptase to amplify the specific cDNA from a pool of total fish mRNA. Next, insert the cDNA into a T-DNA vector that contains a high-efficiency plant promoter and enhancer, and transform the recombinant T-DNA into *Agrobacterium* (see Fig. 19.5). Finally, spray the transformed *Agrobacterium* onto plant cells and then grow embryos from single cells under selection for T-DNA insertion. (If the T-DNA vector included a gene for herbicide resistance, you would add the herbicide to the cultures of the plant cells.) Embryos that survive selection should express the fish antifreeze gene cDNA under control of a plant promoter.

b. Researchers did find fish antifreeze protein in plants, but it did not seem to function. The most likely possibility is that key posttranslational modifications were not made to the fish protein in plant cells. A second possibility to consider is that the antifreeze protein in fish does not work by itself, but instead it functions only in conjunction with a cofactor (another protein or even a small molecule) that is found in fish but not in plants.

19-8.

a. The most straightforward way to make a transgene that would inhibit the function of a particular gene is through RNA interference. An RNA interference transgene should have a promoter at both the 5' end and the 3' end of a complete or partial cDNA for the gene; the 5' end promoter makes the sense transcript, and the 3' end promoter makes an antisense transcript. The sense and antisense transcripts hybridize to form double-stranded RNAs that will be processed into siRNAs, which will bind RISC and target the endogenous gene transcripts for degradation.

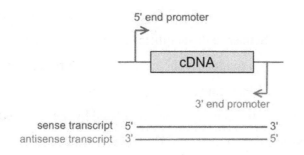

Another possibility is to construct a transgene that expresses a dominant negative allele of the gene. This strategy would be more difficult; you would have to understand a lot about the structure and function of the gene product to design a dominant negative allele, and probably high levels of overexpression of the transgene would be required for it to have a chance to knock down gene function. Moreover, even when they work, dominant negative alleles rarely inhibit the function of the wild-type allele completely.

b. An RNAi construct for the *CFTR* gene could be made that consists of one or a few of the large number of exons of the gene, and two copies of a strong lung-specific promoter oriented as shown in the answer to part (a). The transgene could be incorporated into the mouse genome by pronuclear injection. Because the insertion sites and copy numbers vary in different lines, the levels of interfering RNA expressed are line-specific. Thus, in different transgenic lines, *CFTR* gene expression would be inhibited to different extents. To determine whether or not *CFTR* gene mRNA is effectively degraded, lung cell mRNA from normal mice, null mutant mice and different lines of RNAi transgenic mice would be purified and used to make cDNA. The cDNA would be used as a template for PCR with primer pairs that amplify exons of *CFTR*. If *CFTR* mRNA is degraded by RNAi in a specific line, an amplification product should be detected when the cDNA from the normal mice is used as a template, but no amplification product (or much less) should be obtained using the cDNA from that RNAi line and no amplification product from the cDNA of the null mice. (As an alternative to PCR, you could also perform RNA-Seq to determine the residual level of expression.) Mouse lines in which the *CFTR* transcripts are degraded successfully would be analyzed to determine if they have a phenotype similar to humans with cystic fibrosis. For the *CFTR* gene, it may be possible to generate a dominant negative by using a very strong lung promoter to overexpress an allele that makes a mutant protein that cannot function as a chloride ion regulator (due to a deletion in the ORF or a missense mutation), but can insert into the cell membrane. As above, the transgene would be transferred to the mouse genome by pronuclear injection. The mutant protein, if expressed at much higher levels than normal CFTR, potentially could out-compete the normal protein for space at the cell membrane. You could then determine if the mice with the transgene have a mutant phenotype similar to humans with cystic fibrosis.

19-9.

a. In the diagrams that follow, IR = inverted repeat; *ori* = origin of replication that allows the plasmid to be maintained in *E. coli*. A key point is that the plasmid on the left that contains the transgene has *Tol2* inverted repeats, and the plasmid on the right that supplies *Tol2* transposase protein does not.

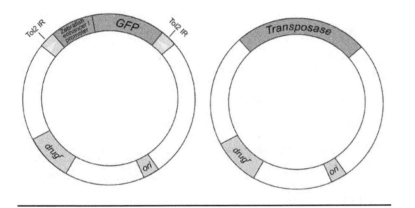

b. Using a medaka fish transposon (*Tol2*) in zebrafish means that there is no endogenous source of Tol2 transposase. Thus, once inserted in the zebrafish genome, the transgene will be stable.

Section 19.3

19-10.

a. Some genes in the mouse genome might be haploinsufficient for an essential function in undifferentiated ES cells. For these genes, cells heterozygous for knockouts will die and cannot be maintained as a cell line.

b. Some knockouts that are viable as heterozygotes in totipotent ES cells could be haploinsufficient for the function of key tissues later in mouse development. Mice with these knockouts would be inviable.

c. *Fam* is haploinsufficient in ES cells, and so it is not possible to use ES cells to make an entire mouse that is *Fam-/ Fam+*, let alone a homozygous knockout mouse (*Fam -/ Fam-*). To ask if *Fam* is required for mouse eye development, a researcher could make a conditional knockout mouse using the Cre/loxP recombination system. A construct that could be introduced into the mouse *Fam* gene by homologous recombination in ES cells is shown in the following diagram:

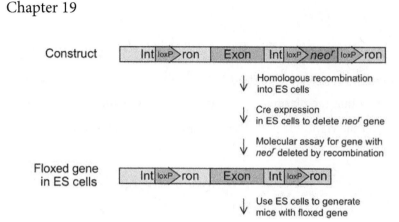

The mouse would also have a *cre* gene (expresses Cre recombinase protein) controlled by an eye-specific enhancer. Eye specific Cre expression would result in deletion of the floxed exon of *Fam* (the *purple* exon in the preceding diagram) only in eye cells. Thus in a mouse heterozygous for a wild-type *Fam* gene and a floxed *Fam* gene (*Fam+/Fam floxed*), the eyes would be *Fam+/Fam-* (exon deleted), while all of the other cells in the animal are *Fam+/Fam floxed* (exon not deleted). The eyes of these mice might display a mutant phenotype if *Fam+* is haploinsufficient in eyes. Mice that lack all *Fam+* function in their eyes could be generated by crossing two *Fam+/Fam floxed* heterozygotes to obtain a *Fam floxed /Fam floxed* homozygote. Eye-specific Cre expression in such a homozygote would result in deletion of the floxed exon in both *Fam floxed* gene copies, and homozygous *Fam- / Fam-* eye cells.

d. As *Fam* is haploinsufficient for viability in ES cells, it is likely also haploinsufficient in most mouse cells. Thus, it seems likely that two copies of *Fam+* are required for viability of eye cells and thus that *Fam+/Fam-* eyes would be absent because the heterozygous eye cells would die. Another possible outcome is that *Fam+* levels are less crucial in the eye than in ES cells, and so the cells live but the eyes don't develop properly and are malformed. Yet a third result could be that only parts of the eye are missing or formed abnormally, meaning that *Fam* is required for proper development of specific parts of the eye. Finally, it is possible that the eye would be transformed into another organ – for example, an antenna. Mutations resulting in transformations of one body part into another are called *homeotic mutations*. This would mean that *Fam* is *homeotic gene* – a gene pivotal in making cell fate decisions.

19-11.

a. The diagram below shows a construct for knocking out the yeast *H2A* gene. The blue rectangles can be sequences homologous to the *H2A* gene and at each end as shown, or 5' or 3' to the *H2A* gene (not shown). Homologous recombination between the *H2A* gene in the yeast genome and the linear construct leads to replacement of the normal allele with the allele containing the *kan^r* gene in the middle of the open reading frame. This allele should be nonfunctional (a null allele).

b. (i) By recombinant DNA technology you would make a plasmid containing the *kan^r* gene inserted into the *H2A* open reading frame. (ii) You would then make a linear fragment containing the interrupted *H2A* gene as indicated in the preceding diagram. You could make this linear fragment by cutting it out of the plasmid with restriction enzymes or by PCR amplifying the desired sequences from the plasmid. (iii) You would transform yeast with the linear DNA fragment and select for kanamycin-resistant colonies. (iv) You would analyze the *H2A* genomic region of single colony using PCR and sequencing of the PCR product to check for insertion via homologous recombination.

c. You would expect that the *H2A* gene is essential because its protein product is a critical part of nucleosomes (review Chapter 11). You would thus perform the gene targeting in a diploid strain and would plan to knock out only a single allele. (Gene targeting is sufficiently inefficient that it would be unlikely to knock out both copies of the gene simultaneously.) In a diploid, a wild-type gene copy will remain to prevent the successfully targeted yeast cell from dying.

d. If haploid *H2A* knockouts are viable, such a result would mean that, counter to expectation, *H2A* is not an essential gene. The most likely explanation would that the yeast genome contains another gene that makes a protein very similar to H2A and that can substitute functionally for the H2A protein in nucleosomes.

19-12.

The idea is to synthesize a PCR primer pair that will amplify the *neo^r* gene template and at the same time add loxP sites to the two ends of the gene. This can be done by synthesizing long primers that contain the 34 nt loxP site, and also ~20 nt of the *neo^r* gene. In addition, the very 5' end of each primer will include a restriction site (RE) that is not found elsewhere in the PCR amplification product but is found in the intron into which this DNA fragment will be ligated. As shown in the following diagram, the PCR product will have the same restriction site at both ends (RE), and loxP sites flanking the *neor* gene.

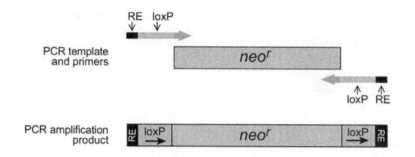

You can now cut the PCR product with the restriction enzyme and ligate it into a plasmid containing the intron that has been cut with the same restriction enzyme that leaves the same sticky ends:

19-13

a. Because LCA is due to loss of *RPE65* gene function, a mouse knockout could be used to generate a model for LCA. As is true of most loss-of-function mutations, the LCA phenotype is recessive and appears only in homozygotes or in transheterozygotes for two different alleles. Thus, the mouse model would need to be homozygous for the knockout allele. If these knockout mice are blind, then *RPE65* likely functions similarly in mice and humans.

b. The procedure you would use to create a mouse model for fragile X syndrome would depend on which aspect of the disease you wanted to study. Because the disease is caused by loss of *FMR-1* gene function, a knockout could model the disease phenotype. It turns out that the *FMR-1* gene in mice is located on the murine X chromosome as well. Male mice hemizygous for the knockout and female mice homozygous for the knockout in fact show phenotypes that are highly reminiscent of the symptoms of fragile-X syndrome seen in human children. (On the other hand, if you want to study how new mutant alleles arise from permutation alleles, or how the expansion of CGG repeat number inhibits *FMR-1* expression, you could generate a knockin with additional CGG repeats).

c. Huntington disease is caused by a gain-of-function allele of *Htt* that makes a protein with an abnormally long polyQ region. To study the disease phenotype, how the mutant protein functions, or the process by which a pre-mutation allele becomes a disease allele, a knockin that adds CAG repeats to the mouse gene's coding region at the same position these repeats are found in the human Htt would be needed. Such knockin mouse models with 150 CAG repeats have indeed been created, and they show late onset neurodegeneration. Pharmaceutical companies can use these mice to establish whether candidate drugs will alleviate the symptoms, although the models are difficult to use because the onset is quite late compared to the life span of the mouse.

19-14

a. The object is to knockin into the mouse *FGFR3* gene the missense mutation (G380R) that causes achondroplasia when present in the human gene. It turns out that the corresponding mutation in the mouse *FGFR3* gene is G374R. [The mutation is a single base change: GGG (Gly) to AGG (Arg). The mouse and human proteins are of slightly different sizes, explaining the difference in the numbering.] The knockin construct and the final mutation it makes in the mouse *FGFR3* gene are shown in the following diagram:

b. TALENs could also be used to generate the same mutation in the mouse *FGFR3* gene. First, design synthetic genes for two TALEN proteins that will bind to base pair sequences flanking the GGG codon for G374. Next, use *in vitro* transcription to make mRNAs from each TALEN gene. Inject the two different kinds of TALEN mRNAs into the cytoplasm of one cell stage mouse embryos (zygotes), along with linear DNAs containing the G374R point mutation. The TALEN proteins will be synthesized in embryonic cells by translation of the mRNAs, and the TALEN proteins will cut mouse chromosomes at the position of the nucleotides encoding G374 of the *FGFR3* gene. The ends produced by this cleavage promote homologous recombination between the mouse chromosome and the linear DNA. You will next need to implant the injected embryos into surrogate mothers. When these animals are born, you then test the mouse pups for cells with the mutation using a PCR assay. Because the injected mice that test positive for the mutation are likely mosaic for mutant and normal cells, you need to backcross these mice to normal mice. If cells in the germ line have the mutation, the gametes they produce will generate non-mosaic heterozygotes in the next generation.

19-15

a. To express GFP, the gene trapping construct must integrate within an intron of a gene. The gene trapping construct is in essence an exon, and if it inserts between the exons of a mouse gene, it can potentially be incorporated into a spliced mRNA. Because of its poly-A addition site, the construct will become the final exon of the altered gene.

b. Only a fraction of mice with the gene trapping transgene integrated into an intron will express GFP. This statement is true even if we assume that the transgene will always be spliced into the mRNA made from the primary transcript of the altered gene. First, the construct can insert in two different orientations with respect to the promoter. Only the orientation where the *GFP* open reading frame ends up in the transcript could possibly result in GFP protein expression. Second, the position of the transgene with respect to other exons matters. If the transgene inserts between exons that both contain 5'UTR sequences, then the ATG of the transgene should signal the beginning of GFP translation, and GFP should be made. If the transgene inserts between coding exons, then translation will have begun upstream and the ATG of the GFP cDNA must be in frame with the ORF of the preceding exon in order for GFP protein to be translated; the chances of this occurring are only 1 in 3 (if the orientation is correct). Finally, if ORFs are in frame, GFP amino acids will be attached at the C terminus of the protein encoded by the preceding exon(s). As part of a hybrid protein, GFP may or may not fold correctly, and thus fluorescence may or may not be detectable.

c. If the transgene inserts such that GFP protein is made without other amino acids attached to it [see part (b)], then the information from enhancer trapping and gene trapping is substantially similar; GFP would be reporting the pattern of expression of the regulatory elements of the gene that trapped it. However, one subtle difference between the patterns of expression revealed by the two methods exists. If the gene trapping construct inserts between exons that both contain 5'UTR sequences, then the mRNA expressing GFP will have 5'UTR sequences from the mouse gene. The 5'UTR sequences could influence the translation or stability of the mRNA for GFP, perhaps in a tissue-specific way. An enhancer trap construct has its own 5'UTR, so such effects could not be observed. If GFP inserts such that is made as the C terminus of a hybrid protein [see part (b)], then information about protein subcellular localization could potentially be revealed, especially if the N-terminal portion of the hybrid protein contains all or most of the normal protein encoding by the gene at the insertion site. If the N-terminal part of the protein is able to go to its normal location in the cell (for example, a particular organelle), the attached GFP will fluoresce there. In an enhancer trap line, GFP would not be expressed as a hybrid protein, so this information would not be available.

d. Both enhancer trap insertions and gene trap insertions can generate mutations in genes at their insertion sites. However, a successfully trapped gene is more likely than a trapped enhancer to be associated with a mutation in the gene. An enhancer trap construct can express GFP without the transgene inserting into the gene. A gene trap construct, however, must insert into an intron of the gene in order for GFP to be made. The stop codon that ends the GFP ORF will stop further translation of the mRNA and thus will prevent translation of any amino acids encoded by exons downstream of the insertion site.

19-16

a. A transgene in which the B cell regulatory region is fused to a *myc* cDNA introduced into the mouse genome by pronuclear injection should increase the frequency of tumor formation in the mouse immune system.

b. The transgenic mice described in part (a) would express the *myc* cDNA in B cells throughout the life of the organism. In this part of the problem, we are exploring how to turn on *myc* overexpression starting at a defined point in the organism's development. One way to overexpress Myc in B cells starting at 1 week of age is to generate a transgene like the one shown in the following diagram, which can be introduced into the mouse genome by pronuclear injection. (In the diagram, the B cell regulatory region contains both a promoter and a B cell-specific enhancer; T= transcription termination sequence.) If the mice also contain a *hs-cre* construct and are heat-shocked when they are one week old, Cre expression will cause the B cell enhancer to flip, so that now it expresses *myc* instead of *GFP*. The GFP gene in this construct serves two purposes. First, it is a positive control to ensure that mice have in fact been transformed by the construct. Second, you can make sure that the heat shock worked as desired if the B cells stop expressing GFP and thus lose their fluorescence.

Another construct that would work has loxP sites in the same orientation flanking *GFP;* the *GFP* cDNA, initially transcribed in B cells, will be deleted when Cre is expressed:

Chapter 19

Section 19.4

19-17.

a. To generate a mouse that expresses Pax6 everywhere it is expressed normally except in its eyes, introduce a transgene that expresses the reverse complement of *Pax6* cDNA from an eye-specific enhancer. The latter construct will inhibit endogenous *Pax6* expression in the eye by RNAi. That is, eye cells will have double-stranded *Pax6* RNA that can be processed into *Pax6* siRNAs; these in turn will lead to degradation of *Pax6* mRNAs.

b. A mouse strain with a floxed *Pax6* gene and *hs-cre* transgene would enable the scientist to turn off *Pax6* expression by heat-shocking the mice at any age. The mouse would need to be homozygous for the floxed *Pax6* because if a normal copy of *Pax6* remained in the genome, its expression would be unaffected by the heat shock. As Cre expression is not eye-specific, the mice would likely die at some point after heat shock due to the loss of Pax6 function in essential organs. One way around this problem would be to express the reverse complement of *Cre* cDNA from a transgene with a pancreas-specific promoter [see part (a)].

c. The knockin construct shown at the top of the figure that follows would generate the floxed *Pax6* gene presented at the bottom of the figure. Note that the *GFP* gene within the floxed *Pax6* gene is divided into two pieces (a 5' piece containing a mouse basal promoter and the 5' UTR, and a 3' piece with the codons for the GFP amino acids), and a transcript made with the intervening sequences. Prior to heat shock, a mouse with the floxed *Pax6* gene would make *Pax6* as normal, because all the alterations of the gene are within introns, so the *GFP* and loxP sequences would be spliced out of the primary transcript. However, such a mouse would be unable to make GFP prior to heat shock because the *GFP* sequences are interrupted. The mice homozygous for the floxed allele also have a transgene that expresses Cre only in the eye. Recombination catalyzed by Cre will delete exon 2 from the floxed gene only in the eye. *Pax6* will become inactivated in eye cells. Simultaneously, the promoter and ORF of *GFP* are brought together (the endogenous *Pax6* enhancer will work with the mouse promoter that drives *GFP* expression) so the cells with no *Pax6* function will fluoresce in green.

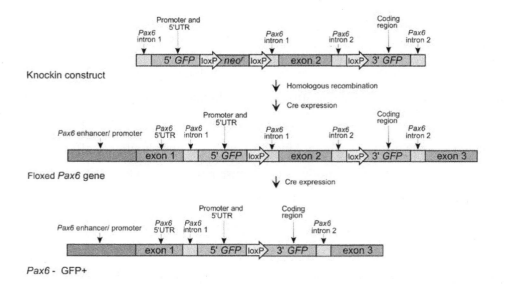

Knockin construct

Floxed *Pax6* gene

Pax6 - GFP+

19-18.

a. Some human diseases do not show symptoms until an advanced age. As the lifespan of the mouse is shorter, mice age faster. Thus, depending on the biochemistry and physiology underlying the disease, it is possible that the mice homozygous for the knockout will die of natural causes before the effects of the knockout will become manifest. As discussed in Problem 13(c) in this chapter, this phenomenon has in fact lessened the utility of mouse models for Huntington disease.

b. Homozygosity for some loss-of-function mutations in humans may not be lethal, yet it may cause disease phenotypes in individuals who are born. Homozygosity for knockouts of the corresponding gene might be lethal *in utero* in mice. Thus, homozygous mice could not suffer from the same condition because these mice could never be born. One way to circumvent this issue is to generate a mouse model for the disease using a conditional knockout where the gene can be inactivated in a specific tissue and time after birth.

c. If mice have several copies of a gene, a knockout for only one of these copies is likely to be without effect, because the other copies could supply the gene product. Two strategies could allow investigators to deal with this issue. First, all the copies of the gene could be knocked out sequentially to model the loss-of-function disease in humans. Alternatively, an RNAi transgene could potentially knock down or knock out expression of all of the copies if a single siRNA could be designed that was homologous to all of these genes.

d. Mice from different inbred lines could have distinct alleles of modifier genes (suppressors and enhancers) resulting in differing expressivity of a knockout mutant phenotype; in fact, the mutant phenotype might not be observed at all in some genetic backgrounds. If a particular knockout mouse does not show a mutant phenotype, it might be useful to outcross it to a different strain and then regenerate the homozygotes. Mixing two different genetic backgrounds might eliminate some suppressors and reveal a human disease-like phenotype.

e. Knockout mice in which the expression of nearby genes is disrupted might display phenotypes completely unrelated to the human disease being studied. It would thus be difficult to know which phenotypes are associated with the knocked-out gene, and which with the nearby gene. Possible ways to deal with this situation include making different kinds of knockouts that should not affect adjacent genes (for example, using gene targeting to introduce a nonsense mutation into the gene of interest or knocking down the function of this gene by RNA interference).

19-19.

a. The following figure diagrams a knockin construct that would allow you to tag the full-length protein product of the gene in question with GFP. You would obtain the GFP coding sequences from a cDNA, and you would use recombinant DNA technology to insert the GFP sequences in frame with the gene's ORF just upstream of the stop codon. In this way, the altered gene will encode a fusion protein in which all the amino acids of the gene product are followed at the C terminus by GFP. The neo^r gene is required as a selectable marker to identify ES cells that have integrated the knockin construct by homologous recombination.

(Note that in the diagram above, if the Stop codon is located in the final exon, the *light blue* rectangle to the right of the "exon" labeled as "intron" would simply be genomic DNA 3' to the gene. In this case, it might not be necessary to remove the neo^r gene.)

b. The knockin strategy has the advantage that the *gene X* regulatory sequences do not need to be characterized because they are already present in *gene* X on the mouse chromosome. Suppose that you employed instead a transgene that would express a Protein X-GFP fusion protein. To ensure that the fusion protein is made in those cells in which *gene X* is normally expressed, the transgene would have to contain a DNA fragment with the *gene X* regulatory sequences. You would have to conduct several experiments to identify such a DNA fragment.

19-20.

Alteration of the genome of human germ-line cells raises so many ethical issues that it is illegal in most countries. One major concern is that genome alterations passed through the germ line would affect every cell in the body of resulting progeny, and could easily produce unanticipated phenotypic consequences in these people and in their descendants for generations to come. These changes may not easily be reversed. In addition, many ethicists are concerned about the ramifications of altering genomes to enhance specific characteristics of their children and their descendants: Will the alterations truly aid the progeny, or would they instead simply reflect what the parents currently think about the desirability of particular traits? How can one draw the line?

19-21.

a. Retroviral vectors deliver to the target cells double-stranded DNA copies of the therapeutic gene to the nucleus, and these copies are then incorporated by reverse transcriptase/endonuclease into a chromosome. AAV vectors deliver to the target cells double-stranded DNA gene copies that remain extrachromosomal.

b. The advantage of retroviral vectors is that the therapeutic gene is stable in a chromosome. By contrast, when using AAV vectors, because the therapy gene is extrachromosomal, the DNA degrades eventually and the gene therapy must be repeated. However, the main drawback of retroviral vectors is that they can cause mutation when the therapeutic gene integrates into the chromosome. If the integration event interrupts a gene, the result would be a loss of function mutation. The integration event could alternatively be a gain-of-function mutation if the strong enhancer in the retroviral vector long terminal repeat (LTR) causes a nearby gene to be overexpressed. Another drawback of retroviral vectors is that human cells tend to mount a stronger immune response to retroviruses than to AAVs.

19.22

a. The dominant *RPE65* mutant allele must be a gain-of-function mutation because the loss-of-function *RPE65* alleles that cause LCA are recessive to wild-type; *RPE65* is not haploinsufficient.

b. The kind of gene therapy used for LCA would not work for retinitis pigmentosa caused by the dominant *RPE65* allele. The gene therapy strategy for LCA was replacement of the loss-of-function alleles with a wild-type gene copy. A therapy gene for retinitis pigmentosa would somehow have to inhibit the function of the dominant mutant *RPE65* allele or gene product.

19.23

a. The issue for designing an siRNA that will prevent the expression of the mutant allele specifically is that siRNAs can bind to and inhibit expression of mRNAs without perfect sequence complementarity. The dominant mutations in disease alleles often are single base changes that alter a codon. Thus, it is possible that an siRNA with perfect complementarity for the disease allele would still be able to inhibit expression of the normal allele because only a single base pair is different. One way that scientists try to get around this problem is to look for silent base pair differences in the normal and mutant allele that an interfering RNA could discriminate between. If such polymorphisms were found, then it might be possible to design interfering RNAs that differ from the wild-type allele in the patient at more than one position. The problem is even more acute in the case of rare dominant alleles that cause overexpression of a normal protein product; here, the mRNAs produced by the mutant and wild-type allele could be identical. The problem could be circumvented only if the mRNAs produced by the two alleles were not in fact identical because of silent polymorphisms.

b. Triplet repeat disorders like Huntington disease always present a challenge to design an interfering RNA that would target only the mutant allele. The reason is that the difference between the normal and disease allele is not a base substitution, but a difference in copy number of a triplet repeat. Because the triplet repeat region in normal alleles is usually longer than an interfering RNA (~21-30 nt), it is impossible to design an interfering RNA that would base pair only with a mutant allele that has an expanded triplet repeat region. As described in part (a), one potential way around this problem is to target silent sequence differences in the wild-type and mutant alleles.

Chapter 20 Sequencing and Analyzing Genomes

Synopsis:

This chapter describes the tools and goals of genome sequence analysis. The highest resolution genomic map is a long-range DNA sequence maps compiled from the sequences of subclones which provides the complete sequence of the entire genome. The subclones may be derived either from previously mapped large insert clones (hierarchical shotgun approach) or directly from the genome (whole-genome shotgun approach). In recent years, a new generation of "massively parallel" sequencing strategies have been developed that greatly increase the speed with which researchers can sequence genomes. At the same time these methods have greatly reduced the costs associated with sequencing projects.

This work has led to a variety of major insights of human and model organism genomes:

- there are surprisingly few genes in the human genome, only ~ 21,000;
- genes fall into 2 major classes - noncoding RNA genes and protein coding genes;
- repeat sequences constitute >50% of the human genome, with some having evolved to become genes or control sequences;
- the genome contains different types of gene organization, including gene families, gene-rich regions and gene deserts;
- evolution can occur by the lateral transfer of genes from one organism to another;
- different human races have very few, if any, uniquely distinguishing genes;
- the sequences of microbes, plants and animals all employ the same genetic code and show a remarkable similarity;
- The Human Genome Project has catalyzed the development of high-throughput equipment for the studies of genomics and proteomics.
- The Human Genome Project has led to paradigm changes in our approaches to biology and medicine. For the first time it is becoming possible to take a systems approach where all the elements of a system are studied (see Chapter 24).

Key Words:

genome the entire collection of *chromosomes* in each cell of an organism.

Human Genome Project an initiative to determine the complete sequence of the human *genome*.

genomics a branch of biology dedicated to the study of whole *genomes*.

bioinformatics the science of using computational methods to decipher the biological meaning of information contained within organismal systems.

shotgun a sequencing approach in which the overlapping fragments to be sequenced have been randomly generated by shearing (via sonication) or by partial digestion with *restriction enzymes.*

somatic gene therapy remedial measures in which a replacement *gene* is inserted into the affected tissue where the gene is expressed to compensate for a faulty gene.

germline gene therapy a genetic engineering technique that modifies the DNA of *germ cells* that are passed on to progeny.

Significant Elements:

The problems in this chapter use many of the techniques that were introduced in chapter 14, including restriction mapping, cloning, probing, PCR and dideoxy (Sanger) sequencing. After reading the chapter and thinking about the concepts, you should be able to:

♦ Describe the rationale for the Human Genome Project

♦ Describe the two alternative methods used to sequence the human genome

♦ Explain how computational methods are used to analyze genome sequences

♦ Describe the advantages of massively parallel sequencing strategies

♦ Intelligently discuss the ethical ramifications of living in the post-genomic era

Solutions to Problems:

Vocabulary

20-1.

i. 5; **ii.** 3; **iii.** 4; **iv.** 1; **v.** 2 ; **vi.** 6

Section 20.1 – The Evolution of Whole Genome Sequencing

20-2.

The HGP represents an example of hypothesis-generating research (in contrast to hypothesis-driven research). Such exploratory strategies aim to generate data that can be used to stimulate scientific thought and thus lead to the future development of testable hypotheses. In this sense the sequence data of the HGP can be thought of as intellectual infrastructure. For example, many of the ideas/techniques explored in subsequent chapters used the HGP as their foundation. While the HGP is generally thought of by the scientific community as a great success, there is no doubt that the costs were massive (~ $3billion). Would these resources have been better spent on more traditional hypothesis driven research? Has the HGP fulfilled its promise? Everyone has their own opinion, so there is no right or wrong answer. However, it is clear that the HGP has revolutionized the discipline of biology and has forever changed how scientists practice genetics.

Section 20.2 – Sequencing and Assembling Entire Genomes

20-3.

The four cosmids are aligned below. Notice that the third cosmid had to be flipped over for the alignment.

20-4.

a. The monkey DNA of all the BACs in the genomic library is joined to the vector at exactly the same place in the vector, and you know (or can easily determine) the sequence of the BAC vector itself. Thus, you could generate two sequencing primers that would hybridize in all of the clones to the BAC vector just on either side of the inserted monkey DNA. If the 5' to 3' orientation of these primers is correct, the DNA sequence obtained would be of the monkey DNA. The same two primers would enable you to find thousands of different monkey STSs. In the figure below the oval shows the entire BAC clone (the vector DNA is the heavy line and the monkey DNA is the lighter line). The arrows represent the PCR primers with the 3' end of each primer at the arrowhead.

b. We don't know the extent of any of the monkey sequences in the BAC clones other than a general knowledge of the amount of insert DNA that can be cloned into the BAC vector (see part d., next page). We can only determine the order of the BAC clones and the STSs. One way to begin assembling the map is to align the BACs that share sequences in common. The data shows that BAC A contains the STS sequences 4, 5, 7 and 10. BAC A must therefore overlap the ends of BAC B (sequence 4), BAC C (sequence 5) BAC D (sequence 7) and BAC E (sequence 10) as shown below. The map would be equivalent if flipped horizontally with STS 3 at the left end rather than the right end.

c. The minimal tiling path (the fewest BAC clones needed to cover the entire region) would be BAC clones C, B, and A. Clones D and E have redundant sequences that are also found in C, B, or A.

d. BAC clones can accept DNA inserts between 100 and 500 kb long. The minimal tiling path consists of 3 BAC clones, so the contig could range from somewhat less than 300 kb long (because of the overlaps remaining in the minimal tiling path) to somewhat less than 1500 kb long.

20-5.

There are two non-overlapping contigs. The double-stranded sequence of the two contigs is:

5' CAAATAGCAGCAAATTACAGCAATATGAAGAGATCATACAGTCCACTGAA 3'
3' GTTTATCGTCGTTTAATGTCGTTATACTTCTCTAGTATGTCAGGTGACTT 5'
This contig is composed of the first and fifth sequences.

The second contig is:

5' GTAGTATCTCCTTTTAAAAATCTCATTTCCTTTAGGGCATTTTCAAATTC 3'
3' CATCATAGAGGAAAATTTTTAGAGTAAAGGAAATCCCGTAAAAGTTTAAG 5'
This contig is composed of the fourth and sixth sequences.

The second and third sequences do not overlap with each other or with any of the other sequences.

20-6.

Recall that you can read approximately 500-800 nucleotides from a single sequencing reaction. If the repetitive sequence of DNA is longer than this size, then all of the data obtained from the reaction will be derived from the repeated sequence. If the repetitive sequence is repeated many times in the genome, you might not be able to tell from where in the genome the copy you have sequenced is derived. Thus, repetitive sequences longer than 500 bp (like transposons) will constitute a problem, as will long tandem arrays of simple DNA like $(AT)_n$. The array type of repetitive sequences pose an additional problem: such sequences are very difficult to clone at all, and the clones that are obtained often contain deletions or other rearrangements.

Repeats that are dispersed around the genome are not a problem when using the hierarchical shotgun strategy. This strategy analyzes individual BACs that might contain only a single copy of the repetitive sequence, so shotgun sequencing of an entire BAC could proceed without complications. The repetitive sequence would simply be a part of the long region contained in the BAC.

The sequencing of such repetitive sequences is more complicated when using the whole genome shotgun approach. Some information can be derived if a particular sequence is partially composed of a repetitive sequence and partially composed of adjacent "single-copy" DNA found only once in the genome. However, more information is needed. The Celera Corporation's whole genome shotgun strategy involves generating clones with known insert sizes of about 2 kb, 10 kb, and 200 kb. They then sequence the two ends of each clone and retain the information that these two ends are related to each other (that is, one of the sequences is say ~200 kb away from the other sequence). Thus, even if one end is repetitive DNA, it can be connected to a single location because of its relationship with the other end.

Both types of sequencing strategies encounter major difficulties in dealing with tandemly repeated sequences. If these stretches are very long then it becomes hard to tell where within the stretch a particular copy of the sequence is located. Fortunately, in most cases the repeats are not exact: for example, in a stretch of $(AT)_n$, a C or G may occasionally appear to provide a guidepost indicating a particular location. But even so, such regions of the genome are refractory to sequencing, particularly given the problems in cloning them in the first place. Regions around centromeres, for example, may have more than 1 Mb of tandemly repeated simple sequences. As a result, when scientists claim that a genome project for a particular species is complete, they are not necessarily being completely accurate, because such regions may be excluded from the data. In general, this is not a problem, since regions with simple repeats don't usually contain any genes, but it is a source of frustration for scientists interested in studying centromeres.

20-7.

The region may have many genome-wide repeat sequences; or the region may be duplicated at other sites in the genome. Some regions of the genome are unclonable (e.g., centromeric and telomeric sequences) and therefore it is not possible to get the information to design PCR primers. Long stretches of repeated DNA cannot be PCR amplified - the primers must be unique sequences (e.g., AT_n can span hundreds of kb of DNA).

20-8.

The whole genome shotgun sequencing strategy involves randomly shearing the entire genomic DNA to make a plasmid library with ~2 kb inserts, a plasmid library with ~10 kb inserts and a BAC library with ~200 kb inserts. Sequence the 2 kb and the 10 kb inserts for a 6-fold and 3 fold coverage, and then sequence the ends of the BAC clones for 1-fold coverage. The limitations: some genomic sequences cannot be cloned (e.g., heterochromatin) and some sequences get rearranged or deleted when cloned (e.g., some tandemly arrayed repeats).

Section 20.3 – Bioinformatics: Analyzing Genomes
20-9.

a. Once the new gene is sequenced, the predicted amino acid sequence of the protein product can be examined for protein domains or functional units. Tell-tale features of protein sequences are motifs that have been shown to have specific functions in other proteins such as transcription factors. Using comparisons between sequenced genomes of different species you can find orthologous genes. You can also look for paralogous genes (other members of a gene family) within a species. If a function is known for one member of the gene family it is possible to get an idea of the function of another member.

b. Northern blot analysis to discover in which tissues the gene is transcribed provides useful clues about function. Knocking out a gene and looking for a phenotype caused by the knock-out is another type of analysis that might provide functional information on the gene.

20-10.

a. It indicates that there are regions of the chromosome where genes are clustered.

b. The centromere corresponds to the largest gene desert.

c. The CFTR is on the long arm of the chromosome

d. The CFTR gene is trancribed in the direction of the green arrow which is pointing away from the centromere.

e. There are approximately 24 exons in the CFTR gene. It is an approximation as the exons are predicted by computer analysis, and not by a comparison to an actual protein sequence.

20-11.

a. The zinc-finger motif is a DNA sequence that encodes the amino acids capable of forming the zinc finger in a protein. Such domains allow these proteins to bind to specific DNA sequences, suggestions suggesting that the protein is a transcription factor.

b. Similarity with a previously identified gene suggests that the two genes arose by duplication of a common ancestor and could be part of a gene family.

20-12.

Not all human genes have been accurately identified: small genes are hard to identify (e.g. small functional RNAs of 25 bp or less); genes expressed only at the RNA level are difficult to identify (tRNAs, rRNAs, snoRNAs and snRNAs); there could be hundreds or thousands of genes encoding small peptides that are hard to find. Genes that are rarely expressed or that have unusual codon usage patterns are difficult to find. Another factor is that the human proteome is much more complex than that of the nematode, and this comes about due to shuffling of functional modules - the human genome evolved many new arrangements that alter the domain architecture. Combinatorial amplification at the DNA level, as seen with the antibody gene segments, and at the RNA level, seen with alternate splicing, also increases the level of complexity of the proteome. The human genome has more paralogs and chemical modifications of proteins. Humans have >400 different chemical reactions that affect protein structure, so a human cell can have 20,000 different types of mRNAs and 200,000 different proteins.

Section 20.4 – Next Generation Sequencing

19-13.

Next generation sequencing (NGS) is an umbrella term that encompasses a wide range of sequencing technologies that have both increased the speed and reduced the costs associated with DNA sequencing. Some of the most popular platforms are the Roche454 pyrosequencing method, the Illumina sequencing by synthesis method, and Life Technologies Ion Torrent system. While all use unique and proprietary technology, one characteristic clearly separates these methodologies from Sanger sequencing: their massively parallel nature. A typical Sanger machine can run at most a total of 384 reactions in parallel. Next generation methods in contrast can run hundreds of thousands to millions of reactions in parallel. This has allowed for sequencing on a scale not before thought possible. In turn, these advancements have led to great reductions in the costs associated with sequencing.

20-14

Some simple calculations will serve to illustrate the advantages of the massively parallel design. A typical Sanger sequencing reaction generates ~600 bp of sequence. Since a typical Sanger machine can run at most 384 reactions in parallel, a single run of the machine can generate ~ 230,300 bps of sequence. In contrast, a single reaction of a pyrosequencer generates 400 bp of sequence. However, 1.6 million reactions can be run in parallel generating 640,000,000 bps of sequence. Even though the pyrosequencer takes 8 hrs per run (compared to ~ 2 hours for a Sanger machine), the massively parallel design clearly increases the speed with which sequence data can be generated. In addition the cost per base generated is also greatly reduced.

20-15

The system is based upon the fact that the incorporation of a nucleotide during the process of DNA synthesis results in the generation of one pyrophosphate molecule. Thus the number of pyrophosphates generatedduring each "flow" of A, G, C, or T, is proportional to the number of nucleotides incorporated. To measure the amount of pyrophosphate, a series of biochemical reactions are used in which the final by-product is light. First, pyrophosphate is converted to ATP by ATP sulphurylase in the presence of adenosine 5'-phosphosulphate. Next, the ATP is used to convert luciferin to oxyluciferin and light through the action of the enzyme luciferase. Since the amount of light is proportional to the number of nucleotides incorporated, the light produced can be quantified (using an extremely sensitive digital camera) and used to estimate how many A, G, C, or T's were incorporated during each flow.

20-16

Remember that the question asks for the sequence of the template strand. From reading the flowgram you can infer that the sequence of the non-template strand is 5'-TCA GAT CCG TGG GTG G-3'. Thus, the sequence of the template strand is 5'-CCA CCC ACG GAT CTG A-3'

Section 20.5 – Repercussions of the Human Genome Project

20-17

The decision to sequence one's genome is a personal choice that should not be taken lightly. As costs continue to decrease to the point where it will be practical for almost everyone to obtain their own sequence, this is a question you will almost certainly need to grapple with in the not-too-distant future. The main advantage of obtaining your sequence lies in the ability to identify sequence variants that are indicators of disease, and thus can precipitate early diagnosis and medical action. However, not all diseases are treatable. If you possessed a DNA variant that predisposed you to certain medical conditions that could not be treated or prevented would you want to know? Would knowing lead to unnecessary anxiety and worry? Furthermore, at present the predictive power of genome sequencing is somewhat limited. The biological consequences of many variants are unknown or incompletely understood. Thus, much of the information present in a personal genome sequence is unusable. Another important issue relates to privacy. Who would have access to the sequence information? Could government or private organizations use this data against you (i.e. deny insurance or employment on the basis of your DNA)? In any event, the ability to accurately correlate genetic variation with disease states will continue to improve as more and more genomes are sequenced. Thus, these questions are likely to become more and more relevant to you and your family with every passing year.

Chapter 21 Global Genetic Analysis

Synopsis: This chapter introduces you to genetic analysis on a global (i.e. genome-wide scale). The methodologies described in this chapter owe their existence to the intellectual infrastructure provided by the Human Genome Project. This is because any "omics" experiment is dependent on knowing the genome sequence of the organism under study. For example, without accurate annotation of the genome, it would be impossible to create gene chips for use in expression profiling or ChIP-chip analysis. It is important to note that these technologies require interdisciplinary expertise. For instance, the execution of an expression profiling experiment requires expertise from the realms of biology, chemistry, genetics, and physics. For this reason many of the platforms discussed in this chapter represent a fusion of the efforts of both publically funded scientists and privately funded industry.

To correctly answer the questions that appear in this chapter, you will need to understand both the biological and technical aspects of the platforms described. The ultimate goal is for you to develop the ability to properly interpret the data derived from different "omics" platforms.

Key Terms:

haplotype a specific combination of *linked alleles* in a cluster of related *genes.* A contraction of the phrase "haploid genotype."

hybridization the natural propensity of complementary single-stranded molecules of *DNA* or *RNA* to base-pair and form stable double helixes.

genome-wide association study (GWAS) the application of *SNP* chip genotyping to large populations of people for the purpose of discovering genetic associations between particular SNPs and traits.

epigenetic a state of gene functionality that is not encoded within the DNA sequence but that is still heritable from one generation to the next. It can be accomplished and maintained through a chemical modification of DNA such as methylation.

DNA microarray a collection of oligonucleotides attached to a solid surface.

chromatin immunoprecipitation (ChIP) a procedure used by scientists to identify specific DNA sequences that are bound, *in vivo*, to proteins of interest.

Comparative genomic hybridization A molecular cytogenetic method used to screen cells for DNA gains and losses at the chromosomal level

Human Genome Project an initiative to determine the complete sequence of the human *genome.*

Significant Elements:

After reading the chapter and thinking about the concepts, you should be able to

- Compare and contrast traditional genetic analysis with the global analyses described in this chapter
- Describe how gene-chips are designed and constructed
- Explain the role of nucleic acid hybridization in the measurement of gene expression levels and in the characterization of protein-DNA interactions
- Define comparative genome hybridization and explain how it is used in a clinical setting
- Describe the goals of genome-wide association studies with respect to understanding the genetics of complex traits
- Explain how epigenetic modifications are characterized on a genome-wide level

Solutions to Problems:

Vocabulary

21-1.

i. 2; **ii.** 3; **iii.** 1; **iv.** 5; **v.** 4

Section 21.1 – Gene Expression Profiling

21-2.

The fluorescence intensity produced upon scanning the array with a laser beam exciting either the Cy3 or Cy5 fluorophore (attached to the cDNA). The more cDNA hybridizes to the probe, the greater the fluorescence intensity.

21-3.

a. <u>Black</u> – this gene is either not transcribed or is transcribed at very low, undetectable levels in both the normal tissue and in the cancerous tissue. <u>Green</u> – the mRNA for this gene accumulates to higher levels in normal tissue than in the tissue from the tumor so it is likely that the transcription of this gene is turned down in the cancerous cells. <u>Red</u> - the mRNA for this gene accumulates to higher levels in cancerous tissue than in normal tissue so it is probable that the transcription of this gene is turned up in the cancerous cells. <u>Yellow</u> – the mRNA for these genes accumulates to the same level in both kinds of tissue.

b. You would most likely choose a gene that gives a red signal on the microarray. If the level of the mRNA goes up in the tumor relative to normal cells the over-expression of the protein product of this gene may contribute to cancer. A drug that inactivates such a protein might be able to stop the cancer from proliferating.

21-4.

a. The person whose PCR products were labeled with rhodamine (red) is a heterozygote with the M1 sequence on one homologue and the M2 sequence on the other homologue. The other person, whose DNA is labeled with fluorescein, is heterozygous for M3 and M6. Remember that the DNA on the chromosomes is double-stranded, not single-stranded as shown for the oligonucleotide sequences.

b. In this particular case, the DNA sequence of the PCR products from both individuals would appear identical. The sequencing would show that both people have the sequence: 5' ACT(TG)ACCGAGAGA(GA)CCTGCG 3'. The two nucleotides within a set of parentheses would show up in the same position in the sequencing reactions. When you consider the left set of parentheses you can tell that both people are heterozygous at this position with the sequence 5' ACT(T)ACC... on one homologue and 5' ACT(G)ACC... on the other homologue. Likewise you would know that both people were heterozygous for G and A at the second position. This particular case is unusual; the reason these sequences are ambiguous as determined from DNA sequencing of the PCR products is that this short region of the genome has two polymorphisms that are independent of each other. The only way to find the precise genotype of both homologues of both people (for example that the 5' ACT(T)ACC polymorphism is part of the same allele as the 5' AGA(A)CCT polymorphism) is to do the microarray experiment described in part (a) above.

c. The results shown in part (a) demonstrate that this method of oligonucleotide microarrays can be used to genotype single nucleotide polymorphisms. Since you can put many oligonucleotides on a single microarray theoretically this technique can be used to simultaneously genotype anyone for a large number of the most important disease-causing polymorphisms. It is not clear that the method will "scale up" so easily, since you would have to simultaneously PCR amplify many genomic regions (from all the disease genes of interest), and this might contribute to inefficiencies in the PCR or high background noise upon hybridization.

21-5. cDNAs are labelled by including Cy3 (orCy5) tagged dCTP during cDNA synthesis. Thus a cDNA 2000 bp in length would be expected to have (on average) 10 times the fluorescence of a 200 bp cDNA. Thus, one could only conclude that gene X was expressed at a higher level than gene Y if the cDNAs happened to be of the same length.

21-6. The data indicates that the adult (green) produces transcripts A and B, while larvae (red) express only transcript C. The fact that the exon 5 spot fluoresces green indicates that the adult expresses transcript A and that the larvae do not. The fact that the exon 2 spot fluoresces red indicates that the larvae expresses A and/or C. However, we already know that variant A is not expressed by the larvae, thus it must be expressing only variant C. This also indicates that the adult is not expressing transcript C. Given the above, the fact that the exon 4 spot is yellow indicates that the adult must be producing transcript B and the larvae must be producing transcript C.

Section 21.2 – "ChIP-on chip" and ChIP-Seq Analyses"

21-7. Red and yellow spots on the array indicate that the corresponding segments of DNA are enriched (i.e. overrepresented) in the antibody treated sample, relative to the non-antibody treated sample. Thus these 15 regions of the genome represent likely binding sites for the Drz1 transcription factor.

21-8. The resolution could be increased by fragmenting the DNA into smaller sized fragments (e.g. 50-100 bp in length).

Section 21.3 – Comparative Genome Hybridization

21-9.

a. The data shows that 21 out of the 23 chromosomes are found in 2 copies (diploid). However chromosomes 12 and the X are present in three copies (triploid). Note that a portion of chromosome 11 is found only in one copy, so this cell line is also heterozygous for a large deletion of much of the long arm of chromosome 11 and for a shorter deletion in the long arm of chromosome 13.

b. A virtual karyotype of normal cells from the same person should show two copies of all regions in the genome. As was discussed in Chapter 16, people with cancers are often genetic mosaics, consisting of both normal cells with normal karyotype and tumor cells having abnormal karyotypes.

c. This karyotyping method will only detect changes in the number of copies of a region or an entire chromosome. Therefore it will not detect balanced inversions or translocations. Neither heterozygosity nor homozygosity for these types of rearrangements changes the gene dosage. It might also be difficult to detect small deletions or duplications. The detection of such small rearrangements would depend on both the size of the individual DNA fragments being analyzed in each spot and on the density of these spots along the chromosome.

d. Any region of the genome with a change in dosage may contain a gene that contributes to leukemia. Thus regions on chromosomes 11 and 13 might contain genes that cause cancer when dosage is decreased while chromosome 18 and the X chromosome might have genes that contribute to leukemia when there are extra copies, (when the dosage is increased).

e. The changes in gene dosage (number) discussed in part (d) cannot affect the viability of cells since tumor cells with these changes grow and divide perfectly well (too well in fact).

Section 21.4 – Genome-wide Association Studies

21-10.

Single nucleotide polymorphisms, or SNPs, are the most common form of genetic variation in the genome. SNPs arise from single-base substitutions resulting in the creation of two variants of a DNA sequence that differ by a single nucleotide. With the advent of microarray technology, the analysis of SNPs in the genomes of many people allows for the identification of SNP-trait associations. A confounding factor in genetic association studies is population stratification (differences in allele frequencies of different subpopulations when compared to the population). This can lead to positive associations, not because of a true link between SNP and trait, but simply because one has sampled from populations of different ancestries. Using family based data reduces the effects of population stratification.

21-11.

To ensure the internal validity of the experiment by showing that random differences in subsample composition do not affect the identification of important loci.

21-12.

One possibility would be to engage in ChIP-chip (or ChIP-Seq) analysis. In this way one could determine the genomic binding sites of the protein in question. If binding sites consistently appeared in a subset of promoters, then one could hypothesize that it acted as a transcription factor. Furthermore, by examining the functions of the target genes, one might be able to infer the biological role of the protein with respect to pathogenesis.

Section 21.5 – Epigenomics

21-13. Untreated DNA: >>CCTCGGAAGGA**C**TCAGGC**C**G>>
                                             <<GGAGCCTT**CC**TGAGT**C**CGG**C**<<

21-14. The detection of aberrant methylation patterns has been shown to be effective for both the diagnosis and prognosis of many diseases. Furthermore, as described in the case of the *MGMT* gene, methylation patterns can also be used to predict the response of cancerous tumours to different drug regimes. However, at present, the number of validated associations between epigenetic states and disease (or other) traits are limited. Thus, in order to realize the full diagnostic and prognostic potential, many more reference genomes (both normal and diseased) need to be analyzed.

Chapter 22 Proteomics

Synopsis: In this chapter we explore the world of proteomics and describe the experimental techniques used by researchers to 1) analyze protein expression in different cell types, 2) analyze post-translational modifications that take place within these cell types, 3) define protein interaction networks, and 4) better understand the relationship between the structure of protein interaction networks and their biological functions. Achieving these goals are crucial to the understanding of biological processes since the cellular protein complement is known to organize itself into complex and dynamic structural and/or functional interaction networks. By integrating data obtained from proteomics research with genetic and phenotypic data, it may be possible to elucidate how perturbations of these networks affect cellular or organismal phenotype.

Key Terms:

proteome the complete set of unique *proteins* encoded by a given *genome.*

proteomics the global analysis of the *proteins* present in a particular cell type or organism under a defined set of environmental conditions.

yeast two-hybrid system an assay, performed in the budding yeast, Saccharomyces cerevisiae, developed as a means of identifying protein-protein interactions.

recombinant DNA molecules a combination of DNA molecules of different origin that are joined using *recombinant DNA technologies.*

mass spectrometry an analytical method for identifying the components of a sample by means of the separation of gaseous ions according to mass and charge.

isotope-coded affinity tags reagent comprised of a chemical modifying group linked to an affinity group through a mass encoded linker.

Significant Elements:

After reading the chapter and thinking about the concepts, you should be able to

- Define the term proteome and be able to clearly describe the goals of proteomics research
- Describe the technologies used to create protein interaction maps
- Appreciate the role of robotics in conducing high-throughput proteomics research
- Relate the characterization of protein interaction networks to the emergence of cellular/organismal phenotypes
- Explain how isotope-coded affinity tags are employed to analyze dynamic changes in protein expression
- Describe how protein arrays can be used to perform genome-wide analytical studies

Solutions to Problems:

<u>Vocabulary</u>

22-1.

i. 4; **ii.** 2; **iii.** 1; **iv.** 3

Section 22.1 – What is Proteomics and How Does It Relate to Genetics, Medicine, and Network Biology?

22-2.

a. The genome defines the total genetic content in one set of chromosomes. The transcriptome is the total population of mRNAs (derived from the transcription of genes encoded within the genome) that is expressed in a single cell or cell type. The proteome is the complete set of unique proteins (derived from the translation of mRNAs) that are expressed in a cell.

b. The complexity of eukaryotic gene regulation sometimes confounds the use of the terms described in part **a**. For example, patterns of gene expression change as a function of the environment, cell type and development. Furthermore, after being transcribed, a single primary transcript may be subject to alternative splicing. Again, different cell types will often produce different splice variants as a function of developmental or environmental cues. Lastly, proteins can be chemically modified after translation. For example, a given protein might exist in a phosphorylated or a non-phosphorylated state (other examples of post-translational modifications include glycosylation, ubiquitination, and acetylation). Again these modifications have the capacity to alter the structural and/or biochemical properties of the protein. Thus, when referring to the transcriptome or proteome of an organism, one should specify the cell type under study, the growth conditions used, and the developmental stage of the organism.

Section 22.2 – Genome-Level Proteomic Interaction Analysis: The Yeast Two-Hybrid System

22-3.

a. False. Transcription factors do not bind DNA via covalent linkages.

b. False. The expression of the reporter gene increases if there is an interaction.

c. False. Fusions to the activation and DNA binding domain are created.

22-4.

a. Yes. The reporter gene is present within the yeast nuclear genome. Therefore the fusion proteins must be able to translocate from the cytoplasm to the nucleus in order to activate transcription.

b. Not all proteins will be able to enter the nucleus. For example, they may be too large to enter through the nuclear pore, or localize to other subcellular compartments through targeting sequences.

22-5. Sarah is correct. Yeast cells are used simply as a "living test-tube" so-to-speak. Using recombinant DNA technology one can fuse the sequences encoding the Gal4 AD and DBD to DNA sequences of any origin (i.e. sequences encoding proteins found in any organism of interest).

22-6.

a. False positive: The two proteins under study interact and activate the reporter gene in yeast cells, but **do not** interact in the cell type in which the proteins are normally expressed.

False negative: The two proteins under study do not interact and thus do not activate the reporter gene in yeast cells, but **do** interact in the cell type in which the proteins are normally expressed.

b. One of the proteins under study may not be correctly modified in yeast (e.g. a kinase that normally phosphorylates the protein may not be present in yeast) leading to a failed interaction. In the presence of the kinase in its natural cell type the protein is phosphorylated. This may change its conformation, and thus promote binding to its partner.

c. The fusion proteins may be expressed at higher levels than when under the control of their natural promoters. This can lead to abnormally high protein concentrations that can result in non-specific binding.

d. If available it would be useful to clone a DNA sequence encoding a protein sequence known to interact with your bait, and to use this construct to assay the interaction in the two-hybrid system. If the interaction is detected, it likely implies that the bait is properly folded and is localized to the nucleus. To prevent false negatives it is important to confirm that the fusion protein is indeed expressed (perhaps through Western blotting), and that the bait can indeed localize to the nucleus. To prevent false-positives, it is important to ensure that the bait does not have the ability to activate the reporter independently.

Section 22.3 – Genome-Level Proteomic Interaction Analysis: Affinity Purification Coupled to Mass Spectrometry

22-7.

a. No. In the biological applications discussed in the text, proteins all possess the same charge.

b. No. Sanger and next generation methods are used for DNA sequencing.

c. Yes. The sequence of a protein can be determined upon analysis of the spectrum generated after the peptide enters the collision cell.

d. No. Expression profiling and RNA-seq methods are used to quantify mRNA levels.

e. Yes. The height of the peaks in the spectrum provide a basis for the quantification of protein levels.

22-8. The data from the normal pancreatic cell line shows that Rb interacts with four peptide fragments that do not appear in the cancerous line (DDAFTDSLQLDVVGDSAVDEFEK, WIGPVDFSSSDEELVDVSASVLPELK, SSTLPSADPQLQSQPSLNLSPVMSR, LCIYTDGSIRPEELLQMELLLVNK). Likewise Rb in the cancerous line interacts with four fragments not found in the immunoprecipitate from the normal cell line (APPPGLPAETIK, DLKPENILVTSGGTVK, ACQEQIEALLESSLR, MEHQLLCCEVETIR). Upon conducting a database search (BLASTP) the fragments specific to the normal cell line define the E2F protein, and inhibitor of RB. Upon conducting a database search (BLASTP) the fragments specific to the cancerous cell line define Cdk4 and Cyclin D1. Thus, one hypothesis is that the Rb in the cancer line is abnormally interacting with Cdk4/Cyclin D1 due to an absence of E2F, and that this abnormal interaction is driving cell cycle progression and proliferation. One could test this by treating the normal cell line with siRNA's targeting Rb and assessing the resulting phenotype.

Section 22.4 – Analyzing Dynamic Changes in Protein Expression

22-9.

a. False. The ICAT reagent contains a thiol specific reactive group, a linker region comprised of either hydrogen or deuterium, and a biotin tag.

b. True.

c. False. ICAT quantifies changes in protein expression from two different cellular states.

22-10. Typically fragments separated by exactly 8 Da are used to compare peak height. If a peptide were to be completely absent in one of the two conditions tested, it would then be impossible to conduct the comparison.

22-11. The ultimate level of expression will depend on factors affecting the rates of production and degradation of the mRNA and the production and degradation of the protein. Thus, one simple explanation would be to assume that for these 80 proteins whose levels change, the regulation of protein levels must occur predominantly at the post-transcriptional level. This can involve differences in the rates of translation of different mRNAs or differences in the rates at which different proteins are degraded.

22-12. Three fragments would be produced as a result of treatment with trypsin (MDFFR, VVENQQPPATMPLNVSFTNR, NYDLDYDSVQPYFYCDEEENFYQQQQQSELQPPAPSEDIWK). The weights of the three fragments are 786Da, 2582 Da, and 5766 Da. Thus, the Myc peptide is not present in any of the given spectrums.

Chapter 23 Functional Genomics

Synopsis: In this chapter we discuss how genome sequence data can be exploited to analyze both gene function and genome architecture. As illustrated in the figure that opens this chapter, the Human Genome Project represented "the end of the beginning". In other words the availability of genome sequence data represents not an endpoint in genetics research, but instead the beginning of a new scientific era (referred to as the post-genomic era). Research of the post-genomic era seeks to define the function, regulation, and interaction of all gene products in a genome. In this way researchers hope to further illuminate the complex relationship between genotype and phenotype. By its very nature functional genomics relies on high throughput techniques that produce vast data sets describing the characteristics of the genes/gene-products governing cellular physiology. The establishment of these data sets have in turn necessitated the development of philosophies and techniques – collectively defining the discipline of systems biology (discussed in Chapter 24) – that are aimed at understanding how the interaction of cellular components give rise to higher order biological phenomenon. When reading this chapter, pay special attention to how traditional genetic techniques have been cleverly adapted to provide genome-wide functional information.

Key Terms:

functional genomics the branch of genetics that seeks to define the function, regulation, and interaction of all gene products in a genome.

knockout construct a DNA construct that is introduced into a cell type of interest to replace (via homologous recombination) a specific open reading frame from its start to stop codons. The construct generally contains a gene encoding a selectable marker.

homologous recombination the exchange of DNA strands of similar or identical nucleotide sequence.

selectable markers antibiotic resistance genes and other vector genes that make it possible to pick out cells harbouring a particular DNA molecule.

DNA microarray a collection of oligonucleotides attached to a solid surface.

genetic barcode a short, unique, nucleotide sequence used to identify cells of a given genotype.

RNA interference (RNAi) the sequence-specific modulation of eukaryotic gene expression by a 21–24-nucleotide-long RNA molecule referred to as micro-RNA if it is encoded within the genome and short interfering RNA if it is introduced into the cell by scientists or infectious agents. These small, specialized RNAs prevent the expression of specific genes through complementary base pairing. In the most common natural form of RNAi, primary miRNA-containing transcripts are processed sequentially with the enzymes Drosha and Dicer to produce a mature miRNA that is loaded onto an RNA-induced silencing complex (RISC). RISC binds to complementary mRNA targets, causing mRNA degradation or reduced translational activity.

gene knockdown a method for reducing gene expression that exploits the cellular RNAi machinery.

transfection the transformation of mammalian cells via the uptake of DNA from the medium.

synthetic lethality when an individual carrying mutations in two different genes dies, even though individuals carrying either mutation alone survive.

Significant Elements:

After reading the chapter and thinking about the concepts, you should be able to

- Describe the origins of functional genomics research
- Define, compare and contrast the disciplines of functional genomics and systems biology
- Explain how the genome-wide budding yeast gene deletion set was created and how it is used to provide functional information
- Explain how our knowledge of RNAi is exploited to carry out functional genomics studies in developmentally complex eukaryotes
- Describe how synthetic genetic array analysis identifies hub and non-hub genes
- Illustrate the importance of hub and non-hub genes with respect to determining phenotype in outbred populations

Solutions to Problems:

Vocabulary

23-1.

i. 2; **ii.** 3; **iii.** 1

Section 23.1 – What is Functional Genomics?

23-2.

Several characteristics differentiate functional genomics research from traditional genetic analysis. Some of these characteristics include the discipline's inherent global scale, in which all gene-products in a genome (as opposed to one or a few genes) are examined in parallel. This global perspective in turn makes the discipline dependent on high-throughput methods requiring interdisciplinary expertise. Furthermore, the vast data sets produced by these approaches has in turn necessitated the development of philosophies and techniques (defining the discipline of systems biology) that are aimed at understanding how the interaction of cellular components give rise to higher order biological phenomenon.

23-3. Essential genes are those whose expression is required for life (i.e. cells with deletions for essential genes are non-viable under all growth conditions). For budding yeast, it would be possible to define essential genes by creating a set of diploids in which each strain is heterozygous for different gene deletion. A diploid cell heterozygous for deletion of an essential gene would produce only 2 (out of 4) viable progeny when induced to sporulate. Diploids heterozygous for deletion of a non-essential gene would in contrast produce four viable spores upon sporulation.

Section 23.2 – The Genome-wide Budding Yeast Gene Deletion Set

23-4. Obtain the set of barcoded budding yeast haploid gene deletion strains. Equal amounts of each strain could then be inoculated into two independent cultures. Incubate one at room temperature and the other at 42°C (for a predetermined amount of time). At the end of this period, isolate genomic DNA from each culture and amplify the bar codes by PCR (the room temperature sample being amplified while incorporating the Cy3 fluorophore, and the 42°C sample being amplified while incorporating the Cy5 fluorophore). Combine and then competitively hybridize the samples to a bar code array. Strains deleted for genes with a role in the heat shock response will be underrepresented in the 42°C sample relative to the control. This in turn would lead to increased hybridization of Cy3 labelled barcodes (relative to Cy5 labelled barcodes). Thus, spots on the array corresponding to genes with a role in the heat shock response will fluoresce green.

23-5. When considering this question it is important to note that useful information could be obtained using both approaches. In fact, the approaches complement each other. Thus, in a perfect world, where time and money are not an issue, it would be most fruitful to undertake both strategies. In forward genetic screens random mutations are generated (e.g. by treatment with a mutagen) in a population of cells or individuals. Those cells or individuals displaying a specific phenotype are then isolated for further study. In this method many different alleles (both gain and loss of function) of a single gene can be isolated. However, the identity of the gene that has been mutated is not immediately known. In fact identifying the affected gene may be difficult and cumbersome. In reverse genetics the phenotypic effects of disrupting the function of a known gene (i.e. a sequenced and annotated gene) is determined. In this method one knows from the outset the identity of the gene. However, most methods (e.g. RNAi, knockouts) create only loss of function mutations. Thus this approach will not provide multiple alleles for each gene involved in the process under study and thus cannot provide as much functional information when compared to a forward approach.

23-6.

a. (i) An array in which DNA sequences representing expressed portions of every gene in the genome are spotted on the slide. (ii) This type of array is used for expression profiling.

b. (i) An array in which DNA sequences representing non-coding regions of the genome are spotted on the slide. (ii) This type of array can be used to identify the binding sites of any given DNA binding protein through ChIP-chip or ChIP-Seq

c. (i) An array in which DNA sequences representing unique gene deletion identifiers (i.e. barcodes) are spotted on the slide. (ii) This type of array can be used to assess the growth of barcoded strains in functional genomics experiments.

Section 23.3 – Using RNA interference to Probe Gene Function

23-7. Yes, it would indeed be possible to create such a screen. One strategy would be to first create a strain that expresses 1) a GFP reporter gene and 2) a dsRNA targeting the GFP mRNA. In this way one has created a strain of worm that does not display any green fluorescence in its tissues since the mRNA coding for the GFP protein is destroyed. Next, one could use RNAi to systematically knockdown the expression of all *C. elegans* genes one by one. This provides a simple and efficient method with which to identify genes involved in RNAi. The knockdown of such genes would abrogate the silencing, resulting in expression of the GFP reporter which could be assayed by monitoring the level of green fluorescence within the tissues of the worm.

23-8. This is an open-ended question with many possibilities. The simplest manner in which to start would be to determine if they define essential genes by creating gene deletion mutants. If non-essential, one could culture the mutants under different growth conditions and determine if they displayed any obvious phenotypes relative to a wild-type control (e.g. alterations in growth rate, morphological abnormalities). As described in section 23.4, SGA analysis might also provide clues as to their biological function through the potential of clustering them to a gene group with a known biological role.

23-9. A scale-free genetic interaction network is one in which most genes have only a few interactions, and a small number of genes (the hubs) have many interactions. This architecture suggests that hub genes are particularly important in determining complex phenotypes since they "buffer" genetic variation in many other genes.

23-10. Hub genes exhibit synthetic lethal interactions with a large number of other genes. Since a hub gene is so inter-connected, variation in only one of its many interactors has the potential to result in an overt phenotype (if the hub is also abrogated). In contrast, abrogation of a nonhub (that is connected only to the hub) would result in an overt phenotype only if the hub was also abrogated.

Thus, hub genes have the potential to buffer variation in any of its many interactors, whereas a nonhub does not have that potential. By virtue of this characteristic, hubs are thought to be particularly important in determining complex phenotypes (e.g. disease) since they buffer the variation in many other genes.

Section 23.4 – Synthetic Genetic Arrays: Understanding the Principles of Genome Architecture

23-11. Based upon the results of SGA analysis in model systems, it is thought that most genes will act as disease-specific alleles (specifiers), whereas a small number of hub genes will act as modifiers for multiple, unrelated diseases. This is because, with the loss of a hub, the individual has lost the capacity to buffer variation in a wide subset of interacting genes. In contrast, variation in a specifier (nonhub) will result in a phenotype only if the hub is also abrogated.

23-12. A variant of SGA that makes use of barcoded gene deletion mutants is called dSLAM (diploid based synthetic lethality analysis using microarrays). This technique makes use of a pooled set of heterozygous deletion strains (i.e. equal amounts of each strain are grown together in the same culture). This culture is mass transformed with a barcoded gene deletion cassette targeting a specific gene (defining the query). Similar to SGA, double-mutant haploids are selected and their relative abundance quantified by PCR amplifying strain-specific bar codes and measuring their microarray hybridization intensities relative to a control pool of haploid single mutants (in which the query has not been deleted).

Chapter 24 Systems Biology

Synopsis:

Systems biology is a newly emerging field that attempts to define all the components of a biological system and understand how they function in conjunction with one another. This relies on the tools and strategies of global genetic analysis, proteomics, and functional genomics. The fundamental questions of systems biology include:

1. What are the elements of the system (proteins, cells, etc)?
2. What are the physical associations among the elements?
3. How do other biological systems that connect to the system under study change with perturbations of the original system?
4. How do the system's elements, their associations and their relations to changes in the biological context explain its emergent properties?

Systems biology is a developing science. Systems biologists must practice cross-disciplinary biology with teams of biologists, computer scientists, chemists, engineers, mathematicians and physicists. These teams must develop new, high-throughput measuring instruments to generate global data sets, and then develop the computational tools to analyze and annotate this data.

Key Terms:

biological system any complex network of interacting molecules or groups of cells that function in a coordinated manner through dynamic signalling.

systems biology a discipline that seeks to describe the multiple components of a *biological system* and analyze the complex interactions of these components both within the system and in relation to the components of other systems.

emergent properties traits and behaviours that arise from the operation of a *biological system* as a whole; *immunity* and *tolerance* are two emergent properties of the immune system.

Human Genome Project an initiative to determine the complete sequence of the human *genome*.

hysteresis a system that has a different threshold for the transition from the OFF to the ON state, compared with the transition from the ON to the OFF state.

biomarkers molecules that are present under specific conditions or when a disease is present.

network motifs patterns of interaction that recur throughout biological networks.

Significant Elements:

After reading the chapter and thinking about the concepts, you should be able to

♦   Understand the tools and technologies of systems biology and what types of data they collect

- Define the concept of emergence and explain how it can be applied to different biological systems

- Use differential equations to model transcriptional activation and repression

- Define the concept of a network motif and provide a biological example

- Intelligently discuss the systems approach with respect to understanding the manifestation of disease

Solutions to Problems:

Vocabulary

24-1.

i. 4; **ii.** 3; **iii.** 1; **iv.** 2

Section 24.1 – What is Systems Biology?

24-2.

Emergent properties are characteristics/attributes that can be observed only from examining the operation of a system as a whole. There are numerous examples that can be drawn from your everyday experience. The ability of a bicycle to locomote is one simple case in point. A collection of bicycle components properly assembled allows your leg muscles to propel the bicycle in any direction at great speeds. However, if the system were perturbed (e.g. the chain was missing, or the tire was flat) this emergent property would be abrogated. Furthermore, if one had never seen a bicycle before, it would be exceedingly difficult to infer this attribute from the detailed examination of the individual parts alone. This is to say the individual properties of steel, aluminum, rubber, or other components of the bicycle do not in and of themselves indicate the emergent properties (e.g. locomotion) of the system as a whole.

24-3.

The fundamental concepts that define a biological system are: 1) the elements of the system – proteins, cells, etc.; 2) the physical associations among the elements. These are often represented in a graphic representation of a network with nodes representing individual proteins and connections or edges representing physical interactions between the proteins; 3) the biological context of the system, and how perturbations to the system affect it – within individual cells types (prostate cells) or within an entire organism (yeast or mice or humans); 4) how the association of the system's elements and their relation to changes in the biological context explain its emergent property (the property that arises from the operation of the entire system, like the ability of the heart to pump blood).

24-4.

a. Engineers are critical in developing new high throughput measuring instruments necessary to study emergent properties in systems biology.

b. Mathematicians and computer scientists are necessary to develop new computational tools to organize, annotate, analyze, integrate and model the accumulated data.

24-5.

Gene regulatory networks examine the interactions of transcription factors with their cognate *cis*-control elements. These networks receive information from different sources and then they ingrate and modify this input and send the transformed information to various protein networks. Protein networks are sets of interacting proteins and other molecules such as metabolites that execute a particular biological function. Protein networks channel biological information and use it to execute particular functions such as signal transduction, physiological responses, development and metabolism – networks are dynamic. A catalog of *cis*-control elements would be part of a gene regulatory network as it could define specific transcription factors involved in a process such as gut development. To gain a further understanding of the network you need to understand what environmental information affects the network via signal transduction pathways and other inputs, how the network integrates and modifies these inputs and the output of the transformed information to various protein networks.

24-6.

The sequences of the entire genomes of humans, and other model organisms like *E. coli*, yeast, and mice, provide a genetics parts list of all the genes and the proteins they encode. The study of human genome defined the basic blocks of DNA, proteins, and other molecules that systems biology hopes to fit together into networks. These blocks include *cis*-control elements, the discovery and definition of many transcription factors and regulatory cascades, where transcription factors affect many different genes. This also defined many of the complex molecular machines and protein networks, and enforced the idea that biological information is hierarchic – it starts with digital DNA, progresses through mRNA, protein, molecular machines, networks, cells, networks of cells and tissues to individual organisms, populations of organisms to ecosystems.

The Genome Projects also drive the development of powerful computational tools which make it possible to acquire, store, analyze, integrate, display and model biological information. The high-throughput platforms for genomics and proteomics enable the acquisition of global data sets of differing types of biological information. Scientists can now gather global data sets from the genetic and environmental perturbations (experimental manipulations) of the biological systems of the model organisms and thus learn how to do systems biology in more complex organisms. The use of comparative genomics allows scientists to begin to determine the logic of life for individual organisms, (e.g. what type of energy generating systems does an organism use?) and to determine how that logic has changed in different evolutionary lineages.

24-7.

a. True

b. True;

c. False

d. False

e. True – there are about 6,000 genes in the yeast genome and <u>very little alternate mRNA splicing</u>, protein processing and protein modification increase the number of variations of these gene products;

f. True

g. True

h. False

i. False

j. True;

k. True

Section 24.2 – A Familiar Example: The *lac* Operon as a Logical Circuit

24-8. This system acts as a tryptophan sensor that outputs a particular rate of tryptophan biosynthesis as a <u>function</u> (in the mathematical sense of the term) of the current cellular level of tryptophan. In this sense the system acts as an analog computational device in which the system uses tryptophan levels as an input to determine/calculate the optimal rate of tryptophan synthesis for the cell. If the number of *trp* codons in the leader were increased, then this would result in the system being more prone to ribosome stalling, thus leading to greater levels of tryptophan biosynthesis. If the affinity of regions 3 and 4 were increased then transcriptional termination would be more likely, leading to decreased levels of tryptophan biosynthesis. Decreasing the affinity between regions 3 and 4 would of course have the opposite effect. Note that an examination of the number of *trp* codons, or the affinity of regions 3 and 4 in isolation would not allow you to infer the emergent properties of the system. This would only be possible when considering the system as a whole.

Section 24.3 – A Not-So-Familiar Example: Hysteresis

24-9.

You should ask your friend lots of questions: What exactly is the biological system that he is perturbing? Does he know all of the elements in this system? Some of the cytokines may be the output of the system, but does he know all of the outputs? Or all of the inputs? If he is measuring protein levels, he has only one type of biological information, and systems biology cannot be done with just a single type of information – this is closer to discovery science because systems biology requires the integration of different types of information. Also, your friend is not looking at the other systems whose behaviors will be altered by the knockout perturbations – there are no contextual studies. You could argue that your friend's research is not systems biology.

24-10.

From our biological perspective, hysteresis refers to an attribute exhibited by certain switch-like regulatory networks. A switch exhibiting hysteresis has a different threshold for the transition from the OFF state to the ON state, compared with the transition from the ON state to the OFF state. One example of hysteresis from the world of physics involves the behaviour of rubber bands. In this case it takes more energy to initially stretch the rubber band, than it does to keep the rubber band in the stretched position. This property makes hysteretic systems particularly suited to controlling cell cycle transitions. By being hysteretic, cell cycle control systems can prevent unwanted reversals in the cell division cycle. This is to say, it takes more activity to drive a cell into mitosis than it does to keep a cell in mitosis once it has been initiated (thus making the transition from M phase to G2 very unlikely). In cases such as these the cell benefits from committing itself to complete a process once the process has been initiated. Imagine, for example, the chaos that would ensue if a cell in anaphase slipped back into G2 phase leading to the decondensation of chromosomes.

Section 24.4 – Mathematical Modelling of Transcriptional Regulation

24-11.

a. The Hill equation for an activator, $\dfrac{\beta(X^*)^n}{K^n + (X^*)^n}$

b. K, represents the concentration of activator protein at which the promoter activity of the *SLA3* gene is at half-maximal value.

c. The steady state level of the message can be calculated using the equation $Y_{m(steady\ state)} = b_m/a_m$. In this case $b_m = 5$ molecules/min and $a_m = 0.2$/min. Thus the steady state level is 25 molecules.

d. The steady state level of the protein can be calculated using the equation $Y_{p(steady\ state)} = b_p/a_p$. We are told that the protein is produced at a rate of 60 molecules per hour (or 1 molecule per minute) for every molecule of message. At steady state there are 25 molecules of message thus, $b_p = 25$ molecules per minute. The degradation rate is 0.25, thus $Y_{p(steady\ state)} = 25$ molecules/0.25 min^{-1}, or 100 molecules.

e. To answer this question we first need to calculate the promoter activity of the wild-type system.

$$Promoter\ activity\ of\ SLA3 = \frac{\beta(X^*)^n}{K^n+(X^*)^n} = 300(100)^1/(50^1 + 100^1) = 200\ units$$

In the mutant system $a_p = 0.5$/min. Thus the steady state level of activator is 50 molecules. Thus in this case

$$Promoter\ activity\ of\ SLA3 = \frac{\beta(X^*)^n}{K^n+(X^*)^n} = 300(50)^1/(50^1 + 50^1) = 150\ units$$

Thus expression is decreased by 25%.

Section 24.5 – Network Motifs

23-12.

In this case, the behaviour is opposite to that of a feed forward loop with AND logic. With OR logic, the system maintains expression even if the input is momentarily lost. That is to say, there is no delay in activation, but there is a delay in deactivation when the signal is lost. This allows for continuing expression of a system even when the input fluctuates.

Section 24.6 – A Systems Approach to Disease

24-13.

a. True

b. True

c. True

d. True

e. True.

Chapter 25 Synthetic Biology

Synopsis: In this chapter we explore the revolutionary and exciting new discipline of synthetic biology. This discipline represents an important new step in the evolution of genetics research. Instead of simply reading/analyzing genomes, the field has now progressed to the point where researchers know enough to create user-defined genetic circuits that can be expressed within cells. These circuits impart rationally designed characteristics that permit the cell type to carry out biological processes of medical or industrial importance. More recent research has shown that it is even possible to create entire synthetic genomes. This opens up a Pandora's Box of possibilities, from which scientists might one day have the ability to create completely novel and artificial life forms. These technologies, if applied conscientiously, have the potential to solve some of the most pressing needs of society. However, the ability to create synthetic life forms raises some important ethical considerations that society needs to quickly address.

Key Terms:

biological system any complex network of interacting molecules or groups of cells that function in a coordinated manner through dynamic signalling.

synthetic biology a discipline focused on the design and construction of novel biological pathways, organisms or devices.

biobricks DNA sequences used as building blocks for the design and assembly of larger synthetic biological circuits with defined functions.

genetic toggle switch a synthetically constructed bistable gene-regulatory network.

repressilator a synthetically constructed gene regulatory network whose output oscillates with a defined period.

multiplex automated genome engineering (MAGE) an experimental method for the rapid introduction of mutations in *E. coli* at many targeted locations.

synthetic genomics the engineering and manipulation of an organism's genetic material on a genome-wide scale.

homologous recombination the exchange of DNA strands of similar or identical nucleotide sequence.

Significant Elements:

After reading the chapter and thinking about the concepts, you should be able to

♦ Describe how synthetic gene circuits are created in order to impart user-defined characteristics

♦ Provide examples of common synthetic gene circuits and their functions

♦ Define synthetic biology and relate this new discipline to the Human Genome Project

♦ Evaluate the potential benefits (and limitations) of synthetic strategies

♦ Compare and contrast genome engineering with traditional recombinant DNA technology

- ◆ Describe the methods used to synthesize and assemble entire genomes
- ◆ Intelligently discuss the ethical ramifications of synthetic biology

Solutions to Problems:

Vocabulary

25-1.

i. 4; **ii.** 3; **iii.** 2; **iv.** 1

Section 24.1 – What is Synthetic Biology?

25-2.

To achieve this goal one would need to construct a feed forward loop that outputs GFP expression. Upstream of this would be a secondary regulator capable of activating transcription of the GFP construct. Upstream of this would be a master regulator capable of activating transcription of both the secondary regulator and the GFP construct (and which is itself stimulated by the presence of arabinose in the growth media). As the framework for this system already exists naturally in *E. coli*, one would only need to introduce a construct in which the GFP coding sequence was placed under control of the *araBAD* promoter.

Section 25.2 – Synthetic Biology: The First Synthetic Gene Circuits

25-3.

i. Circuit #2 would be more switchlike. The cascade like structure makes the system act (for all intents and purposes) in a more cooperative manner. ii. It would take longer for circuit #2 to propagate a signal since the signal must proceed through the multiple layers of the cascade. iii. Circuit #2 would be more resistant to small random fluctuations. The delay created by the cascade-like structure of the network would most likely act to average out fluctuations in input and thereby mitigate the effects of random fluctuations.

25-4.

a. Create a construct in which GFP is under the control of a strong constitutive promoter. In *E. coli* this could be done by placing the GFP coding sequence under the control of the BBa_J23100 promoter (available through the Biobricks website).

b. Create an *E. coli* strain expressing 1) a construct that constitutively expresses the *tetR* repressor and 2) a construct in which GFP is under the control of the $P_LtetO-1$ promoter. In this way GFP will normally be repressed, but can be de-repressed by the addition of aTc.

c. Create a construct in which GFP is under control of a promoter containing both the $P_LtetO-1$ and *Ptrc-2* elements. Express in an *E. coli* strain that constitutively expresses the *tetR* repressor and the *lacI* repressor. In this way the system would be de-repressed only in the presence of both aTc and IPTG.

Section 25.4 – Multiplex Automated Genome Engineering

25-5.

In the scenario described in the text the researchers had a simple assay with which to select for cells showing increased lycopene production (the researchers simply examined colonies for those that displayed a red colour). What if such a simple assay did not exist for the traits to be selected? In these cases the technique would be much slower and cumbersome since it would not be a trivial exercise to select for the appropriate variants.

Section 25.5 – Synthetic Genomics

25-6.

This is an open-ended question with no correct answer. However, your recommendations would undoubtedly include 1) creating procedures for assessing the risks associated with the creation (and possible release into the environment) of a given synthetic organism, 2) the creation of reliable containment and control mechanisms, such as "suicide genes", 3) the screening of oligonucleotide synthesis orders (to prevent the synthesis of organisms that could be used as biological weapons, 4) increased public education.

25-7.

Mycoplasma spp. are among the simplest free living organisms on the planet. Genome sizes for this group are very small and range from 0.6-1.0 Mbp and contain between 500-1000 genes. Thus, these bacteria represent a logical first step in the creation of synthetic genomes. Now that this step has been taken, researchers can move on to synthesizing larger and more complex genomes.

25-8.

To start it would be important to stress that with dwindling oil supplies, the discovery of new fuels is a pressing societal need. As demonstrated by J.C. Venter and colleagues harnessing the power of biology has proven to be one of the most promising avenues with respect with this goal. Furthermore, proof-of-principle has already been established, and the methodologies and techniques fully validated. All that remains is to begin applying these principles to specific applications. For this to take place the panel's venture capital is required.

25-9.

A variation of PCR in which a series of short, overlapping oligos prime DNA synthesis, ultimately producing a contiguous piece of DNA (see 25.13). PCA (Polymerase Cycling Assembly) is used in synthetic genomics to create DNA cassettes bearing user defined sequences.

25-10.

Using the provided sequence one would create a series of oligonucleotides that together represent the entire genome of the virus. The oligos would be created so that they share complementarity and overlap. In this way one could use PCA to create four 6kb cassettes that together define the genome (Figure 25.13). These cassettes could in turn be introduced into budding yeast along with a linearized plasmid vector. Each end of the vector and each end of each cassette would be designed to share overlapping complementarity with adjacent cassettes. The budding yeast cells, recognizing the homology, would then be able to recombine the fragments into one contiguous circular DNA molecule containing the vector and the contiguous 24kb cassette (see figure 25.14). At this point, one could begin iteratively altering the sequence to determine the effects of these changes on the pathogenicity of the virus.

25-11.

While any technology can be used negatively, ethical reviews have concluded that these technologies show great promise with respect to both technological and medical applications. Furthermore, these same ethical reviews have led to the adoption of regulatory guidelines for the safe use of the approach.